HIGH–SPEED MATHEMATICS

By

LESTER MEYERS

1947

D. VAN NOSTRAND COMPANY, Inc.

TORONTO   NEW YORK   LONDON

NEW YORK

D. Van Nostrand Company, Inc., 250 Fourth Avenue, New York 3

TORONTO

D. Van Nostrand Company (Canada), Ltd., 228 Bloor Street, Toronto

LONDON

Macmillan & Company, Ltd., St. Martin's Street, London, W.C. 2

PRINTED IN THE UNITED STATES OF AMERICA

Dedicated to the

ROYAL SOCIETY OF ARTS, LONDON

whose certificate in Accounting, awarded the
author at the age of seventeen, inspired the
long-anticipated preparation of this book

PREFACE

This book has been prepared primarily to serve men and women engaged in business—executives, salesmen, purchasing agents, engineers, bookkeepers and general office workers.

Its purpose is threefold—namely, to show: (1) how a wide variety of problems in business mathematics can be computed *quickly;* (2) how these problems can be computed *mentally* or with a minimum of pencil-and-paper work; and (3) how, by means of one checking method or another, the possibility of *errors in computation can be virtually eliminated.* The third purpose is no less important than the others for, as every businessman knows, some errors can be very costly. An unhurried study of this book should make it possible for the average reader to acquire the ability to compute the answers to thousands of different problems without making a single mistake.

A knowledge of short-cuts in business mathematics is of great practical importance. Everybody in business is constantly confronted by mathematical problems of one kind or another, and one's business life can be made not only more profitable but more interesting and more pleasurable, when a wide variety of problems which may seem to be unsolvable without pencil and paper can be worked quickly, mentally and accurately in less time than it takes the uninitiated to pick up a pencil or depress the keys of a calculating machine.

Speed and accuracy are acquired through the mastery of technique—and techniques are the rock on which this book is built. These are not trick methods, but methods adapted to the rule rather than the exception. And once the technique of a short-cut is understood, the reader will find that its application with speed and accuracy is simple and easy, regardless of the seeming complexity of the problem.

Nothing more than a knowledge of simple arithmetic is necessary to understand the techniques discussed in these pages. There is no bothersome terminology to be memorized. There is not a word about algebra in the entire volume. Anyone who knows the simple rules of addition, subtraction, multiplication and division can sail through this book quickly and easily.

There is a range and richness to this fascinating subject, and for any reader who takes his business life seriously this book holds forth an additional promise of a satisfying adventure—an adventure of mental excursions to a world where one not only *sees* relationships between numbers, but *feels* them and *plays* with them . . . a world where computations become fun instead of work.

It is my hope that this book will constitute a welcome contribution to business—to executives and salesmen, because it will save them precious minutes and be of added service when the use of pencil and paper is not expedient; to employers, because it will help speed up production in bookkeeping and other departments; and, last but not least, to bookkeepers and general office workers, for whom the ability to compute speedily and accurately is a valuable attribute which will not fail to impress an employer.

I wish to express a deep obligation to my many business friends for their generous and valuable suggestions. For their kindness in looking over parts of the chapter on stocks and bonds, I am indebted to Mr. Fred C. Moffatt, chairman of the Public Relations Committee of the New York Curb Exchange, and to Mr. John G. Forrest, financial editor of *The New York Times*. And it is a special pleasure to thank Miss Harriet Bukarest for the diligence with which she applied herself to the tedious task of typing the manuscript.

LESTER MEYERS

May 1947
New York, N. Y.

CONTENTS

CHAPTER I—THERE IS A SHORT-CUT FOR VIRTUALLY EVERY MULTIPLICATION PROBLEM

ARTICLE

CONTENTS

CHAPTER II—THE BREAKDOWN METHOD OF MULTIPLICATION

CHAPTER III—THE "DOUBLE-AND-HALVE" METHOD OF MULTIPLICATION

CHAPTER IV—MORE TRICKS IN MENTAL ARITHMETIC

CHAPTER V—MORE SHORT-CUTS IN MULTIPLICATION

CHAPTER VI—ALIQUOT PARTS

CHAPTER VII—PERCENTAGES AND DISCOUNTS

CHAPTER VIII—PREPARING AND CHECKING BILLS

CONTENTS

CHAPTER XI—SIMPLE INTEREST

CHAPTER XII—AVOIDING ERRORS IN ADDITION

CONTENTS

CHAPTER XIII—AVOIDING ERRORS IN SUBTRACTION

CHAPTER XIV—DIVISION CAN BE AS SIMPLE AS MULTIPLICATION

CHAPTER XV—THE "DOUBLE-AND-DOUBLE" METHOD OF DIVISION

CONTENTS

CHAPTER XX—PARTIAL PAYMENTS AND INTEREST ON UNPAID BALANCES

CHAPTER XXI—COMPOUND INTEREST AND ANNUITIES

CONTENTS

LIST OF TABLES

HOW TO READ THIS BOOK

As has been pointed out, anyone who knows the simple rules of addition, subtraction, multiplication and division can easily understand the techniques discussed in this book. However, any reader who is not sure of himself when confronted by problems which involve decimals and fractions is urged to make a careful study of Chapter XXIII, preferably before he has progressed very far in his study of the other chapters. A quick review of this chapter is all that will be needed to understand any of the techniques discussed in the rest of the book.

Attention is called to the interrelation between Chapter I and Chapter II. For the sake of clarity and simplicity it was considered advisable to separate the subject matter of these two chapters. Should the reader have cause to hesitate even for a moment in following any of the discussions in Chapter I, he will find it helpful to read some of the material in Chapter II.

When he comes across what may appear to be a surprisingly simple problem, he should remember that the answer is to be computed by the method discussed in the text. In this way he will learn to compute mentally and with almost unbelievable ease a great many problems the solutions to which he would never heretofore have attempted without the use of pencil and paper.

The inclusion of stars and article references in the problem sections is an important feature of the book and should help speed up the reader's progress in his studies. The most practical way to use the article references is to work the problem first, and then —unless the reader is perfectly sure that he used the right technique—to check with the text in the indicated article.

INTRODUCTION

A brief glance through the table of contents will suffice to reveal the scope of this book. The author does not know of any other work that professes the object here sought—namely, to provide the reader with a wealth of ideas so he may know how to compute many different problems mentally and in the twinkling of an eye, and to conserve his time and energy in solving those problems which may require the use of pencil and paper.

To illustrate what is meant by being able to solve a problem in the twinkling of an eye, the reader is asked to multiply 35 by 28 the way he would ordinarily, then to turn to Example 1 in Art. 16 and learn how problems of this nature can be worked mentally in a few seconds. Let him also multiply 76 by 44 in his own way, then turn to Example 5 in the same article. Does the reader know how to compute a product with a multiplier like 436 without multiplying by more than a single digit? He will learn a simple and effortless way of doing so if he will refer to Example 9 in Art. 16.

The solution to the problem $5\frac{1}{2}$ times 126 may require pencil-and-paper work on the part of many; but the answers to this problem and to any number of others like it can be computed in just a few seconds with practically no effort and with full confidence in their accuracy by an incredibly simple method explained in Art. 20. And the same holds true for the problems $17\frac{1}{2}$ times 28 and $403\frac{1}{2}$ times 16, as explained in Art. 22.

A section of the book which will doubtless intrigue many is Chapter V, "More Short-Cuts in Multiplication." It shows among other things how one mixed number can be multiplied by another—for example, $8\frac{3}{7}$ times $8\frac{4}{7}$—mentally, in a few seconds, and with confidence and assurance.

Perhaps no other part of the book gave the author more pleasure in the preparation than the two chapters on the subject of division.

Examples of three typical problems in these chapters, each of which the reader will quickly learn to solve in a matter of seconds and without pencil and paper, are the division of 572 by 44, the division of 560 by $2\frac{1}{3}$, and how to find the number of gross in 9072.

Some of the aforementioned examples are stressed because the respective techniques are discussed in three of the most important chapters in this book. They are Chapter II, "The Breakdown Method of Multiplication," Chapter III, "The 'Double-and-Halve' Method of Multiplication," and Chapter XV, "The 'Double-and-Double' Method of Division." It is believed that many readers—those with an aptitude for figures and others who have always disliked mathematics—will discover here the key to something which may always have been a locked door to them. These chapters might be described as the core of the entire book. They contain information of much significance to anyone who wishes to learn some of the most important "secrets" of speed and accuracy in business mathematics. Although the terms "breakdown method," "double-and-halve method" and "double-and-double method" may not be quite in accord with pedagogic procedure, the license of using them seems warranted because they describe the techniques of the methods most satisfactorily.

The reader, on whose part no previous knowledge of the subject is presupposed, will find in Chapter VII, "Percentages and Discounts," many interesting facts about per-cent rates, which hitherto may have escaped his notice. He will learn, for instance, how to compute the answer to virtually any interest problem in a few simple steps; how to compute percentages like 32 per cent of $27.50 and 16 per cent of $37.50 mentally, and in just a few seconds.

It would be impossible in the confines of this Introduction to emphasize in detail all of the other important parts of this book, for what may be important to one reader may not be quite so important to another. Stress, however, might be laid upon the following discussions: Art. 64, which explains a quick way of mentally converting price per gross to price per unit—a comparatively unknown method which the author believes will be a pleasant revelation to many readers; Art. 70, which shows how even a simple problem like 37 times 24 can be computed in at least six different ways—a discussion which should enable the reader to develop amazing accuracy in his calculations; Arts. 6 and 106, wherein are discussed short and simple ways of multiplying and dividing by numbers which are divisible by 9; Arts. 117 and 118, on how to divide mentally and quickly by numbers which contain the fraction $\frac{1}{2}$; Art. 121, for information on how different problems which may appear to be difficult to compute without pencil and paper—for example, 36 times $1.0275—can be computed mentally or by writing no more than four figures. And many will experience a special delight when they read in Chapter XVI, "Short-Cutting the Short-Cuts," a perfectly simple procedure which has never before been touched upon in any book on mathematics.

For the benefit of those who have always believed that they were not mathematically inclined, an easy-to-follow chapter on the subject of decimals and fractions has been included at the end of this book. Decimals and fractions are really very simple, and a quick grasp of the subject, made possible by the bird's-eye view presentation in Chapter XXIII, will provide a firm foundation and be of considerable help in attaining skill in the various techniques discussed in the main text.

One peculiarity—the arrangement and substance of the chapters—perhaps needs explanation. Since the aim has been to aid businessmen and businesswomen who are eager to get right down to essentials, much of the material which is found in the conventional texts intended for schoolroom use has been omitted, and no space has been used to discuss the elementary processes of arithmetic. The subject of speed in computing the answers to problems of the kind most frequently encountered in business—those concerned with multiplication—starts with the first chapter. And, whereas in conventional texts addition and subtraction are usually treated in the opening pages, their discussion, confined practically entirely to avoiding errors in these operations, has been reserved for Chapters XII and XIII.

The starring of problems at the end of the articles is another interesting feature. Realizing that many would like to read this book with arm-chair comfort, stars have been placed before those problems which can be worked mentally. In this way the reader who chooses to do so can quickly pass over those problems which require paper work. Of more than 1500 problems (exclusive of illustrations) in this book, at least 500 are calculable mentally. So the reader can look forward to a thoroughly interesting and profitable time without going to the trouble of writing a single figure.

It is suggested that good use be made of the article references which follow the answers to many of the problems. These references are to previously discussed techniques which might be used advantageously in computing the answers. It should be remembered that this book is primarily one of techniques. So that, although it is important to obtain the correct answer, it is equally important to obtain the answer quickly and easily and, wherever possible, mentally.

Many readers will find it interesting to note the rich variety of the subject matter of the illustrations and problems at the end of the articles. These illustrations and problems are made up from facts about hundreds of different products, materials, operations, services and business practices, as shown in the list at the end of the book.

Abundantly illustrated and completely void of intricate and useless exercises, this book will provide a valuable foundation to any reader who gives to it the surprisingly little effort needed—a foundation that will save for him *time* . . . the *physical effort* spent in making computations by conventional methods . . . and the expenditure of *mental energy* which often accompanies the hope that an important computation made by the conventional method is correct.

CHAPTER I

THERE IS A SHORT-CUT FOR VIRTUALLY EVERY MULTIPLICATION PROBLEM

It is hoped that few readers of this book will need to be informed that to multiply a number by 10, all that is necessary is to place a zero after the last figure; or, if there is a decimal point in the number, to move the decimal point one place to the right. Thus 47 multiplied by 10 becomes 470, and 38.9 multiplied by 10 equals 389. Similarly, the product of 47 multiplied by 100 is 4700, and 38.9 multiplied by 100 equals 3890.

All this may seem elementary—and it is. Yet many individuals with an aptitude for figures fail to apply this rule when multiplying by such numbers as $7\frac{1}{2}$, 9, 35, 45, 97, 185; or fail to take advantage of it for purposes of quick mental computation.

As a preliminary to the many other interesting and important short-cuts discussed in this book, the first four articles in this chapter show how it is possible to make many computations rapidly and easily—and oftentimes mentally—by the simple expedient of multiplying by 10 or by a multiple of 10, adding or subtracting a small mentally computed partial product.

1. How to Multiply Quickly by 5, 15, $7\frac{1}{2}$, 9, 18, 11, $12\frac{1}{2}$, $112\frac{1}{2}$, .125.

1-a. Multiplying by 5. Let us begin with a simple example: 5 times 48. To solve this problem the average individual would use the conventional method, going to the trouble of multiplying 8 by 5, setting down a zero and carrying 4, multiplying the 4 in the multiplicand by 5 and adding 4 to the product. Actually, this problem could readily be calculated mentally. Five is half of 10; why not, then, multiply 48 by 10 mentally and divide the result by 2 mentally? Or, if you like, divide 48 by 2 mentally and multiply the result by 10 mentally?

No matter how many figures it contains, the multiplicand can be multiplied by 5 mentally without any trouble at all and without the need to write down the multiplicand or the multiplier. Thus 5 times 184726 can be multiplied mentally as easily as 5 times 48; dividing 184726 by 2 mentally we write down the result, 92363, and annexing a zero supplies the answer, 923630.

1-b. Multiplying by 15. Here, too, there is no need to write down the multiplicand or the multiplier, or to multiply by 10 and by 5 on paper. We know that if 10 times the multiplicand is added to 5 times the multiplicand the total equals 15 times the multiplicand. To multiply 782 by 15, then, all we need to do is add to the result of 782 multiplied by 10 (which is 7820) the result of 782 multiplied by 5 (which is half of 7820).

Notice in the following illustration the fewer figures and the simplicity of the procedure in computing the preceding problem under the suggested short method, as compared with the longer conventional method.

Conventional Method	*Short Method*		
782	782 multiplied by 10 *	=	7820
× 15	782 times 5 ($\frac{1}{2}$ of 7820) *	=	3910
3910	782 multiplied by 15 *		= 11730
782			
11730			

1-c. Multiplying by $7\frac{1}{2}$. Can you multiply 44 by $7\frac{1}{2}$ mentally in a few seconds? If not, you will very likely be able to do so presently. Seven and a half is equivalent to three fourths of 10.

---

* This data is given here only for the purpose of explanation. In actual practice only the products and their sum or difference, as the case may be, need be written down.

Stated another way, $7\frac{1}{2}$ is equivalent to 10 minus one fourth of 10. To multiply 44 by $7\frac{1}{2}$, then, we simply multiply 44 by 10 and subtract from the result one fourth of the result. Thus 44 multiplied by 10 equals 440; one fourth of 440 is 110; 440 minus 110 equals 330. Three seconds is all it should take to do this simple problem mentally.

A more difficult example is $392.36 multiplied by $7\frac{1}{2}$. Yet this should take but a few seconds longer. No need to write down $392.36 or $7\frac{1}{2}$, and no need to multiply by 7 and by $\frac{1}{2}$. Merely write down the result of $392.36 multiplied by 10, and subtract one fourth, thus:

$$\$392.36 \text{ multiplied by } 10 = \$3923.60$$
$$- \quad 392.36 \text{ times } 2\frac{1}{2} \ (\tfrac{1}{4} \text{ of } \$3923.60) = \quad 980.90$$

$$\$392.36 \text{ multiplied by } 7\frac{1}{2} = \$2942.70$$

1-d. Multiplying by 9. Nine is the equivalent of 10 minus 1. Bearing this in mind how would you go about multiplying 8754 by 9? Would you multiply each digit by 9? . . . first 4, then 5, then 7, and lastly 8? I hope not. You would find it more practical to set down the result of 8754 multiplied by 10, and then subtract 8754, thus:

$$8754 \text{ multiplied by } 10 = 87540$$
$$- 8754 \qquad\qquad = 8754$$

$$8754 \text{ multiplied by } 9 \ = 78786$$

This simple method makes possible the computation of many different types of problems mentally. In computing 89 times 9, for instance, we need but to subtract 89 from 890, and in a few brief seconds we know that the answer is 801.

1-e. Multiplying by 18. As a multiplier 18 is an interesting number. It is the equivalent of 20 minus one tenth of 20. Let us multiply 8439 by 18, first by the conventional method, then by the short method which makes use of the aforementioned observation, and notice the ease and simplicity of the latter method.

Conventional Method

    8439

$\times$ 18

  67512

  8439

 151902

Short Method

8439 multiplied by 20 mentally $= 168780$

$-$ 8439 times 2 ($\frac{1}{10}$ of 168780) $= 16878$

8439 multiplied by 18 $= 151902$

The short method is obviously simpler and speedier than the conventional method.

1-f. Multiplying by 11. There is no need, in multiplying by 11, to multiply each figure in the multiplicand by 11. Write down the multiplicand; then, directly below, 10 times the multiplicand, and add. Thus 93 multiplied by 11 equals the sum of 93 and 930, or 1023.

When the multiplicand contains but two figures and their sum does not exceed 9, there is a still shorter way of multiplying by 11. Simply set down the multiplicand, leaving a little space between the figures, then insert in this space the sum of the two figures. Thus 43 multiplied by 11 equals 473; 70 multiplied by 11 equals 770, and so on.

To multiply a three-figure number in which the sum of the last two figures does not exceed 9, the method is equally simple. The last two figures are multiplied by 11 by the method described in the previous paragraph, and the result is added to the product of the hundreds digit multiplied by 11. Thus 834 multiplied by 11 equals 374 plus 8800, or 9174.

1-g. Multiplying by $12\frac{1}{2}$. Just as $7\frac{1}{2}$ is the equivalent of 10 *minus* one fourth of 10, $12\frac{1}{2}$ is the equivalent of 10 *plus* one fourth of 10. Or, we may say, $12\frac{1}{2}$ is one eighth of 100—so that the product of $12\frac{1}{2}$ times a number is equivalent to the product of 100 times that number, divided by 8. We, therefore, have a choice of two methods in multiplying by $12\frac{1}{2}$.

A little practice will enable one to determine which is the better method for the solution of any given problem. In computing $12\frac{1}{2}$ times 800, for instance, the second method is better, for 800 is easily divided by 8 mentally. The same would apply to numbers like 400, 1200, 48, 96. On the other hand, a problem like 137 multiplied by $12\frac{1}{2}$ might be computed more easily by the first method—that is, by multiplying by 10 and adding to the product one fourth of the product.

1-h. Multiplying by 112½. A careful study of the multipliers discussed in this article so far will contribute to a quick appreciation of the short method of multiplying by $112\frac{1}{2}$. Note in the following illustration the simplicity and ease of the short method as compared with the conventional method.

Conventional Method	*Short Method*	
174	174 multiplied by 100	$= 17400$
$\times\ 112\frac{1}{2}$	174 times $12\frac{1}{2}$ ($\frac{1}{8}$ of 17400) $=$	2175
87	174 multiplied by $112\frac{1}{2}$	$= 19575$
348		
174		
174		
19575		

The advantage of the short method is so obvious that comment is hardly necessary. Under the short method only fourteen figures were written down, only one operation (in division) was necessary, and only two numbers had to be added. Under the conventional method twenty-three figures were written down, and four numbers had to be added.

1-i. Multiplying by .125. It is worth remembering that 125 is exactly one eighth of 1000, and that .125 is exactly one eighth of 1. Thus 327 multiplied by 125 equals 327000 divided by 8; and 327 multiplied by .125 equals 327 divided by 8. It is much easier to divide by the one digit (8) than to multiply by the three digits (125).

PROBLEMS

* **1.** Without putting pencil to paper and without hesitating for a moment read, from left to right, the product of 5 times $648.32.
Ans. $3241.60.

* **2.** Compute by the process of division the weight of 5 bushels of barley. (One bushel of barley weighs 48 pounds.)   *Ans.* 240 pounds.

3. What is the cost of a rug of 15 square yards quoted at $4.62 a square yard?   *Ans.* $69.30.

4. If the air express rate from Brownsville, Texas, to Montevideo, Uruguay, is $1.68 per pound, what would the transportation cost be on a shipment weighing 15 pounds?   *Ans.* $25.20.

* **5.** At $88.00 an acre what is the value of $7\frac{1}{2}$ acres of land?
Ans. $660.00.

6. If a gallon of cottonseed oil weighs $7\frac{1}{2}$ pounds, what would the weight be of 136 gallons?   *Ans.* 1020 pounds.

7. A manufacturer uses a certain type of paper by the square foot but buys it by the square yard. How many square feet will he obtain from 260 square yards?   (One square yard equals 9 square feet.)
Ans. 2340 square feet.

8. A girl can produce 187 machinery parts in one day. How many might she be expected to produce in 9 days?   *Ans.* 1683.

9. A cosmetic manufacturer finds that the net weight of a pint bottle of a newly created product is 18 ounces. Compute the number of ounces that would be necessary to fill one gross of these pint bottles.
Ans. 2592 ounces.

10. A contractor agrees to complete a job in 28 working days. If his labor cost is $18 a day, what would he have to pay out in labor for the 28 days?   *Ans.* $504.00.

* **11.** If a cow gives an average of 23 pounds of milk a day, how many pounds of milk will she give in 11 days?   *Ans.* 253 pounds.

* **12.** Compute the total number of square inches in 11 square feet. (One square foot equals 144 square inches.)   *Ans.* 1584 square inches.

* **13.** If a gallon of molasses weighs $12\frac{1}{2}$ pounds, what would 176 gallons weigh?   *Ans.* 2200 pounds.

14. A manufacturer decides to dispose of 3 gross of miscellaneous equipment parts at a flat price of $12\frac{1}{2}$ cents each. What would the total charge amount to?   *Ans.* $54.00.

15. A manufacturer produces $112\frac{1}{2}$ dozen units a month at a net profit of $4.80 per dozen. What is his total net profit per month? *Ans.* $540.00.

16. Three men put in a total of $112\frac{1}{2}$ hours work on a job. If their rate of pay is $1.36 an hour, what is the amount of their combined earnings?   *Ans.* $153.00.

17. Compute the height of a stack of 160 metal plates each of which is .125 inches thick.   *Ans.* 20 inches.

18. A manufacturer signs an order for 10 gross of screws at $0.125 each. What will this bill of goods cost him?   *Ans.* $180.00.

2. How to Multiply Quickly by 45, 35, 125, 180, $17\frac{1}{2}$. With the foregoing devices as a guide, the reader will quickly perceive the time-saving advantages of using short methods for multiplying by these numbers.

2-a. Multiplying by 45. This number is equivalent to 50 minus 5. To multiply by 50 is a simple matter, for 50 is one half of 100. Five, on the other hand, is one tenth of 50. All one need do, then, to multiply by 45 is multiply by 50 and subtract from the product one tenth of the product.

Example 1: Multiply 34 by 45.

Solution: 34 times 50 ($\frac{1}{2}$ of 3400) = 1700
    − 34 times 5 ($\frac{1}{10}$ of 1700) =   170
    _____
    34 multiplied by 45   = 1530

2-b. Multiplying by 35. Thirty-five is the sum of 25 and 10. The sum of 25 times the multiplicand plus 10 times the multiplicand—two easily computed partial products—is therefore equivalent to the product of 35 times the multiplicand.

Example 2: Multiply 432 by 35.

Solution: 432 times 25 ($\frac{1}{4}$ of 43200) = 10800
    432 times 10   =   4320
    _____
    432 multiplied by 35   = 15120

2-c. Multiplying by 125. In line with the explanation in Art. 1-i, the multiplication of a number by 1000 and the division of the product by 8 is equivalent to multiplying by 125. However,

125 is also equivalent to 100 plus one fourth of 100. When the multiplicand is easily divisible by 4, the latter method is more suitable, particularly because the computation may be made more quickly. The following two illustrations will make this point clear.

Example 3: Multiply 122 by 125.

Solution: 122 times 125 ($\frac{1}{8}$ of 122000) = 15250

Example 4: Multiply 36 by 125.

Solution: 36 times 100   = 3600
36 times 25 ($\frac{1}{4}$ of 3600) =   900

---

36 multiplied by 125   = 4500

It is obviously easier to compute one fourth of 3600 and add the result to 3600 than to divide 36000 by 8.

2-d. Multiplying by 180. The method recommended here is similar to that used in multiplying by 18. Simply multiply by 200 and deduct from the product one tenth of the product.

Example 5: Multiply 68 by 180.

Solution: 68 times 200 (6800 times 2) = 13600
− 68 times 20 ($\frac{1}{10}$ of 13600)   =   1360

---

68 multiplied by 180   = 12240

2-e. Multiplying by $17\frac{1}{2}$. This number is equivalent to 20 minus one eighth of 20. The procedure is very simple.

Example 6: Multiply 128 by $17\frac{1}{2}$.

Solution: 128 times 20 (1280 times 2) = 2560
− 128 times $2\frac{1}{2}$ ($\frac{1}{8}$ of 2560)   =   320

---

128 multiplied by $17\frac{1}{2}$ = 2240

PROBLEMS

★ 1. If the fire insurance rate on the contents of a house is 45 cents per $100, what would the premium amount to on contents valued at $26,000?
Ans. $117.00.

2. How many revolutions will be made in 45 minutes by a motor whose speed is 2100 rpm (revolutions per minute)?   *Ans.* 94,500.

3. Compute the weight of 172 cubic feet of dry elm wood, the average weight of which is 35 pounds per cubic foot.   *Ans.* 6020 pounds.

4. At the rate of 35 cents per square foot what would it cost to treat a floor 18 feet long and 17 feet wide?   *Ans.* $107.10.

5. The express charge on a carton weighing 100 pounds shipped from New York to Cleveland is $2.56. Compute the cost of shipping a carton weighing 125 pounds between these points. (Note that shipments in excess of 100 pounds are charged on a pro rata basis; thus the cost of shipping 150 pounds between the points mentioned would be $1\frac{1}{2}$ times $2.56.)   *Ans.* $3.20.

6. Estimate the cost of 125 bushels of corn at $1.34 per bushel.
Ans. $167.50.

7. If the average weight of a bale of waste cotton is 638 pounds, what would the total weight be of 180 bales?   *Ans.* 114,840 pounds.

8. Compute the cost of 180 shares of stock purchased at $13\frac{1}{2}$—that is, at $13.50 per share.   *Ans.* $2430.00.

9. A fruiterer buys sixteen 12-quart baskets of cherries. If the baskets weighed $17\frac{1}{2}$ pounds each, what is the total weight of his purchase?
Ans. 280 pounds.

★ 10. A contractor wishes to estimate the total area of the outside walls of a building, excluding the space occupied by the window openings. How many square feet will he need to deduct if each of the 22 window openings has an area of $17\frac{1}{2}$ square feet?   *Ans.* 385 square feet.

3. How to Multiply Quickly by Numbers Near 100, as 99, 98, 97, 103; and by Numbers Near 1000, as 999, 998, 997. The method illustrated is obviously the only one that should be used in computing problems of this nature. The author would feel apologetic for including this article, were it not for the fact that this method is not commonly practiced.

Example 1: Multiply 147 by 99.

Solution: 99 = 100 − 1.   We therefore multiply 147 by 100 and subtract 147 from the result, thus:

$$\begin{aligned} 147 \text{ times } 100 \quad &= 14700 \\ -\ 147 \quad &= 147 \end{aligned}$$

147 multiplied by 99 = 14553

Example 2: Multiply 216 by 98.

Solution: 98 = 100 − 2.

$$\begin{aligned} 216 \text{ times } 100 \quad &= 21600 \\ -\ 216 \text{ times } 2 \quad &= 432 \end{aligned}$$

216 multiplied by 98 = 21168

Example 3: Multiply 1347 by 97.

Solution: 97 = 100 − 3.

$$\begin{aligned} 1347 \text{ times } 100 \quad &= 134700 \\ -\ 1347 \text{ times } 3 \quad &= 4041 \end{aligned}$$

1347 multiplied by 97 = 130659

Example 4: Multiply 238 by 103.

Solution: Multiply 238 by 100 and add 3 times 238.

$$\begin{aligned} 238 \text{ times } 100 \quad &= 23800 \\ 238 \text{ times } 3 \quad &= 714 \end{aligned}$$

238 multiplied by 103 = 24514

Example 5: Find the cost of 98 pounds of plastic belting at $1.84 a pound.

Solution: $1.84 times 100 = $184.00
             − $1.84 times 2 =   3.68

$1.84 times 98 = $180.32

To multiply by numbers near 1000—as 999, 998, 997, etc.—the procedure is the same as in multiplying by numbers near 100, except that instead of multiplying by 100 we multiply by 1000.

PROBLEMS

1. A dry goods dealer has several bolts of cloth whose combined length is 97 yards. What would he receive if the entire quantity brought an average price of $3.40 a yard?   *Ans.* $329.80.

2. What would the dealer receive for the cloth mentioned in the foregoing problem if the combined length equaled 103 yards and the average price received was $2.86 a yard?   *Ans.* $294.58.

★ **3.** Ceylon cinnamon featherings are packed in bales averaging 99 pounds each. What would the total weight be of 340 bales?

Ans. 33,660 pounds.

4. If medium-bold, bleached cardamon seeds average 198 to one ounce, how many seeds would be needed to fill 437 one-ounce containers?

Ans. 86,526.

★ **5.** In August, 1946, hogs were selling at $22.00 per 100 pounds. What did this price bring on sales of (a) 999 pounds, (b) 998 pounds, (c) 997 pounds?   *Ans.* (a) $219.78; (b) $219.56; (c) $219.34.

4. How to Multiply Quickly by Numbers Near an Even Hundred, as 185, 288, 389, 497; and by Numbers Near an Even Thousand, as 1195, 2956, 3988, 4980. Here the procedure is similar to that in the preceding article, except that the computation entails an additional operation or two. The illustrations that follow explain themselves.

Example 1: Multiply 273 by 185.

Solution: 273 times 200 $= 54600$
        − 273 times 15 (2730 plus 1365) $= 4095$
        _____
        273 multiplied by 185 $= 50505$

Example 2: Multiply 178 by 288.

Solution: 178 times 300 $= 53400$
        − 178 times 12 $= 2136$
        _____
        178 multiplied by 288 $= 51264$

Example 3: Multiply 419 by 389.

Solution: 419 times 400   = 167600
       — 419 times 11   =   4609

---

419 multiplied by 389 = 162991

Example 4: Multiply 1269 by 497.

Solution: 1269 times 500   = 634500
       — 1269 times 3   =   3807

1269 multiplied by 497 = 630693

Example 5: Multiply 3728 by 1195.

Solution: 3728 times 1200   = 4473600
       — 3728 times 5 ($\frac{1}{2}$ of 37280) =   18640

3728 multiplied by 1195   = 4454960

Example 6: Multiply 5784 by 2956.

Solution: 5784 times 3000   = 17352000
       — 5784 times 44 (23136 times 11) =   254496

5784 multiplied by 2956   = 17097504

Example 7: Multiply 4732 by 3988.

Solution: 4732 times 4000   = 18928000
       — 4732 times 12   =   56784

4732 multiplied by 3988 = 18871216

Example 8: Multiply 7326 by 4980

Solution: 7326 times 5000   = 36630000
       — 7326 times 20   =   146520

7326 multiplied by 4980 = 36483480

Example 9: What would it cost to have 3875 leaflets printed at $8.45 per 1000?

Solution: 4000 at $8.45 per 1000   = $33.80
            —   125 at $8.45 per 1000 ($\frac{1}{8}$ of $8.45) =   1.06
            _____

                3875 at $8.45 per 1000   = $32.74

PROBLEMS

1. A manufacturer's representative guarantees to sell a minimum quantity of 185 units per month. If the selling price is $28.50 per unit, what should the minimum total sales be per month?   *Ans.* $5272.50.

2. If a hardware item purchasable by the gross costs $13\frac{1}{2}$ cents each, what would 2 gross (288) cost?   *Ans.* $38.88.

3. A private trade school graduated 389 students in a twelve-month period. If the amount received from each student for tuition and supplies averaged $43.50, what was the total amount taken in for the year?
Ans. $16,921.50.

4. The total weight of three bags of coffee is 497 pounds. Compute the cost at $0.17695 per pound.   *Ans.* $87.94.

5. A manufacturer wants to know, without waiting until the payroll records have been made up, the amount earned in the current week by 35 girls who put in a total of 1195 hours. Each girl was employed at the rate of 74 cents an hour. What was the total of the girls' earnings for the week?   *Ans.* $884.30.

6. A paint manufacturer sold 2956 gallons of one of his specialties in one year. If his net profit was $0.347 per gallon, what was his total net profit on this item for the year?   *Ans.* $1025.73.

7. If the import duty on peanut butter is 7 cents per pound, what would the duty amount to on 3988 pounds?   *Ans.* $279.16.

8. Compute the cost of 4980 pounds of cottonseed oil at 17.8 cents per pound.   *Ans.* $886.44.

5. A Short Way of Multiplying by Numbers Which Can Be Factored, Such as 24, 32, 56, 64, 121. If you wished to multiply quickly by any of these numbers, would you multiply first by one digit, then by the other? That would not be the shortest method. A speedier way would be to multiply by factors.

The number 24, for example, might be broken up into the factors 8 and 3 (the product of 8 multiplied by 3 being 24). Or it may be broken up into the factors 6 and 4, or 12 and 2. For our purposes the most convenient factors of 32 are 8 and 4; of 56, 8 and 7; of 64, 8 and 8; of 121, 11 and 11.

The following example will serve to illustrate the time-saving significance of multiplication by factors as compared with the conventional method.

Example 1: Multiply 827 by 24.

Solution by the	*Solution by the*
Conventional Method	*Short Method*
827	827
× 24	× 8
3308	6616
1654	× 3
19848	19848

Observe that under the conventional method eighteen figures had to be set down and the computation involved an operation in addition. Under the short method no addition was necessary, and only fourteen figures were set down. Actually it was not necessary to set down more than nine figures: the partial product 6616, and the final product 19848.

In multiplying by 32 the procedure is the same. To multiply 374 by 32, for instance, we would multiply first by 8, then by 4. Eight times 374 equals 2992, and 2992 multiplied by 4 equals 11968.

The procedure in multiplying by 56, 64 and 121 would be along exactly the same lines.

Example 2: Compute the cost of 64 square feet of Plexiglas at $4.12 per square foot.

Solution: 8 times $4.12 = $ 32.96
8 times $32.96 = $263.68

1. What would it cost to ship a carton weighing 24 pounds by air express from Miami, Florida, to Santiago, Chile, at the rate of $1.38 per pound? *Ans.* $33.12.

2. The specific gravity of cork is .24, which means that the weight of cork is .24 times the weight of an equal volume of water. If one cubic foot of water weighs 62.5 pounds, what would the weight be of one cubic foot of cork? *Ans.* 15 pounds.

3. If the moisture content of anthracite is 3.2%, how much moisture may be expected in 26.5 short tons of anthracite? (A short ton equals 2000 pounds.) *Ans.* 1696 pounds.

4. If a drum of calcium chloride occupies 8.7 cubic feet of space, how much space would be occupied by 32 drums? *Ans.* 278.4 cubic feet.

5. What would it cost to have 73 dozen belts sewn at the rate of 56 cents per dozen? *Ans.* $40.88.

6. The walls of a building exterior are to be given 2 coats of paint. The total area, excluding the open spaces, is 5600 square feet. If it takes $3.74 worth of paint to apply 2 coats to 100 square feet, what would be the total cost of the paint used on the job? *Ans.* $209.44.

7. A pump delivers $18\frac{1}{8}$ gallons of water per stroke. How many gallons will it deliver in 64 strokes? *Ans.* 1160 gallons.

8. Compute in square feet the area of a yard 137 feet long and 64 feet wide. *Ans.* 8768 square feet.

9. A foot of $1\frac{5}{8}$-inch diameter wire rope weighs 4.09 pounds. How much would 121 feet weigh? *Ans.* 494.89 pounds.

10. The labor cost of 4 men employed on a contract job is $6.23 per hour. If it required 121 man-hours to complete the job, what was the total labor cost? *Ans.* $753.83.

6. A Short Way of Multiplying by Numbers Which Are Divisible by 9, Such as 27, 36, 45, 54, 63, 72, 81. In Art. 1-d we learned that to multiply by 9 it is much simpler to multiply by 10 and subtract from the result one tenth of the result. Thus 34 multiplied by 9 equals 340 minus 34.

The same principle may be applied with equally good effect to numbers which are multiples of 9. To multiply by 27, for instance, we would multiply by 30 and subtract from the result one tenth of the result. Similarly, the multiplier 36 would be changed to 40, 45 would be changed to 50, 54 to 60, and so on.

The object of this method is, of course, to save time and effort by reducing the number of partial products to a minimum. Thus to multiply by 72 we would multiply by only one digit (8) instead of by two digits (2 and 7). Using this number in an example let us multiply 643 by 72, first by the conventional method, then by the short method, and observe the time-saving advantage of the latter method.

Conventional Method	Short Method
643	643
× 72	× 80
——	——
1286	51440
4501	− 5144
——	——
46296	46296

It is much easier to take one tenth of a number than to multiply by any digit, particularly if it is a high number, like 7, 8 or 9.

The use of this method need not necessarily be confined to two-digit multipliers. The multiplier 270 would be treated in exactly the same manner as the multiplier 27, the number 270 being changed to 300 instead of to 30.

Example: A fault detector makes possible the inspection of sheet rubber at a speed of 450 feet per minute. At this rate how many feet of sheet rubber can be inspected in an 8-hour day?

Solution: 8 hours equals 480 minutes.

$$50 \text{ times } 480 \ (\tfrac{1}{2} \text{ of } 48000) \quad = \quad 24,000$$
$$- \ \ 5 \text{ times } 480 \ (\tfrac{1}{10} \text{ of } 24000) \quad = \quad 2,400$$

$$45 \text{ times } 480 \quad\quad\quad\quad\quad\quad = \quad 21,600$$
$$450 \text{ times } 480 \ (10 \text{ times } 21600) = 216,000$$

Ans. 216,000 feet.

PROBLEMS

1. For the fiscal year beginning July 1, 1946, the New York City real estate tax was set at $2.70 on each $100 of assessed valuation. If a parcel of property is assessed at $28,600 how much tax would the owner have to pay? *Ans.* $772.20.

2. A manufacturer receives an order for 536 boxes. Each box requires the use of 27 square feet of lumber. How much lumber will be used to fill the order? *Ans.* 14,472 square feet.

3. At the price of 36 cents per yard of plastic film, what would 734 yards cost? *Ans.* $264.24.

4. Compute the total weight of 34 crates of cauliflower weighing 36 pounds each. *Ans.* 1224 pounds.

5. In preparing estimates on large jobs, printers take into consideration the higher cost of printing in color. For yellow ink, for instance, it is customary to add 45% to what the cost would have been if the portion to be printed in yellow were printed in black. If the area to be printed in yellow is 78 square inches of form surface per 1000 impressions, what area would actually be considered in arriving, for cost purposes, at a figure representing an equivalent area printed in black ink? *Ans.* 113.1 square inches.

6. If the import duty on surgical mirrors is 45%, how much duty would be payable on a shipment valued at $317.50? *Ans.* $142.88.

7. The average weight of loose, broken anthracite is 54 pounds per cubic foot. How many pounds would fill a space of 235 cubic feet? *Ans.* 12,690 pounds.

8. It takes 6 boys paid at the rate of 70 cents an hour and 4 men paid at $1.10 an hour 54 hours to complete the construction of a machine. What is the total labor cost? *Ans.* $464.40.

9. If the gross weight of a box of spermaceti is 63 pounds, what is the gross weight of 23 boxes? *Ans.* 1449 pounds.

10. Compute the weight of 63 cubic feet of dry sycamore, using the average weight of 37 pounds per cubic foot for the wood of the tree of this species. *Ans.* 2331 pounds.

11. If it takes 72 cents worth of a certain ingredient to make 4 ounces of a high-quality cosmetic, how much of this material would be required to make a sufficient quantity of the product to fill 5 gross 4-ounce jars? *Ans.* $518.40.

12. Compute the value of 72 yards of material at $2.17 per yard. *Ans.* $156.24.

13. At the market quotation of $3.60 per 100 pounds of potatoes, what would 81 sacks cost? (A sack of potatoes weighs 112 pounds.) *Ans.* $326.59.

14. Estimate the value of 81 acres of land at $173 per acre. *Ans.* $14,013.00.

7. In Multiplication It Is Usually Better to Consider the Larger Number the Multiplicand and the Smaller Number the Multiplier. If we were to compute the problem 3 multiplied by 1700, it is obvious that the simplest procedure would be to multiply 1700 by 3 rather than 3 by 1700. In other words, we should use 3 (the smaller number) rather than 1700 (the larger number) as the multiplier.

The same procedure would be used in computing such problems as 28 times 19, 382 times 29, 483 times 73. It is easier to multiply by two digits than by three, by the digit 1 than by any other digit.

On the other hand, the problem 17 multiplied by 300 would call for a slightly different treatment. Transposition in this instance is not necessary. All we need do here is to multiply 17 by 3 and annex two zeros. Neither would transposition be necessary to compute the problem 18 multiplied by 51. It is very convenient to say, "18 multiplied by half a hundred equals 900, and 18 added equals 918." And in the problem 45 times 111, rather than multiply 111 by 45, we need but jot down the partial products 4500, 450 and 45, and add them. (Or, in solving the last problem, the still shorter method described in Art. 1-f may be used; this would reduce the computation to the sum of 4500 and 495.)

Example: A machine takes candy in a plastic state, then forms, cuts and wraps it at the rate of 600 pieces per minute. At this rate how many pieces of candy can be cut and wrapped in $2\frac{1}{2}$ hours?

Solution: $2\frac{1}{2}$ hours equals 150 minutes.

100 times 150 = 15,000
600 times 150 (6 times 15,000) = 90,000

Ans. 90,000 pieces.

The transposition of multiplicand and multiplier is only advisable obviously in certain instances. In computing the product of 87 multiplied by 344, for instance, it would be better to multiply by 344 rather than by 87 for, in the first place, the digit 4 occurs twice in 344 and, secondly, it is easier to multiply by the digits 3 and 4 than by the digits 7 and 8.

Having in mind the techniques discussed in the preceding articles, would you transpose the multiplicands and multipliers in any of the following problems? Just answer *yes* or *no*.

1. 9.75 multiplied by 12.5.   *Ans.* No.
2. 24 multiplied by $7\frac{1}{2}$.   *Ans.* No.
3. 15 multiplied by 14.   *Ans.* Yes.
4. 88 multiplied by $112\frac{1}{2}$.   *Ans.* No.
5. 43 multiplied by 700.   *Ans.* No.
6. 180 multiplied by 74.   *Ans.* Yes.
7. 17.5 multiplied by 16.5.   *Ans.* Yes.
8. 37 multiplied by 45.   *Ans.* No.
9. 125 multiplied by 87.   *Ans.* Yes.
10. 99 multiplied by 68.   *Ans.* Yes.
11. 103 multiplied by 497.   *Ans.* Yes.
12. 13 multiplied by 64.   *Ans.* Yes.
13. 23 multiplied by 27.   *Ans.* No.
14. 36 multiplied by 17.   *Ans.* Yes.

8. Transposing Multiplicand and Multiplier Is Particularly Helpful in Monetary Calculations. To the uninitiated the computation of the problem 25 times 35 cents would probably call for the use of pencil and paper. The average person would, in all likelihood, proceed to multiply 25 by 5, 25 by 30, and add the partial products. This is really unnecessary.

Consider how simple the mental calculation of the aforementioned problem becomes when multiplicand and multiplier are transposed, that is, when the problem 25 times 35 cents is changed to read 35 times 25 cents. The multiplication of 25 cents by 35 resolves itself into the simple problem, "How much is 35 quarters?" Since there are four quarters in a dollar, 35 quarters equals $8\frac{3}{4}$ dollars, or $8.75.

A problem calling for a little more effort is $25\frac{1}{2}$ times 60 cents. The numbers transposed, the problem becomes 60 times $25\frac{1}{2}$ cents. A good procedure in this instance would be to make two separate calculations: 60 quarters are $15.00, and 60 times $\frac{1}{2}$ cent equals 30 cents; total, $15.30.

Incidentally, the latter method of solving a multiplication problem by adding two separate and easily computed little calculations may be used with good effect in computing different types of problems. By this method 70 times 26 cents could be solved mentally very quickly: 70 quarters are $17.50, 70 times 1 cent equals 70 cents; total, $18.20. Eighty times 28 cents could be computed with equal ease: 80 quarters are $20.00, 80 times 3 cents equals $2.40; total, $22.40.

Or take a problem in which the multiplier contains a decimal: 25.7 times 65 cents. Transposed, the problem becomes 65 times $25\frac{7}{10}$ cents, which can be quickly computed as follows:

65 quarters	= $16.25
65 times $\frac{7}{10}$ cents ($6\frac{1}{2}$ times $7\cancel{c}$) =	.46

65 times $25\frac{7}{10}$ cents	= $16.71

Example: Estimate the cost of thirteen 1-gallon bottles of vitamin syrup at $11.40 per gallon.

Solution:
13 times $11.00 (11 times $13.00)	= $143.00
13 times $0.40 (4 times $1.30)	= 5.20

13 times $11.40	= $148.20

PROBLEMS

Compute the answers to the following problems:

  * **1.** 36 cents multiplied by $50\frac{1}{4}$.   *Ans.* $18.09.
  * **2.** 74 cents multiplied by 26.   *Ans.* $19.24.
    3. 50.4 cents multiplied by 63.   *Ans.* $31.75.
  * **4.** $2.25 multiplied by 88.   *Ans.* $198.00.
  * **5.** $64.00 multiplied by 126.   *Ans.* $8064.00.
  * **6.** 96 cents multiplied by $75\frac{3}{4}$.   *Ans.* $72.72.
    7. $45\frac{1}{2}$ cents multiplied by 86.   *Ans.* $39.13.

9. How to Multiply Quickly and Easily by 56, 67, 78, 89. Here is another energy-saving little short-cut. Note that each of these numbers can be increased to 100 by the addition of a number which consists of like digits. Fifty-six added to 44 equals 100; 67 added to 33 equals 100; 78 plus 22, and 89 plus 11, equals 100.

What would be simpler, then, when dealing with these multipliers, than to multiply by 100 and deduct the product of the multiplicand times 44, 33, 22 or 11, as the case may be? Instead of multiplying by 5 and by 6, when the multiplier is 56, it is but necessary to subtract 44 times the multiplicand from 100 times the multiplicand. The same procedure would be used to multiply by 67 and 78. The multiplier 89 is the simplest of all, for here the number to be subtracted is arrived at in a single calculation—namely, 11 times the multiplicand.

It will be recalled that the number 56, included in this article heading, was also discussed in Art. 5, where it was shown that in dealing with multipliers of this nature it is speedier to multiply by their factors than by their digits, thus eliminating the need for adding partial products. In choosing the technique for multiplying by 56 one may be guided by the nature of the multiplicand. The multiplicand 204, for instance, lends itself admirably to the factor method—for 204 can be multiplied mentally by either of the factors 7 and 8 without any effort—whereas the number 143 may be more easily multiplied by 56 by the method indicated in this article.

Following are some interesting examples with their solutions. Note that to multiply by 44, 33 or 22, one has the choice of multiplying first by 11 (by the method discussed in Art. 1-f), then by 4, 3 or 2, as the case may be; or, one may compute, respectively, 4, 3 or 2 times the multiplicand and add 10 times the result.

Example 1: Multiply 143 by 56.

Solution: 100 times 143   = 14300
      −   44 times 143 (4 times 1573) = 6292

         56 times 143   = 8008

Example 2: Multiply 724 by 67.

Solution: 100 times 724   = 72400
      −   33 times 724 (3 times 7964) = 23892

         67 times 724   = 48508

Example 3: Multiply 283 by 78.

Solution: 100 times 283   = 28300
       − 22 times 283 (2 times 3113) = 6226

        78 times 283   = 22074

Example 4: Multiply 836 by 89.

Solution: 100 times 836 = 83600
       − 11 times 836 = 9196

        89 times 836 = 74404

As the reader may have noticed by this time, the above technique provides two advantages: First, instead of multiplying by two different digits in each instance, we multiply only by one; second, instead of multiplying by the high digits 5, 6, 7, 8 and 9, our multipliers are confined to the low and easy digits 1, 2, 3 and 4.

With the multipliers 560, 670, 780 and 890 it is but necessary to work the problem as though these numbers were 56, 67, 78, and 89 respectively, by the method indicated in this article, and then multiply the result by 10.

Example 5: Compute the cost of 890 gallons of paint at $3.15 a gallon.

Solution: 100 times $3.15   = $ 315.00
       − 11 times $3.15   =   34.65

        89 times $3.15   = $ 280.35
        890 times $3.15 (10 times $280.35) = $2803.50

PROBLEMS

1. A department store advertises a hardware item as a Saturday special and, as a result, sells 369 units at a gross profit of 56 cents per unit. What did the store's total gross profit on this item amount to for the day?   *Ans.* $206.64.

2. What will a dealer have to pay for 56 radios purchased at a flat price of $16.85 each?   *Ans.* $943.60.

3. Compute the cost of 83 short tons of newsprint rolls at the market price of $67.00 per short ton. *Ans.* $5561.00.

4. What will 670 yards of 28-inch denim cost at the market price of $0.256 per yard? *Ans.* $171.52.

5. At 78 cents a square foot what would it cost to treat a concrete floor having an area of 326.5 square feet? *Ans.* $254.67.

6. A manufacturer finds that a product he is about to put on the market requires the use of 78 square feet of canvas. If he expects to sell 3 gross units how much canvas will he need? *Ans.* 33,696 square feet.

7. A salesman's commission is 89 cents per instrument. If he receives an order for 240 units, what commission will he have earned on the sale? *Ans.* $213.60.

8. The gross weight of a tub containing 20 pounds of butter is 28 pounds. Find the gross weight of 89 tubs. *Ans.* 2492 pounds.

10. How to Multiply Quickly and Easily by $68\frac{1}{2}$, 79, $89\frac{1}{2}$. In the previous article we found it very convenient, in dealing with certain multipliers, to multiply first by 100. In this article we will find that the same technique can be applied to another class of numbers. Whereas in the previous article the difference between 100 and the multiplier consisted of two like digits, here the difference constitutes a number in which one part is an exact multiple of the other. Thus 100 minus $68\frac{1}{2}$ equals $31\frac{1}{2}$, and 30 is exactly two times $1\frac{1}{2}$; 100 minus 79 equals 21, and 20 is exactly 20 times 1; 100 minus $89\frac{1}{2}$ equals $10\frac{1}{2}$, and here, too, one part of the difference is exactly 20 times the other part.

The following illustrative examples demonstrate how one can multiply by any of the numbers under discussion with a minimum expenditure of effort.

Example 1: Multiply 817 by $68\frac{1}{2}$.

Solution:

$$
\begin{array}{lll}
100 \text{ times } 817 & & = 81700 \\
-\left\{ \begin{array}{l} 30 \text{ times } 817 \\ 1\frac{1}{2} \text{ times } 817 \ (\frac{1}{2} \text{ of } 2451) \end{array} \right. & \begin{array}{l} = 24510 \\ = 1225\frac{1}{2} \end{array} & \\
& & = 25735\frac{1}{2} \\
\hline
68\frac{1}{2} \text{ times } 817 & & = 55964\frac{1}{2}
\end{array}
$$

Example 2: Multiply $347.28 by 79.

Solution: 100 times $347.28   = $34728.00

— $\begin{cases} 20 \text{ times } \$347.28 = \$6945.60 \\ 1 \text{ times } \$347.28 = 347.28 \end{cases}$

                                                    =   7292.88

79 times $347.28   = $27435.12

Example 3: Multiply $413.52 by 89½.

Solution: 100 times $413.52   = $41352.00

— $\begin{cases} 10 \text{ times } \$413.52 = \$4135.20 \\ \frac{1}{2} \text{ of } \$413.52 = 206.76 \end{cases}$

                                                    =   4341.96

89½ times $413.52   = $37010.04

Note that here, as in the previous article, instead of having to multiply by two high digits, we multiply by a single low digit and divide the partial product by 20.

PROBLEMS

1. There are approximately 876, 2d, common wire nails in one pound. What quantity might be expected to be contained in a keg whose net weight is 79 pounds?   *Ans.* 69,204.

2. Maple wood has a specific gravity of .79. What would the weight be of 143 cubic feet? Compute the answer to the nearest pound. (One cubic foot of water weighs 62.5 pounds.)   *Ans.* 7061 pounds.

3. If there are 3.71 feet of 1-inch diameter 3-strand Manila rope in one pound, how many feet would there be in 68½ pounds?
                                                    Ans. 254.135 feet.

4. Two girls are employed at the rate of 86 cents an hour. What is the amount of their combined earnings if each is entitled to 34¼ hours pay?   *Ans.* $58.91.

5. A dealer disposed of 89½ yards of material at $2.46 a yard. How much did he receive?   *Ans.* $220.17.

6. If one foot of $\frac{3}{8}$-inch straight link chain weighs 1.58 pounds, what would 89$\frac{1}{2}$ feet weigh?   *Ans.* 141.41 pounds.

11. A Short Way of Multiplying by Three-Digit Numbers Which Are Divisible by 11, Such as 374, 572, 781. Having in mind the simple process by which *two*-digit numbers can be multiplied quickly by 11 (Art. 1-f), let us see how easy it is to multiply by three-digit numbers which are divisible by 11.

Let us suppose we wish to multiply 647 by 374.   Now 374 is divisible by 11.   In order words, it is the product of 11 times 34. So that 11 times the product of 34 times 647 would produce the same result as 374 times 647.

Let us compute the answer to this problem, first by the conventional method, then by the short method, and consider the advantage of this short-cut.

Conventional Method	Short Method
647	647
374	34
—	—
2588	2588
4529	1941
1941	—

34 times 647 = 21998
340 times 647 = 219980

Conventional Method answer: 241978

241978

Under the conventional method it was necessary to have three separate partial products; under the short method, only two partial products, for—having already computed 34 times 647—it was unnecessary to compute 340 times 647.   True, under the short method the partial products and the answer contain twenty-four figures, compared with but eighteen figures under the conventional method, but the effort-saving advantage of eliminating the need for multiplying by 7 and the reduction of the possibility of error more than compensates for the effortless writing down of the extra few figures.

It is interesting to observe that there are 36 three-digit numbers divisible by 11, as follows:

121	231	341	451	561	671	781	891
132	242	352	462	572	682	792	
143	253	363	473	583	693		
154	264	374	484	594			
165	275	385	495				
176	286	396					
187	297						
198							

For the last number in each column of this tabulation there is a still shorter method of multiplying by 11, and this will be discussed in a succeeding article. For the number 275, too, there is a shorter method, for this number may be broken up into the two numbers 250 and 25—so that to multiply by 275 it is but necessary to multiply by 250 and add one tenth of the result.

The first two numbers—namely, 121 and 132—are especially interesting for this reason: 121 being the product of 11 times 11, and 132 being the product of 11 times 12, it is but necessary (when the multiplier is 121) to first multiply by 11, or (when the multiplier is 132) to first multiply by 12, then to add 10 times the partial product.

Example 1: Multiply 483 by 121.

Solution: 11 times 483   = 5313
           110 times 483 (10 times 5313) = 53130

———

           121 times 483   = 58443

Example 2: Multiply 583 by 132.

Solution: 12 times 583   = 6996
           120 times 583 (10 times 6996) = 69960

———

           132 times 583   = 76956

Example 3: The production capacity of a plant manufacturing mechanical pencils is 682 gross per 8-hour day. If the plant operated continually for 128 business days, how many gross pencils would be produced in that time?

Solution: 62 times 128   = 7,936
620 times 128 (10 times 7936) = 79,360

682 times 128   = 87,296

Ans. 87,296 gross pencils.

PROBLEMS

1. Compute the weight of a strip of ice occupying 17.25 cubic feet. (The weight of one cubic foot of ice is 57.2 pounds.) *Ans.* 986.7 pounds.

2. Brazilian green coffee in double jute burlap bags weighs 132 pounds per bag. How much will 326 bags weigh? *Ans.* 43,032 pounds.

3. If a foot of flat bar steel $1\frac{3}{4}$ inches wide and $1\frac{1}{8}$ inches thick weighs 6.71 pounds, what will $76\frac{1}{4}$ feet weigh? Compute the answer to the nearest pound. *Ans.* 512 pounds.

4. How much will 26.75 bales of Spanish moss weigh if the weight of a full bale is 17.6 pounds? *Ans.* 470.8 pounds.

5. Compute the total yardage in each of the following cases:

(a) 143 pounds of narrow print cloth measuring 4.63 yards to the pound. *Ans.* 662.09 yards.

(b) 253 pounds of wide, gray drill fabric of which there are 1.94 yards to the pound. *Ans.* 490.82 yards.

(c) 341 pounds of cord fabric at $23\frac{1}{4}$ yards per pound.

Ans. $7928\frac{1}{4}$ yards.

12. How to Multiply Quickly and Easily by Numbers Which When the Unit Digit Is Increased to 10 Constitute a Multiple of the Number Added, e.g., 38 Increased to 40, 57 to 60, $28\frac{1}{2}$ to 30, $47\frac{1}{2}$ to 50, 133 to 140, 237 to 240. The method of dealing with these multipliers might be regarded as a refinement of the technique discussed in Art. 6. Familiarity with the speedy way of multiplying by 27, 36, etc., will make an understanding of the method to be discussed here a very simple matter.

Just as the unit digits in the multipliers considered in Art. 6 were increased to 10 (27 increased to 30, 36 to 40, etc.), so the unit digits with which we are concerned here are also increased to 10. Thus 38 is increased to 40, 57 to 60, and so on.

The only difference is in the next step. In increasing to 10 the unit digit of two-figure multipliers divisible by 9 (as for example 27 increased to 30) the tens digit of the new number is exactly the same as the number added to the original multiplier. Here (38 increased to 40, 57 to 60, etc.) the tens digit of the new number is a *multiple* of the number added to the original multiplier— 4 being a multiple of 2, 6 a multiple of 3, and so on. Conversely— and this applies equally to the multipliers treated in Art. 6—the number added to the original multiplier is an aliquot part of the increased number—that is, it is exactly divisible into it. Thus $1\frac{1}{2}$ (added to $28\frac{1}{2}$ to increase this number to 30) is one twentieth of 30, and $2\frac{1}{2}$ (added to $47\frac{1}{2}$ to bring it up to 50) is one twentieth of 50.

It is plain, therefore, that to multiply by 38, instead of multiplying by 8 and by 3, we might multiply by 40 and subtract from the result one twentieth of the result. Similarly, to multiply by $28\frac{1}{2}$, we might multiply by 30 and subtract from the result one twentieth of the result. And so on.

Example 1: Multiply 28 by 38.

Solution: 40 times 28   = 1120
  − 2 times 28 ($\frac{1}{20}$ of 1120) =   56
  _____
  38 times 28   = 1064

Example 2: Multiply \$119.46 by $28\frac{1}{2}$.

Solution: 30   times \$119.46 (3 times \$1194.60) = \$3583.80
  − $1\frac{1}{2}$ times \$119.46 ($\frac{1}{20}$ of \$3583.80) =   179.19
  _____
  $28\frac{1}{2}$ times \$119.46   = \$3404.61

In multiplying by three-digit numbers in which the increased number constitutes a multiple of the number added to the original multiplier, a procedure in reverse makes it possible to limit the number of partial products to two. In other words, instead of multiplying first by the hundreds and tens digits we multiply first by the number added to the original multiplier. The procedure will be explained better with illustrations.

Example 3: Multiply $129.43 by 133.

Solution: (Note that the partial product of 140 times $129.43 is computed *after* and is written *above* the first partial product.)

Second step: 140 times $129.43
(20 times $906.01) = $18,120.20 (B)

First step: — 7 times $129.43 = 906.01 (A)

---

133 times $129.43
(B minus A) = $17,214.19

Example 4: Multiply 429 by 237.

Solution:

Second step: 240 times 429 (80 times 1287) = 102960 (B)

First step: — 3 times 429 = 1287 (A)

---

237 times 429 (B minus A) = 101673

A noteworthy example of the frequency with which the technique demonstrated in Examples 3 and 4 may be used is a paragraph in an announcement made by the New York State Division of Placement and Unemployment Insurance concerning unemployment insurance tax rebates to be distributed to employers in the year 1946. The report of the announcement as published in *The New York Times* for September 14, 1946, is as follows:

Under the terms of distribution announced yesterday employers with the best records will get back an amount equal to 1.18 per cent of their taxable payrolls for the calendar year 1945. This represents 43.6 per cent of the unemployment insurance taxes they were liable for in 1945 and will have the effect of reducing their 1945 tax rate from the 2.7 per cent of payrolls, specified by law, to 1.52 per cent.

In this single paragraph are four per cent rates, and each one of them exemplifies the flexibility of the technique discussed in this

TABLE I

THREE-DIGIT NUMBERS WHICH WHEN THE UNIT DIGITS ARE INCREASED
TO 10 CONSTITUTE MULTIPLES OF THE NUMBERS ADDED *

To Multiply by	A Subtract the Product of the Multiplicand Times	B And Add the Product of the Figure Obtained in the First Computation (A), Times
114	6	20
116	4	30
117	3	40
118	2	60
133	7	20
145	5	30
147	3	50
152	8	20
156	4	40
158	2	80
177	3	60
178	2	90
218	2	110
232	8	30
234	6	40
236	4	60
237	3	80
238	2	120
245	5	50
276	4	70
312	8	40
316	4	80
327	3	110
345	5	70
354	6	60
356	4	90
357	3	120
413	7	60
414	6	70
436	4	110
445	5	90
472	8	60
474	6	80
476	4	120
483	7	70
534	6	90
545	5	110
623	7	90

* Note that to multiply by any of these numbers it is necessary to compute
only two partial products, as indicated in Examples 3 and 4 in Art. 11.

article. Note in the following illustration the practicability of multiplying by these per-cent rates by this technique:

2.7 is the equivalent of 3 minus .3
43.6 is the equivalent of 44 minus .4
1.18 is the equivalent of minus .02 plus 60 times .02
1.52 is the equivalent of minus .08 plus 20 times .08

Example 5: A manufacturer's taxable payroll for the year 1945 was \$113,620.00. If he was credited with a rebate of 1.18% of this figure, how much of a refund should he have received?

Solution:

Second step: 1.2% of \$113,620.00 (60 times
                         \$22.724)   = \$1363.44
First step: − .02% of \$113,620.00 ($\frac{2}{100}$ of
                         1% of \$113,620.00, or
                         twice \$11.362)   =   22.724
_____

          1.18% of \$113,620.00   = \$1340.72

A delightful study of the numbers dealt with in this discussion and others of a similar nature will be found in Table I.

PROBLEMS

1. If a ton of soft coal occupies 38 cubic feet, what space will be occupied by 62 tons?   *Ans.* 2356 cubic feet.

2. If a bushel basket of plums weighs 57 pounds, how many pounds will 73 baskets weigh?   *Ans.* 4161 pounds.

3. A barrel of brewer's pitch occupies 11.7 cubic feet. Compute the amount of space that would be occupied by 37 barrels?
                                               Ans. 432.9 cubic feet.

4. Find the cost of 234 machine parts priced at $28\frac{1}{2}$ cents each.
                                               Ans. \$66.69.

5. An employee receiving time-and-a-half pay for time put in over 40 hours in one week, works a total of 45 hours from Monday to Saturday. If his rate of pay is 86 cents an hour, what will he have earned for the week? (Hint: 40 hours plus 5 hours overtime is equivalent to $47\frac{1}{2}$ hours straight time.)   *Ans.* \$40.85.

6. What will the transportation charges amount to on a carton weighing 133 pounds shipped by air express from New York to Augusta, Maine, if the air express rate between these points on shipments exceeding 40 pounds in weight is 9.21 cents per pound?   *Ans.* $12.24.

13. A Short Way of Multiplying by Numbers in Which One Part Is an Exact Multiple of, or Is Exactly Divisible into, the Rest of the Number, e.g., 84, 48, 123, 312, 1938, 3612, $73\frac{1}{2}$, $1894\frac{1}{2}$. A studied observation will reveal an interesting fact about these numbers. Note that in 84, 80 is exactly twenty times the rest of the number (the unit digit 4), and that in 48 the 8 is exactly two tenths of 40; that in 123, 120 is exactly 40 times 3, and that in 312 the 12 is four hundredths of 300.

Observation of relationships of this nature saves time and labor in working problems, as will be seen in the illustrations that follow.

Example 1: Multiply 234 by 84.

Solution: 4 times 234   =   936
        80 times 234 (20 times 936) = 18720
        _____

        84 times 234   = 19656

Example 1A: Multiply 234 by 48.

Solution: 40 times 234   =   9360
        8 times 234 ($\frac{2}{10}$ of 9360) =   1872
        _____

        48 times 234   = 11232

Example 2: Multiply 431 by 123.

Solution: 3 times 431   =   1293
        120 times 431 (40 times 1293) = 51720
        _____

        123 times 431   = 53013

Example 2A: Multiply 431 by 312.

Solution: 300 times 431   = 129300
        12 times 431 ($\frac{4}{100}$ of 129300) =   5172
        _____

        312 times 431   = 134472

Example 3: Multiply 3467 by 1938.

Solution: 1900 times 3467   = 6587300
        38 times 3467 ($\frac{2}{100}$ of 6587300) =   131746

___

        1938 times 3467   = 6719046

Example 3A: Multiply 3467 by 3819.

Solution: 19 times 3467   =   65873
         3800 times 3467 (200 times 65873) = 13174600

___

         3819 times 3467   = 13240473

Example 4: Multiply 1237 by 3612.

Solution: 12 times 1237   =   14844
         3600 times 1237 (300 times 14844) = 4453200

___

         3612 times 1237   = 4468044

Example 4A: Multiply 1237 by 1236.

Solution: 1200 times 1237   = 1484400
          36 times 1237 ($\frac{3}{100}$ of 1484400) =   44532

___

         1236 times 1237   = 1528932

In the following illustrations the multiplier contains a fraction.

Example 5: Multiply 637 by $73\frac{1}{2}$.

Solution: 70   times 637   = 44590
        $3\frac{1}{2}$ times 637 ($\frac{1}{20}$ of 44590) = $2229\frac{1}{2}$

___

        $73\frac{1}{2}$ times 637   = $46819\frac{1}{2}$

Example 6: Multiply 428 by $1894\frac{1}{2}$.

Solution:

90	times 428	= 38520
$4\frac{1}{2}$	times 428 ($\frac{1}{20}$ of 38520)	= 1926
1800	times 428 (20 times 38520)	= 770400

$1894\frac{1}{2}$ times 428	= 810846

In the foregoing examples multipliers were used in which a part of the number is divisible into the rest of the number an *exact* number of times. Exact divisibility, however, need not constitute a limitation of the use of this method, as will be evident in the illustration that follows.

Example 7: Multiply 368 by $186\frac{1}{2}$.

Solution:

$\frac{1}{2}$	of 368	= 184
6	times 368	= 2208
180	times 368 (30 times 2208)	= 66240

$186\frac{1}{2}$ times 368	= 68632

The use of this technique need not be confined to multiplication problems in which either factor contains fewer than five figures. But in dealing with numbers of five figures it may not have the same time-saving advantage in all instances, though its use in proving computations is highly recommended. The following example, however, is of particular interest because in the multiplicand as well as in the multiplier one part of the number is an exact multiple of the other.

Example 8: Multiply 16482 by 243.

Solution:

3 times 82	=	246
240 times 82 (80 times 246)	=	19680

243 times 82	=	19926
243 times 16400 (200 times 19926)	=	3985200

243 times 16482	= 4005126

The reader is urged to try a few examples of his own, making use of Tables II, III and IV, which list numbers in which divisibility is exact. Skill in the technique may be further developed by trying examples with numbers in which divisibility is not exact, as 365, 728½ and 286.

Readers whose appetite is whetted by the fascinating study in Table IV will be interested to know that this short-cut method of multiplication can be extended to still other numbers, as follows.

8976 (8800 plus 176), 176 representing $\frac{2}{100}$ of 8800
7854 (7700 plus 154), 154 representing $\frac{2}{100}$ of 7700
7931 (7700 plus 231), 231 representing $\frac{3}{100}$ of 7700
6732 (6600 plus 132), 132 representing $\frac{2}{100}$ of 6600
6798 (6600 plus 198), 198 representing $\frac{3}{100}$ of 6600

Four-digit numbers of this nature are few. But the mathematically inclined will be quick to recognize the time-saving advantage of always being on the lookout for ideal combinations of figures as exemplified in these numbers. If one is to multiply by a number like 6798, it certainly is much simpler to multiply by the two digits 6 and 3 than by the four digits 6, 7, 9 and 8.

TABLE II

Two-Figure and Three-Figure Numbers in Which the Unit Digit Is Divisible into the Rest of the Number an Exact Number of Times

The Unit Digit Is Divisible into the Rest of the Number	Unit Digit							
	2	3	4	5	6	7	8	9
90 times	182	273	364	455	546	637	728	819
80 times	162	243	324	405	486	567	648	729
70 times	142	213	284	355	426	497	568	639
60 times	122	183	244	305	366	427	488	549
50 times	102	153	204	255	306	357	408	459
40 times	82	123	164	205	246	287	328	369
30 times	62	93	124	155	186	217	248	279
20 times	42	63	84	105	126	147	168	189

TABLE III

THREE-FIGURE NUMBERS IN WHICH THE HUNDREDS DIGIT, TAKEN AS AN INDIVIDUAL NUMBER, IS DIVISIBLE INTO THE REST OF THE NUMBER AN EXACT NUMBER OF TIMES *

Relationship Between the Hundreds Digit, Taken as an Individual Number, and the Rest of the Number	Hundreds Digit							
	2	3	4	5	6	7	8	9
100 ninths	218	327	436	545	654	763	872	981
100 eighths	216	324	432	540	648	756	864	972
100 sevenths	214	321	428	535	642	749	856	963
100 sixths	212	318	424	530	636	742	848	954
100 fifths	210	315	420	525	630	735	840	945
100 fourths	208	312	416	520	624	728	832	936
100 thirds	206	309	412	515	618	721	824	927
100 halves	204	306	408	510	612	714	816	918

* Note the interesting relationship between the numbers in this table and the numbers in Table II. By lifting the unit digit in any number in Table II and placing it ahead of the hundreds digit (or ahead of a zero when there is no hundreds digit) we obtain the corresponding number in Table III. Thus 182 in Table II becomes 218 in Table III; 82 (which is the same as 082) becomes 208, 328 becomes 832, and so on.

In Examples 5, 6 and 7 we saw that the use of the technique under discussion may be extended to numbers containing the fraction $\frac{1}{2}$. The method can, in fact, be used very conveniently with other numbers too. Since $5\frac{1}{2}$ is half of 11, and $2\frac{3}{4}$ is half of $5\frac{1}{2}$, it is easy to see that in a number like $2202\frac{3}{4}$, $2\frac{3}{4}$ is exactly divisible into 2200—11 is $\frac{1}{200}$ of 2200, $5\frac{1}{2}$ is $\frac{1}{400}$ of 2200, and $2\frac{3}{4}$ is $\frac{1}{800}$ of 2200.

Example 9: Multiply 1684 by $2202\frac{3}{4}$.

Solution: 2200 times 1684 (11 times 336800)   = 3704800

$2\frac{3}{4}$ times 1684 ($\frac{1}{800}$ of 3704800 or $\frac{1}{8}$ of 37048)   =   4631

$2202\frac{3}{4}$ times 1684   = 3709431

The number $2102\frac{1}{3}$ is another typical example. If we multiply $2\frac{1}{3}$ by the denominator in the fraction we see at a glance that the product 7 is exactly divisible into 2100. Seven is $\frac{1}{300}$ of 2100, and $2\frac{1}{3}$, which is one third of 7, is $\frac{1}{900}$ of 2100. It is a simple

TABLE IV

SHOWING THE EXTENSIVE NUMBER OF FOUR-FIGURE COMBINATIONS IN WHICH
THE FIRST TWO FIGURES ARE AN EXACT MULTIPLE OF, OR ARE EXACTLY
DIVISIBLE INTO, THE LAST TWO FIGURES

Numbers 11 to 19

2211	1122	3015	1530
3311	1133	4515	1545
4411	1144	6015	1560
5511	1155	7515	1575
6611	1166	9015	1590
7711	1177		
8811	1188	3216	1632
9911	1199	4816	1648
		6416	1664
2412	1224	8016	1680
3612	1236	9616	1696
4812	1248		
6012	1260	3417	1734
7212	1272	5117	1751
8412	1284	6817	1768
9612	1296	8517	1785
2613	1326	3618	1836
3913	1339	5418	1854
5213	1352	7218	1872
6513	1365	9018	1890
7813	1378		
9113	1391	3819	1938
		5719	1957
2814	1428	7619	1976
4214	1442	9519	1995
5614	1456		
7014	1470		
8414	1484		
9814	1498		

TABLE IV (*Continued*)

Numbers 21 to 29

4221	2142	5025	2550
6321	2163	7525	2575
8421	2184		
		5226	2652
4422	2244	7826	2678
6622	2266		
8822	2288	5427	2754
		8127	2781
4623	2346		
6923	2369	5628	2856
9223	2392	8428	2884
4824	2448	5829	2958
7224	2472	8729	2987
9624	2496		

Numbers 31 to 39

6231	3162	7035	3570
9331	3193		
		7236	3672
6432	3264		
9632	3296	7437	3774
6633	3366	7638	3876
9933	3399		
		7839	3978
6834	3468		

Numbers 41 to 49

8241	4182	9246	4692
8442	4284	9447	4794
8643	4386	9648	4896
8844	4488	9849	4998
9045	4590		

matter, therefore, when the multiplier is $2102\frac{1}{3}$, to multiply first by 2100, then to add to the result $\frac{1}{900}$ of the result.

Example 10: Multiply 4914 by $2102\frac{1}{3}$.

Solution: 2100 times 4914   = 10319400

    $2\frac{1}{3}$ times 4914 ($\frac{1}{900}$ of 10319400 or $\frac{1}{9}$

      of 103194)   =   11466

    $2102\frac{1}{3}$ times 4914   = 10330866

To the reader who is as yet unaccustomed to working problems of this nature the application of the technique to certain numbers may seem labyrinthine. With a little practice, however, the method may become amazingly simple. Furthermore, it offers an excellent means of checking computations worked by other methods.

There are any number of variations or combinations in which one part of a number is an exact multiple of, or is exactly divisible into, the other part. Taking the number 4221, for instance, here are just a few of the many possible variations.

$4210\frac{1}{2}$ ($10\frac{1}{2}$ is $\frac{1}{400}$ of 4200, and 4200 is 400 times $10\frac{1}{2}$)
$4205\frac{1}{4}$ ($5\frac{1}{4}$ is $\frac{1}{800}$ of 4200, and 4200 is 800 times $5\frac{1}{4}$)
$4215\frac{3}{4}$ ($15\frac{3}{4}$ is $\frac{3}{800}$ of 4200, and 4200 is $\frac{1}{3}$ of 800 times $15\frac{3}{4}$)

Or take the number 6416.

6408 (6400 is 800 times 8, and 8 is $\frac{2}{100}$ of 400)
6406 (6 is $\frac{1}{1000}$ of 6000, and 6000 is 1000 times 6)
6403 (3 is $\frac{1}{2000}$ of 6000, and 6000 is 2000 times 3)
6402 (2 is $\frac{1}{200}$ of 400, and 400 is 200 times 2)
$6401\frac{1}{2}$ ($1\frac{1}{2}$ is $\frac{1}{4000}$ of 6000, and 6000 is 4000 times $1\frac{1}{2}$)

It is interesting to observe that combinations similar to those in Table IV can be had in five-figure numbers in which the middle figure is a zero. Thus in 77011 the first two digits are an exact multiple of the last two digits, just as they are in 7711; and that in 11077 the last two digits are an exact multiple of the first two digits, just as they are in 1177. It should be noted, however, that while one pair of digits is an exact multiple of the other pair, the values in the two sets of numbers are different. Thus in 7711 the first two digits (whose value is 7700) is the equivalent of seven *hundred* times 11, whereas in 77011 the first two digits (whose value is 77000) is the equivalent of seven *thousand* times 11.

EXERCISES

Multiply 723.4 by each of the following numbers, using the procedure indicated:

1. 63. Multiply by 3 and add 20 times the result.
2. 284. Multiply by 4 and add 70 times the result.
3. 567. Multiply by 7 and add 80 times the result.
4. 328. Multiply by 8 and add 40 times the result.
5. 1860. Multiply by 60 and add 30 times the result.
6. 1470. Multiply by 70 and add 20 times the result.
7. 642. Multiply by 600 and add $\frac{7}{100}$ of the result.
8. 756. Multiply by 700 and add $\frac{8}{100}$ of the result.
9. 936. Multiply by 900 and add $\frac{4}{100}$ of the result.
10. 1272. Multiply by 1200 and add $\frac{6}{100}$ of the result.

PROBLEMS

1. Compute the total number of yards contained in 84 pounds of typewriter cambric of which there are 5.06 yards to the pound.
Ans. 425.04 yards.

2. A power hack saw makes 126 strokes per minute. If it worked continually for 2 hours and 3 minutes, how many strokes would it have made in that time? *Ans.* 15,498 strokes.

3. If a bushel of wheat makes 315 loaves of bread each weighing one pound two ounces, how many loaves of this weight can be made with 473 bushels of wheat? *Ans.* 148,995 loaves.

4. Compute the value in dollars and cents of 876 Venezuelan bolivars, quoted at 30.15 cents per bolivar. *Ans.* $264.11.

5. How many quart bottles can be filled from 34 barrels, each having a capacity of 31½ gallons? *Ans.* 4284.

6. If the capacity of a U. S. dry barrel is 7056 cubic inches, what would be the cubic inch capacity of 13.75 dry barrels?
Ans. 97,020 cubic inches.

7. What is the amount of a fire insurance premium on a $2,400,000 policy issued at the rate of $0.0426 per $100?   *Ans.* $1022.40.

8. Convert 387 grains to grams. (To convert grains to grams multiply by .0648.)   *Ans.* 25.0776 grams.

9. Five cows produced a total of 43,364 pounds of milk during one year. The next year their production increased 12.3%. What was their total production in the second year? Compute the answer to the nearest pound.   *Ans.* 48,698 pounds.

14. A Short Way of Multiplying by Three-Digit Numbers in Which When Increased to an Even Hundred the Hundreds Digit Is Exactly Divisible into, or Is an Exact Multiple of, the Number Added, e.g., 288, 360, 576, 693, 897. Except for the nature of the numbers to be considered here the method of procedure is essentially the same as that discussed in preceding articles. While in Arts. 9 and 10 we saw the advisability, in dealing with certain multipliers having a value of less than 100, of first multiplying by 100, and while in Art. 12 we found it convenient, in dealing with other types of multipliers, to first increase the unit digit to 10, here we are going to increase three-digit numbers to an even hundred.

It will be interesting to observe that several numbers which are multiples of a gross lend themselves perfectly to the application of this short-cut method of multiplication. The number 288, for instance, equals 2 gross; 576 equals 4 gross; 720, 5 gross, and so on.

Example 1: Multiply 647 by 288.

Solution:

$$300 \text{ times } 647 = 194100$$
$$-\ 12 \text{ times } 647\ (\tfrac{4}{100} \text{ of } 194100) = 7764$$

$$288 \text{ times } 647 = 186336$$

Example 2: Multiply $538.26 by 360.

Solution:

$$400 \text{ times } \$538.26 = \$215{,}304.00$$
$$-\ 40 \text{ times } \$538.26\ (\tfrac{1}{10} \text{ of } \$215{,}304.00) = 21{,}530.40$$

$$360 \text{ times } \$538.26 = \$193{,}773.60$$

Example 3: Multiply $273\frac{1}{6}$ by 576.

Solution:

$$600 \text{ times } 273\tfrac{1}{6} \ (100 \text{ times } 1639) = 163900$$
$$- \ 24 \text{ times } 273\tfrac{1}{6} \ (\tfrac{4}{100} \text{ of } 163900) = 6556$$

$$576 \text{ times } 273\tfrac{1}{6} \qquad\qquad\qquad = 157344$$

Note in the foregoing illustration the helpfulness of our imaginative reach when confronted by a multiplicand which contains a fraction. Instead of multiplying by 6, 7 and 5, and then adding the fourth partial product of $\frac{1}{6}$ of 576, we simply added 100 times the product of $273\frac{1}{6}$ multiplied by 6 to $\frac{4}{100}$ of the result. In the example that follows the fruitfulness of this method is even more apparent.

Example 4: Multiply $813\frac{1}{7}$ by 693.

Solution:

$$700 \text{ times } 813\tfrac{1}{7} \ (100 \text{ times } 5692) = 569200$$
$$- \ 7 \text{ times } 813\tfrac{1}{7} \phantom{\ (100 \text{ times } 5692)} = 5692$$

$$693 \text{ times } 813\tfrac{1}{7} \qquad\qquad\qquad = 563508$$

The illustration that follows is a noteworthy example of the usefulness of the technique indicated in Examples 3 and 4 in Art. 12.

Example 5: Multiply $\$16.33\frac{1}{3}$ by 897.

Solution:

Second step.　$900 \text{ times } \$16.33\tfrac{1}{3}$
$$(300 \text{ times } \$49.00) = \$14,700.00$$
First step.　$- \ 3 \text{ times } \$16.33\tfrac{1}{3} = 49.00$

$$897 \text{ times } \$16.33\tfrac{1}{3} \qquad = \$14,651.00$$

Example 6: If a sheet of asbestos mill board 42 by 48 inches weighs 5.82 pounds, how much will 239 sheets of these dimensions weigh?

Solution: 6 times 239 $= 1434$
    $-$ .18 times 239 ($\frac{3}{100}$ of 1434) $= \quad 43.02$

   5.82 times 239 $= 1390.98$

           Ans. 1390.98 pounds.

Exercises

Multiply 258 by each of the following numbers, using the technique indicated:

1. 297. Multiply by 300 and subtract $\frac{1}{100}$ of the result.
2. 285. Multiply by 300 and subtract $\frac{1}{20}$ of the result.
3. 294. Multiply by 300 and subtract $\frac{2}{100}$ of the result.
4. 396. Multiply by 400 and subtract $\frac{1}{100}$ of the result.
5. 392. Multiply by 400 and subtract $\frac{2}{100}$ of the result.
6. 475. Multiply by 500 and subtract $\frac{5}{100}$ of the result.
7. 594. Multiply by 600 and subtract $\frac{1}{100}$ of the result.
8. 528. Multiply by 600 and subtract $\frac{12}{100}$ of the result.
9. 784. Multiply by 800 and subtract $\frac{2}{100}$ of the result.
10. 873. Multiply by 900 and subtract $\frac{3}{100}$ of the result.

Problems

1. What would the total net weight be of 138 pint containers of cream containing 28% butter fat, if cream of this butter-fat content weighs 8.37 pounds per gallon? Compute the answer to the nearest pound. *Ans.* 144 pounds.

2. Find the cost of $3\frac{3}{4}$ dozen units at $2.97 per dozen. *Ans.* $11.14.

3. Steam at 100° C. has a weight of 0.598 grams per liter. Compute the weight of 374 liters. *Ans.* 223.652 grams.

4. A square foot of iron 0.072 inches thick weighs 2.88 pounds. What will 37 square feet weigh? *Ans.* 106.56 pounds.

5. A barrel of cement weighs 376 pounds. Find the weight of 34 barrels. *Ans.* 12,784 pounds.

6. If a 4-inch pump has a discharge capacity of 380 gallons per minute, how many gallons would be discharged in 4 hours 17 minutes? *Ans.* 97,660 gallons.

7. Pure chromium weighs 6.93 grams per cubic centimeter. Compute the weight of 492 cubic centimeters. *Ans.* 3409.56 grams.

8. A foot of flat bar steel $\frac{5}{16}$ inches thick and 7 inches wide weighs 7.44 pounds. How much will 276 feet weigh? *Ans.* 2053.44 pounds.

9. In 1946 the import duty on hats for women and girls, valued at over \$9.00 but not over \$12.00 per dozen, was $41\frac{2}{3}$ cents each, plus 25%. On that basis what duty would an importer have to pay on a shipment of 4 gross hats purchased at \$10.50 per dozen. (Hint: The 25% is computed on the purchase price—namely, \$10.50 per dozen.) *Ans.* \$366.00.

15. A Short Way of Multiplying by Four-Digit Numbers in Which When Increased to an Even Hundred the Thousands and Hundreds Digits Are Alike and, Taken Together, Are an Exact Multiple of, or Are Exactly Divisible into, the Number Added, e.g., 8756, 3267, 4378, 2189, 2156, 4312. In order to quickly appreciate and understand the method to be taken up now, the reader will find it of value to review the procedure studied in Art. 9. He will note that the numbers dealt with in that article—namely, 56, 67, 78 and 89—occur as the last two digits in some of the numbers mentioned in the heading of the present article.

In Art. 9 we discovered that to multiply by 56, 67, 78 or 89, it is simpler to first multiply by 100, then to subtract the product of the multiplicand times 44, 33, 22 or 11, as the case may be. This procedure is more convenient because it is easier to multiply by 11 or a multiple of 11 than to multiply by pairs of digits like 56, 67, 78 and 89.

We will now find it convenient to use a similar technique for multiplying by a variety of four-digit numbers. Note that when 8756 is increased to 8800 there is a distinct relationship between the number added (44) and the increased number (8800)—44 is exactly $\frac{1}{200}$ of 8800. Similarly, when 3267 is increased to 3300, the number added (33) is exactly $\frac{1}{100}$ of 3300; when 4378 is increased to 4400, the number added (22) is exactly $\frac{1}{200}$ of 4400; and when 2189 is increased to 2200, the number added (11) is exactly $\frac{1}{200}$ of 2200. On the other hand, when 2156 is increased to 2200, 22 is exactly divisible into 44, the number added; and when 4312 is increased to 4400, 44 is exactly divisible into 88.

Having in mind the related technique discussed in Arts. 12, 13 and 14, the reader will scarcely need to be instructed further in the time-saving method now under consideration. The following illustration with the solution worked both by the conventional

method and the short method, and the explanatory paragraph that
follows, will point to its important benefits.

Example 1: Multiply 2738 by 8756.

Solution:

Conventional
Method	*Short Method* *	
2738	8000 times 2738	$= 21904000$
8756	800 times 2738 ($\frac{1}{10}$ of 21904000)	$= 2190400$
16428	8800 times 2738	$= 24094400$
13690 $-$	44 times 2738 ($\frac{1}{200}$ of 24094400 or $\frac{1}{2}$	
19166	of 240944)	$= 120472$
21904		
	8756 times 2738	$= 23973928$
23973928		

The technique of the short-cut method illustrated provides an
interesting study for more than one reason. The total number
of figures written down in the solution by the short method is 37,
compared with only 36 by the conventional method, and it might
seem that the conventional method is therefore to be preferred.
The test for the value of a short-cut, however, is not always how
few figures need to be written down in the computation. The
time-saving and effort-saving factors and the assurance of accuracy are of greater importance. In the solution by the conventional method four partial products were taken, and we all know
from experience that the likelihood of an error occurring in the
total is greater when many partial products must be added than
when only two lines of figures are added. Furthermore, the likelihood of error is even greater when the partial products, as in
solutions by the conventional method, are "angular" products.

* The data accompanying the computations is, of course, shown only by
way of explanation. In actual practice only the products and their sum or
difference, as the case may be, need be written down.

Example 2: Multiply 3918 by 3267.

Solution:

3000 times 3918	= 11754000
300 times 3918 ($\frac{1}{10}$ of 11754000)	= 1175400

3300 times 3918	= 12929400
− 33 times 3918 ($\frac{1}{100}$ of 12929400) =	129294

3267 times 3918	= 12800106

Example 3: Multiply 4362 by 4378.

Solution:

4000 times 4362	= 17448000
400 times 4362 ($\frac{1}{10}$ of 17448000)	= 1744800

4400 times 4362	= 19192800
− 22 times 4362 ($\frac{1}{200}$ of 19192800 or	
$\frac{1}{2}$ of 191928)	= 95964

4378 times 4362	= 19096836

Example 4: Multiply 5291 by 2189.

Solution:

2000 times 5291	= 10582000
200 times 5291 ($\frac{1}{10}$ of 10582000)	= 1058200

2200 times 5291	= 11640200
− 11 times 5291 ($\frac{1}{200}$ of 11640200 or	
$\frac{1}{2}$ of 116402)	= 58201

2189 times 5291	= 11581999

Example 5: Multiply 1.637 by 2156.

Solution:

2000 times 1.637 (2 times 1637)	= 3274
200 times 1.637 ($\frac{1}{10}$ of 3274)	= 327.4

2200 times 1.637	= 3601.4
− 44 times 1.637 ($\frac{2}{100}$ of 3601.4 or 2	
times 36.014)	= 72.028

· 2156 times 1.637	= 3529.372

Example 6: Multiply .0578 by 4312.

Solution:

4000 times .0578 (4 times 57.8)	=	231.2
400 times .0578 ($\frac{1}{10}$ of 231.2)	=	23.12

4400 times .0578	=	254.32
— 88 times .0578 ($\frac{2}{100}$ of 254.32 or 2 times 2.5432)	=	5.0864

4312 times .0578	=	249.2336

Thus far we have considered multipliers in which the first two digits of the increased number are a multiple of 11. The same technique, however, can be used with other numbers. too, as will be seen in the following illustrations.

Example 7: The jewelers' weight known as the carat is equal to 3.168 grains. Compute the weight of 237 carats.

Solution:

32 times 237 (8 times 948)	=	7584
— .32 times 237 ($\frac{1}{100}$ of 7584)	=	75.84

31.68 times 237	=	7508.16
3.168 times 237 ($\frac{1}{10}$ of 7508.16)	=	750.816

Ans. 750.816 grains.

Example 8: A square foot of steel plate 0.165 inches thick weighs 6.732 pounds. Compute to the nearest half pound the weight of 473 pounds of this material.

Solution: 68 times 473

66 times 473		
(6 times 5203)	=	31218
2 times 473	=	946

	=	32164
— .68 times 473 ($\frac{1}{100}$ of 32164)	=	321.64

67.32 times 473	=	31842.36
6.732 times 473 ($\frac{1}{10}$ of 31842.36)	=	3184.236

Ans. 3184 pounds.

EXERCISES

Multiply 3742 by each of the following numbers, using the method indicated:

1. 8712.   Multiply by 8800 and subtract $\frac{1}{100}$ of the result.
2. 6567.   Multiply by 6600 and subtract $\frac{1}{200}$ of the result.
3. 6578.   Multiply by 6600 and subtract $\frac{1}{300}$ of the result.
4. 4389.   Multiply by 4400 and subtract $\frac{1}{400}$ of the result.
5. 5489.   Multiply by 5500 and subtract $\frac{1}{500}$ of the result.
6. 6589.   Multiply by 6600 and subtract $\frac{1}{600}$ of the result.
7. 7689.   Multiply by 7700 and subtract $\frac{1}{700}$ of the result.
8. 3234.   Multiply by 3300 and subtract $\frac{2}{100}$ of the result.
9. 9834.   Multiply by 9900 and subtract $\frac{2}{300}$ of the result.
10. 2167.   Multiply by 2200 and subtract $\frac{3}{200}$ of the result.

PROBLEMS

1. A printer takes an order for 10,000 booklets at $31.75 per thousand. If he can deliver only 9867 booklets, for what amount will the invoice to the purchaser be made out?   *Ans.* $313.28.

2. If the average weight of the fleeces obtained by a sheep breeder is 11.27 pounds, how many pounds of wool might be expected if 2112 sheep are shorn?   *Ans.* 23,802.24 pounds.

3. Convert 346 cubic feet to cubic inches. (To convert cubic feet to cubic inches multiply by 1728.)   *Ans.* 597,888 cubic inches.

4. A jobber makes a gross profit on a cosmetic item of $0.835 per dozen bottles. If he sold a total of 3588 dozen bottles how much gross profit will he have made?   *Ans.* $2995.98.

5. Estimate the value of 65.67 acres at $86.50 per acre.

    Ans. $5680.46.

6. The conversion of pounds of cement to bags is effected by multiplying by 0.0106383. How many bags will hold 8778 pounds of cement? Compute the answer to the nearest bag.   *Ans.* 93 bags.

7. If a 36-inch wide twill fabric weighs 19.21 ounces per square yard, how many ounces would 2134 square yards weigh?   *Ans.* 40,994.14 ounces.

8. If 1000 feet of $\frac{3}{4}$-inch wire strapping weighs 38.2 pounds, how many pounds would be required to furnish 4378 feet? Compute the answer to the nearest pound.   *Ans.* 167 pounds.

9. A radio manufacturer wishes to determine the total quantity in stock of a part of which he has $23\frac{1}{2}$ pounds. It is known that a 10-pound package contains 2178 of these parts. What quantity may he safely assume to have on hand? Compute the answer to the nearest whole unit.   *Ans.* 5118.

CHAPTER II

THE BREAKDOWN METHOD OF MULTIPLICATION

The effectiveness of practically every mathematical short-cut is dependent upon some manner of breakdown, and to a greater or lesser extent each of the short-cuts discussed so far is the result of such a procedure. We have seen, for instance, that to multiply by 45 it is easier to multiply first by 50 and then to subtract one tenth of the result; that it is sometimes easier to multiply by factors of a number than by its digits. In Art. 13 we learned how to multiply by a number like 3612 by computing only two partial products and, in Art. 15, how to reduce the process of multiplying by some four-digit numbers to the point where it was but necessary to compute one partial product and one simple calculation in division.

The first chapter gave us a background for the appreciation of a new and even more interesting track that will open out for us in the four articles that follow. Here we will consider some of the many ramifications of the breakdown method of multiplication. And one of the things we will discover is that it is not necessary, in using short-cuts, to limit ourselves to two-, three- or four-figure numbers, or to two-, three- or four-figure numbers in which one part is an exact multiple of, or is exactly divisible into, the other part.

Inseparably linked with all time- and labor-saving mathematical procedure, a thorough understanding of the breakdown method of multiplication will enable the reader to have a valuable insight into the virtually unlimited possibilities of short-cuts in business mathematics.

It is suggested that the subject matter of this chapter be studied very carefully, in order that the techniques treated in the articles in succeeding chapters may be quickly grasped. An abundance of illustrations will help pave the way toward a clearer understanding of the method and to proficiency in its use.

16. Multiplying by Two-, Three- and Four-Figure Numbers, Like 12, 26, 35, 39, 48, 52, 76, 128, 135, 165, 436, 362, 2483. The number 12 is a relatively easy number to get along with. But could the reader multiply $3.60 by 12 mentally, without using the uncomfortable process which entails "carrying"? By breaking up 12 into the numbers 10 and 2 the mental computation of the problem becomes remarkably simple: 10 times $3.60 equals $36.00; twice $3.60 is $7.20; $36.00 plus $7.20 equals $43.20.

In multiplying $3.60 by 26 the procedure is even simpler: 25 times $3.60 (one fourth of $360.00) equals $90.00; and $90.00 plus $3.60 equals $93.60.

Example 1: Multiply 28 cents by 35.

Solution: 25 times 28 cents ($\frac{1}{4}$ of $28.00) = $7.00
10 times 28 cents = 2.80
_____

35 times 28 cents = $9.80

Example 2: Multiply 73 cents by 39.

Solution: 40 times 73 cents (4 times $7.30) = $29.20
− 1 times 73 cents = .73
_____

39 times 73 cents = $28.47

Example 3: Multiply 65 cents by 39.8.

Solution: 40 times 65 cents (4 times $6.50) = $26.00
− .2 times 65 cents ($\frac{1}{5}$ of 65 cents) = .13
_____

39.8 times 65 cents = $25.87

Example 4: Multiply 38 cents by 52.

Solution: 50 times 38 cents ($\frac{1}{2}$ of $38.00) = $19.00
2 times 38 cents = .76
_____

52 times 38 cents = $19.76

Example 5: Multiply 44 cents by 76.

Solution: 75 times 44 cents ($\frac{3}{4}$ of $44.00) = $33.00

1 times 44 cents   =   .44

76 times 44 cents   = $33.44

Example 6: Find the cost of 128 units at $4.76 per hundred.

Solution: 100 at $4.76 per hundred   = $4.76

25 at $4.76 per hundred ($\frac{1}{4}$ of $4.76) = 1.19

3 at $4.76 per hundred (3 times .047) =   .14

128 at $4.76 per hundred   = $6.09

Example 7: Multiply 419 by 135.

Solution: 100 times 419   = 41900

25 times 419 ($\frac{1}{4}$ of 41900) = 10475

10 times 419   = 4190

135 times 419   = 56565

Example 8: Multiply 419 by 165.

Solution: 100 times 419   = 41900

50 times 419 ($\frac{1}{2}$ of 41900) = 20950

150 times 419   = 62850

15 times 419 ($\frac{1}{10}$ of 62850) = 6285

165 times 419   = 69135

Example 9: Estimate the value of 436 units at $1.68 per hundred.

Solution: 400 at $1.68 per 100   = $6.72

40 at $1.68 per 100 ($\frac{1}{10}$ of $6.72) =   .67

440 at $1.68 per 100   = $7.39

—   4 at $1.68 per 100 ($\frac{1}{10}$ of .67) =   .07

436 at $1.68 per 100   = $7.32

Example 10: Multiply 784 by 362.

Solution: 300 times 784   = 235200
      60 times 784 ($\frac{1}{5}$ of 235200) =   47040
       2 times 784   =   1568

---

362 times 784   = 283808

Example 11: Find the cost of 2483 parts at 83 cents per hundred.

Solution: 2000 at 83 cents per 100 (2000 at $8.30 per
           1000)   = $16.60
      400 at 83 cents per 100   =   3.32
       80 at 83 cents per 100 ($\frac{1}{5}$ of $3.32) =   .664
        3 at 83 cents per 100 (3 times .0083)   =   .025

2483 at 83 cents per 100   = $20.61

Problems

* 1. If there are 32 teeth per inch in a 12-inch hack saw blade, how many teeth are there in the entire blade? (Which partial products did you add or subtract to arrive at the total?)   *Ans.* 320 plus 64 = 384.

* 2. A machine folds and closes 55 cartons per minute. How many cartons will it do in 2 hours 4 minutes?   *Ans.* 6820.

* 3. Iron weighs .26 pounds per cubic inch. Compute the weight of 29 cubic inches of iron.   *Ans.* 7.54 pounds.

* 4. Find the cost of 26 units at $6.80 per hundred.   *Ans.* $1.77.

5. Convert 687 drams into grams. (Multiply by 3.9.)
Ans. 2679.3 grams.

* 6. By the processes of addition and subtraction find the cost of 8 dozen cigarette cases at $1.35 per dozen.   *Ans.* $10.80.

7. Compute the value of 650 Argentina paper pesos at the cable rate of 24.90 cents per peso.   *Ans.* $161.85.

8. A meter equals 39.37 inches. Which three digits would you use as a short-cut in computing the number of inches in a given number of meters?   *Ans.* 4, 6 and 3.

9. A workman receiving $1.12 per hour and entitled to time and a half for all time put in over 40 hours in one week works a total of 46 hours.

What did he earn for the week?   (Hint: He worked 6 hours overtime, so his pay will be computed on the basis of 49 hours straight time.)

Ans. $54.88.

10. The labor costs in a certain industry average 17.9% of the sales. If the sales for a twelve-month period amount to $630,000.00, what might the expected labor costs be for the year?   *Ans.* $112,770.00.

17. Multiplying by Numbers Which Contain Fractions, Such as $3\frac{7}{8}$, $57\frac{1}{2}$, $58\frac{1}{3}$. Just as in multiplying by 39.8 it is simpler to multiply by 40 and subtract .2 (one fifth) of the multiplicand, so, in multiplying by $3\frac{7}{8}$, $24\frac{8}{9}$, $34\frac{9}{10}$, etc., it is more practicable to multiply by the next whole number and then to subtract $\frac{1}{8}$, $\frac{1}{9}$, $\frac{1}{10}$, respectively, of the multiplicand.

Example 1: Multiply 288 by $3\frac{7}{8}$.

Solution:
$$
\begin{array}{rl}
4 \text{ times } 288 &= 1152 \\
- \ \frac{1}{8} \text{ of } 288 &= \ \ \ \ 36 \\
\hline
3\frac{7}{8} \text{ times } 288 &= 1116
\end{array}
$$

Example 2: Multiply 36 by $24\frac{8}{9}$.

Solution:
$$
\begin{array}{rl}
25 \text{ times } 36 \ (\frac{1}{4} \text{ of } 3600) &= 900 \\
- \ \ \frac{1}{9} \text{ of } 36 &= \ \ \ 4 \\
\hline
24\frac{8}{9} \text{ times } 36 &= 896
\end{array}
$$

Example 3: Multiply $83\frac{1}{2}$ by $34\frac{9}{10}$.

Solution:
$$
\begin{array}{rl}
25 \text{ times } 83\frac{1}{2} \ (\frac{1}{4} \text{ of } 8350) &= 2087.5 \\
10 \text{ times } 83\frac{1}{2} &= \ 835 \\
\hline
35 \text{ times } 83\frac{1}{2} &= 2922.5 \\
- \ \frac{1}{10} \text{ of } 83\frac{1}{2} \ (\frac{1}{10} \text{ of } 83.5) &= \ \ \ 8.35 \\
\hline
34\frac{9}{10} \text{ times } 83\frac{1}{2} &\doteq 2914.15
\end{array}
$$

Note in the following illustration that advantage is taken of the fact that 5 is one tenth of 50, and that $2\frac{1}{2}$ is one half of 5.

Example 4: Multiply $23.60 by $57\frac{1}{2}$.

Solution: 50 times $23.60 ($\frac{1}{2}$ of $2360.00)   = $1180.00
         5 times $23.60 ($\frac{1}{10}$ of $1180.00) =   118.00
         $2\frac{1}{2}$ times $23.60 ($\frac{1}{2}$ of $118.00)   =   59.00

$57\frac{1}{2}$ times $23.60   = $1357.00

A beautiful example of the convenience of the breakdown method is the number $58\frac{1}{3}$. (The reader may be interested to know that in 1946 the import duty on hats and caps for men and boys, valued at over $15.00 but not over $18.00 per dozen, was [in addition to the separate percentage on the valuation] $58\frac{1}{3}$ cents each, which figure is used in the following illustration.)

Example 5: Multiply 432 by $58\frac{1}{3}$ cents.

Solution: 432 times $33\frac{1}{3}$ cents ($\frac{1}{3}$ of $432.00) = $144.00
         432 times 25 cents ($\frac{1}{4}$ of $432.00)   =   108.00

---

432 times $58\frac{1}{3}$ cents   = $252.00

Practically without effort the preceding problem could be worked mentally.

Example 6: Advertised for sale is a 6-story walk-up 41 feet 8 inches by 100 feet. What is the area of the place in square feet?

Solution: 41 feet by 100 feet   = 4100   square feet
         8 inches by 100 feet ($\frac{2}{3}$ foot
            times 100)   = $66\frac{2}{3}$ square feet

---

41 feet 8 inches by 100 feet   = $4166\frac{2}{3}$ square feet

PROBLEMS

1. If blacksmiths' 26-inch tongs weigh $3\frac{7}{8}$ pounds each, how much will 24 tongs weigh?   *Ans.* 93 pounds.

2. Convert $13\frac{15}{16}$ pounds to ounces.   *Ans.* 223 ounces.

★ **3.** One thousand $\frac{1}{4}$-inch soldering lugs weigh 6 pounds. How many soldering lugs might be expected to be contained in a box having a net weight of $3\frac{3}{4}$ pounds?   *Ans.* 625.

★ 4. If the import duty on hemp cordage is $4\frac{7}{8}$ cents per pound, what duty would an importer be obliged to pay on a shipment of 320 pounds?

Ans. $15.60.

5. An acre equals 4840 square yards. Compute the number of square yards in $9\frac{7}{10}$ acres. *Ans.* 46,948.

6. Estimate the value of 471 bushels of corn at $1.63\frac{3}{4}$ per bushel, using the latter figure as the multiplier. *Ans.* $771.26.

★ 7. Estimate the cost of $2\frac{5}{6}$ yards of material at $3.30 per yard.

Ans. $9.35.

★ 8. If a 24-pint crate of beans weighs $16\frac{2}{3}$ pounds, how much will 21 crates weigh? *Ans.* 350 pounds.

9. Crude petroleum weighs 7.75 pounds per gallon. Compute the weight of 32 gallons. *Ans.* 248 pounds.

★ 10. The product of 480 times $41\frac{2}{3}$ cents can be obtained mentally, without putting pencil to paper, in a matter of seconds by breaking up $41\frac{2}{3}$ into two numbers. What are the two numbers? *Ans.* 25 and $16\frac{2}{3}$.

18. Multiplying by Numbers in Which One Part Is a Multiple of a Second or Third Part, e.g., 4536, 16398, 1988384. Readers who enjoyed the last few articles in Chapter I will find a special delight in learning how to multiply by these numbers. Let the procedure in the following illustrations explain itself.

Example 1: Convert 2743 pounds to kilograms. (One pound equals .4536 kilograms.)

Solution: (Note that both the first pair of digits in the multiplier and the last pair are multiples of 9.)

9 times 2743	= 24,687

4500 times 2743 (500 times 24,687 or $\frac{1}{2}$ of 24,687,000)	= 12,343,500
36 times 2743 (4 times 24,687)	= 98,748

4536 times 2743	= 12,442,248
.4536 times 2743	= 1244.2248

Ans. 1244.2248 kilograms.

Example 2: Compute the number of grams in 8674 liters of hydrochloric acid. (One liter of hydrochloric acid weighs 1.6398 grams.)

Solution:

.04 times 8674		=	346.96
1.6 times 8674 (40 times 346.96 or 4			
times 3469.6)		=	13,878.4

1.64 times 8674		=	14,225.36
— .0002 times 8674 ($\frac{1}{200}$ of 346.96 or			
$\frac{1}{2}$ of 3.4696)		=	1.7348

1.6398 times 8674		=	14,223.6252

Ans. 14,223.625 grams.

Example 3: Convert 734 kilometers to U. S. rods. (Multiply by 198.8384.)

Solution:

200 times 734	= 146,800
— 1 times 734	= 734

199 times 734	= 146,066
— .1616 times 734	

$$.16 \text{ times } 734 = \frac{8}{10,000} \text{ of}$$
146,800 or 8 times 14.68 = 117.44
.0016 times 734 = $\frac{1}{100}$ of 117.44 = 1.1744

	= 118.6144

198.8384 times 734	= 145,947.3856

Ans. 145,947.3856 rods.

Example 4: The U. S. standard barrel for fruits and vegetables (except cranberries) has a capacity of 7056 cubic inches. Compute the cubic inch capacity of 679 of these barrels.

Solution: 7000 times 679 (7 times 679,000)   = 4,753,000
　　　　56 times 679 ($\frac{8}{1000}$ of 4,753,000 or 8
　　　　　　times 4753)   =   38,024

7056 cubic inches multiplied by 679   = 4,791,024

Ans. 4,791,024 cubic inches.

Problems

1. What would 116 Canadian free dollars cost at the quoted rate of 90.81 cents?   *Ans.* $105.34.

2. There are 28.35 grams to the ounce. How many grams are there in 342 ounces? (Hint: 28 and 35 are multiples of 7.)   *Ans.* 9695.7 grams.

3. In May, 1946, the average hourly earnings in the newspaper printing and publishing industry was $1.435 per hour. At this rate what would be the approximate total amount earned by a representative group of employees who worked a total of 2378 hours?   *Ans.* $3412.43.

4. Lead has a specific gravity of 11.37. Which two numbers in addition to 3, of which they are multiples, could be used as a substitute for 11.37 in converting cubic feet of lead to pounds? How would you use these numbers?

　　　　Ans. 12 and 6; multiply by 12 and subtract the sum of $\frac{1}{20}$ of the
　　　　result plus $\frac{1}{400}$ of the result.

5. A short way of multiplying by 15.76 is to add two partial products and subtract another. What relationship does the product subtracted have to one of the other products?

　　　　Ans. The product of .24 times the multiplicand is $\frac{3}{100}$ of the
　　　　product of 8 times the multiplicand.

6. How would you obtain the product of 168.5 times a number without having to add more than three lines of figures?

　　　　Ans. Multiply the product of 8 times the multiplicand by 20
　　　　to obtain the product of 160 times the multiplicand.

7. There are 10,890 square feet in a British rod. Compute the number of square feet in 372 British rods by a process of multiplication in which the number 372 is multiplied by no other digit than 1.

　　　　Ans. 4,051,080 square feet.

8. A cubic centimeter of liquid mercury weighs 13.596 grams. And there are 1398.56 dry pints in a cubic yard. By a short-cut method only two digits need be used to obtain the product of any number of times either of these numbers. In both instances the two digits are alike. What are they? *Ans.* 1 and 4.

9. The picul is a measure of weight used in Borneo. It is the American equivalent of 135.64 pounds. Compute the weight of 78.6 piculs, without multiplying by any other digits than 1, 3 and 6. *Ans.* 10,661.304 pounds.

10. If a mailing list of 10,896 saw-mill and lumber manufacturers can be purchased at $12.50 per thousand, what would the cost of the entire list be? *Ans.* $136.20.

19. The Use of the Breakdown Method of Multiplication Is Especially Advantageous in Dealing with Decimal Fractions. The use of decimal numbers, either as multiplicands or as multipliers, frequently necessitates the pointing off of decimal places in the answer. This in itself is quite simple, but there is always the possibility of pointing off the wrong number of places. A safer and shorter method of multiplication is the breakdown method.

Take for instance the problem 365 times .37147. Let us compute this, first by the conventional method, then by the breakdown method.

Conventional Method

$$.37147$$
$$365$$

$$\overline{}$$

185735　　Since there are five decimal places in the
222882　　multiplicand, the same number of decimal
111441　　places must be pointed off in the product. So
　　　　　that our answer is 135.58655.

$$\overline{}$$

13558655

Breakdown Method

300 times .37147 (3 times 37.147) = 111.441
60 times .37147 ($\frac{1}{5}$ of 111.441)　 = 22.288
5 times .37147 ($\frac{1}{2}$ of 3.7147)　 = 1.857

$$\overline{}$$

365 times .37147　　　　　　 = 135.59

Which of the two methods do you think is the shorter and more reliable?

Computed by the conventional method each partial product contains six figures and the total, eight figures, whereas by the breakdown method one partial product contains five figures, another, four, and the total but five. Consider also the greater possibility of error in adding the larger partial products and the possibility of pointing off the wrong number of decimal places in the computation by the conventional method, and you will appreciate the advantage of the safe and speedy breakdown method of multiplication.

A study of the procedure in the following illustration will be found interesting and profitable.

Example 1: Find the cost of 1278 units at $1.86 per hundred.

Solution: 1000 at $1.86 per 100   = $18.60
          250 at $1.86 per 100 ($\frac{1}{4}$ of $18.60)   =   4.65
           25 at $1.86 per 100 ($\frac{1}{10}$ of $4.65)   =   .465
            3 at $1.86 per 100 (3 times .0186) =   .056

1278 at $1.86 per 100   = $23.77

Do you see how we arrive at the price per unit (.0186) in the foregoing illustration? We keep moving the decimal point to the left, saying to ourselves, "If the price per hundred is $1.86, the price of ten is .186, and the price per unit is .0186."

There are any number of variations of the breakdown method of multiplication. Note an interesting adaptation in the following illustration.

Example 2: Find the cost of 48.8 tons at $16.80 per ton.

Solution: 48 tons at $16.00 (96 times $8.00)   = $768.00
         48 tons at .80 ($\frac{1}{20}$ of $768.00)   =   38.40

48 tons at $16.80 per ton   = $806.40
 .8 tons at $16.80 per ton ($\frac{1}{60}$ of $806.40)   =   13.44

48.8 tons at $16.80 per ton   = $819.84

Example 3: The construction of a concrete floor 6 inches thick requires the use of 1.85 cubic yards of concrete per 100 square feet. On this basis how many cubic yards of concrete would be required to build a floor of 342 square feet?

Solution:

300 square feet times 1.85	= 5.55
30 square feet times 1.85 ($\frac{1}{10}$ of 5.55) =	.555
10 square feet times 1.85 ($\frac{1}{3}$ of .555) =	.185
2 square feet times 1.85 ($\frac{1}{5}$ of .185) =	.037

342 square feet times 1.85   = 6.327

Ans. 6.327 cubic yards of concrete.

A type of problem not so frequently encountered, but important nonetheless, is this: Multiply $2175.25 by .1346286. A quick glance at these figure will indicate that to solve this problem by the conventional method would call for at least six partial products, each containing at least six figures. Done by the breakdown method the computation is simple, quick and easy:

$2000.00 times .1346286 (2 times $134.6286) =	$269.257
100.00 times .1346286	= 13.463
50.00 times .1346286 ($\frac{1}{2}$ of $13.463)	= 6.732
25.00 times .1346286 ($\frac{1}{2}$ of $6.732)	= 3.366
.25 times .1346286 ($\frac{1}{100}$ of $3.366)	= .034

$2175.25 times .1346286   = $292.85

The breakdown method of multiplying dollars and cents has definite time-saving advantages, and the reader is urged to drill himself in the technique; if he has occasion to do any calculating at all, the use of this method will save him many precious minutes, he will have less need for calculating machines, and he will save much mental and nervous energy besides. It would be hopeless to attempt to illustrate all or even any considerable number of the many possible adaptations of the breakdown method, and it is hoped that the many illustrations and problems in this chapter have helped the reader to gain an intimate working knowledge of this very important time-saving process.

PROBLEMS

1. Multiply .479 by 298. *Ans.* 142.742.

2. How many yards are there in 317.5 pounds of fabric of which there are 8.97 yards to the pound? *Ans.* 2847.975 yards.

3. A cubic foot of asphaltum weighs 87.3 pounds. Estimate the weight of 26.35 cubic feet. Compute the answer to the nearest pound. (Hint: 87.3 is equivalent to 90 minus 2.7.) *Ans.* 2300 pounds.

4. The skaulpuna is a Swedish unit of measurement which is equal to .0937 American pounds. Compute to the nearest whole unit the weight in pounds of $284\frac{1}{2}$ skaulpunas. (Hint: $284\frac{1}{2}$ is equivalent to 300 minus $15\frac{1}{2}$.) *Ans.* 27 pounds.

5. If 1000 feet of $\frac{3}{4}$-inch packing-case strapping weigh 38.2 pounds, what should 843 feet weigh? Compute the answer to the nearest quarter of a pound. *Ans.* $32\frac{1}{4}$ pounds.

6. Compute the cost of 14 bags (132 pounds to the bag) of Santos coffee at the market quotation of $0.21695 per pound. *Ans.* $400.92.

CHAPTER III

THE "DOUBLE-AND-HALVE" METHOD OF MULTIPLICATION

One of the most helpful of all mathematical short-cuts is a device which the author chooses to call the "double-and-halve" method. It is a simple little trick, and the wonder is that so many successful businessmen with a mathematical background never think of using it.

The principle of the process is based on the fact that when two factors in a multiplication problem are multiplied and divided, respectively, by the same value, the product is not affected.

The illustrations in this chapter demonstrate the ease and simplicity with which many problems can be computed mentally or with a minimum of pencil and paper work by this uncommonly used method.

20. How to Multiply Mentally and Quickly by $2\frac{1}{2}$, $3\frac{1}{2}$, $4\frac{1}{2}$, $5\frac{1}{2}$. To compute 62 times $2\frac{1}{2}$ all one need do is to multiply half of 62 (31) by twice $2\frac{1}{2}$ (5). With practically no effort at all, it is seen that 5 times 31 equals 155.

The same procedure applies to the multipliers $3\frac{1}{2}$, $4\frac{1}{2}$ and $5\frac{1}{2}$. Thus $3\frac{1}{2}$ times 24 is equivalent to 7 times 12. By the same token $4\frac{1}{2}$ times 16 equals 9 times 8, and $5\frac{1}{2}$ times 126 equals 11 times 63. The last problem, by the way, may recall to the reader's mind the interesting rule explained in Art. 1-f, by which 11 times 63 can be computed in a fraction of a second, and with virtually no possibility of error.

The term "double-and-halve" method was chosen primarily for its descriptive value, and for the reason that factors in a multiplication problem can be changed more easily in this than in any other ratio. However, the value by which multiplicand and multiplier may be multiplied and divided, respectively, need not

66

necessarily be limited to 2; any other value may be used to exactly the same effect. Thus $2\frac{1}{2}$ times 440 would be computed more conveniently by multiplying and dividing the factors, respectively, by 4 instead of by 2, changing the problem to read 10 times 110. Similarly, the factors in the problem $3\frac{1}{2}$ times 330 might be multiplied and divided, respectively, by 3, changing the problem to read $10\frac{1}{2}$ times 110.

Example: A machine for de-airing pottery has a capacity of $3\frac{1}{2}$ tons per hour. At this rate how many tons of pottery can be de-aired by this machine in 14 hours?

Solution: $3\frac{1}{2}$ times 14 is equivalent to 7 times 7, which equals 49.

Ans. 49 tons.

PROBLEMS

* **1.** When insurance is paid in advance for 3 years the premium is $2\frac{1}{2}$ times the one-year premium. If the premium for one year is \$32.24 what would it be for 3 years?   *Ans.* \$80.60.

* **2.** Asbestos cement sheets in the $\frac{1}{4}$ inch thickness weigh approximately $2\frac{1}{2}$ pounds per square foot. Compute the weight of each of the following sheets: (a) 42 by 48 inches; (b) 48 by 48 inches; (c) 42 by 96 inches.   *Ans.* (a) 35 pounds; (b) 40 pounds; (c) 70 pounds.

* **3.** If the average daily consumption of corn silage by one sheep is $3\frac{1}{2}$ pounds, how many pounds would 64 sheep consume in 30 days?

Ans. 6720 pounds.

* **4.** Asbestos board is used for fireproof lining of floors, etc. If a board 42 by 48 inches in the $\frac{3}{64}$ inch thickness weighs $3\frac{1}{2}$ pounds, what would 18 boards weigh?   *Ans.* 63 pounds.

* **5.** A group of anglers catch a total of 42 codfish which have an average weight of $4\frac{1}{2}$ pounds. Estimate in two seconds the weight of the entire catch.   *Ans.* 189 pounds.

* **6.** A baked cork used for insulation is supplied in bags of 7 cubic feet capacity. If one cubic foot of this material weighs approximately $4\frac{1}{2}$ pounds, what would the weight be of 22 bags? (Hint: $4\frac{1}{2}$ times 22 is equivalent to 9 times 11.)   *Ans.* 693 pounds. (*Arts. 1-f, 3*)

* **7.** A machine wraps 5 bouillon cubes in a packet at the rate of 68 packets per minute. At this rate how many packets can be wrapped in $5\frac{1}{2}$ hours?   *Ans.* 22,440 packets.

* 8. The huacaya sheep yields a fleece weighing approximately $5\frac{1}{2}$ pounds. On this basis what would the fleece yield be of 162 huacaya sheep?   *Ans.* 891 pounds. (*Art. 1-f*)

21. How to Multiply Mentally and Quickly by Numbers Which Contain Fractions Other Than $\frac{1}{2}$.

We saw in the previous article that multiplication problems in which one of the factors contains the fraction $\frac{1}{2}$ lend themselves very conveniently to computation by the double-and-halve method. This process may be used with equal facility in the case of numbers containing other fractions. Thus the problem of finding the area of a floor 8 feet 4 inches long by 24 feet wide is simplified by multiplying the length by 3 and dividing the width by 3, changing the problem to read 25 feet by 8 feet; and we see at a glance that the answer is 200 square feet. Note that we multiplied and divided respectively by 3 because 3 is also the denominator of the fraction $8\frac{1}{3}$, the equivalent in feet of 8 feet 4 inches.

This technique is just as easy to apply to the fraction $\frac{3}{4}$. A good example is $2\frac{3}{4}$, which is the number of bushels in a hectoliter. To find the number of bushels in 28 hectoliters, for instance, we proceed by changing $2\frac{3}{4}$ into a whole number. The denominator of the fraction being 4, we multiply $2\frac{3}{4}$ by 4 and divide 28 by 4, which gives us the equivalent of 11 times 7. Without any further effort whatever we know that there are 77 bushels in 28 hectoliters.

The same technique may be applied with equally good effect to mixed numbers containing tens and hundreds digits as well as unit digits. Thus to do the problem $317\frac{1}{3}$ times 24 we multiply and divide respectively by 3, obtaining the equivalent of 952 times 8. It is interesting to note that in the solution to this problem it is necessary to write down only four figures, compared with 19 by the conventional method, to say nothing of the greater laboriousness of the latter process.

PROBLEMS

* 1. Estimate the volume in cubic feet of a box of these dimensions: length, 12 feet; width, 18 feet; depth, $7\frac{1}{3}$ feet.

                                             Ans. 1584 cubic feet. (*Art. 16*)

  ★ **2.** Compute the number of feet in $203\frac{1}{3}$ rods. One rod equals $16\frac{1}{2}$ feet. (Hint: 610 times $5\frac{1}{2}$ is equivalent to 305 times 11.) *Ans.* 3355 feet.

  ★ **3.** If the coastwise freight rate on coal shipped from New York to Portland, Maine, on quantities of 700 tons or less, is $2.75 per ton, what would it cost to transport 32 tons of coal between these two points?
Ans. $88.00. (*Art. 1-f*)

  ★ **4.** A water tank for the use of horses and cattle is 8 feet long, 3 feet 3 inches wide, and 2 feet 3 inches deep. How many gallons of water will it hold, filled to a depth of 2 feet? (One cubic foot equals $7\frac{1}{2}$ gallons.)
Ans. 390 gallons.

  ★ **5.** A tank has a capacity of 640 cubic feet. Compute the weight of water filled to three fourths of its depth. (One cubic foot of water weighs $62\frac{1}{2}$ pounds.) *Ans.* 30,000 pounds.

  ★ **6.** If there are 6400 $2\frac{1}{2}$-ounce tacks to the pound, how many tacks of this size should there be in 4 pounds 2 ounces? (Pencil and paper should be used to write the answer only.) *Ans.* 26,400.

  ★ **7.** A San Francisco insurance salesman is asked by a creamery to estimate the annual premium on a Manufacturer's and Contractor's Liability insurance policy based on an annual payroll of $73,250.00. If the rate in California on insurance of this nature is 8 cents per $100 of payroll, what would the premium amount to? *Ans.* $58.60.

  ★ **8.** A road 16 feet wide and one mile long is filled with aggregate one inch thick. If the quantity of aggregate used on this job is 261 cubic yards, how much would be needed to fill a road $2\frac{2}{9}$ miles long and 32 feet wide, one inch thick? *Ans.* 1160 cubic yards.

  ★ **9.** If rails weigh $43\frac{1}{3}$ pounds per foot, what would be the weight in tons of the rails used to lay one mile of track? (One mile equals 5280 feet, and one ton equals 2000 pounds.) *Ans.* 114.4 tons.

22. How to Multiply Mentally by 14, 16, 18, 24 and Higher Even Numbers.

The principle of the method discussed in this article is based on the fact that it is easier to multiply mentally by one digit than by two. The whole "secret" to the method, then, is to convert the two-digit multiplier to a single digit. Thus to compute 18 times $54\frac{1}{2}$, 18 is halved and $54\frac{1}{2}$ is doubled. This changes the problem to read 9 times 109, which can be computed in but a fraction of the time it would take to work the original problem by the conventional method.

  Here, as in the preceding two articles, it will be seen that two factors in a multiplication problem may be multiplied and divided, respectively, by a number other than 2 to equally good advantage. Changing the aforementioned problem to 3 times 327 instead of to 9 times 109 does not affect the product.

As a matter of fact it makes no difference whether, in doubling and halving, a factor is changed or the product is changed, so long as the doubling process is offset by the halving process. Thus the problem $12\frac{1}{2}$ times 16 might very conveniently be solved by multiplying $12\frac{1}{2}$ by 8, instead of by 16, and completing the computation by multiplying the product by 2.

Another illustration is $17\frac{1}{2}$ times 28. This problem is equivalent to 35 times 14 or 70 times 7; and we see by inspection that the answer is 490.

Even when the multiplicand is a large number the double-and-halve method may be used to advantage, though the use of pencil and paper may be necessary to some extent. Thus the problem $3481.84 multiplied by 14 would be computed by first multiplying mentally by 2 and writing down the partial product $6963.68, then multiplying this product mentally by 7 and writing down the answer, $48,745.76.

Example: What is the total length of 406 logs, each 16 feet long?

Solution: Revising the problem to read 812 times 8, we see by inspection, without any need for putting pencil to paper, that the answer is 6496, for 8 times 800 equals 6400; 8 times 12 equals 96; and 6400 plus 96 equals 6496.   *Ans.* 6496 feet.

It is interesting to observe that in some instances the change may be made "in midstream," so to speak; that is, a part of the problem is worked with the figures as originally given, and the rest of the problem is done with changes in the multiplicand and multiplier. An example of such a problem is 48 times $1.03. The solution by this method follows:

48 times $1.00	= $48.00
48 times .03 (12 times .12 computed mentally) =	1.44

48 times $1.03	= $49.44

A noteworthy benefit of the double-and-halve method of multiplication is its use in helping to eliminate the need for pencil and paper when these physical accessories are neither available nor practical to use. On a train journey, in an airplane, when in bed with the lights out, in a conversation, or at a conference where it may be necessary to make a quick computation without the use of pencil and paper, it is a decided advantage to be able to do mentally a problem like 16 times 65 without having to multiply by 6 and carry 3. Using the double-and-halve method, the problem can be readily computed mentally by changing it successively to 8 times 130, 4 times 260, twice 520; and with practically no effort at all, and as easily as counting sheep, the answer 1040 comes to mind. Or take the problem $403\frac{1}{2}$ times 16; by the double-and-halve method we obtain the equivalent of 807 times 8, and without any further effort the answer 6456 becomes obvious. The time-saving advantages and the reduction in the possibility of error of the double-and-halve method of multiplication cannot be over-emphasized.

Problems

* **1.** A merchant plans to include in an advertising campaign the use of 1400 booklets at a cost of $6.00 per hundred. Using the double-and-halve method, and taking no more than 2 seconds to do it, compute mentally the total cost of the booklets.   *Ans.* $84.00.

* **2.** A 10-ton Diesel locomotive hauls trains of fourteen 3500-pound loads ten times daily over a certain distance. How many pounds are hauled by this locomotive in a day?   *Ans.* 490,000 pounds.

* **3.** A shoe machine sews 60 buttons per minute, feeding and attaching 16 stitches to each button. How many stitches does this machine make in a continuous operation of 1 hour 40 minutes?   *Ans.* 96,000.

* **4.** A concrete mix in the $1:2\frac{3}{4}:4$ proportion calls for the use of 6.2 sacks of cement for each 100 square feet of area 4 inches thick. If concrete of this mix and thickness is to be laid on floors having a total area of 1800 square feet, how many sacks of cement will be needed to make the mix?   *Ans.* 111.6 sacks.

* **5.** A furrier receives a shipment of skins of which there are to be 18 to the pound. If the net weight of the shipment is 17 pounds, how many skins were received?   *Ans.* 306 skins.

*6. Basing your answer on a consumption of 40 pounds of corn silage per head per day, how many pounds of silage may be expected to be consumed by a herd of 14 dairy cows in 24 days?   *Ans.* 13,440 pounds.

*7. Compute the number of bottles that can be washed in three 8-hour days by a machine having a capacity of 600 bottles an hour.

Ans. 14,400.

23. How to Multiply Quickly by 140, 160, 180, 220, 240, 270, 280, 360, etc. Here the method is substantially the same as that described in the preceding article. The only difference is that instead of multiplying and dividing by 2 or by 3, we multiply and divide by 20 or 30, as the case may be, reducing the multiplier to a single-digit number.

Thus 140 times 37 would be changed to 7 times 740; 160 times 129 would become 8 times 2580; 180 times $2.71 would be restated as 9 times $54.20; and the problem 220 times 72 would, by this method, be changed to read 11 times 1440.

The same method would apply to the rest of the multipliers mentioned in this article heading. However, in changing numbers greater than 240 it is advisable to divide and multiply, respectively, by 30 or 40, etc., rather than by 20. Thus 270 times 17 would be changed to 9 times 510, and 360 times 173 might be restated to read 12 times 5190. The problem 280 times 83, on the other hand, might be computed more conveniently by multiplying and dividing, respectively, by 40, changing the problem to read 7 times 3320.

The process of multiplying and dividing factors by 30 or 40 need not necessarily be confined to problems in which the multiplier is greater than 240. It may be used to excellent advantage in converting multipliers like 180 and 160. Thus the problem 180 times $33\frac{1}{3}$ might be changed advantageously by multiplying and dividing, respectively, by 30, making it read 6 times 1000. One hundred and sixty times $21.50 might be changed with good effect to read 4 times $860.00. And a problem like 180 times $16\frac{2}{3}$ can be computed mentally and quickly by changing it to read 3 times 1000.

Note that in the following illustration the multiplication and division by 5 makes the problem calculable mentally in a matter of seconds.

Example: In 1925 the average yield of cotton per acre was 165 pounds. Today the yield is well in excess of 210 pounds. Taking the latter figure as an average yield, how much more cotton would be produced on 2200 acres today than in 1925?

Solution: The difference between 210 pounds and 165 pounds is 45 pounds. 45 times 2200 is equivalent to 9 times 11,000, and we see instantly that the answer is 99,000.   *Ans.* 99,000 pounds more.

The reader should not lose sight of the prime objective of the double-and-halve method, which is to make possible the mental computation of a large variety of problems and, when mental computation might be a little difficult or hazardous, to shorten the process of computation by reducing the amount of pencil-and-paper work and eliminating entirely the need for addition.

Problems

★ **1.** A seven-hold ship can be loaded at the rate of 140 tons an hour. Estimate the number of tons that can be loaded in $32\frac{1}{2}$ hours.

Ans. 4550 tons.

2. If the gross weight of a wood box of fresh apples is 276 pounds, how much would 160 boxes weigh?   *Ans.* 44,160 pounds.

★ **3.** A manufacturer announces that he plans to produce a new stove every 20 seconds—that is, 180 an hour. If he is successful in carrying out his plans how many stoves will he be able to produce in a 45-hour week?   *Ans.* 8100 stoves.

★ **4.** If a generator produces 220 cubic feet of hydrogen per hour, what volume would be produced in 17 hours?

Ans. 3740 cubic feet. (*Art. 1-f*)

5. A perforated metal is made with 240 holes to the square inch. Estimate the number of holes contained in a sheet 18 by 28 inches.

Ans. 120,960 holes. (*Art. 22*)

★ **6.** How many pounds of material will be sifted in 9 hours 20 minutes by a turbine sifter having a capacity of 270 pounds per hour?

Ans. 2520 pounds. (*Art. 21*)

★ **7.** The raw material used in the manufacture of leather belting is known as the strap butt, which has an area of approximately $19\frac{1}{4}$ square feet. Estimate the total area of a lot of 280 strap butts.

Ans. 5390 square feet. (*Art. 21*)

★ **8.** If on irrigated land, alfalfa yields $8\frac{1}{3}$ tons of dry hay per acre, how much dry hay may be expected from 360 acres of irrigated land?

Ans. 3000 tons. (*Art. 21*)

CHAPTER IV

MORE TRICKS IN MENTAL ARITHMETIC

Fortified with a knowledge of the breakdown method of multiplication as explained in Chapter II, the reader will readily appreciate the short-cuts considered in the following articles.

24. Many Different Problems in Which the Multiplier Is 12 or a Single Digit, Such as 6, 7, or 9, Can Be Computed Mentally with Very Little Effort. If you had to multiply 34 by 6 mentally would you do it by the conventional method? Would you write down 34, with 6 underneath it, and proceed to multiply 4 by 6, setting down 4 and carrying 2, and so on? This would indeed be an unnecessarily laborious process.

Consider this simpler way: think of the multiplicand as 30 plus 4. Now multiply each of these numbers (30 and 4) separately by 6 and add the products. Six times 30 equals 180; 6 times 4 equals 24; 180 plus 24 equals 204.

Three-digit numbers are no more difficult to manipulate by this method than two-digit numbers. The problem 128 times 7, for instance, would be worked in this way: 7 times 100 equals 700; 7 times 20 equals 140, and 700 plus 140 equals 840; 7 times 8 equals 56, and 840 plus 56 equals 896. That is the *theory* of the method—actually it is unnecessary to say to oneself, audibly or inaudibly, "7 times 20 equals 140," or "7 times 8 equals 56." It would save time and avoid confusion to say merely, "700, plus 140 equals 840, plus 56 equals 896."

Nine is another interesting number in this connection. Here we will find that in some instances it is just as easy to multiply by 10 and then to subtract—first the hundreds, then the tens, and finally the unit digits—as to multiply each digit by 9 and add the partial products. Thus taking the problem 228 times 9, the computations by both methods would be as follows:

Method A: 228 times 10   = 2280
          2280 minus 228   = 2080 minus 28
          2080 minus 28   = 2060 minus 8
          2060 minus 8   = 2052

Method B: 200 times 9   = 1800
          1800 plus 180 (9 times 20)   = 1980
          1980 plus 72 (9 times 8)   = 2052

And here, as in many other instances throughout the book, some readers will prefer the first method and others the second.

The multiplier 12 is perhaps the most interesting of all because one can multiply by this number in many different ways. In the case of multiplicands with low digits, as for example 109, 213, 342, the most practical method might be to multiply each digit separately, starting with the hundreds. Thus to multiply 109 by 12 we would say, "1200 and 108 equals 1308." And to multiply 213 by 12 we might say, "2400 and 120 equals 2520, and 36 equals 2556." On the other hand, to multiply 826 by 12, it may be found easier to multiply 825 by 12 (which equals 3300 times 3), and quick as a flash we should note that the answer is 9900 plus 12, or 9912. And if the problem were 185 times 12, it would be very convenient to say, "10 times 185 equals 1850, and 370 (twice 185) equals 2220." Or, since by doubling 185 the multiplicand is reduced to a two-digit number and the multiplier to a one-digit number, we might say, "185 times 12 equals 370 times 6; 300 times 6 equals 1800, and 420 (6 times 70) equals 2220."

Example: Estimate mentally the value of 12 instrument panels at $2.37 each.

Solution: 12 times $2.00   = $24.00
            12 times $0.30 = $3.60; and $24.00 = $27.60
            12 times $0.07 = $0.84; and $27.60 = $28.44

Ans. $28.44.

The endless variety of ways in which multiplicands and multipliers can be manipulated will be readily apparent. No one method is the best in every instance or the most suitable for all individuals, and it is hoped that a studied concentration of the examples given will help develop the reader's mathematical thinking so he will acquire the instinct of being able to quickly determine the most practical method by which he can most readily compute any type of problem.

PROBLEMS

The following problems should be worked without pencil and paper.

★ **1.** Find the cost of 12 yards of cloth at $2.43 per yard. *Ans.* $29.16.

★ **2.** How much work, in terms of watt-hours, is done by a 12-horsepower motor? (One horsepower equals 746 watts. And the work done by one watt in one hour is equivalent to one horsepower.)

Ans. 8952 watt-hours.

★ **3.** Compute the cost of 6 shirts at $3.43 each.   *Ans.* $20.58.

★ **4.** It takes 2.46 cubic yards of concrete to construct an 8-inch thick concrete floor of 100 square feet. How many cubic yards of concrete will be required to make in the same thickness a floor having an area of 600 square feet?   *Ans.* 14.76 cubic yards.

★ **5.** Elevator insurance is usually issued at so much per unit. If the rate in Connecticut for elevators in office and bank buildings is $53.00 per unit per year, what would the premium be for one year on 7 elevators in this classification?   *Ans.* $371.00.

★ **6.** One bundle of 500 feet of galvanized pipe ⅛ inch thick weighs 123 pounds. How much will 7 bundles weigh?   *Ans.* 861 pounds.

★ **7.** Shortage of stock makes it necessary for a printer to deliver only 9000 letterheads on an order for 10,000. At the price per thousand of $7.30, what would the 9000 letterheads cost?   *Ans.* $65.70.

★ **8.** Estimate the value of 9 dozen bracelets at $4.35 per dozen.

Ans. $39.15.

25. How to Multiply Mentally by a Power of 2, e.g., 4, 8, 16, etc. An especially significant nugget of arithmetical knowledge is the "successive" method of multiplying mentally by a power of 2.

To multiply 73 by 4, for instance, it is not necessary to use the conventional method, multiplying 3 by 4, writing down 2 and carrying 1, and so on. Even if the conventional method were used to obtain the answer mentally, it would have a drawback for, in mental computations which necessitate carrying, errors are likely to occur. A shorter method is to double the multiplicand and keep on doubling the products as many times as the multiplier can be factored by 2, or as many times as may be necessary.

Four, for example, contains the "2 factor" twice; so that the problem 73 times 4 would be calculable mentally in this fashion: twice 73 equals 146, and twice 146 equals 292.

If the multiplier were 8 instead of 4, we would continue the process once more, saying to ourselves, "twice 292 equals 584." And if the multiplier were 16, the answer would be twice 584, or 1168.

Is it not likely, you might ask, to lose track of the number of times the multiplicand is multiplied by 2?   Not if the procedure is systematic.   A good way to insure this is to restate the problem at each stage of the calculation.   Thus taking the problem 29 times 16, we would say, "29 times 16 equals 58 times 8, equals 116 times 4, equals 232 times 2, equals 464."

In many instances the problem becomes easily calculable mentally without breaking the multiplier down to 2.   Thus after the problem 35 times 16 has been changed to 70 times 8, the answer becomes evident immediately—8 times 7 equals 56, and annexing a zero supplies the answer, 560.   Similarly, $22\frac{1}{2}$ times 16 equals 45 times 8, equals 90 times 4; and we know in a flash that the answer is 360.

Example: Compute mentally the cost of 16 tons of steel scrap at $17.75 per ton.

Solution: 16 at $17.75
           equals 8 at $35.50,
           equals 4 at $71.00,
           equals 2 at $142.00,
           equals $284.00.

Naturally, this method could not be used very conveniently when the multiplicand we start with consists of three or more figures, or with multipliers that are greater than 16 or 32. Nonetheless, it is a significant short-cut which, in addition to saving time, will add pleasure and satisfaction to your mathematical adventures.

Problems

The following problems should be worked without pencil and paper, and the answers should be written down only after they have been computed mentally.

★ **1.** What would it cost to ship a 4-pound package from Miami, Florida, to Salinas, Ecuador, at the air express rate of 86 cents a pound?
Ans. $3.44.

★ **2.** Convert 4 kilograms to pounds. (1 kilogram equals 2.205 pounds.)
Ans. 8.82 pounds.

★ **3.** If a lantern burns 28 hours on a pint of oil, how many hours will it burn on a gallon?   *Ans.* 224 hours.

★ **4.** What is the cost of 8 chairs at $12.65 each?   *Ans.* $101.20.

★ **5.** The peck is a unit of dry measure. It is equal to 16 pints. How many pints are there in 17 pecks?   *Ans.* 272 pints.

★ **6.** Gun metal, a soft bronze, is formed with 16 parts of copper to one of tin. Compute the number of parts of copper that would be necessary to use with 23 parts of tin in the making of this metal.
Ans. 368 parts of copper.

★ **7.** A workman hired at an hourly rate of $1.17 decides to quit at the end of the fourth day. If he worked a total of 32 hours, how much pay will be coming to him?   *Ans.* $37.44.

★ **8.** A woman's hosiery machine has a capacity of 32 dozen pairs an hour. How many dozen pairs can be produced with this equipment in 37 hours?   *Ans.* 1184 dozen pairs.

26. How to Compute Mentally, Multiplication Problems in Which One Factor Is a Small Sum of Money, the Other a Whole Number. It is unfortunate but true that many individuals do not know how to use the decimal system for solving multiplication problems in which one factor is a small sum of money.

In Art. 8 we learned that sometimes the transposition of factors in a multiplication problem makes the product instantly apparent. We saw, for instance, that by changing the problem 25 times 35 cents to read 35 times 25 cents, the answer was immediately obvious. In this article we shall make an attempt to visualize the fractional relationship between $1.00 and amounts under $1.00, and to learn another useful method of dealing with multiplicands having a value of less than a dollar.

Let us begin with a review of a few simple facts. Ninety cents is the equivalent of $1.00 less one tenth of $1.00; 55 cents is half a dollar plus one tenth of half a dollar; $57\frac{1}{2}$ cents is half a dollar, plus one tenth of half a dollar, plus a half of one tenth of half a dollar; 45 cents is half a dollar less one tenth of half a dollar; $1.05 is $1.00 plus one twentieth of $1.00.

If you are not accustomed to working with figures this may seem a little confusing at first. It will probably be much clearer after observing the steps in the following solutions:

Example 1: Multiply 90 cents by 35 mentally.

Solution: 35 times $1.00 = $35.00
  − 35 times .10   =   3.50
_____

       35 times .90   = $31.50

Example 2: Multiply 55 cents by 46 mentally.

Solution: 46 times .50   = $23.00
          46 times .05 ($\frac{1}{10}$ of $23.00) =   2.30
_____

          46 times .55   = $25.30

Example 3: Multiply $57\frac{1}{2}$ cents by 36 mentally.

Solution: 36 times .50   = $18.00
          36 times .05 ($\frac{1}{10}$ of $18.00) =   1.80
          36 times .02$\frac{1}{2}$ ($\frac{1}{2}$ of $1.80) =   .90
_____

          36 times .57$\frac{1}{2}$ = $20.70

Example 4: Multiply 45 cents by 84.

Solution: 84 times .50   = $42.00
  − 84 times .05 ($\frac{1}{10}$ of $42.00) =   4.20
_____

       84 times .45   = $37.80

In problems in which the multipliers contain but a few digits, as in the preceding four illustrations, it is comparatively easy to perform the entire computation mentally. With large multipliers the computation may be speeded by writing down the partial products. Thus in computing $57\frac{1}{2}$ cents multiplied by 286 it might help to write down the products of 286 times 50 cents, 286 times 5 cents and 286 times $2\frac{1}{2}$ cents, and, of course, the sum of these products to obtain the final result. It would be good practice, though, to learn to add small sums like these mentally.

Here is an easy and interesting example: Multiply 98 cents by 20. In this case either of two methods may be used. This problem is the equivalent of $9.80 multiplied by 2, and without giving it a second thought we see that the answer is $19.60. Or we may take the product of $1.00 multiplied by 20, and subtract the product of 20 times 2 cents—two perfectly simple calculations which should enable one to arrive at the answer to a problem of this kind in a matter of seconds.

Another problem of this nature is 96 cents multiplied by 12. But here it would obviously be simpler to say, "12 times $1.00 equals $12.00; 12 times 4 cents equals .48; $12.00 minus .48 equals $11.52."

Let us take another example: 119 times 98 cents. One hundred and nineteen times $1.00 equals $119.00; 119 times 2 cents equals $2.38; $119.00 minus $2.38 equals $116.62.

Example 5: Estimate the cost of a 52-pound roll of kraft paper at $8\frac{1}{2}$ cents per pound.

Solution: 50 times $8\frac{1}{2}$ cents ($\frac{1}{2}$ of $8.50) = $4.25
　　　　　 2 times $8\frac{1}{2}$ cents　　　　　　 = 　.17

　　　　　 52 times $8\frac{1}{2}$ cents　　　　　　 = $4.42

It goes without saying that while the purpose of this discussion is to indicate the ease with which sums under $1.00 may be multiplied mentally, the same method may be used to advantage in the case of sums over $1.00, as demonstrated in the illustration that follows:

Example 6: Multiply $1.05 by 460.

Solution: 460 times $1.00   = $460.00
        460 times .05 ($\frac{1}{20}$ of $460.00) =   23.00

        460 times $1.05   = $483.00

PROBLEMS

The following problems should be worked without pencil and paper, and the answers should be written down only after they have been computed mentally.

* **1.** 81 times 25 cents.   *Ans.* $20.25.
* **2.** 26 times 48 cents.   *Ans.* $12.48.
* **3.** 36 times 23 cents.   *Ans.* $8.28.
* **4.** 19 times 60 cents.   *Ans.* $11.40.
* **5.** 76 times 42 cents.   *Ans.* $31.92.
* **6.** 88 times 30 cents.   *Ans.* $26.40.
* **7.** 45 times 78 cents.   *Ans.* $35.10.
* **8.** 55 times 46 cents.   *Ans.* $25.30.
* **9.** 69 times 40 cents.   *Ans.* $27.60.
* **10.** 98 times 52 cents.   *Ans.* $50.96.

Using as many as possible of the short-cuts discussed in preceding articles, work the following problems with a minimum of pencil-and-paper work.

11. 9 times $18.36.   *Ans.* $165.24. (*Art. 1-d*)
12. 11 times $4.30.   *Ans.* $47.30   (*Art. 1-f*)
13. 14 times $48.08.   *Ans.* $672.00. (*Art. 22*)
14. 15 times $8.36.   *Ans.* $125.40. (*Art. 1-b*)
15. 125 times $2.48.   *Ans.* $310.00. (*Art. 2-c*)
16. 104 times $1.63.   *Ans.* $169.52.   (*Art. 3*)
17. 64 times $1.16.   *Ans.* $74.24.   (*Art. 5*)
18. 72 times $3.11.   *Ans.* $223.92.   (*Art. 5*)
19. 89 times $2.54.   *Ans.* $226.06.   (*Art. 9*)
20. 69 times $4.36.   *Ans.* $300.84. (*Art. 10*)

27. Seemingly Difficult Multiplication Problems Can Be Solved with Surprisingly Little Paper Work. In the preceding article we learned how to compute mentally and with a minimum of effort such problems as 35 times 90 cents, 46 times 55 cents, etc. Here we shall learn how to compute more difficult problems in a fraction of the time ordinarily taken, with a minimum of pencil-and-paper work, and with reasonable assurance of accuracy.

Taking the problem 65 cents multiplied by 44, observe that the digits in the multiplier are alike. It is not difficult to multiply 65 cents by 4 mentally; twice 65 cents equals $1.30, and twice $1.30 equals $2.60. Now if 4 times 65 cents equals $2.60, 40 times 65 cents equals 10 times $2.60, or $26.00. Adding $2.60 and $26.00 gives us our answer, $28.60. The only figures we needed to write down, if any, were $2.60 and $26.00. We did not need to write down their sum, for these simple values can be added mentally with little difficulty.

Now see how easy it is to do the problem 35 cents multiplied by 4.4 mentally. Twice 35 cents equals 70 cents; therefore, 4 times 35 cents equals $1.40. Now if 4 times 35 cents equals $1.40, .4 times 35 cents equals one tenth of $1.40, or 14 cents. All we need to do now is add .14 to $1.40, and we have the answer, $1.54. All the figures we needed to write down, if any, were $1.40 and .14.

Here is an interesting example: 5.9 times 35 cents. Remember what we did when we multiplied by 9 (Art. 1-d); we found it easier to multiply first by 10 and then to subtract one tenth of the result. Using this method here, we multiply 35 cents by 6, which gives us $2.10, and subtract one tenth of 35 cents. The only figures we need to write down, if any, are $2.10 and .03 or .04, a total of five figures.

Another typical illustration is 93 times $0.296. Notice that $0.296 is the equivalent of $0.30 minus $0.004. This problem might be computed on paper as follows:

$0.30 multiplied by 93 (3 times $9.30)   = $27.90
— $0.004 multiplied by 93 (4 times $0.093) =   .37
_____

$0.296 multiplied by 93   = $27.53

A somewhat similar example is 1804 times $0.489. Notice that .489 is the equivalent of .50 minus .011. The computation would be as follows:

$0.50 multiplied by 1804 ($\frac{1}{2}$ of $1804.00)   = $902.00
− $0.011 multiplied by 1804 ($18.04 plus $1.80) =   19.84

$0.489 multiplied by 1804   = $882.16

This solution required no multiplying at all. We simply worked with decimal points, which is much simpler than multiplying 1804 by 9, then by 8, and finally by 4, and then adding the three partial products to obtain the answer.

The problem 225 times $0.224 is interesting for a different reason. Here we have the choice of two methods:

Method A: 200 times $0.224 (twice $22.40) = $44.80
          25 times $0.224 ($\frac{1}{4}$ of $22.40) =   5.60

---

          225 times $0.224   = $50.40

Method B: 225 times $0.20 ($\frac{1}{5}$ of 225.00)   = $45.00
          225 times $0.02 ($\frac{1}{10}$ of 45.00)   =   4.50
          225 times $0.004 ($\frac{1}{5}$ of 4.50)   =   .90

---

          225 times $0.224   = $50.40

Method A is, of course, the shorter.

In the example 5.2 times 55 cents we also have two choices of computation. One choice is to multiply 50 cents by 5.2, and add one tenth of the product; the other is to multiply 55 cents by 5 and add .2 (one fifth) of 55 cents.

Here is a type of problem which occurs frequently in business: 60 cents multiplied by 39.9. Notice that the multiplier is short of .1 to make it the nice round number 40. The quickest method of computation, therefore, would be:

          40 times $0.60 (4 times $6.00) = $24.00
        −   .1 times $0.60   =   .06

          39.9 times $0.60   = $23.94

A good illustration of how unnecessary it is at times to use the conventional method of multiplication is the problem 16 times $8.03. We have here two simple little problems in one: 16 times

$8.00, and 16 times $0.03.   Both problems can be computed
mentally with ease, so why go to the trouble of setting down multiplicand and multiplier, writing down, in all, five lines of figures?
Sixteen times $8.00 equals $128.00; 16 times $0.03 equals $0.48;
total $128.48.   (To compute 16 times 8 mentally, we simply take 8
times 8, and double the result.)

An unusually interesting example of the little need for paper
work in computing many problems is demonstrated by the following: The Agricultural Census of 1945 (preliminary) shows West
Virginia as having 99,128 farms averaging 88.4 acres in size. Now
to compute the total farm acreage we can multiply the number of
farms by the number of acres, or vice versa. Note that either
method can be worked by the technique discussed in Art. 13, as
illustrated:

Method A: 99,128 multiplied by 88.4.

$$99128$$
$$88.4$$

First partial product	39651.2
Second partial product	
(20 times 1st product)	793024
Third partial product	793024

8762915.2

Ans. 8,762,915.2 acres.

Method B: 88.4 multiplied by 99,128.

100,000 times 88.4		= 8,840,000
− 872 times 88.4		
800 times 88.4	= 70720	
72 times 88.4 ($\frac{9}{100}$ of		
70720)	= 6364.8	
	=	77,084.8

99,128 times 88.4	= 8,762,915.2

Ans. 8,762,915.2 acres.

Problems 1 to 6 should be worked without computing more than two partial products in each instance.

1. 164 times $2.74.   *Ans.* $449.36. (*Art. 13*)

2. 325 times $16.50.   *Ans.* $5362.50. (*Art. 13*)

3. 52½ times $0.0288.   *Ans.* $1.51.   (*Art. 13*)

4. 39.7 times $1.23.   *Ans.* $48.83.   (*Art. 16*)

5. 51¼ times $0.32.   *Ans.* $16.40.   (*Art. 13*)

6. 47½ times $4.86.   *Ans.* $230.85. (*Art. 13*)

The following problems should be worked without pencil and paper, and the answers should be written down only after they have been computed mentally.

* 7. If 26-inch duck fabric weighs 16.55 ounces per yard, how much should 32 yards weigh? (Hint: If one yard weighs 16.55 ounces, 16 yards should weigh 16.55 pounds.)   *Ans.* 33.1 pounds.

8. Using the short-cut method for multiplying by 27, compute the cost of a mailing list of 13,500 names at $13.50 per thousand. (Hint: Half of 13,500 is equivalent to 6¾ thousand.)   *Ans.* $182.25. (*Art. 6*)

* 9. Formaldehyde weighs 8.2 pounds per gallon. Estimate the weight of the contents of 24 pint bottles of this compound.   *Ans.* 24.6 pounds.

* 10. If one pound of butter fat makes 1⅙ pounds of butter, how many pounds of butter can be made from 37 pounds of butter fat?

Ans. 43⅙ pounds.

* 11. Compute the amount of wages due a workman for 39 hours at $1.24 an hour.   *Ans.* $48.36. (*Art. 16*)

28. In Computations Requiring Paper Work, Multiplicand and Multiplier Need Not Always Be Written Down. Several times in the preceding pages it was pointed out that in computing many different types of multiplication problems it was unnecessary to write down the multiplicand and the multiplier.

Most of us are in the habit of writing down the multiplicand and, under the multiplicand, the multiplier, as though we were writing an examination paper and wanted to satisfy the examiner that we knew what we were doing. In a great many instances this copying of factors is entirely unnecessary, particularly when the factors are easily observable. Let us say that we were to compute the amount of a sale comprising 478 units at 34 cents each. Both numbers, 478 and 34, are already before our eyes, either on a memo or on some kind of business form. It would, therefore, be a waste of time to copy these numbers on a scratch pad. Why not proceed with the computation using the figures that are already before us, writing down nothing more than the product of 4 times 478 and 30 times 478?

Example: A manufacturer rents a loft 127 feet long by 28 feet wide. What is the total floor space of the loft?

Solution: 125 times 28 ($\frac{1}{8}$ of 28000) = 3500

        2 times 28   =   56

---

    127 times 28   = 3556

Ans. 3556 square feet.

In the foregoing problem it was even unnecessary to write down 3500 and 56, for $\frac{1}{8}$ is equivalent to $\frac{1}{2}$ of $\frac{1}{4}$, and since $\frac{1}{4}$ of 28,000 equals 7000, $\frac{1}{8}$ of 28,000 equals 3500; and 3500 plus twice 28 equals 3556.

The time- and energy-saving advantages of eliminating this unnecessary appendage from calculations are especially important to those who continually work with figures, and the reader is urged not to underestimate the value of this significant, although uncommonly practiced, short-cut.

Problems

The following problems should be worked without pencil and paper, and the answers should be written down only after they have been computed mentally.

  ★ **1.** 25 gallons at $1.96 a gallon.   *Ans.* $49.00. (*Art. 2*)

  ★ **2.** $7\frac{1}{4}$ hours at $1.60 an hour.   *Ans.* $11.60. (*Art. 21*)

  ★ **3.** 27 times 23.   *Ans.* 621.   (*Art. 6*)

  ★ **4.** 48 at $26\frac{1}{4}$ cents each.   *Ans.* $12.60. (*Art. 21*)

  ★ **5.** 29 times 16.   *Ans.* 464.   (*Art. 16*)

  ★ **6.** $7\frac{1}{2}$ dozen at $4.80 a dozen.   *Ans.* $36.00. (*Art. 1-c*)

  * 7. 98 at 14 cents each.   *Ans.* $13.72.   (*Art. 3*)
  * 8. 36 times $15.25.   *Ans.* $549.00.   (*Arts. 21, 1-d*)
  * 9. 104 times $23.00.   *Ans.* $2392.00. (*Art. 3*)
  * 10. 1008 units at $21.35 a gross.   *Ans.* $300.00. (*Art. 1-g*)

Compute the answers to the following problems with a minimum of pencil-and-paper work and without writing down the multiplicands and multipliers.

  11. The total weight of 17 barrels of oysters, each barrel weighing 375 pounds.   *Ans.* 6375 pounds. (*Art. 13*)

  12. The area in square feet of a room 22 feet 2 inches long by 24 feet wide.   *Ans.* 532 square feet. (*Art. 2*)

  13. The total weight of 33 bales of cinnamon sticks, each bale weighing 112 pounds.   *Ans.* 3696 pounds. (*Art. 1-f*)

  14. The cost of treating a floor having an area of 450 square feet, at $1.30 per square foot.   *Ans.* $585.00. (*Arts. 2-a, 6*)

  15. The weight of 96 cubic feet of water, the weight of one cubic foot of water being $62\frac{1}{2}$ pounds.   *Ans.* 6000 pounds. (*Art. 3*)

  16. Compute the total number of pounds in $16\frac{1}{4}$ long tons. (Hint: Multiply 16.25 by 2000 and add $\frac{12}{100}$ of the result.)
                                 Ans. 36,400 pounds. (*Art. 13*)

  17. The commission earned by a broker on 167 units at $3.15 a unit.
                                 Ans. $526.05. (*Art. 13*)

  18. The number of cubic feet of space occupied by $17\frac{1}{2}$ cords of wood. (A cord of wood equals 128 cubic feet.)   *Ans.* 2240 cubic feet. (*Art. 16*)

  19. At 4.7 yards of $36\frac{1}{2}$-inch wide print cloth to the pound, the number of yards in 19 pounds.   *Ans.* 89.3 yards. (*Art. 16*)

  20. The weight of $7\frac{1}{3}$ cubic feet of Portland cement. (One cubic foot of Portland cement weighs 183 pounds.)   *Ans.* 1342 pounds. (*Arts. 1-f, 21*)

29. How to Compute Mentally Costs, Invoice Extensions, etc., When the Price or Rate Given Is per 100 or per 1000. Ask the average person to compute *mentally* the value of 9 articles priced at $26.00 per hundred or the value of 23 articles at $20.00 per thousand, and the chances are he may prefer to walk a mile.

Yet nothing could be simpler.

To solve the first problem we need but to determine the price per unit, and this much can be done without performing any calculation whatever; the decimal point is simply moved two places to the left. So that instead of reading $26.00 per hundred we read 26 cents each. Nine times 26 cents is the equivalent of 10 times 26 cents cents minus 26 cents, which equals $2.34, all of which could be done mentally.

In our second problem, 23 at $20.00 per thousand, the price is equivalent to $2.00 per hundred. Two dollars per hundred is 2 cents each, and 23 times 2 cents equals 46 cents. And this problem, too, could be computed mentally in less time than it takes to pick up a pencil.

Let us try a slightly more difficult problem: 38 at $35.00 per thousand. This is the same as $3.50 per hundred, which is $3\frac{1}{2}$ cents each. Our problem now becomes 38 times $3\frac{1}{2}$ cents, which, by the "double-and-halve" method (Chapter III), may be restated as 19 times 7 cents. We know in a flash that 20 times 7 cents equals $1.40, and subtracting 7 cents supplies the answer, $1.33.

Example: An advertisement of the War Assets Administration announces the availability of braid at $0.88 per 100 yards. Estimate mentally the cost of 10,250 yards of this material.

Solution: 10,000 yards at $0.88 per 100 yards (100
      times $0.88)   = $88.00
   250 yards at $0.88 per 100 yards ($2\frac{1}{2}$
      times $0.88, or 10 times $0.22) = 2.20

_____

10,250 yards at $0.88 per 100 yards   = $90.20

Problems

* 1. At the market quotation of $6.76 per 100 pounds, what is the value of 203 pounds of rosin?   *Ans.* $13.72. (*Art. 3*)

2. At the wholesale price of $3.46 per 100 pounds, how much is 390 pounds of fluid milk worth?   *Ans.* $13.49. (*Art. 16*)

3. In June, 1946, lambs were quoted at $16.75 per 100 pounds. Estimate the cost of 408 pounds.   *Ans.* $68.34. (*Art. 3*)

4. Compute the cost of 4 dozen oilers at $13.10 per 100.
                Ans. $6.29. (*Art. 16*)

5. One hundred feet of asphalt-felt joints, 4 inches wide and $\frac{3}{4}$ inch thick, weigh 140 pounds. Find the weight of 126 feet.
           Ans. 176.4 pounds. (*Art. 16*)

6. At \$2.80 per 1000 yards, what is the cost of 216 yards of satin ribbon? *Ans.* \$0.61. (*Art. 13*)

7. Compute the value of (a) 2075 board feet of Western Pine at \$40.07 per 1000, and (b) 1160 board feet of Southern Pine at \$46.03 per 1000. *Ans.* (a) \$83.14; (b) \$53.39. (*Art. 16*)

8. What would 1508 common brick cost at \$18.20 per 1000?

Ans. \$27.44. (*Art. 16*)

9. One thousand sheets of 16 substance writing paper, 22 by 34 inches, weigh 64 pounds. An advertising campaign calls for the use of 1125 sheets of this stock, including the quantity allowed for waste. What should the net weight of the purchase be? *Ans.* 72 pounds. (*Art. 2-c*)

10. If it takes 8.5 hours to glue by hand the covers to 1000 96-page sewed books, size 12 by 9 inches, how long would it take to glue the covers to 240 of these books? *Ans.* 2.04 hours. (*Art. 16*)

30. How to Compute Mentally Little Problems in Which the Price per Unit Contains Several Decimal Places. The decimal point needlessly confuses many individuals who are otherwise good at figures.

Consider the problem \$0.331 multiplied by 40. In Chapter III we learned that when factors in a multiplication problem are multiplied and divided, respectively, by the same number, the product is not affected. What would be simpler, then, than to reduce the multiplier in this problem to a single-digit number? By dividing 40 by 10 and multiplying \$0.331 by 10 our problem becomes 4 times \$3.31. Applying the method described in Art. 24, we can compute this problem mentally as follows: 4 times \$3.00 equals \$12.00; 4 times \$0.30 equals \$1.20; and 4 times \$0.01 equals \$0.04. The mental computation and addition of these three little partial products should be virtually effortless.

An additional advantage of reducing the multiplier to a single-digit number in a problem of this nature is that it makes possible at a glance an approximation of the answer. In the problem in the preceding paragraph, for instance, we can see instantly that the answer will be greater than \$12.00 but less than \$16.00.

In the problem 36 times \$1.0275, however, it is not necessary to convert the multiplier to a single-digit number. A better method of procedure would be as follows:

36 times $1.00   = $36.00
36 times $0.025 (18 times 5 cents) =   .90
36 times $0.0025 ($\frac{1}{10}$ of .90)   =   .09

---

36 times $1.0275   = $36.99

The above illustration is, of course, for the purpose of explanation only. With a little practice the mental computation of such a problem should be a comparatively simple matter.

A problem of a different type is $0.346 multiplied by 7. Here the reader's attention is again called to the method discussed in Art. 24, namely, that in mental multiplication it is useful to think of some numbers as a group of separate numbers. Instead of multiplying $0.346 by 7 by the conventional method, which would make it necessary to remember the last figure of each partial product and carry the rest of the product, we make three separate little computations, adding one computation to the other as it is made. Our problem would, therefore, be computed as follows: 7 times $0.30 ($2.10) plus 7 times $0.04 ($0.28) equals $2.38; plus 7 times $0.006 ($0.04) equals $2.42. It is really as simple as that, and the fact that your interest has carried you to this point is a good indication that you will find it so.

PROBLEMS

★ 1. How much would a dealer have to pay for 70 gallons of gas at $0.104 per gallon?   *Ans.* $7.28.

2. Find the cost of 640 yards of printcloths at $0.1415 per yard.
Ans. $90.56.

★ 3. What is the worth of 49 pounds of antimony at the market quotation of $0.1612 per pound?   *Ans.* $7.90. (*Art. 16*)

4. Compute the value of 360 pounds of lard at $0.1905 per pound.
Ans. $68.58. (*Art. 6*)

★ 5. How much is 7 pounds of zinc worth at $0.0869 per pound?
Ans. $0.61.

6. The cost of a factory operation is $0.1825 per unit. If the work is turned over to a contractor who can supply the units at 14 cents each, how much would the manufacturer save on 25 gross?   *Ans.* $153.00.

★ 7. A factory inspector finds that 7 in every 100 parts used in the production of an office device are defective. If 2500 of these parts were purchased at $0.0432 each, how much credit will the purchaser be entitled to upon the return of the defective parts? *Ans.* $7.56. (*Art.* 13)

8. It costs $0.0355 to produce a toy motorboat retailing at 10 cents. If the manufacturer's selling price is 78 cents a dozen, how much gross profit will he make on a sale of 5 gross units? *Ans.* $21.24.

31. How to Compute Mentally Little Problems in Which the Price per Unit Is a Fraction of a Cent. It often helps to visualize a problem and make a rough guess at the answer before attempting its computation. This is particularly true of mentally calculable problems in which the multiplier is a small number and the price per unit a fraction of a cent.

As an illustration, let us take the problem 38 articles at $1.50 per thousand. To facilitate calculation let us restate the problem to read 38 articles at 15 cents per hundred. Now 15 cents per hundred is equivalent to $1\frac{1}{2}$ cents for ten. It is obvious that it will make no difference in the answer whether the quantity is 38 or 40, so let us call it 40. Forty at $1\frac{1}{2}$ cents for 10 equals 6 cents.

Let us take another example: 123 at $1.28 per thousand. This is the same as 123 at $0.128 per hundred. One hundred units would cost .13. Since the price per unit is but a fraction of a cent, let us change 23 to 25, 25 being exactly one fourth of 100. One fourth of 13 cents (the price per 100) is 3 cents. Adding 13 cents and 3 cents gives us our answer, 16 cents.

PROBLEMS

The following problems provide an excellent opportunity for practice in mental computation without the use of pencil and paper.

* **1.** 27 at $1\frac{3}{4}$ cents each. *Ans.* $0.47.

* **2.** 29 at $1.25 per hundred. *Ans.* $0.36.

* **3.** 98 at $1.06 per hundred. *Ans.* $1.04.

* **4.** 47 at $2.30 per hundred. *Ans.* $1.08.

* **5.** 90 at $0.87 per hundred. *Ans.* $0.78.

* **6.** 110 at $4.13 per hundred. *Ans.* $4.54.

* **7.** 23 at $2.75 per hundred. *Ans.* $0.64.

* **8.** 76 at $3.00 per thousand. *Ans.* $0.23.

* **9.** 104 at $4.90 per thousand. *Ans.* $0.51.

* **10.** 334 at $3.69 per thousand. *Ans.* $1 23.

CHAPTER V

MORE SHORT-CUTS IN MULTIPLICATION

This chapter presents a miscellaneous collection of short-cuts which are more or less independent of the rest of the material in this book. A cursory examination of the following articles will indicate that a large variety of problems, in the solution of which much valuable time is ordinarily wasted, can be computed with surprising rapidity. The methods outlined are more easily illustrated than described.

32. How to Square Numbers Ending in 5. Disregard for a moment the unit digit 5. Add 1 to the rest of the number in the multiplicand; multiply the result by the rest of the number in the multiplier, and consider the product as hundreds. Now add the square of the unit digit 5.

Example 1: Square 45.

Solution: 4 times 5 equals 20; 100 times 20 = 2000
5 times 5   =   25
_____

45 times 45   = 2025

Example 2: Square 185.

Solution: 18 times 19 equals 342; 100 times 342 = 34200
5 times 5   =   25
_____

185 times 185   = 34225

To square a number which ends with a zero but whose last digit is 5, disregard the zero and annex two zeros to the result, as shown in the illustration that follows:

Example 3: A waterproofing product adapted for application to wood and metal surfaces covers approximately 350 square feet per gallon. Find the approximate number of square feet that would be covered by 350 gallons of this material.

Solution:

3 times 4 equals 12; 100 times 12 =	1,200
5 times 5 =	25

35 times 35 =	1,225
350 times 350 =	122,500

Ans. Approximately 122,500 square feet.

It is interesting to note that for every zero after the 5 in the number to be squared, two zeros are annexed to the result. Thus to square 4500, four zeros would be annexed to the product of 45 times 45; to square 85,000, six zeros would be annexed to the product of 85 times 85; and so on.

PROBLEMS

★ **1.** Compute in square feet the area of a room 25 feet by 25 feet.

Ans. 625 square feet.

2. Find the area of a circle whose radius is 35 inches. (The formula for finding the area of a circle is πr^2, π being equal to 3.1416, and r^2 meaning radius squared. The radius is a straight line extending from the center of a circle to the circumference. The answer to this problem will therefore be arrived at by finding the product of 3.1416 times 35 times 35 inches.)

Ans. 3848.46 square inches.

3. Compute the area of a sphere whose diameter is 55 inches. (The formula for finding the area of a sphere is πD^2. D^2 means diameter squared. The diameter is the length of a straight line through the center of an object from side to side.) *Ans.* 9503.34 square inches.

4. Estimate the area of a cylinder having a radius of 6.5 inches and a height of 8 inches. (The formula for finding the area of a cylinder is $2\pi r^2$ plus $2\pi rh$—h meaning height or length. The answer to this problem therefore will be obtained by adding two products: the product of 2 times 3.1416 times 6.5 times 6.5 inches plus the product of 2 times 3.1416 times 6.5 times 8 inches.) *Ans.* 592.1916 square inches.

5. Estimate the volume of a cylinder having a radius of 7.5 inches and a height of 9 inches. (The formula for finding the volume of a cylinder is $\pi r^2 h$.) *Ans.* 1590.435 cubic inches.

33. How to Square Numbers Containing the Fraction $\frac{1}{2}$.   Add 1 to the whole number in the multiplicand and multiply the result by the whole number in the multiplier.   Now add the square of the fraction $\frac{1}{2}$.

Example 1: Square $6\frac{1}{2}$.

Solution: $\quad$ 6 times 7 $\quad = 42$

$\qquad\quad\ \ \frac{1}{2}$ times $\frac{1}{2}\ =\quad \frac{1}{4}$

$\qquad\quad\ \ 6\frac{1}{2}$ times $6\frac{1}{2} = 42\frac{1}{4}$

Example 2: Square $17\frac{1}{2}$.

Solution: $\quad$ 17 times 18 $\quad = 306$

$\qquad\quad\ \ \frac{1}{2}$ times $\frac{1}{2}\ =\quad\ \ \frac{1}{4}$

$\qquad\quad\ \ 17\frac{1}{2}$ times $17\frac{1}{2} = 306\frac{1}{4}$

Example 3: What would the import duty amount to on a shipment of sheepswool sponges valued at \$2250.00, at the rate of $22\frac{1}{2}\%$?   (Note that $22\frac{1}{2}\%$ of \$2250.00 is equivalent to $22\frac{1}{2}$ times \$22.50.)

Solution: $\quad$ 22 times 23 (2 times 253) $= 506$

$\qquad\quad\ \ \frac{1}{2}$ times $\frac{1}{2}\qquad\qquad\quad\ =\quad\ \ \frac{1}{4}$

$\qquad\quad\ \ 22\frac{1}{2}$ times $22\frac{1}{2}\qquad\qquad = 506\frac{1}{4}$

$$\textit{Ans. }\$506.25.$$

PROBLEMS

* 1. How many square yards are there in a square rod?   (One rod equals $5\frac{1}{2}$ yards.) $\qquad$ *Ans.* $30\frac{1}{4}$ square yards.

2. How many square feet are there in a square rod?   (One rod equals $16\frac{1}{2}$ feet.) $\qquad$ *Ans.* $272\frac{1}{4}$ square feet. (*Art. 22*)

3. From a sheet of asbestos measuring 4 feet by 8 feet, fifty equal squares of $9\frac{1}{2}$ by $9\frac{1}{2}$ inches are cut.   Assuming that there is no waste in cutting, how many square inches of the original sheet will remain?

$$\textit{Ans. }95\frac{1}{2}\text{ square inches. }(\textit{Art. 5})$$

4. Find the area of a hexagon whose diameter is $8\frac{1}{2}$ inches. (A hexagon is a 6-sided figure all of whose angles are equal. To find the area of a hexagon the square of the diameter is multiplied by 0.866.)

Ans. 62.5685 square inches.

★ **5.** In a right triangle (a triangle in which one of the angles is a right angle—that is, 90 degrees) the square of the hypotenuse (the side opposite the right angle) is equal to the sum of the squares of the other two sides. If one of the two sides is $4\frac{1}{2}$ feet long, and the other $6\frac{1}{2}$ feet, what is the area of the square of the hypotenuse? *Ans.* $62\frac{1}{2}$ square feet.

34. How to Square Any Number of Two Digits. Square the tens digit and consider the result as hundreds; add the square of the unit digit; then add 20 times the product of the tens digit multiplied by the unit digit.

Example 1: Square 79.

Solution: 7 times 7 equals 49; 100 times 49 = 4900
9 times 9   =   81
7 times 9 equals 63; 20 times 63   = 1260

—————————————————————————

79 times 79   = 6241

Example 2: Square 84.

Solution: 8 times 8 equals 64; 100 times 64 = 6400
4 times 4   =   16
8 times 4 equals 32; 20 times 32   = 640

—————————————————————————

84 times 84   = 7056

Example 3: When the lumber of the black gum tree is saturated with water it contains about 43 pounds of water per cubic foot. Compute the amount of water contained in 43 cubic feet of this lumber when it is so saturated.

Solution: 4 times 4 equals 16; 100 times 16 = 1600
3 times 3   =   9
4 times 3 equals 12; 20 times 12   = 240

—————————————————————————

43 times 43   = 1849

Ans. 1849 pounds of water.

PROBLEMS

1. Compute the area of a square whose sides measure 67 feet.

Ans. 4489 square feet.

2. A 46-inch square is marked off in each of the four corners of a room 40 by 60 feet. How many square inches are marked off altogether?

Ans. 8464 square inches.

*3. The end of a piece of lumber is 16 inches square. What is the area of the end surface?   *Ans.* 256 square inches.

* 4. A retailer sold 37 packages of milk powder at 37 cents each. How much did he receive?   *Ans.* $13.69.

* 5. A man worked 38 hours. His rate of pay is $1.38. How much did he earn?   *Ans.* $52.44.

35. How to Find the Product of Two Factors When the Sum of the Unit Digits Is 10 and the Rest of the Number Is the Same in Both Factors. The rule here is the same as when squaring a number ending in 5 (Art. 32) except that, instead of squaring the unit digit 5, one unit digit is multiplied by the other unit digit.

Example 1: Multiply 86 by 84.

Solution: 8 times 9 equals 72; 100 times 72 = 7200
4 times 6   =   24

86 times 84   = 7224

Example 2: Multiply 41 by 49.

Solution: 4 times 5 equals 20; 100 times 20 = 2000
9 times 1   =   9

41 times 49   = 2009

Example 3: Multiply 237 by 233.

Solution: 23 times 24 equals 552· 100 times 552 = 55200
3 times 7   =   21

237 times 233   = 55221

Example 4: Compute mentally the area in square inches of a sheet of asbestos mill board 42 by 48 inches.

Solution: 4 times 5 equals 20; 100 times 20 = 2000

2 times 8   =   16

_____

42 times 48   = 2016

Ans. 2016 square inches.

PROBLEMS

★ **1.** Compute the number of cubic feet in 23 cubic yards. (One cubic yard equals 27 cubic feet.)   *Ans.* 621 cubic feet.

★ **2.** If a chest of tea weighs 84 pounds, how much will 86 chests weigh?
Ans. 7224 pounds.

★ **3.** There are 38 feet of 3-strand Manila rope $\frac{5}{16}$ inch in diameter to the pound. Compute the number of feet that would be represented by 32 pounds.   *Ans.* 1216 feet.

★ **4.** What would the total weight be of 53 cartons of precipitated chalk, each having a gross weight of 57 pounds?   *Ans.* 3021 pounds.

5. If there are 76 strips of an asphalt roof shingle to the square, how many strips would be required to cover 7400 square feet of roof surface? (The word "square," as used in the building industry, denotes 100 square feet.)   *Ans.* 5624 strips.

6. The gross weight of a barrel of buckwheat is 217 pounds. Compute the gross weight of 213 barrels.   *Ans.* 46,221 pounds. (*Art. 1-f*)

★ **7.** The cuadra is a unit of measurement used in Uruguay. The American equivalent is 1.82 acres. Estimate the number of acres in 188 cuadras.   *Ans.* 342.16 acres. (*Art. 1-e*)

8. What is the value of 812 pounds of refined lead at the wholesale price of $0.0818 per pound?   *Ans.* $66.42.

9. A machine operated by a single individual can turn out 146 springs per hour. How many springs will be turned out by 4 machines in one week, if each of the 4 operators works a total of 36 hours per week?
Ans. 21,024 springs. (*Art. 22*)

★ **10.** A coal-crushing machine has a capacity of 113 tons per hour. How many tons of coal can be crushed in 3 weeks if the machine is operated for 39 hours each week?   *Ans.* 13,221 tons. (*Art. 1-f*)

36. How to Find the Product of Two Factors, Each Containing a Fraction, in Which the Whole Numbers Are Alike and the Sum

of the Fractions Is 1. Add 1 to the whole number in the multiplicand; multiply the result by the whole number in the multiplier; then add the product of the fractions.

Example 1: Multiply $9\frac{1}{4}$ by $9\frac{3}{4}$.

Solution: 9 times 10 $= 90$

$\qquad \frac{1}{4}$ times $\frac{3}{4} = \quad \frac{3}{16}$

$\qquad 9\frac{1}{4}$ times $9\frac{3}{4} = 90\frac{3}{16}$

Example 2: Multiply $4\frac{1}{3}$ by $4\frac{2}{3}$.

Solution: 4 times 5 $= 20$

$\qquad \frac{1}{3}$ times $\frac{2}{3} = \quad \frac{2}{9}$

$\qquad 4\frac{1}{3}$ times $4\frac{2}{3} = 20\frac{2}{9}$

Example 3: Multiply $8\frac{3}{7}$ by $8\frac{4}{7}$.

Solution: 8 times 9 $= 72$

$\qquad \frac{3}{7}$ times $\frac{4}{7} = \quad \frac{12}{49}$

$\qquad 8\frac{3}{7}$ times $8\frac{4}{7} = 72\frac{12}{49}$

Example 4: If $1\frac{1}{5}$ gallons of coconut oil can be obtained from 25 pounds of copra, how many gallons of the oil would be yielded by 45 pounds of copra? (Note that 45 pounds is equivalent to $1\frac{4}{5}$ times 25 pounds.)

Solution: 1 multiplied by 2 $= 2$

$\qquad \frac{1}{5}$ multiplied by $\frac{4}{5} = \quad \frac{4}{25}$

$\qquad 1\frac{1}{5}$ times $1\frac{4}{5} \qquad = 2\frac{4}{25}$

Ans. $4\frac{4}{25}$ gallons.

PROBLEMS

* 1. If a girl can pack $3\frac{2}{3}$ gross units in one hour, how many gross units might she be expected to pack in 3 hours 20 minutes?

Ans. $12\frac{2}{9}$ gross units.

* 2. A chemist can produce in one hour a sufficient quantity of a liquid preparation to fill 31 quart bottles. At this rate how many gallons of the material could be produced in $7\frac{1}{4}$ hours?   (Hint: 31 quarts equal $7\frac{3}{4}$ gallons.)   *Ans.* $56\frac{3}{16}$ gallons.

   ★ **3.** Compute the cost of $8\frac{2}{5}$ yards of material costing $8.60 a yard. (Hint: $8.60 equals $8\frac{3}{5}$.)   *Ans.* $72.24.

   ★ **4.** Compute the total yardage of $9\frac{1}{6}$ lengths of material, each measuring $9\frac{5}{6}$ yards.   *Ans.* 90 yards 5 inches.

   ★ **5.** If $6\frac{1}{4}$ sacks of Portland cement are required to make one cubic yard of a $1:2\frac{1}{4}:3$ mix concrete, how many sacks of Portland cement will be needed to make $6\frac{3}{4}$ cubic yards of concrete of this mix?

                                           Ans. $42\frac{3}{16}$ sacks.

   ★ **6.** How many acres are there in a piece of land $4\frac{3}{8}$ miles long by $4\frac{5}{8}$ miles wide?   (One square mile equals 640 acres.)   *Ans.* 12,950 acres.

37. How to Find the Product of Factors Ending with Zeros. Eliminate the zeros after the last significant figure in each factor, compute the problem with the remaining figures, then annex to the product as many zeros as were eliminated.

Example 1: Multiply 2300 by 350.

Solution: Eliminate the three zeros, and multiply 35 by 23.

$$
\begin{array}{ll}
23 \text{ times } 25 \ (\tfrac{1}{4} \text{ of } 2300) & = 575 \\
23 \text{ times } 10 & = 230 \\
\hline
23 \text{ multiplied by } 35 & = 805
\end{array}
$$

Annexing three zeros, we arrive at the answer, 805000.

Example 2: Multiply 16040 by 1020.

Solution: Note that we eliminate only those zeros *after the last significant figure.*

$$
\begin{array}{ll}
1604 \text{ times } 100 & = 160400 \\
1604 \text{ times } 2 & = 3208 \\
\hline
1604 \text{ multiplied by } 102 & = 163608
\end{array}
$$

Annexing two zeros, we arrive at the answer, 16,360,-800.

Example 3: How many apples can be pared and cored in 30 hours by a machine operating at a speed of 2400 apples an hour?

Solution: 3 times 24 = 72

Annexing three zeros, gives us 72,000.

Ans. 72,000 apples.

PROBLEMS

★ 1. Estimate the total weight of 120 Indian bales of cotton having an average weight of 600 pounds.   *Ans.* 72,000 pounds.

★ 2. Compute the number of square rods in 30 acres. (One acre equals 160 square rods.)   *Ans.* 4800 square rods.

★ 3. If a power excavating bucket can handle 800 cubic yards per hour, what volume would be moved in 60 hours?   *Ans.* 48,000 cubic yards.

★ 4. A full coil of $\frac{3}{8}$ inch diameter Manila rope weighs 60 pounds. Estimate the weight of 330 coils.   *Ans.* 19,800 pounds.

★ 5. If there are 520 whole black peppercorns to the ounce, how many would there be in 10 pounds?   *Ans.* 83,200. (*Art. 22*)

★ 6. What is the capacity in cubic feet of a ditch 20 feet deep, 8 feet wide and 200 feet long?   *Ans.* 32,000 cubic feet.

★ 7. A cord of wood yields about 1500 pounds of excelsior. How many pounds of excelsior could be obtained from 260 cords?

Ans. 390,000 pounds. (*Art. 1-b*)

★ 8. If granite weighs 170 pounds per cubic foot, how much will 320 cubic feet weigh?   *Ans.* 54,400 pounds.

★ 9. Compute the number of pounds in 40 long tons. (A long ton equals 2240 pounds.)   *Ans.* 89,600 pounds.

★ 10. An unskilled workman can cut 35 squares in one hour. If 5 men of equal capacity are hired to do this work, how many squares should be ready at the end of four 40-hour weeks?   *Ans.* 28,000.

38. How to Multiply Quickly by $\frac{3}{4}$. The conventional method of multiplying by $\frac{3}{4}$ is to multiply by 3 and divide by 4. A much simpler method is to take half of the multiplicand and add to it half of the half.

Example 1: Multiply 84 by $\frac{3}{4}$.

Solution: $\frac{1}{2}$ of 84   = 42
$\frac{1}{4}$ of 84 ($\frac{1}{2}$ of 42) = 21

$\frac{3}{4}$ of 84   = 63

Example 2: Compute the cost of 170 shares at $11.75 per share.

Solution: 17 times $11.00   = $ 187.00
17 times $0.50 ($\frac{1}{2}$ of $17.00)   =   8.50
17 times $0.25 ($\frac{1}{2}$ of $8.50)   =   4.25

---

17 times $11.75   = $ 199.75
170 times $11.75 (10 times $199.75) = $1997.50

Ans. $1997.50.

PROBLEMS

★ **1.** Find the cost of $\frac{3}{4}$ gross of screws at $9.60 a gross.   *Ans.* $7.20.

★ **2.** What is the value of $\frac{3}{4}$ yard of fabric at $2.60 a yard?   *Ans.* $1.95.

★ **3.** Compute the amount due a workman for $\frac{3}{4}$ hour at $1.40 an hour.
Ans. $1.05.

★ **4.** Compute the amount due an employee for 30 hours of work at $33.60 per 40-hour week.   *Ans.* $25.20.

★ **5.** What should a grocer charge for 9 eggs at 75 cents a dozen?
Ans. $0.57.

★ **6.** What is the worth of 75 machine parts at $4.30 per hundred?
Ans. $3.23.

★ **7.** How much should a jobber charge for 750 units at $16.00 per thousand?   *Ans.* $12.00.

★ **8.** How many square inches are there in $\frac{3}{4}$ of a square foot? (One square foot equals 144 square inches.)   *Ans.* 108 square inches.

★ **9.** How many pounds are there in $\frac{3}{4}$ of a metric ton? (A metric ton equals 2205 pounds.)   *Ans.* $1653\frac{3}{4}$ pounds.

★ **10.** State the equivalent in yards of $\frac{3}{4}$ of a mile. (A mile equals 1760 yards.)   *Ans.* 1320 yards.

★ **11.** Compute the weight of 750 board feet of American Elm. (One thousand board feet of American Elm weigh 2920 pounds and, should the reader be interested to know, a board foot is the equivalent of one square foot one inch thick.)   *Ans.* 2190 pounds.

★ **12.** What is the expired amount of an annual insurance premium costing $37.00, nine months after the insurance has been in force? *Ans.* $27.75.

39. How to Multiply by a Number Containing a Fraction. First step: multiply by the whole number. Second step: if it is seen that the multiplicand is exactly divisible by the denominator of the fraction, divide by the denominator and multiply the result by the numerator.   If exact divisibility is not possible, or if a quick glance does not reveal the possibility, multiply by the numerator, then divide the result by the denominator.   Now add the results obtained in the two steps.

Example 1: Multiply 243 by $3\frac{7}{9}$.

Solution: 243 times 3 $= 729$
            243 divided by 9 equals 27; 27 times 7 $= 189$
            _____
            243 times $3\frac{7}{9}$ $= 918$

Example 2: Multiply 142 by $4\frac{3}{11}$.

Solution: (Note that in this illustration the second plan is followed in multiplying by the fraction.)

142 times 4 $= 568$
142 times 3 equals 426; 426 divided by 11 $= \;38\frac{8}{11}$
_____
142 times $4\frac{3}{11}$ $= 606\frac{8}{11}$

Although the aforementioned rule applies to fractions of any denominator, the breakdown method often is very useful in problems of this kind.   The problem in the following illustration is typical:

Example 3: Multiply 378 by $6\frac{4}{7}$.

Solution: 378 times 6 $= 2268$
            378 times $\dfrac{3\frac{1}{2}}{7}$ ($\frac{1}{2}$ of 378) $=\;\;189$
            378 times $\dfrac{\frac{1}{2}}{7}$ ($\frac{1}{7}$ of 189) $=\;\;\;27$
            _____
            378 times $6\frac{4}{7}$ $= 2484$

Example 4: Convert $7\frac{5}{8}$ long tons to pounds.   A long ton equals 2240 pounds.

Solution: 7 times 2240   = 15,680
$\frac{4}{8}$ of 2240 ($\frac{1}{2}$ of 2240) =   1,120
$\frac{1}{8}$ of 2240 ($\frac{1}{4}$ of 1120) =   280
———————————————————————
$7\frac{5}{8}$ times 2240   = 17,080

Ans. 17,080 pounds.

PROBLEMS

Note that in Problems 1 to 6 the multiplicand is exactly divisible by the denominator in the fraction. This makes it more practical to divide first the multiplicand by the denominator and then to multiply the result by the numerator. In Problems 7 to 12, on the other hand, divisibility is not exact, so here the reverse procedure is preferable—that is, to multiply first by the numerator and then to divide the result by the denominator.

1. Compute the total number of units in $6\frac{2}{9}$ gross.

Ans. 896. (*Art. 21*)

2. One cubic inch of platinum weighs 11.28 troy ounces. How many troy ounces will $7\frac{2}{3}$ cubic inches weigh?   *Ans.* 86.48 troy ounces.

3. Convert $5\frac{2}{3}$ pounds to kilograms. (One pound equals 0.4536 kilograms.)   *Ans.* 2.5704 kilograms.

4. A 20-foot diameter cast-in-place silo requires 78 vertical reinforcing bars, each 14 feet 8 inches long. Compute the total length of the bars.

Ans. 1144 feet. (*Art. 21*)

5. The net weight of a box of 90-pound, 10 by 20 inch, tin-plate sheets is 129 pounds. If there are 225 sheets to the box, what should the total net weight be of the contents of two boxes and 100 loose sheets? (Hint: 100 sheets equals $\frac{4}{9}$ of 225 sheets.)   *Ans.* $315\frac{1}{3}$ pounds.

6. There are 231 cubic inches in one gallon. Estimate the number of cubic inches in $7\frac{4}{11}$ gallons.   *Ans.* 1701 cubic inches.

7. Compute the value of $16\frac{2}{3}$ yards of material at $4.14 a yard. (Hint: $16\frac{2}{3}$ is exactly one sixth of 100.)   *Ans.* $69.00.

8. If a bar of steel weighs 1 pound 6 ounces per foot of its length, what will 29 feet weigh?   *Ans.* 39 pounds 14 ounces.

9. How much will $38\frac{4}{9}$ square feet of calf leather cost at $0.536 per square foot?   *Ans.* $20.61.

10. One cubic foot of water weighs $62\frac{1}{2}$ pounds. Estimate the weight of $6\frac{7}{10}$ cubic feet.   *Ans.* 418.75 pounds.

11. How many cubic inches are there in 13 pints? (Hint: One gallon equals 231 cubic inches, and 13 pints equal $1\frac{5}{8}$ gallons.)

Ans. $375\frac{3}{8}$ cubic inches.

12. Estimate the total area of 73 sheets of steel each of which measures 12 inches by 2 feet 5 inches. (Hint: 12 inches by 2 feet 5 inches equals $2\frac{5}{12}$ square feet.)   *Ans.* $176\frac{5}{12}$ square feet.

40. How to Multiply One Two-Digit Number by Another in One Line. The method illustrated may be a little confusing, and for this reason it is not particularly recommended, although it may be used to advantage in proving calculations. The technique is primarily one of mentally combining partial products.

Instead of attempting to follow the rule it probably will be simpler to observe the procedure.

Example: Multiply 23 by 45.

Solution: 23

                                                45
                                            ─────────

5 times 3 = 15. Write down 5, carry 1   5
5 times 2 = 10; 4 times 3 = 12; 10 plus 12
   plus 1 we carried = 23. Write down 3,
   carry 2   3
4 times 2 = 8, plus the 2 we carried   = 10

                                              ─────────
                                                1035

PROBLEMS

1. A merchant purchased 26 shark leather skins, each having an area of 17 square feet. How many square feet did he purchase in all?

Ans. 442 square feet.

2. If the speed of loading an ocean-going vessel is 23 tons per hatch per hour, how many tons will have been loaded in 16 hours on 3 hatches?

Ans. 1104 tons.

3. Estimate the total weight in ounces of 48 Guatemalan avocados having an average weight of 29 ounces.   *Ans.* 1392 ounces.

4. Specifications for the treatment of a floor surface call for the use of 34 pounds of asphalt per 100 square feet. If the total floor area is 3700 square feet how many pounds of asphalt will be needed to effect the treatment?   *Ans.* 1258 pounds.

5. A flat pan trough measures 37 by 74 inches. What is its area in square inches? *Ans.* 2738 square inches.

6. Calculate the weight of 28 cubic feet of earth weighing 73 pounds per cubic foot. *Ans.* 2044 pounds.

7. If a lubricating oil cooler has a capacity of 67 gallons per minute, how many gallons could be cooled in 58 minutes? *Ans.* 3886 gallons.

8. In an industrial abattoir carcasses are passed from the slaughtering pen to the cooling room at the rate of 83 per hour. At this rate of speed how many carcasses could be handled in 36 hours? *Ans.* 2988.

9. There are approximately 78 oval-head steel rivets, 4 inches in diameter in one pound. Estimate the number of rivets of this size in 26 pounds. *Ans.* 2028.

10. A businessman obligates himself to pay $46.00 every week for 37 weeks. How much will he have paid in all when his obligations have been met? *Ans.* $1702.00.

CHAPTER VI

ALIQUOT PARTS

No study of business mathematics would be complete without due consideration to the subject of aliquot parts.

With the techniques of the breakdown method of multiplication (Chapter II) and the double-and-halve method (Chapter III) as a background, a knowledge of aliquot parts will enable the reader to solve many different problems involving decimals and fractions speedily and with interesting results. The three subjects—the breakdown method, the double-and-halve method, and aliquot parts—necessarily overlap each other, and if the reader feels he has not thoroughly mastered the techniques of the first two methods he is urged to review them.

In this chapter frequent use will be made of the decimal point, and it would be well for readers who do not feel thoroughly at home in dealing with decimals to glance through the pages of Chapter XXIII before proceeding with the study of the articles that follow.

41. The Significance of Decimal Fractions Like .25, .12$\frac{1}{2}$, .37$\frac{1}{2}$, .62$\frac{1}{2}$, and Their Variations. "Aliquot," as defined in Funk & Wagnalls Dictionary, means "contained in something else an exact number of times: said of a part or division: as, 6 is an aliquot part of 12 and 18."

Having in mind this definition, it is easy to understand that 25 cents is an aliquot part of a dollar—it is one fourth of a dollar; so is 12$\frac{1}{2}$ cents an aliquot part of a dollar—it is one eighth; and 6$\frac{1}{4}$ cents, which is one half of 12$\frac{1}{2}$ cents, is one sixteenth of a dollar. Each of these values is contained in one dollar an exact number of times. The value 37$\frac{1}{2}$ cents, on the other hand, is not strictly an aliquot part of a dollar, but 12$\frac{1}{2}$ cents (which is one third of $37\frac{1}{2}$ cents) is. And so for practical purposes we may extend our definition to include values such as $37\frac{1}{2}$ cents too.

Thus if we wish to find the product of 36 times 25 cents, we need but to multiply 36 by $\frac{1}{4}$ and consider the answer as dollars. To find the product of 24 times $12\frac{1}{2}$ cents, we would multiply 24 by $\frac{1}{8}$. Similarly, to multiply $6\frac{1}{4}$ cents by 32, we would restate the problem to read $\frac{1}{16}$ dollar multiplied by 32, and promptly we should know that the answer is $2.00.

All of us know that $33\frac{1}{3}$ is exactly one third of 100 or, stated another way, 100 times one third. So that to multiply 138 by

TABLE V

Decimal Fractions and Their Corresponding Values as Aliquot Parts of 1

Decimal Fractions	Aliquot Parts of 1
.50	$\frac{1}{2}$
.33$\frac{1}{3}$	$\frac{1}{3}$
.66$\frac{2}{3}$	$\frac{2}{3}$
.25	$\frac{1}{4}$
.75	$\frac{3}{4}$
.20	$\frac{1}{5}$
.40	$\frac{2}{5}$
.16$\frac{2}{3}$	$\frac{1}{6}$
.12$\frac{1}{2}$	$\frac{1}{8}$
.37$\frac{1}{2}$	$\frac{3}{8}$
.62$\frac{1}{2}$	$\frac{5}{8}$
.87$\frac{1}{2}$	$\frac{7}{8}$
.08$\frac{1}{3}$	$\frac{1}{12}$
.06$\frac{1}{4}$	$\frac{1}{16}$

$33\frac{1}{3}$ we need but to annex two zeros to 138 and divide the result (13800) by three.

And since $66\frac{2}{3}$ is exactly twice $33\frac{1}{3}$, we should find the product of a number times $66\frac{2}{3}$ by first finding the product of the number times $33\frac{1}{3}$ and then multiplying the result by 2.

The reader's interest and pleasure in studying the following illustrations will possibly be enhanced by an examination of Table V—"Decimal Fractions and Their Corresponding Values as Aliquot Parts of 1."

Example 1: Find the product of 384 times $12\frac{1}{2}$ cents.

Solution: 384 times $12\frac{1}{2}$ cents ($\frac{1}{8}$ of $384.00) = $48.00

Example 2: Multiply 160 by $6\frac{1}{4}$ cents.

Solution: 160 times $12\frac{1}{2}$ cents ($\frac{1}{8}$ of $160.00) = $20.00

160 times $6\frac{1}{4}$ cents ($\frac{1}{2}$ of $20.00) = $10.00

Example 3: Multiply 135 by $62\frac{1}{2}$ cents.

Solution: (Note that $62\frac{1}{2}$ cents is the sum of 50 cents plus $12\frac{1}{2}$ cents.)

135 times 50 cents ($\frac{1}{2}$ of $135.00) = $67.50
135 times $12\frac{1}{2}$ cents ($\frac{1}{8}$ of $135.00 or $\frac{1}{4}$ of $67.50) = $16.87\frac{1}{2}$

135 times $62\frac{1}{2}$ cents = $84.38

Thus far we have dealt with numbers which are aliquot parts of a dollar or, we might say, aliquot parts of 100. Let us now consider some illustrations which reflect the significance of aliquot parts of units of measurement.

Example 4: How many pints are represented by .375 gallons?

Solution: (Note that .375 is the equivalent of $\frac{3}{8}$.) $\frac{1}{8}$ of a gallon is one pint. Therefore $\frac{3}{8}$ of a gallon equals 3 pints.

In the foregoing illustration the decimal equivalent of $\frac{3}{8}$ was shown as .375 rather than as .37$\frac{1}{2}$. When the last figure in a decimal number is 5 the fraction $\frac{1}{2}$ may be substituted for the 5 to simplify computation. It will quickly be seen that $\frac{37\frac{1}{2}}{100}$, which is another way of writing .37$\frac{1}{2}$, has exactly the same value as $\frac{375}{1000}$, which is another way of writing .375.

Example 5: Compute the number of inches in $4.08\frac{1}{3}$ yards.

Solution: 4 yards equals 4 times 36 inches   = 144 inches
   $.08\frac{1}{3}$ yards equals $\frac{1}{12}$ of 36 inches =   3 inches

---

$4.08\frac{1}{3}$ yards   = 147 inches

Example 6: How many units are there in $3.06\frac{1}{4}$ gross?

Solution: 3 gross equals 3 times 144   = 432 units
   $.06\frac{1}{4}$ gross equals $\frac{1}{16}$ of 144, or $\frac{1}{8}$ of 72 =   9 units

---

$3.06\frac{1}{4}$ gross   = 441 units

Repeated reference to Table V will help toward a thorough understanding of the succeeding three articles and will prepare the reader for the chapter dealing with percentages. An understanding of aliquot parts is virtually essential in dealing with percentages. Suppose, for instance, you wanted to calculate $8\frac{1}{3}$ per cent of a number. Even without remembering that $8\frac{1}{3}$ is exactly one twelfth of 100, experience with numbers will enable you to quickly determine that $8\frac{1}{3}$ is one third of 25, and therefore one twelfth of 100; that $16\frac{2}{3}$ is one half of $33\frac{1}{3}$ and therefore one sixth of 100, and so on.

PROBLEMS

Using Table V as a guide, if necessary, write the decimal equivalents of the following fractions·

1	$3\frac{5}{8}$	*Ans.* $3.62\frac{1}{2}$.
2.	$4\frac{2}{3}$	*Ans.* $4.66\frac{2}{3}$.
3.	$18\frac{1}{5}$	*Ans.* 18.2.
4.	$13\frac{1}{12}$	*Ans.* $13.08\frac{1}{3}$.
5.	$7\frac{1}{3}$	*Ans.* $7.33\frac{1}{3}$.
6.	$31\frac{3}{8}$	*Ans.* $31.37\frac{1}{2}$.
7.	$19\frac{11}{12}$	*Ans.* $19.91\frac{2}{3}$.
8.	$162\frac{3}{5}$	*Ans.* 162.6.
9.	$9\frac{5}{6}$	*Ans.* $9.83\frac{1}{3}$.
10.	$4\frac{7}{16}$	*Ans.* $4.43\frac{3}{4}$.

Compute the answers to the following problems with a minimum of pencil-and-paper work.

11. How much cord would be required to obtain 136 pieces, each of which is to be $4.37\frac{1}{2}$ inches long?   *Ans.* 595 inches.

12. If a bottle of liquid contains $\frac{4}{5}$ of a quart, how many quarts would be necessary to fill 186 bottles? Give your answer in decimal form.

Ans. 148.8 quarts.

13. As a result of competition a manufacturer offers a discount of $66\frac{2}{3}\%$ from his list prices. His customers, in other words, will pay only $33\frac{1}{3}\%$. On this basis what would a purchaser have to pay for a bill of goods which, at the list price, would have amounted to \$273.90?

Ans. \$91.30.

14. The time-card of an employee paid by the hour shows that he worked 6 hours 36 minutes. If his rate of pay is \$1.36 an hour how much will he have earned? *Ans.* \$8.98.

15. For having exceeded his quota of sales, a salesman receives a bonus of $12\frac{1}{2}\%$ of his commission on the total amount of business written in a specified 4-week period. If his total was \$1410.00 and his rate of commission $27\frac{1}{2}\%$, what is the amount of his bonus? *Ans.* \$48.47.

42. How to Multiply by Near-Aliquot Numbers Like .27$\frac{3}{4}$, .27$\frac{1}{4}$, .31$\frac{1}{4}$, .13$\frac{1}{3}$, etc. Reference to Table VI will show that the fraction .27$\frac{1}{2}$ is equivalent to the sum of .25 plus one tenth of .25. Thus to multiply 440 by .27$\frac{1}{2}$ we should add one fourth of 440, which is 110, to one tenth of 110, which is 11, obtaining the total of 121.

But suppose we wish to multiply by .27$\frac{3}{4}$. The difference between .27$\frac{3}{4}$ and .27$\frac{1}{2}$ is exactly $\frac{1}{4}$ of .01. To multiply 440 by .27$\frac{3}{4}$, then, it is only necessary to add to the product of 440 times .27$\frac{1}{2}$, the product of 440 times $\frac{1}{4}$ of .01, which is 1.1. And we see immediately that the answer is 122.1.

Similarly, to multiply 440 by .27$\frac{1}{4}$ we should simply subtract 440 times $\frac{1}{4}$ of .01 from the product of 440 times .27$\frac{1}{2}$, giving us the answer 119.9.

Example 1: Compute the value of 192 units at $7\frac{1}{4}$ cents each.

Solution: 192 times $12\frac{1}{2}$ cents ($\frac{1}{8}$ of \$192.00) = \$24.00

192 times $6\frac{1}{4}$ cents ($\frac{1}{2}$ of \$24.00)	= \$12.00
192 times 1 cent	= 1.92

192 times $7\frac{1}{4}$ cents	= \$13.92

The foregoing illustration is of special interest, since the computation by the method demonstrated presupposes a knowledge of the two techniques referred to in the introduction to this chapter. Our knowledge of aliquot parts and the breakdown method of multiplication led us to subdivide the multiplier $7\frac{1}{4}$ into $6\frac{1}{4}$ and 1; and our knowledge of the double-and-halve method directed us to multiply by $12\frac{1}{2}$ instead of by $6\frac{1}{4}$, because to multiply by 100 and divide by 8 (the equivalent of multiplying by $12\frac{1}{2}$) is much simpler than to multiply by 100 and divide by 16 (the equivalent of multiplying by $6\frac{1}{4}$).

TABLE VI

INDIRECT OR NEAR-ALIQUOT PARTS

Values	Ratios	Sub-Ratios
$.07\frac{1}{2}$	$.10 - .02\frac{1}{2}$	$.02\frac{1}{2}$ equals $\frac{1}{4}$ of .10
$.09$	$.10 - .01$	$.01$ equals $\frac{1}{10}$ of .10
$.11$	$.10 + .01$	$.01$ equals $\frac{1}{10}$ of .10
$.11\frac{1}{4}$	$.10 + .01\frac{1}{4}$	$.01\frac{1}{4}$ equals $\frac{1}{8}$ of .10
$.11\frac{1}{2}$	$.12\frac{1}{2} - .01$	$.01$ equals $\frac{1}{100}$ of 1
$.13\frac{1}{3}$	$.10 + .03\frac{1}{3}$	$.03\frac{1}{3}$ equals $\frac{1}{3}$ of .10
	or $.33\frac{1}{3} - .20$	$.33\frac{1}{3}$ equals $\frac{1}{3}$ of 1
$.13\frac{1}{2}$	$.12\frac{1}{2} + .01$	$.01$ equals $\frac{1}{100}$ of 1
$.13\frac{3}{4}$	$.12\frac{1}{2} + .01\frac{1}{4}$	$.01\frac{1}{4}$ equals $\frac{1}{10}$ of $.12\frac{1}{2}$
$.15$	$.10 + .05$	$.05$ equals $\frac{1}{2}$ of .10
$.17\frac{1}{2}$	$.12\frac{1}{2} + .05$	$.05$ equals $\frac{1}{2}$ of .10
	or $.20 - .02\frac{1}{2}$	$.02\frac{1}{2}$ equals $\frac{1}{8}$ of .20
$.18$	$.20 - .02$	$.02$ equals $\frac{1}{10}$ of .20
$.22\frac{1}{2}$	$.20 + .02\frac{1}{2}$	$.02\frac{1}{2}$ equals $\frac{1}{8}$ of .20
	or $.25 - .02\frac{1}{2}$	$.02\frac{1}{2}$ equals $\frac{1}{10}$ of .25
$.23\frac{1}{3}$	$.20 + .03\frac{1}{3}$	$.03\frac{1}{3}$ equals $\frac{1}{6}$ of .20
$.23\frac{3}{4}$	$.25 - .01\frac{1}{4}$	$.01\frac{1}{4}$ equals $\frac{1}{20}$ of .25
$.24$	$.25 - .01$	$.01$ equals $\frac{1}{100}$ of 1
$.26$	$.25 + .01$	$.01$ equals $\frac{1}{100}$ of 1
$.26\frac{2}{3}$	$.16\frac{2}{3} + .10$	$.16\frac{2}{3}$ equals $\frac{1}{6}$ of 1
	or $.20 + .06\frac{2}{3}$	$.06\frac{2}{3}$ equals $\frac{1}{3}$ of .20
$.27\frac{1}{2}$	$.25 + .02\frac{1}{2}$	$.02\frac{1}{2}$ equals $\frac{1}{10}$ of .25
$.33\frac{3}{4}$	$.30 + .03\frac{3}{4}$	$.03\frac{3}{4}$ equals $\frac{1}{8}$ of .30
$.35$	$.25 + .10$	$.10$ equals $\frac{1}{10}$ of 1

The problem 376 times 24 cents might be computed in a similar manner. From the product of 376 times 25 cents ($94.00) we subtract the product of 376 times 1 cent ($3.76) and, mentally, without the need for putting pencil to paper, we arrive at the answer, $90.24.

The multiplier $.13\frac{1}{3}$ can be manipulated in any number of ways, thus:

Example 2: Find the product of 60 times $.13\frac{1}{3}$.

Solution:

Method A: Here $.13\frac{1}{3}$ is broken up into .1, which is $\frac{1}{10}$, and $.03\frac{1}{3}$, which is $\frac{1}{3}$ of $\frac{1}{10}$.

$$
\begin{array}{ll}
.1 \text{ of } 60 & = 6 \\
.03\frac{1}{3} \text{ of } 60 \ (\frac{1}{3} \text{ of } 6) & = 2 \\
\hline
.13\frac{1}{3} \text{ of } 60 & = 8
\end{array}
$$

Method B: By this method $.13\frac{1}{3}$ will be considered as $\frac{1}{3}$ of .4.

$.13\frac{1}{3}$ of 60 $(\frac{1}{3}$ of $\frac{4}{10}$ of 60$) = 8$

Method C: Note that here we will look upon the number $.13\frac{1}{3}$ as the equivalent of $.33\frac{1}{3}$ minus .2.

$$
\begin{array}{ll}
.33\frac{1}{3} \text{ times } 60 \ (\frac{1}{3} \text{ of } 60) & = 20 \\
- \ .2 \text{ times } 60 \ (\frac{1}{5} \text{ of } 60) & = 12 \\
\hline
.13\frac{1}{3} \text{ times } 60 & = \ \ 8
\end{array}
$$

Method B is obviously the simplest manner of procedure in the above example because $\frac{4}{10}$ of 60 can be easily computed mentally. However, if instead of 60 we were dealing with a number like $23.47, it would, of course, be more practical to compute the answer by either of the other methods.

The number $.35\frac{1}{3}$ lends itself to similar handling because it is the sum of $.33\frac{1}{3}$ plus .02. Thus $.35\frac{1}{3}$ times a number could be computed by adding one third of 100 times the multiplicand to .02 times the multiplicand. Similarly, to find the product of a number times $.26\frac{2}{3}$ we could first multiply by $.16\frac{2}{3}$ (which is one sixth of 1), and then add .1 times the multiplicand.

It is interesting to observe that $.26\frac{2}{3}$ can also be split up very conveniently into the numbers .2 and $.06\frac{2}{3}$—$.06\frac{2}{3}$ being exactly one third of .2. Note the convenience of this split-up in the following illustration:

Example 3: Multiply 96 by $.26\frac{2}{3}$.

Solution: .2 times 96 (2 times 9.6) $= 19.2$
$.06\frac{2}{3}$ times 96 ($\frac{1}{3}$ of 19.2) $=$ 6.4

$.26\frac{2}{3}$ times 96 $= 25.6$

Our study of aliquot parts thus far has been concentrated on fractions. The technique, however, is not altered one bit when the multiplier, for instance, is $27\frac{3}{4}$ instead of $.27\frac{3}{4}$. The result of multiplying by $27\frac{3}{4}$ is simply 100 times the result obtained in multiplying the same number by $.27\frac{3}{4}$.

Problems

Compute the answers to the following:

  ★ **1.** 88 times $.11\frac{1}{2}$ *Ans.* 10.12.
  ★ **2.** 60 times $.13\frac{1}{3}$ *Ans.* 8. (*Art. 21*)
  ★ **3.** 72 times $.13\frac{1}{2}$ *Ans.* 9.72.
  ★ **4.** 160 times $.13\frac{3}{4}$ *Ans.* 22.
  ★ **5.** 96 times $.22\frac{1}{2}$ *Ans.* 21.6.
  ★ **6.** $23\frac{1}{3}$ times 36   *Ans.* 840.
      7. $23\frac{3}{4}$ times 348   *Ans.* 8265.
      8. $26\frac{2}{3}$ times $198.60   *Ans.* $5296.00.
      9. $27\frac{1}{2}$ times $23.00   *Ans.* $632.50.
   10. $33\frac{3}{4}$ times $47.56   *Ans.* $1605.15.

Compute the cost of sending a 33-word cablegram to each of the following countries at the NLT ("delivery not earlier than the first morning after filing") rate per word indicated.

  ★ **11.** Great Britain—$6\frac{2}{3}$ cents. (Hint: $6\frac{2}{3}$ equals one third of 20, or one fifth of $33\frac{1}{3}$.)   *Ans.* $2.20.

★ 12. Midway Islands—$9\frac{2}{3}$ cents. (Hint: $9\frac{2}{3}$ equals 10 minus one third of 1.)   *Ans.* \$3.19.

★ 13. Mauritania—$19\frac{2}{3}$ cents. (Hint: $19\frac{2}{3}$ equals 20 minus one third of 1.)   *Ans.* \$6.49.

★ 14. French Equatorial Africa—$16\frac{2}{3}$ cents. (Hint: $16\frac{2}{3}$ equals one sixth of 100.)   *Ans.* \$5.50.

★ 15. French Cameroons—$20\frac{2}{3}$ cents. (Hint: $20\frac{2}{3}$ equals $16\frac{2}{3}$ plus 4.)

Ans. \$6.82. (*Art. 25*)

★ 16. Transjordania—$14\frac{2}{3}$ cents. (Hint: $14\frac{2}{3}$ equals $16\frac{2}{3}$ minus 2.)

Ans. \$4.84.

★ 17. Togoland—$27\frac{1}{3}$ cents. (Hint: $27\frac{1}{3}$ equals $33\frac{1}{3}$ minus 6.)

Ans. \$9.02. (*Art. 24*)

★ 18. Madeira Island—$13\frac{1}{3}$ cents. (Hint: $13\frac{1}{3}$ equals one third of 40.)

Ans. \$4.40.

Equally interesting results can be obtained with the near-aliquot fractions in the following problems:

19. Find the number of cubic inches in $3\frac{8}{27}$ cubic feet. (Hint: $\frac{9}{27}$ equals $\frac{1}{3}$, and there are 1728 cubic inches in a cubic foot.)

Ans. 5696 cubic inches.

20. An aluminum paint suitable for use on weather-exposed galvanized iron can be made with a paste vehicle and an oil varnish. If 2 pounds of the paste mixed with 1 gallon of the varnish yield 1 gallon $1\frac{1}{4}$ pints, how many gallons of aluminum paint will 25 times the aforementioned quantities yield? (Hint: $1\frac{1}{4}$ pints equals $\frac{5}{32}$ gallon.) *Ans.* $28\frac{29}{32}$ gallons.

21. A formula for making 100 pounds of parchment red ink calls for the use of 8 pounds of varnish. If it is desired to make only $38\frac{1}{2}$ pounds of this ink how much varnish will be required? Compute the answer to the nearest ounce.   *Ans.* 3.08 pounds.

★ 22. Of one variety of corner beads, used in the building industry, 1000 lineal feet weigh 320 pounds. How much will 1625 lineal feet weigh?

Ans. 520 pounds.

23. Gerald Nixon's share in his company's profits is $.16\frac{1}{3}$. If the profit to be divided amounts to \$8,463.20, how much will Mr. Nixon receive? (Hint: $16\frac{1}{3}$ equals $16\frac{2}{3}$, which is one sixth of 100, minus one third of 1.)   *Ans.* \$1382.32.

43. How to Multiply by a Mixed Number in Which the Fraction Is an Aliquot Part of the Rest of the Number, e.g., 20.2, 75.25, $80\frac{4}{5}$, $75\frac{3}{8}$, $625\frac{5}{8}$. The subject of aliquot parts affords an interesting study in connection with mixed numbers—that is, numbers made up of one or more whole units and a fraction. When the mixed number $20\frac{1}{5}$, for example, is written in decimal form—namely, 20.2, it is seen at a glance that .2 is exactly $\frac{1}{100}$ of 20. To multiply by $20\frac{1}{5}$, then, there is no need to divide the multiplicand by 5 to obtain one fifth of the multiplicand; simply multiply by 20 and add $\frac{1}{100}$ of the result.

When the number $75\frac{1}{4}$ is written as 75.25 it is quickly seen that 75 is 300 times .25 and, conversely, that .25 is $\frac{1}{300}$ of 75. So that to multiply by 75.25 it is but necessary to compute one fourth of the multiplicand and add 300 times the result.

The same procedure might be taken in multiplying by $80\frac{4}{5}$, which is the equivalent of 80.4, for 80 is exactly 200 times .4.

The method is simple, quick and easy, as will be seen in the following demonstration:

Example 1: Find the product of $75\frac{3}{8}$ times 74.

Solution: (Note that $\frac{3}{8}$, besides being an aliquot part of 1, is also an aliquot part of 75, for it is divisible into 75 exactly 200 times.)

75 times 74 ($\frac{3}{4}$ of 7400)	= 5550
$\frac{3}{8}$ of 74 ($\frac{1}{200}$ of 5550 or $\frac{1}{2}$ of 55.5) =	27.75

$75\frac{3}{8}$ times 74	= 5577.75

Example 2: Multiply 328 by $625\frac{5}{8}$.

Solution: (Note that 625 is $\frac{5}{8}$ of 1000. So that to multiply by the fraction $\frac{5}{8}$, it is but necessary to take $\frac{1}{1000}$ of the result obtained in multiplying by 625.)

500 times 328 ($\frac{1}{2}$ of 328000)	= 164000
125 times 328 ($\frac{1}{4}$ of 164000)	= 41000

625 times 328	= 205000
$\frac{5}{8}$ times 328 ($\frac{1}{1000}$ of 205000) =	205

$625\frac{5}{8}$ times 328	= 205205

Example 3: If a linear yard of 34-inch wide No. 3 duck fabric weighs 24.72 ounces, how many ounces should 116 yards weigh?

Solution: 24 times 116 (12 times 232)   = 2784
.72 times 116 ($\frac{3}{100}$ of 2784) =   83.52

24.72 times 116   = 2867.52

Ans. 2867.52 ounces.

PROBLEMS

Work the following problems with a minimum of pencil-and-paper work, and write the answers in decimal form.

1. $4\frac{3}{8}$ times $8\frac{4}{5}$.   (Hint: $\frac{4}{5}$ is one tenth of 8.)   *Ans.* 38.5.

2. 234 times 15.3.   *Ans.* 3580.2.

3. $71\frac{1}{2}$ times 20.25.   *Ans.* 1447.875.

4. $3\frac{1}{9}$ times $18\frac{18}{25}$.   (Hint: $\frac{18}{25}$ is exactly $\frac{1}{25}$ of 18; and 18 times $3\frac{1}{9}$ can be computed mentally without any effort.)   *Ans.* 58.24.

5. $7\frac{2}{11}$ times $22\frac{11}{20}$.   (Hint: $\frac{11}{20}$ is the equivalent of $\frac{1}{40}$ of 22, so the answer to this problem will be the sum of 22 times $7\frac{2}{11}$ plus $\frac{1}{40}$ of the result.)   *Ans.* 161.95.

6. Estimate the cost of making the following shipments by air express from New York at the rate per pound indicated. It is interesting to observe that, in each instance, the last two figures in the rate equal $\frac{7}{100}$ of one third of the first two figures; thus in the rate of 12.28 cents, .28 is $\frac{7}{100}$ of 4; in 15.35, .35 is $\frac{7}{100}$ of 5; in 18.42, .42 is $\frac{7}{100}$ of 6; in 21.49, .49 is $\frac{7}{100}$ of 7; and in 24.56, .56 is $\frac{7}{100}$ of 8.

(a) 67 pounds to Euclid, Ohio, at 12.28 cents.   *Ans.* $8.23.
(b) 53 pounds to Dunbar, West Virginia, at 15.35 cents.   *Ans.* $8.14.
(c) 42 pounds to Newport, Kentucky, at 18.42 cents.   *Ans.* $7.74.
(d) 47 pounds to Augusta, Georgia, at 21.49 cents.   *Ans.* $10.10.
(e) 54 pounds to Evansville, Indiana, at 24.56 cents.   *Ans.* $13.26.

44. How to Multiply by a Mixed Number in Which When Increased to the Next Whole Unit the Fraction Added Is an Aliquot Part of the New Number, e.g., 19.8, 74.75, 79.2, 11.7, 13.3, 23.6. A moment's reflection will reveal an interesting relationship between the first three numbers in the heading of this article and the first three numbers in the heading of Art. 43. The numbers are different, yet the partial products necessary to compute the answers are exactly the same. Thus whereas in multiplying by 20.2 (see Art. 43) we multiplied by 20 and *added* $\frac{1}{100}$ of the result, here, in multiplying by 19.8, we multiply by 20 and *subtract* $\frac{1}{100}$ of the result.

The same procedure would be followed in finding the product of a number times 74.75—the equivalent of 75 minus .25, .25 being a very convenient value to subtract, since it is one third of $\frac{1}{100}$ of 75. It is easier to multiply by 75 and subtract from the result $\frac{1}{300}$ of the result than to multiply by 74 (which requires the computation of two separate partial products) and by .75.

Similarly to find the product of 79.2 times a number, it is easier to multiply by 80 and subtract $\frac{1}{100}$ of the result (.8 being $\frac{1}{100}$ of 80), thus:

Example 1: Multiply 734 by 79.2.

Solution: 80 times 734   = 58720
    —   .8 times 734 ($\frac{1}{100}$ of 58720) =   587.2

_____

    79.2 times 734   = 58132.8

Example 2: Find the product of 93 times 11.7.

Solution: 12 times 93   = 1116
    —   .3 times 93 (3 times 9.3) =   27.9

_____

    11.7 times 93   = 1088.1

Example 3: Multiply 247 by 13.3.

Solution: (13.3 is equivalent to 14 minus .7. Our procedure here, however, is a little different from that in Examples 1 and 2. Instead of multiplying first by the whole number 14 and then subtracting $\frac{1}{20}$ of the result, we will find it more convenient to first compute the product of .7 times the multiplicand, to multiply the result by 20, then to subtract the first product from the second. This technique was described and illustrated in Art. 12.)

Second step: 14 times 247 (20 times 172.9) = 3458
First step: —   .7 times 247 (7 times 24.7) =   172.9

13.3 times 247   = 3285.1

Example 4: Multiply 138 by 23.6.

Solution:

Second step: 24 times 138 (60 times 55.2 or 6
                    times 552)   = 3312
First step: —   .4 times 138 (4 times 13.8)   =   55.2

23.6 times 138   = 3256.8

Example 5: The dessiatine is a Russian unit of measurement equivalent to 2.6997 acres. How many acres are there in 87 dessiatines?

Solution: 3 times 87   = 261
          — .3003
                  .3 times 87 ($\frac{1}{10}$ of
                      261)   = 26.1
                  .0003 times 87
                      ($\frac{1}{10000}$ of 261) =   .0261
                                                 = 26.1261

2.6997 times 87   = 234.8739

Ans. 234.8739 acres.

If the subject of aliquot parts is new to him, the reader is urged to make an assiduous study of Tables II and III. He should not attempt to memorize all of the ratios in Table III; more important is an understanding of the method by which these ratios are determined. Moreover, a thorough understanding of the principle will help him to quickly determine the common fraction equivalents and ratios of many values not included in the tables.

PROBLEMS

Design a form headed as in the specimen tabulation shown below, and, in the manner indicated in this specimen, show how you would use your knowledge of aliquot parts and the breakdown method of multiplication (Chapter II) to multiply by each of the following numbers. For example, to show how you would multiply by 9.3, write .3 in the plus section of the column headed "First Step," and 30 in the plus section of the column headed "Second Step." And so on.

SPECIMEN TABULATION

To Multiply by	First Step		Second Step	
	Add or Subtract, as the Case May Be, the Multiplicand Times the Number Indicated Here		Add or Subtract, as the Case May Be, the Product Obtained in the First Step, Times the Number Indicated Here	
	Add	Subtract	Add	Subtract
9.3	.3		30	
19.8	20			$\frac{1}{100}$
11.8		.2	60	

   ★ **1.** 3.18.   *Ans.* 3 plus $\frac{6}{100}$ of 3.

   ★ **2.** 14.7   *Ans.* Subtract .3 and add 50 times .3.

   ★ **3.** 16.2.   *Ans.* .2 plus 80 times .2.

   ★ **4.** 21.6.   *Ans.* 20 plus $\frac{8}{100}$ of 20.

   ★ **5.** 9.6.   *Ans.* 10 minus $\frac{4}{100}$ of 10.

   ★ **6.** 5.4.   *Ans.* 6 minus $\frac{1}{10}$ of 6.

   ★ **7.** 16.8.   *Ans.* .8 plus 20 times .8.

   ★ **8.** 18.6.   *Ans.* .6 plus 30 times .6.

   ★ **9.** 11.4.   *Ans.* Subtract .6 and add 20 times .6.

   ★ **10.** 7.6.   *Ans.* Subtract .4 and add 20 times .4.

★ **11.** 15.6.   *Ans.* Subtract .4 and add 40 times .4.

★ **12.** 45.9.   *Ans.* 46 minus .1.

★ **13.** 32.7.   *Ans.* Subtract .3 and add 110 times .3.

★ **14.** 92.7.   *Ans.* Subtract .3 and add 310 times .3.

★ **15.** 5.97.   *Ans.* Subtract .03 and add 200 times .03.

★ **16.** 39.8.   *Ans.* Subtract .2 and add 200 times .2.

★ **17.** 23.8.   *Ans.* Subtract .2 and add 120 times .2.

★ **18.** 47.4.   *Ans.* Subtract .6 and add 80 times .6.

★ **19.** 69.3.   *Ans.* Subtract .7 and add 100 times .7.

★ **20.** 23.4.   *Ans.* Subtract .6 and add 40 times .6.

CHAPTER VII

PERCENTAGES AND DISCOUNTS

A consideration of aliquot parts is logically followed by a study of percentages and discounts, for in the arithmetic of business no other problems occur more frequently, and in no other problems is the rapid speed of computation made possible by a knowledge of aliquot parts better exemplified.

Readers who, in the preceding chapters, found the slightest difficulty understanding the illustrations which involved the decimal point are advised to study Chapter XXIII before proceeding further. This study will enable the reader to benefit fully from the techniques described in the following articles.

45. Quick Ways of Deducting the Per-Cent Rates of 20, 30, 40, 60, 70, 80 and 90. Time and again the author has seen the simplest per cents computed the long way, when much time and labor might have been saved by the use of a short-cut.

Take, for instance, the problem $300.00 less 20 per cent. Here is how this is commonly computed:

Long Way

$$
\begin{array}{rr}
 & \$300.00 \\
20\% & 60.00 \\
\hline
 & \$240.00 \\
\end{array}
$$

The above method is needlessly long. It calls for two operations: the calculation of 20 per cent of the base and the subtraction of the percentage from the base. Two operations are really unnecessary, for this reason: the discount, we are told, is 20 per cent, and so the *net* amount, or the figure we wish to arrive at, is 80 per cent (100 minus 20 equals 80) of $300.00. Our problem, therefore, can

122

be solved in *one* operation by calculating 80 per cent of $300.00. And what could be simpler? Eighty per cent of *one* hundred dollars is $80.00; therefore 80 per cent of *three* hundred dollars equals three times $80.00, or $240.00. No need for any subtraction, and no need to use pencil and paper.

If the base had been $324.60 instead of $300.00, the solution would be no more difficult. Eighty per cent is the equivalent of eight tenths; so that all we need do is divide $324.60 by 10 and multiply the quotient ($32.46) by 8, which can be done mentally and effortlessly. There is no need to write down $324.60 and 80 per cent. A mental picture of the changed position of the decimal point makes it a comparatively simple matter to multiply by 8 and write the answer, $259.68, directly into the record or document concerned without using any scratch paper whatever.

In any problem involving the deduction of a per cent like 20, 30, 40, 60, 70 or 80, the thing to do, therefore, is to determine the per cent that is *payable* and then multiply the gross amount by that per cent.

Example 1: Compute $736.00 less 30%.

Solution: $736.00 less 30% is equivalent to 70% of $736.00, or $\frac{7}{10}$ of $736.00.

$\frac{1}{10}$ of $736.00   = $ 73.60

_____

$\frac{7}{10}$ of $736.00 (7 times $73.60) = $515.20

Example 2: Compute $89.40 less 60%.

Solution: $89.40 less 60% is equivalent to 40% of $89.40, or $\frac{4}{10}$ of $89.40.

$\frac{1}{10}$ of $89.40   = $ 8.94

_____

$\frac{4}{10}$ of $89.40 (4 times $8.94) = $35.76

With the per-cent rates of 10 and 90 the procedure is even simpler. In calculating $18.60 less 10 per cent, for instance, there is really no calculating to do at all; from $18.60 we merely deduct one tenth ($1.86). On the other hand, problems which call for the deduction of 90 per cent are the simplest of all percentage problems, for their solution does not call for deductions or computations of any kind; the decimal point is simply moved one place to the left, and the resulting number constitutes the answer. Thus $143.00 less 90 per cent equals $14.30.

Problems

1. Compute the net amount due on a bill for $84.60 less a discount of 20%. *Ans.* $67.68.

2. The list price of a mechanical testing device is $185.00. If the purchaser is offered a trade-in allowance of 30% for his old machine, how much will the new machine cost him in exchange? *Ans.* $129.50.

★ **3.** If a 650-pound steer lost 40% of its weight in dressing, what was the weight of the carcass? *Ans.* 390 pounds.

4. The elimination of waste motion and other unnecessary time-consuming factors in a production plant enabled a manufacturer to announce a 60% discount off list prices. On this basis how much would a customer have to pay on a purchase which, at the list price, amounts to $318.40? *Ans.* $127.36.

5. A new automobile cost $875.00. If it lost 70% of its value through wear and tear, what is its present worth? *Ans.* $262.50.

★ **6.** The 80% co-insurance clause is a stipulation in many fire insurance policies which provides for full payment of damage if the property is insured for 80% of its value and the damage does not exceed the face value of the policy. In other words, if property valued at $76,000 and insured for 80% of its value was damaged to the extent of $10,000, the company would pay the full amount of the damage. Compute the loss sustained by the owner of property valued at $43,000, completely destroyed by fire, and insured for only 80% of its value. *Ans.* $8600.00.

★ **7.** A manufacturer is forced by a strike to lay off 90% of his help. If he had 230 employees on his payroll before the strike, what was the extent of his skeleton force? *Ans.* 23.

46. Quick Ways of Calculating the Per-Cent Rates of $32\frac{1}{2}$, $37\frac{1}{2}$, $42\frac{1}{2}$, $47\frac{1}{2}$, $52\frac{1}{2}$, $57\frac{1}{2}$, $62\frac{1}{2}$ and $67\frac{1}{2}$. If the reader has studied carefully the chapter entitled "Aliquot Parts," he will appreciate the interesting way in which many different per-cent rates lend themselves to short-cut calculation.

Let us take two problems for each of eight different rates—one in which we are to find only the percentage, the other in which the net amount is required—and observe the simplicity and rapidity of their solution by a method based on our combined knowledge of aliquot parts and the breakdown method of multiplication. In the case of five of these rates, an alternative method of computation will be indicated, and it is suggested that the reader acquire the habit of computing the answer by one method and proving it by the other method.

Example 1: Find $32\frac{1}{2}\%$ of $180.00.

Solution:

Method A: 25% of $180.00 ($\frac{1}{4}$ of $180.00) $\qquad$ = \$45.00
$\qquad$ 5% ($\frac{1}{5}$ of $45.00) $\qquad\qquad$ = $\quad$ 9.00
$\qquad$ $2\frac{1}{2}\%$ ($\frac{1}{2}$ of $9.00) $\qquad\qquad$ = $\quad$ 4.50

$\qquad$ $32\frac{1}{2}\%$ of $180.00 $\qquad\qquad\qquad$ = \$58.50

Method B: 30% of $180.00 (3 times $18.00) $\qquad$ = \$54.00
$\qquad$ $2\frac{1}{2}\%$ ($\frac{1}{40}$ of $180.00 or $\frac{1}{4}$ of $18.00) = $\quad$ 4.50

$\qquad$ $32\frac{1}{2}\%$ of $180.00 $\qquad\qquad\qquad$ = \$58.50

Example 1A: What is the net amount of a sale amounting to $180.00 on which a discount of $32\frac{1}{2}\%$ is allowable?

Solution: The answer will be $67\frac{1}{2}\%$ of $180.00.

Method A: 50% of $180.00 ($\frac{1}{2}$ of $180.00) $\qquad$ = \$ 90.00
$\qquad$ $12\frac{1}{2}\%$ ($\frac{1}{4}$ of $90.00) $\qquad\qquad$ = $\quad$ 22.50
$\qquad$ 5% ($\frac{1}{10}$ of $90.00) $\qquad\qquad$ = $\quad$ 9.00

$\qquad$ $67\frac{1}{2}\%$ of $180.00 $\qquad\qquad\qquad$ = \$121.50

Method B: 60% of $180.00 (6 times $18.00) = \$108.00
$\qquad$ 6% ($\frac{1}{10}$ of $108.00) $\qquad\qquad$ = $\quad$ 10.80
$\qquad$ $1\frac{1}{2}\%$ ($\frac{1}{4}$ of $10.80) $\qquad\qquad$ = $\quad$ 2.70

$\qquad$ $67\frac{1}{2}\%$ of $180.00 $\qquad\qquad\qquad$ = \$121.50

Example 2: Find $37\frac{1}{2}\%$ of \$426.00.

Solution:

Method A: 25% of \$426.00 ($\frac{1}{4}$ of \$426.00) = \$106.50
 $12\frac{1}{2}\%$ ($\frac{1}{2}$ of \$106.50) = 53.25

 $37\frac{1}{2}\%$ of \$426.00 = \$159.75

Method B: $12\frac{1}{2}\%$ of \$426.00 ($\frac{1}{8}$ of \$426.00) = \$ 53.25

 $37\frac{1}{2}\%$ (3 times \$53.25) = \$159.75

Example 2A: What is the net amount payable on a purchase of \$426.00 less $37\frac{1}{2}\%$?

Solution: The answer will be $62\frac{1}{2}\%$ of \$426.00.

Method A: 50% of \$426.00 ($\frac{1}{2}$ of \$426.00) = \$213.00
 $12\frac{1}{2}\%$ ($\frac{1}{4}$ of \$213.00) = 53.25

 $62\frac{1}{2}\%$ of \$426.00 = \$266.25

Method B: $12\frac{1}{2}\%$ of \$426.00 ($\frac{1}{8}$ of \$426.00) = \$ 53.25

 $62\frac{1}{2}\%$ (5 times \$53.25) = \$266.25

Example 3: Find $42\frac{1}{2}\%$ of \$826.00.

Solution:

Method A: 25% of \$826.00 ($\frac{1}{4}$ of \$826.00) = \$206.50
 $12\frac{1}{2}\%$ ($\frac{1}{2}$ of \$206.50) = 103.25
 5% ($\frac{1}{5}$ of \$206.50) = 41.30

 $42\frac{1}{2}\%$ of \$826.00 = \$351.05

Method B: 40% of \$826.00 (4 times \$82.60) = \$330.40
 $2\frac{1}{2}\%$ ($\frac{1}{40}$ of \$826.00 or $\frac{1}{4}$ of \$82.60) = 20.65

 $42\frac{1}{2}\%$ of \$826.00 = \$351.05

Example 3A: Compute the net amount of a sale amounting to $826.00 less $42\frac{1}{2}\%$.

Solution: The answer will be $57\frac{1}{2}\%$ of $826.00.

$$
\begin{aligned}
50\% \text{ of } \$826.00 \ (\tfrac{1}{2} \text{ of } \$826.00) &= \$413.00 \\
5\% \ (\tfrac{1}{10} \text{ of } \$413.00) &= \quad 41.30 \\
2\tfrac{1}{2}\% \ (\tfrac{1}{2} \text{ of } \$41.30) &= \quad 20.65 \\
\hline
57\tfrac{1}{2}\% \text{ of } \$826.00 &= \$474.95
\end{aligned}
$$

Example 4: Find $47\frac{1}{2}\%$ of $785.00.

Solution: Notice that here we *deduct* $2\frac{1}{2}\%$ from 50%.

$$
\begin{aligned}
50\% \text{ of } \$785.00 \ (\tfrac{1}{2} \text{ of } \$785.00) &= \$392.50 \\
- \quad 2\tfrac{1}{2}\% \ (\tfrac{1}{20} \text{ of } \$392.50 \text{ or } \tfrac{1}{2} \text{ of } \$39.25) &= \quad 19.62 \\
\hline
47\tfrac{1}{2}\% \text{ of } \$785.00 &= \$372.88
\end{aligned}
$$

Example 4A: Show the net amount of a sale amounting to $785.00 less $47\frac{1}{2}\%$.

Solution: The answer will be $52\frac{1}{2}\%$ of $785.00.

$$
\begin{aligned}
50\% \text{ of } \$785.00 \ (\tfrac{1}{2} \text{ of } \$785.00) &= \$392.50 \\
2\tfrac{1}{2}\% \ (\tfrac{1}{20} \text{ of } \$392.50 \text{ or } \tfrac{1}{2} \text{ of } \$39.25) &= \quad 19.62 \\
\hline
52\tfrac{1}{2}\% \text{ of } \$785.00 &= \$412.12
\end{aligned}
$$

Example 5: Find $52\frac{1}{2}\%$ of $1042.60.

$$
\begin{aligned}
\textit{Solution: } 50\% \text{ of } \$1042.60 \ (\tfrac{1}{2} \text{ of } \$1042.60) &= \$521.30 \\
2\tfrac{1}{2}\% \ (\tfrac{1}{20} \text{ of } \$521.30 \text{ or } \tfrac{1}{2} \text{ of } \$52.13) &= \quad 26.07 \\
\hline
52\tfrac{1}{2}\% \text{ of } \$1042.60 &= \$547.37
\end{aligned}
$$

Example 5A: Show the net amount of a sale amounting to $1042.60 less $52\frac{1}{2}\%$.

Solution: The answer will be $47\frac{1}{2}\%$ of \$1042.60.

$$50\% \text{ of } \$1042.60 \ (\tfrac{1}{2} \text{ of } \$1042.60) \qquad = \$521.30$$
$$- \ 2\tfrac{1}{2}\% \ (\tfrac{1}{20} \text{ of } \$521.30 \text{ or } \tfrac{1}{2} \text{ of } \$52.13) = \quad 26.07$$

$$47\tfrac{1}{2}\% \text{ of } \$1042.60 \qquad\qquad\qquad = \$495.23$$

Example 6: Find $57\frac{1}{2}\%$ of \$38.80.

Solution: 50% of \$38.80 $(\tfrac{1}{2}$ of \$38.80$) = \$19.40$
$\qquad\quad\ 5\% \ (\tfrac{1}{10} \text{ of } \$19.40) \qquad = \quad 1.94$
$\qquad\quad\ 2\tfrac{1}{2}\% \ (\tfrac{1}{2} \text{ of } \$1.94) \qquad = \quad\ .97$

$$57\tfrac{1}{2}\% \text{ of } \$38.80 \qquad\qquad = \$22.31$$

Example 6A: Show the net amount of a sale amounting to \$38.80 less $57\frac{1}{2}\%$.

Solution: The answer will be $42\frac{1}{2}\%$ of \$38.80.

Method A: 25% of \$38.80 $(\tfrac{1}{4}$ of \$38.80$)$ $\qquad = \$ \ 9.70$
$\qquad\qquad 12\tfrac{1}{2}\% \ (\tfrac{1}{2} \text{ of } \$9.70) \qquad\qquad = \quad 4.85$
$\qquad\qquad\ 5\% \ (\tfrac{1}{5} \text{ of } \$9.70) \qquad\qquad = \quad 1.94$

$$42\tfrac{1}{2}\% \text{ of } \$38.80 \qquad\qquad\quad = \$16.49$$

Method B: 40% of \$38.80 (4 times \$3.88) $\qquad = \$15.52$
$\qquad\qquad 2\tfrac{1}{2}\% \ (\tfrac{1}{40} \text{ of } \$38.80 \text{ or } \tfrac{1}{4} \text{ of } \$3.88) = \quad .97$

$$42\tfrac{1}{2}\% \text{ of } \$38.80 \qquad\qquad\quad = \$16.49$$

Example 7: Find $62\frac{1}{2}\%$ of \$123.84.

Solution:

Method A: 50% of \$123.84 $(\tfrac{1}{2}$ of \$123.84$) = \$61.92$
$\qquad\qquad 12\tfrac{1}{2}\% \ (\tfrac{1}{4} \text{ of } \$61.92) \qquad = \quad 15.48$

$$62\tfrac{1}{2}\% \text{ of } \$123.84 \qquad\qquad = \$77.40$$

Method B: $12\tfrac{1}{2}\%$ of \$123.84 $(\tfrac{1}{8}$ of \$123.84$) = \$15.48$

$$62\tfrac{1}{2}\% \ (5 \text{ times } \$15.48) \qquad\qquad = \$77.40$$

Example 7A: Show the net amount of a sale amounting to $123.84 less $62\frac{1}{2}\%$.

Solution: The answer will be $37\frac{1}{2}\%$ of $123.84.

Method A: 25% of $123.84 ($\frac{1}{4}$ of $123.84)   = $30.96
$12\frac{1}{2}\%$ ($\frac{1}{2}$ of $30.96)   = 15.48

$37\frac{1}{2}\%$ of $123.84   = $46.44

Method B: $12\frac{1}{2}\%$ of $123.84 ($\frac{1}{8}$ of $123.84) = $15.48

$37\frac{1}{2}\%$ (3 times $15.48)   = $46.44

Example 8: Find $67\frac{1}{2}\%$ of $518.80.

Solution:

Method A: 50% of $518.80 ($\frac{1}{2}$ of $518.80)   = $259.40
$12\frac{1}{2}\%$ ($\frac{1}{4}$ of $259.40)   = 64.85
5% ($\frac{1}{10}$ of $259.40)   = 25.94

$67\frac{1}{2}\%$ of $518.80   = $350.19

Method B: 60% of $518.80 (6 times $51.88) = $311.28
6% ($\frac{1}{10}$ of $311.28)   = 31.13
$1\frac{1}{2}\%$ ($\frac{1}{4}$ of $31.13)   = 7.78

$67\frac{1}{2}\%$ of $518.80   = $350.19

Example 8A: Show the net amount of a sale amounting to $518.80 less $67\frac{1}{2}\%$.

Solution: The answer will be $32\frac{1}{2}\%$ of $518.80.

Method A: 25% of $518.80 ($\frac{1}{4}$ of $518.80)   = $129.70
5% ($\frac{1}{5}$ of $129.70)   = 25.94
$2\frac{1}{2}\%$ ($\frac{1}{2}$ of $25.94)   = 12.97

$32\frac{1}{2}\%$ of $518.80   = $168.61

Method B: 30% of $518.80 (3 times $51.88)   = $155.64
$2\frac{1}{2}$% ($\frac{1}{40}$ of $518.80 or $\frac{1}{4}$ of $51.88) =   12.97

$32\frac{1}{2}$% of $518.80   = $168.61

The reader will do well not to leave this article until he has mastered it since the technique illustrated is one of the most interesting and important short-cut techniques in business arithmetic.

PROBLEMS

Compute the odd-numbered problems by Method A, illustrated in the text, and the even-numbered problems by Method B.

1. In a survey made early in 1946 it was found that 12% of the farms being sold were held for less than two years and that the typical resale profit was 30 to 35%. Using the mean per-cent rate of $32\frac{1}{2}$% how much profit would have been made on the sale of a farm in 1946 purchased two years previously for $28,500?   *Ans.* $9,262.50.

2. A bill for $82.70 is subject to a discount of $32\frac{1}{2}$%. What is the net amount due?   *Ans.* $55.82.

3. If the import duty on cotton collar stiffeners is $37\frac{1}{2}$%, what would the duty amount to on an importation valued at $174.36?   *Ans.* $65.39.

4. A flaw in a manufacturing process of a fabric entitled a dealer to an allowance of $37\frac{1}{2}$%. If the fabric in question was billed at $379.40, how much will the dealer be expected to pay in full settlement?

Ans. $237.13.

5. A jobber's gross profit on an item is $42\frac{1}{2}$%. If his cost per unit is $12.38, how much gross profit will he make on a sale of 214 units?

Ans. $1455.20. (*Art. 13*)

6. A job lot of merchandise is purchased at a discount of $42\frac{1}{2}$%. The merchandise consisted of 120 gross springs at $3.00 a gross and 200 screws at $2.00 per hundred. Compute the net amount of the purchase.

Ans. $209.30.

7. Rising prices of materials and increased cost of labor forced a manufacturer to raise the price of his products by $47\frac{1}{2}$%. If one of his items had previously sold for $23.40 per dozen, how much per dozen would the purchaser have to pay after the increase went into effect?

Ans. $34.52.

8. The substitution of lower-priced materials in the production of an upholstered chair enabled a manufacturer to sell at $47\frac{1}{2}$% less than the higher-priced product, which cost $128.00. What was the price of the cheaper chair?   *Ans.* $67.20.

9. A businessman's study of reports leads him to expect that his sales for the year will be $52\frac{1}{2}\%$ higher than in the previous year. If his previous year's sales amounted to $146,700, how much business does he expect to do in the current year?   *Ans.* $223,717.50.

10. The business boom following the end of World War II reduced a businessman's selling costs $52\frac{1}{2}\%$ of his pre-war costs. If his pre-war costs were $30.00 per $100.00 of sales, what were his current selling expenses per $100.00?   *Ans.* $14.25.

11. A real estate company's income in 1946 exceeded its average annual income in the 1930's by $57\frac{1}{2}\%$. If its annual income averaged $18,456.00, how much profit did the company make in 1946?
Ans. $29,068.20.

12. The meat shortage in 1946 coupled with a fire loss reduced a butcher's profits so that his income for the year was $57\frac{1}{2}\%$ of his $6472.00 income in 1945. Estimate his profit for the year 1946.   *Ans.* $3721.40.

13. An improvement in the packaging design of a company's product resulted in an increase in sales of $62\frac{1}{2}\%$. Everything else being equal, how much business might the company expect to do in a 3-month period as a result of this improvement if in the corresponding period of the previous year its sales amounted to $17,188.00?   *Ans.* $27,930.50.

★ 14. A liquid preparation of heavy consistency contains $62\frac{1}{2}\%$ water by volume. If a tank is filled to three fourths of its capacity of 128 cubic feet with a batch of the finished material, how much space is occupied by the materials other than water?   *Ans.* 36 cubic feet.

15. An experiment by a community organization showed that an extension of its cultural activities increased its income by $67\frac{1}{2}\%$. If the quarterly income had previously been $138.40, how much of a quarterly income will the organization expect in the future as a result of this innovation?   *Ans.* $231.82.

16. Neglected pruning of a company's mailing list resulted in a wasted expense of $67\frac{1}{2}$ cents of every dollar spent in an advertising campaign. The cost of the campaign was $836.50. Compute the amount that would have sufficed to do this advertising if the mailing list had been kept up to date.   *Ans.* $271.86.

47. Short-Cuts for Other Per-Cent Rates. The per-cent rates discussed in Arts. 45 and 46 and the rates of 25, 50 and 75 per cent are the most frequently occurring rates in business. However, rates like $38\frac{1}{2}$ per cent and 58 per cent can be calculated by exactly the same technique. The computation, however, might take a few seconds longer, since an additional partial product or two will be necessary.

The rate of $38\frac{1}{2}$ per cent, for instance, might be divided up into 25, $12\frac{1}{2}$ and 1 per cent. The rate of 58 per cent may be subdivided in any of a number of ways: 50, 5, $2\frac{1}{2}$ and $\frac{1}{2}$ per cent; or 60 and 2 per cent; or 50, 5 and 3 per cent. It is all a matter of preference.

Fifty-one per cent would, of course, be broken up into 50 and 1 per cent. Forty-nine per cent also into 50 and 1 per cent, the 1 per cent being deducted from 50 per cent.

The shortest way of computing 94 per cent would be to deduct 6 per cent.

PROBLEMS

Compute the following to the nearest cent.

1. $38\frac{1}{2}\%$ of $74.00.   *Ans.* $28.49.

2. 58% of $93.60.   *Ans.* $54.29.

★ **3.** 51% of $82.30.   *Ans.* $41.97.

4. 49% of $142.50.   *Ans.* $69.82.

5. 94% of $62.75.   *Ans.* $58.98.

6. 37% of $18\frac{3}{4}$ pounds. (Hint: Find $37\frac{1}{2}\%$ and subtract $\frac{1}{2}$ of 1%.)
        Ans. 6.845 pounds.

7. $61\frac{1}{2}\%$ of 120 miles. (Hint: $1\frac{1}{2}\%$ is $\frac{1}{40}$ of 60%.)   *Ans.* 73.8 miles.

8. $2\frac{1}{4}\%$ of $3462.46. (Hint: Find $2\frac{1}{2}\%$ and subtract $\frac{1}{10}$ of the result.)   *Ans.* $77.91.

★ **9.** $3\frac{1}{2}\%$ of $83.26. (Hint: $3\frac{1}{2}\%$ is equivalent to $2\frac{1}{2}\%$ plus 1%.)
        Ans. $2.91.

10. $24\frac{2}{3}\%$ of $192.50. (Hint: Find 25% and subtract $\frac{1}{3}$ of 1%.)
        Ans. $47.48.

11. In 1946 the import duty on plain-back cotton velveteens was $31\frac{1}{4}\%$. Estimate the duty payable on an importation of this merchandise valued at $274.92.   *Ans.* $85.91.

12. A salesman's remuneration is $6.00 a day plus $3\frac{1}{3}\%$ commission on all sales. Compute this salesman's earnings for the week in which his sales amounted to $2418.00. The $6.00 a day arrangement is based on a 5-day week.   *Ans.* $110.60.

13. An agent sold for his principal goods valued at $2346.22. If his commission was $4\frac{1}{2}\%$ how much did he earn on the transaction?
        Ans. $105.58.

14. In behalf of a client a lawyer accepts 85% of a debt amounting to $1734.00 in full payment. Estimate the amount of his fee if he charged a commission of $3\frac{3}{4}\%$.   *Ans.* $55.27.

15. If the net profit of a general merchandise store is $8\frac{1}{2}\%$ of its sales, approximately how much net profit will be made in a year if the average monthly sales amount to $7832.00.   *Ans.* $7988.64.

16. A retailer's sales for the year total $83,420.00. If his net profit is $4\frac{1}{4}\%$ of the sales, what is his income for the year?   *Ans.* $3545.35.

17. In 1946 it was estimated that the production of elevators, escalators and conveyors one year after reconversion would exceed the production in 1939 by 87.8%. If the production in 1939 was $64,100,000, compute the amount of the expected production one year after reconversion. (Hint: The answer can be computed by the breakdown method without having to multiply by more than one digit.)   *Ans.* $120,379,800.

* 18. Promotion experts recommend that a drug store, having an annual sales volume of $50,000, spend a minimum of 0.75 to 1.11% of its sales for promotion. How much is 0.75% of $50,000?   *Ans.* $375.00.

19. A study of 4000 cases showed the following average sales increases in drug stores as a result of the installation of new equipment:

(a) Completely modernized....... 49% increase in total sales
(b) Store front modernized....... 27.7% increase in total sales
(c) Modernized lighting .... 23.5% increase in total sales
(d) Air conditioning............. 22.2% increase in total sales

The proprietor of a drug store decides to make improvements b, c and d. How much of an annual sales volume might be expected as a result if in the previous year the sales amounted to $38,500? (Hint: Add the three per-cent rates, find the percentage, then add the result to $38,500.)
                                                     Ans. $66,759.00.

20. The catalog of a mailing list company shows the following lists to be available:

Automobile retail dealers.................... 193,356 names
Hardware retail stores....................... 29,739 names
Retail druggists .... 61,453 names
Men's furnishings and clothing stores .... 27,361 names
Restaurants .... 121,126 names

It is reported that in a 12-month period—as a result of deaths, bankruptcies, removals, changes in firm names and changes in ratings—the mortality in these classifications was, respectively, 23%, 18%, 21%, 28% and 42%. Assuming that the mortality in the ensuing 12-month period would be about the same, compute the number of changes which might be necessary in each of these lists one year after compilation or correction.   *Ans*. 44,472, 5353, 12,905, 7661 and 50,873, respectively

48. Calculating Percentages When the Base Is a Multiple of a Tenth of a Dollar. Many individuals are confused by problems like 61 per cent of 70 cents. But see how simple the computation really is:

$$61\% \text{ of } \$1.00 \qquad\qquad\qquad\qquad\qquad = \$.61$$
$$\text{therefore } 61\% \text{ of } 10 \text{ cents equals } \tfrac{1}{10} \text{ of } .61 \quad = \quad .061$$
$$\text{therefore } 61\% \text{ of } 70 \text{ cents equals } 7 \text{ times } .061 = \quad .43$$

The reader is here reminded that in the above illustration, as in many of the illustrations in the preceding chapters, the data at the left of the partial products is given only for the purpose of explanation and clarification. In actual practice there is no need to write down the data or the separate calculations, for with just a little experience the mental computation of such problems will become easy and effortless.

In our study of the double-and-halve method (Chapter III) it was shown that when two factors in a multiplication problem are multiplied and divided, respectively, by the same value, the product is not affected. The application of this principle makes the computation of percentages when the base is a multiple of a tenth of a dollar even speedier than the method indicated in the foregoing illustration. Using the same example to illustrate the point, all we need do is multiply .70 by 10 and divide .61 by 10, which changes the problem to read 7 times .061, and we see at a glance that the answer is .43. The time-saving importance of this method will be appreciated after observing the process of computation in the following illustrations. Bear in mind the meaning of the term "per cent." A rate per cent signifies how many per hundred. Thus 43 per cent means 43 per hundred, which may also be written .43.

Example 1: Compute 43% of 30 cents.

Solution: .43 of .30 is the same as .043 times 3, or .13.

Example 2: Compute 37% of 70 cents.

Solution: .37 of .70 is the same as .037 times 7, or .26.

Example 3: Compute $89\frac{1}{2}$% of 80 cents.

Solution: .895 of .80 is the same as .0895 times 8, or .72.

The use of this method may be extended to bases other than multiples of a tenth of a dollar, though in such instances computations may sometimes call for pencil-and-paper work. In the illustrations that follow the problems are similar to those in Examples 1, 2 and 3. There is just a slight modification: in the base amount a unit digit of the same value as the tens digit takes the place of the zero. Thus the zero in 30 is changed to 3.

Example 4: Compute 43% of 33 cents.

Solution: .43 of .33 is the same as .043 times 3.3.

$$
\begin{array}{ll}
.043 \text{ times } 3 & = .129 \\
.043 \text{ times } .3 \ (\tfrac{1}{10} \text{ of } .129) & = .013 \\
\hline
.043 \text{ times } 3.3 & = .14
\end{array}
$$

Example 5: Compute 37% of 77 cents.

Solution: .37 of .77 is the same as .037 times 7.7.

$$
\begin{array}{ll}
.037 \text{ times } 7 & = .259 \\
.037 \text{ times } .7 \ (\tfrac{1}{10} \text{ of } .259) & = .026 \\
\hline
.037 \text{ times } 7.7 & = .29
\end{array}
$$

Example 6: Compute $89\frac{1}{2}$% of 88 cents.

Solution: .895 of .88 is the same as .0895 times 8.8.

$$
\begin{array}{ll}
.0895 \text{ times } 8 & = .716 \\
.0895 \text{ times } .8 \ (\tfrac{1}{10} \text{ of } .716) & = .072 \\
\hline
.0895 \text{ times } 8.8 & = .79
\end{array}
$$

Note the procedure in the following illustrations, in which the unit digit in the base amount is an aliquot part of the rest of the amount. In Example 7, for instance, 4 cents is an aliquot part of 20 cents.

Example 7: Compute 56% of 24 cents.

Solution: .56 of .24 is the same as .056 times 2.4.

$$.056 \text{ times } 2 \qquad\qquad = .112$$
$$.056 \text{ times } .4 \ (\tfrac{1}{5} \text{ of } .112) = .022$$

$$.056 \text{ times } 2.4 \qquad\qquad = .13$$

Example 8: Compute 72% of 42 cents.

Solution: .72 of .42 is the same as .072 times 4.2.

$$.072 \text{ times } 4 \qquad\qquad = .288$$
$$.072 \text{ times } .2 \ (\tfrac{1}{20} \text{ of } .288) = .014$$

$$.072 \text{ times } 4.2 \qquad\qquad = .30$$

Example 9: Compute 29% of 93 cents.

Solution: .29 of .93 is the same as .029 times 9.3.

$$.029 \text{ times } 9 \qquad\qquad = .261$$
$$.029 \text{ times } .3 \ (\tfrac{1}{30} \text{ of } .261) = .008$$

$$.029 \text{ times } 9.3 \qquad\qquad = .27$$

The use of this method may be extended still further. Suppose, for instance, we wished to compute 28 per cent of 85 cents. By the method described, we should first find 28 per cent of 80 cents, then 28 per cent of 4 cents. All we need do now to complete the computation is add 28 per cent of one cent, which is less than half a cent and will, therefore, be disregarded. So that 28 per cent of 85 cents would be equivalent, for all practical purposes, to 28 per cent of 84 cents.

Find the following percentages mentally, computing answers to the nearest cent.

* **1.** 83% of 50 cents.   *Ans.* $0.42.
* **2.** 28% of 40 cents.   *Ans.* $0.11.
* **3.** 34% of 60 cents.   *Ans.* $0.20.
* **4.** 47% of 30 cents.   *Ans.* $0.14.
* **5.** 62% of 70 cents.   *Ans.* $0.43.
* **6.** 78% of 80 cents.   *Ans.* $0.62.
* **7.** 81% of 90 cents.   *Ans.* $0.73.
* **8.** $52\frac{1}{2}$% of 20 cents.   *Ans.* $0.11.

Compute the answers to the following problems without writing down the multiplicands and multipliers.

9. 72% of 55 cents.   *Ans.* $0.40.
10. 57% of 66 cents.   *Ans.* $0.38.
11. 68% of 33 cents.   *Ans.* $0.22.
12. 49% of 22 cents.   *Ans.* $0.11.
13. 24% of 77 cents.   *Ans.* $0.19.
14. 86% of 88 cents.   *Ans.* $0.76.
15. 13% of 99 cents.   *Ans.* $0.13.
16. $31\frac{1}{2}$% of 44 cents.   *Ans.* $0.14.
17. 46% of 82 cents.   *Ans.* $0.38.
18. 73% of 63 cents.   *Ans.* $0.46.
19. 19% of 42 cents.   *Ans.* $0.08.
20. 26% of $52\frac{1}{2}$ cents.   *Ans.* $0.14.
21. 87% of $61\frac{1}{2}$ cents.   *Ans.* $0.54.
22. 35% of 93 cents.   *Ans.* $0.33.
23. $91\frac{1}{2}$% of 84 cents.   *Ans.* $0.77.
24. $62\frac{1}{2}$% of $72\frac{1}{3}$ cents.   *Ans.* $0.45.
25. $27\frac{1}{2}$% of 87 cents.   *Ans.* $0.24.
26. $32\frac{1}{2}$% of 79 cents.   *Ans.* $0.26.
27. 25% of 23 cents.   *Ans.* $0.06.
28. 55% of 32 cents.   *Ans.* $0.18.

Note the near-aliquot per-cent rates in the next two problems.

29. $67\frac{2}{3}$% of 93 cents. (Hint: $66\frac{2}{3}$% is exactly $\frac{2}{3}$.)   *Ans.* $0.63.
30. $63\frac{1}{2}$% of 56 cents. (Hint: $62\frac{1}{2}$% is exactly $\frac{5}{8}$.)   *Ans.* $0.36.

49. Calculating Percentages When the Base Is Less Than One Dollar. In computing per cents of amounts under one dollar, it frequently makes very little difference whether the unit digit of the rate per cent or the unit digit of the base is increased or decreased by a unit or fraction of a unit. The lower the rate per cent, or the smaller the base, the truer this is.

Take for instance the problem 15 per cent of 40 cents, which equals 6 cents. Computed to the nearest penny, $15\frac{1}{2}$ per cent of 40 cents is 6 cents too. And 16 per cent of 40 cents, computed to the nearest penny, is also 6 cents. Likewise, 15 per cent of $40\frac{1}{2}$ cents, as 15 per cent of 41 cents, equals 6 cents.

Let us take an example with a commonly used rate: $33\frac{1}{3}$ per cent of 39 cents. The answer is exactly 13 cents. Thirty-three per cent of 39 cents, computed to the nearest penny, also gives us 13 cents. And 34 per cent of 39 cents does not change our answer of 13 cents. If we increased the base to 40 cents, $33\frac{1}{3}$ per cent, computed to the nearest cent, would still give us 13 cents.

We may conclude, therefore, that in computing per cents of amounts under one dollar, an insignificant change in the per cent rate or in the amount of the base may not affect the answer to any practical extent.

Using this conclusion as a hypothesis, consider the ease with which a problem like $66\frac{1}{2}$ per cent of 90 cents may be computed. If the rate were $66\frac{2}{3}$ per cent (which is exactly two thirds), our answer would be exactly 60 cents. The difference between $66\frac{2}{3}$ per cent and $66\frac{1}{2}$ per cent is but one sixth of 1 per cent, and one sixth of 1 per cent of 90 cents is so insignificant that it may be disregarded. So that for all practical purposes the rate of $66\frac{1}{2}$ per cent, in this instance, may safely be changed to $66\frac{2}{3}$ per cent.

Or take the problem 24 per cent of 47 cents, to be computed to the nearest cent. If the rate were 25 per cent instead of 24 per cent, our answer would be $11\frac{3}{4}$ cents. This, however, exceeds the required answer by 1 per cent of 47 cents. But 1 per cent of 47 cents is less than half a cent and may, therefore, be disregarded.

PROBLEMS

All computations are to be to the nearest cent. (A review of Table V in the preceding chapter may be found helpful.)

* **1.** $55\frac{1}{2}\%$ of 40 cents.   *Ans.* $0.22.
* **2.** $49\frac{1}{2}\%$ of 38 cents.   *Ans.* $0.19.
* **3.** $12\frac{3}{4}\%$ of 56 cents.   *Ans.* $0.07.
* **4.** $12\frac{1}{4}\%$ of 24 cents.   *Ans.* $0.03.
* **5.** $25\frac{1}{2}\%$ of 84 cents.   *Ans.* $0.21.
* **6.** 24.7% of 60 cents.   *Ans.* $0.15.
* **7.** $37\frac{1}{4}\%$ of 28 cents.   *Ans.* $0.10.
* **8.** 38% of 46 cents.   *Ans.* $0.17.
* **9.** 49.8% of 98 cents.   *Ans.* $0.49.
* **10.** 50.86% of 34 cents.   *Ans.* $0.17.
* **11.** $33\frac{1}{3}\%$ of $18\frac{1}{2}$ cents.   *Ans.* $0.06.
* **12.** $16\frac{1}{3}\%$ of 66 cents.   *Ans.* $0.11.
* **13.** 20% of $30\frac{1}{2}$ cents.   *Ans.* $0.06.
* **14.** 25% of 80.5 cents.   *Ans.* $0.20.
* **15.** $62\frac{1}{4}\%$ of 80.2 cents.   *Ans.* $0.50.
* **16.** $74\frac{1}{4}\%$ of 48 cents.   *Ans.* $0.36.
* **17.** $16\frac{5}{8}\%$ of 36 cents.   *Ans.* $0.06.
* **18.** $87\frac{3}{4}\%$ of 80.1 cents.   *Ans.* $0.70.
* **19.** $90\frac{7}{8}\%$ of 20 cents.   *Ans.* $0.18.
* **20.** 55% of $60\frac{1}{4}$ cents.   *Ans.* $0.33.

50. Calculating Percentages When the Base Is an Aliquot Part of $100, $1000, etc. When the base is an aliquot part of $100, $1000, etc., the transposition of the values simplifies the problem. Thus 14 per cent of $50.00 is equivalent to 50 per cent of $14.00, which is $7.00; $32\frac{1}{4}$ per cent of $25.00 is the same as 25 per cent of $32.25, which is $8.06; $11\frac{3}{4}$ per cent of $37.50 produces the same answer as $37\frac{1}{2}$ per cent of $11.75, which is $4.41; and $18\frac{1}{2}$ per cent of $750.00 is equivalent to 750 per cent of $18.50, or $7\frac{1}{2}$ times $18.50, which is $138.75.

The computation of per cents of multiples of $100 is, of course, very simple. The per-cent rate is simply multiplied by the multiple of $100. Sixty-three per cent of $700.00 is equivalent to $63.00 multiplied by 7; 43 per cent of $1100.00 produces the same result as $43.00 multiplied by 11. And so on.

Problems

The computation of these problems without pencil and paper should be found a comparatively simple matter.

★ **1.** 23% of $50.00.   *Ans.* $11.50.
★ **2.** 32% of $27.50.   *Ans.* $8.80.
★ **3.** 16% of $37.50.   *Ans.* $6.00.
★ **4.** 8.8% of $62.50.   *Ans.* $5.50.
★ **5.** 24.16% of $75.00.   *Ans.* $18.12.
★ **6.** 48% of $225.00.   *Ans.* $108.00.
★ **7.** 72.98% of $50.00.   *Ans.* $36.49.
★ **8.** 12.84% of $25.00.   *Ans.* $3.21.
★ **9.** 55% of $120.00.   *Ans.* $66.00.
★ **10.** 44% of $175.00.   *Ans.* $77.00.

Only the partial products and the answers are to be written down in working the following problems.

11. 36.82% of $150.00.   *Ans.* $55.23.
12. 16.72% of $387.50.   *Ans.* $64.79.
13. 64% of $412.50.   *Ans.* $264.00.
14. 72% of $227.50.   *Ans.* $163.80.
15. 40.56% of $662.50.   *Ans.* $268.71.
16. 15.8% of $520.00.   *Ans.* $82.16.
17. 84.24% of $525.00.   *Ans.* $442.26.
18. 8.96% of $737.50.   *Ans.* $66.08.
19. 3.74% of $650.00.   *Ans.* $24.31.
20. 34.3% of $810.00.   *Ans.* $277.83.

51. A Good Way to Check Per-Cent Computations. A good way to prove the result of a per-cent computation might be described as the "minus" method. To prove, for instance, the result of $37\frac{1}{2}$ per cent of any sum, we might deduct $62\frac{1}{2}$ per cent from the original sum (100 minus $37\frac{1}{2}$ equals $62\frac{1}{2}$). The result of $47\frac{1}{2}$ per cent of any sum might be proved by deducting $52\frac{1}{2}$ per cent from the original sum. And so on.

Or, as indicated in some of the illustrations in Art. 46, the rate per cent may be subdivided in two different ways, a separate computation being made for each of the two sets of figures. Thus $32\frac{1}{2}$ per cent might be divided up into 25, 5 and $2\frac{1}{2}$ per cent; or into 30 and $2\frac{1}{2}$ per cent.

PROBLEMS

Prove by the "minus" method the given answers to the following problems.

1. $32\frac{1}{2}\%$ of $46.40 equals $15.08.
2. $37\frac{1}{2}\%$ of $48.96 equals $18.36.
3. $42\frac{1}{2}\%$ of $423.60 equals $180.03.
4. $47\frac{1}{2}\%$ of $365.20 equals $173.47.
5. $52\frac{1}{2}\%$ of $286.40 equals $150.36.
6. $57\frac{1}{2}\%$ of $480.80 equals $276.46.
7. $62\frac{1}{2}\%$ of $153.36 equals $95.85.
8. $67\frac{1}{2}\%$ of $1468.40 equals $991.17.

52. An Ideal Way of Checking and Computing Percentages When the Same Per-Cent Rate Is Used Exclusively on a List of Many Items. When the same rate is used exclusively for computing per cents of many items, there is still a shorter method of proving the calculations than the one explained in the preceding article.

Let us say a manufacturer is about to add to his line of merchandise some new products, and decides to determine the selling prices by adding to the production costs a certain percentage to cover overhead expenses and profit. It is obvious that the selling price of each item must be computed separately. What, however, would be the quickest way to prove the computations? Would it be necessary to prove each computation separately? Not at all.

A short and sure checking procedure would be this:

1. First add the figures of all the items on which the per-cent rates are computed. (In the aforementioned example, these would constitute the production costs.) We will call this Total A.

2. Next add the increased figures, that is, the selling prices. Let us call this Total C.

3. Now compute the same rate per cent of Total A as was used to calculate the individual percentages. If the sum of Total A plus the percentage of Total A equals Total C, it may be reasonably assumed that each of the individual per-cent computations is correct.

The following problem will serve as an illustration. A manufacturer's production costs on five items are $116.80, $122.28, $76.32, $48.94 and $65.76 respectively. The selling price of each item is to be determined by adding 92 per cent to the production costs. Compute the selling price of each item, and prove the five computations in one calculation.

Production Costs	92% of Production Costs	Selling Price (Production Costs Plus 92%)
$116.80	$107.46	$224.26
122.28	112.50	234.78
76.32	70.21	146.53
48.94	45.02	93.96
65.76	60.50	126.26
$430.10 (Total A)	plus $395.69 * equals	$825.79 (Total C)

* The figures in this column need not necessarily be added, as explained in a succeeding paragraph. The total is shown here only for the purpose of clarification.

Following the indicated method of checking, we add the production costs of all five items, which gives us Total A, or $430.10. Now we compute 92 per cent of this amount, which is $395.69. The sum of $430.10 plus $395.69 should equal the total of all the selling prices, Total C. We find that it does. It may, therefore, be taken for granted that the computed selling price of each of the five items is correct.

It should be noted that whereas, for checking purposes, a separate total of the production costs and a separate total of the estimated selling prices must be taken, the individual percentages need not be added. For checking purposes, the total of the percentages is computed in one lump sum, using the total of the production costs as the base.

It should be remembered that in proving the total for the group of selling prices, we have not taken into consideration that an error on the plus side in one instance may have been offset by an error of exactly the same magnitude on the minus side in another instance, in which case the error would not show up in the total for the group. Thus in the example illustrated, if the selling price of the second item were incorrectly shown as $235.78, instead of $234.78, and the selling price of the third item were erroneously shown as $145.53, instead of $146.53, the total would still be $825.79. The fact, however, is that errors of this nature seldom occur, and this method of group checking may be used with assurance and safety.

While the example illustrated deals with production costs and selling prices, there are any number of financial records whose preparation calls for the same or a similar procedure, and the reader will do well to familiarize himself with this method of checking and computing percentages.

PROBLEMS

1. A factory checking operation is estimated to occupy $16\frac{2}{3}\%$ of the total time required to assemble each unit. Compute the amount of time that would be spent in checking the work done in assembling the following: (a) 17 units requiring 3 hours each; (b) 10 units requiring 1 hour 30 minutes each; (c) 8 units requiring 45 minutes each.

Ans. 12 hours.

2. A salesman employed on a straight commission basis of 15% makes 7 sales. These are shown in his company's commission statement as follows:

Amount of Sale	Commission
$ 234.60	$ 35.19
119.20	17.88
408.56	61.29
791.43	118.71
84.78	12.72
512.12	76.81
314.28	47.15
$2464.97	$369.75

Check by a single computation the accuracy of the figure representing the total amount of commission due the salesman.

3. A food-flavor formula requires the use of $6\frac{1}{2}$ ounces of a botanical ingredient for each 100 ounces of the finished product. Four batches of the product are made up as follows: 160, 330, 95 and 125 ounces. Estimate the total number of ounces of the botanical ingredient used in the production of these batches. *Ans.* 46.15 ounces.

4. A dealer is offered an extra discount of $2\frac{1}{2}\%$ if he pays his outstanding bills within three days. These bills are for the following amounts: $80.00, $11.20, $47.18, and $21.62. How much will the dealer save if he accepts the offer? *Ans.* $4.00.

5. If the average ratio of lard yielded by slaughtered hogs is 12.5 pounds per 100 pounds of live weight, how much lard will be produced by the slaughtering of hogs whose live weight totals are 2400 pounds, 1840 pounds, 3795 pounds and 2165 pounds? *Ans.* 1275 pounds.

6. In 1932 the average interest rate on mortgages charged by a New York bank was 5.48% per annum. Compute the bank's total income from the following one-year mortgages at this rate: $18,500, $23,200, $15,000 and $8250. *Ans.* $3559.26.

7. The minimum percentage of copper in alloy steel, as specified by the American Iron & Steel Institute, is 0.60%. Estimate the total amount of copper used to this specification in the following quantities of alloy steel: 36 pounds, 24 pounds, $19\frac{1}{2}$ pounds, $83\frac{1}{2}$ pounds and 17 pounds. (Hint: 0.60% means $\frac{6}{10}$ of 1%.) *Ans.* 1.08 pounds.

8. It has been the experience of dry cleaners who operate many stores that a corner location is worth at least 25% more than one in the middle of a block in the same area. How much profit may be expected in the first year of operation by a dry cleaner who rents a corner store, if two of his other stores, in the same area but in the middle of a block, produced profits in the preceding twelve months of $1244.00 and $1336.00, respectively, and are expected in the ensuing 12-month period to better these figures by 20%? (Hint: To half the sum of $1244.00 and $1336.00 add 20%; then add 25% of the result.) *Ans.* $1935.00.

53. Computing the Net Amount When a Sum Is Subject to Two or More Successive Discounts.

Many businessmen mistakenly believe that the sequence in which two or more discounts are deducted makes a difference. Of course, it does *not* make any difference.

Example 1: Find the net amount of a bill for $650.00 subject to the successive discount rates of 20%, 10% and 5%.

Solution A: In this solution the discounts are deducted in the order in which they are stated in the problem.

$650.00 less 20% = $520.00
520.00 less 10% = 468.00
468.00 less 5% = 444.60

Ans. $444.60.

Solution B: In this solution the discounts are deducted in a different order.

$650.00 less 10% = $585.00
585.00 less 5% = 555.75
555.75 less 20% = 444.60

Ans. $444.60.

Note that in both solutions the answers are identical. The reason is that in any multiplication problem the order in which the values are arranged is immaterial. Percentage computation is, in effect, a process of multiplication; it is a process of multiplying the base by the difference between 1 and the rate per cent. Thus $650.00 less 20 per cent is equivalent to $650.00 multiplied by 80 per cent. And $650.00 less the successive discounts of 20 per cent, 10 per cent and 5 per cent is equivalent to $650.00 multiplied by .80, multiplied by .90, multiplied by .95. In multiplying a series of numbers, the order in which they are multiplied does not affect the result. So that our problem would produce exactly the same result if it were restated as $650.00 multiplied by .90, multiplied by .80, multiplied by .95.

PROBLEMS

Since the sequence in which two or more successive discounts are deducted does not affect the result, in what order would you deduct the discounts in the following problems so as to facilitate computation mentally or with a minimum or pencil-and-paper work? Indicate your answers by numbering the per-cent rates in the first five problems, 1 and 2, and in the last five problems, 1, 2 and 3.

1. $100.00 less $33\frac{1}{3}$% and 10%.   *Ans.* 2, 1.
2. $80.00 less 5% and $12\frac{1}{2}$%.   *Ans.* 2, 1.

   3. $96.00 less $16\frac{2}{3}\%$ and 20%.   *Ans.* 1, 2.
   4. $160.00 less $7\frac{1}{2}\%$ and $37\frac{1}{2}\%$.   *Ans.* 2, 1.
   5. $72.00 less $33\frac{1}{3}\%$ and $62\frac{1}{2}\%$.   *Ans.* 1, 2.
   6. $40.00 less 25%, $12\frac{1}{2}\%$ and $33\frac{1}{3}\%$.   *Ans.* 1, 3, 2.
   7. $135.00 less 20%, $66\frac{2}{3}\%$ and 10%.   *Ans.* 2, 1, 3.
   8. $840.00 less $16\frac{2}{3}\%$, 5% and 10%.   *Ans.* 1, 3, 2.
   9. $120.00 less $2\frac{1}{2}\%$, $33\frac{1}{3}\%$ and 5%.   *Ans.* 2, 1, 3.
  10. $600.00 less 5%, 25% and 10%.   *Ans.* 2, 3, 1.

54. How to Find the Equivalent and the Net Result of Deducting a Series of Successive Discounts. In Art. 45 we saw that when dealing with discounts the process of computing net amounts can be speeded up if, instead of subtracting the amount of the discount, we multiplied by the difference between 100 per cent and the per cent of the discount rate. Thus to find the net amount of $300.00 less 20 per cent, we could obtain the answer very quickly by computing 80 per cent of $300.00 (80 per cent being the difference between 100 per cent and 20 per cent).

This process of multiplying by the difference between 100 per cent and the per cent of the discount rate can be used with excellent effect to compute the net amount of a sum subject to two or more successive discounts. Let us say, for example, that the sum of $200.00 is subject to the successive discounts of 25 per cent and 10 per cent. If we did not know that the equivalent of these two successive discounts is $32\frac{1}{2}$ per cent, we would have to compute first $200.00 less 25 per cent, and then $150.00 (the net amount obtained in the first computation) less 10 per cent, which gives us $135.00. Observe how simple the computation becomes when we calculate $200.00 less the single discount of $32\frac{1}{2}$ per cent; we see immediately that the answer equals $67\frac{1}{2}$ per cent (the difference between 100 per cent and $32\frac{1}{2}$ per cent) of $200.00, or $135.00.

Another example of the speed and simplicity of multiplying by a single equivalent to find the net amount of a sum subject to successive discounts is the series of 40, 10 and 5 per cent rates, which equals 51.3 per cent.

It should be noted, however, that computing by single equivalent values is not always as time-saving. Deducting the successive discounts of 20, 10 and 5 per cent, for example, is equivalent to multiplying by 68.4 per cent, or .684 (which is the difference between 100 per cent and 31.6 per cent—31.6 per cent being the discount rate equivalent of the aforementioned successive per-cent rates). To multiply a sum like $283.19 by .684 would require three separate partial products and about as much pencil-and-paper work as the separate computation of the three discount rates.

However, an understanding of how to find the equivalent of a series of successive discounts or their net result is very important. A businessman, for instance, may be offered a line of merchandise by a manufacturer at a discount of, say, 35 per cent from the list prices; another manufacturer offers the identical merchandise at the same list prices, but at the successive discount rates of 30 per cent and $7\frac{1}{2}$ per cent. He will obviously want to know the equivalent discount of 30 per cent and $7\frac{1}{2}$ per cent and which manufacturer's net prices are lower.

The equivalent value or net result of a series of successive discounts is determined in this manner: Using 1 as the base, we find that 1 (100 per cent) less 30 per cent, for example, equals 70 per cent, or .7; and .7 less 5 per cent (that is, 5 per cent of .7) equals .665, which is the net result.

Knowing the net result we need but to subtract this figure from 100 to obtain the equivalent discount rate. Thus 100 per cent minus $66\frac{1}{2}$ per cent equals $33\frac{1}{2}$ per cent, and this figure is the equivalent of the successive rates of 30 per cent and 5 per cent.

To deduct 30 per cent and 5 per cent, therefore, we have two choices: (1) to deduct the equivalent rate of $33\frac{1}{2}$ per cent; (2) to multiply by $66\frac{1}{2}$ per cent, or .665. And as was pointed out in the opening paragraphs of this article, the latter method is preferred in most instances.

This method of finding the equivalent or net result applies to any series of successive discounts. Thus if a sum were subject to the three successive discounts of 40 per cent, 10 per cent and 5 per cent, we should determine the equivalent net amount as follows:

$$1.0 \text{ less } 40\% = .6$$
$$.6 \text{ less } 10\% = .54$$
$$.54 \text{ less } 5\% = .513$$

So that to compute the net amount of a sum subject to the successive discounts of 40, 10 and 5 per cent, we multiply by .513.

The reader is cautioned not to confuse the equivalent *discount* rate with the *net result* of a series of successive discounts. The net result of deducting 40, 10 and 5 per cent from 1, as shown in the foregoing illustration, is .513. The equivalent discount rate, however, is the difference between 1 and .513—that is, .487. In other words, deducting 48.7 per cent produces the same result as deducting, successively, 40 per cent, 10 per cent, and 5 per cent. But, again—as has been pointed out—a shorter way of finding the net amount of a sum subject to the discount rate of 48.7 per cent is to multiply by .513.

PROBLEMS

Calculate to the nearest tenth of 1%: (a) the number by which to multiply to obtain the net amount of a sum subject to each of the following series of successive discounts; (b) the equivalent discount rate of each series.

1. 20%, 10% and 5%.   *Ans.* (a) .684; (b) 68.4%.
2. 25%, 5% and $2\frac{1}{2}$%.   *Ans.* (a) .695; (b) 69.5%.
3. 10%, 5% and $2\frac{1}{2}$%.   *Ans.* (a) .834; (b) 83.4%.
4. $12\frac{1}{2}$%, 5% and 5%.   *Ans.* (a) .790; (b) 79%.
5. 30%, 10% and 5%.   *Ans.* (a) .599; (b) 59.9%.

Using the "net result" figures obtained in the computation of the foregoing problems, calculate the amounts due on the following invoices:

6. $132.00 less 20%, 5% and 10%.   *Ans.* $90.29.
7. $21.40 less 25%, 5% and $2\frac{1}{2}$%.   *Ans.* $14.87.
8. $95.62 less 5%, $2\frac{1}{2}$% and 10%.   *Ans.* $79.75.
9. $250.00 less 5%, $12\frac{1}{2}$% and 5%.   *Ans.* $197.50.
10. $480.00 less 30%, 5% and 10%.   *Ans.* $287.52.

55. How to Find the Rate Per Cent. One of the most useful bits of knowledge in business mathematics is knowing how to determine the relationship between two values on a percentage basis.

A firm may want to know, for instance, by how many per cent its July sales exceeded the June sales. Or it may have effected economies in its production processes in the fiscal year just ended, and wants to know the relationship on a percentage basis between the production cost per $100.00 worth of merchandise manufactured in the year just ended and the cost of producing an equal amount of finished merchandise in the previous year. There is virtually no end to the number of uses to which a knowledge of how to find the rate per cent may be put.

Let us take some practical examples and observe how, by the process of simple reasoning. the desired information is obtained quickly and easily.

Example 1: A firm's sales for the month of July amounted to $2400.00. Its sales for the previous month were $2000.00. By what rate per cent did the July sales exceed the June sales?

Solution: The July sales exceeded the June sales by $400.00. The problem, therefore, is: What fraction having 100 as the denominator is equivalent to $\frac{400}{2000}$? Stated in the form of an equation

$$\frac{400}{2000} = \frac{x}{100}$$

x being the unknown number, or the rate per cent.

In order that this equation may be clearly understood, let us digress for a few moments and study a simple rule which will probably never be forgotten if it is concentrated on for a little while: *In any fractional equation, the product of the means equals the product of the extremes.*

Let us take the equation $\frac{2}{4} = \frac{3}{6}$. The means are 4 and 3; their product is 12. The extremes are 2 and 6; their product, too, is 12. It is clear, then, that whenever one fraction equals another fraction, the product of the means *must* equal the product of the extremes.

Coming back to the unfinished part of the solution to our problem, $\frac{400}{2000} = \frac{x}{100}$, we have an equation here in which one of the numerators is an unknown quantity. We know, however, that the product of the means equals the product of the extremes. So that $2000x$ equals 40,000. Now, if $2000x$ equals 40,000, all we need do to find what *one* x equals is divide 40,000 by 2000. The answer, of course, is 20. The answer to our problem, then, is that the sales for July exceed the sales for June by 20 per cent.

Example 2: Linseed oil is one of the ingredients of a certain synthetic product. If in the manufacturing process one pound of this oil is used to make 18 pounds of the finished product, what per cent of the weight of the finished product does the weight of the linseed oil constitute?

Solution: The linseed oil content is one eighteenth of the weight of the finished product. Since we want to show this in the form of a percentage, let us write an equation:

$$\frac{1}{18} = \frac{x}{100}$$

Since the product of the means equals the product of the extremes, we know that $18x$ equals 100. One x, therefore, equals 100 divided by 18, or 5.55. The linseed oil content, therefore, is 5.55% of the weight of the finished product.

Example 3: An employee's weekly salary of $52.00 is increased by $8.00. (a) What rate per cent of $52.00 does the increase constitute? (b) What rate per cent of $60.00 does the increase constitute?

Solution: (a) $\dfrac{8}{52} = \dfrac{x}{100}$

$52x = 800$

$x = \frac{800}{52} = 15.4\%$

(b) $\dfrac{8}{60} = \dfrac{x}{100}$

$60x = 800$

$x = \frac{800}{60} = 13.3\%$

In each of the preceding illustrations it was necessary to divide into 100 or a multiple of 100 to find the value of x. In many instances, however, the rate per cent will be obvious at a glance. Thus $\frac{1}{10}$ is equivalent to 10 per cent; $\frac{1}{25}$ equals 4 per cent; $\frac{45}{360}$ equals $\frac{1}{8}$ or $12\frac{1}{2}$ per cent, and so on. Fractions like these shorten the process of computation. The following illustration will help to make this clear.

Example 4: A product costs \$80.00, and sells for \$120.00. What rate per cent of the selling price does the gross profit constitute?

Solution: The gross profit is \$40.00, or one third of the selling price. The rate per cent, therefore, is $33\frac{1}{3}$.

PROBLEMS

★ **1.** On October 1, 1946, the domestic air mail postal rate was reduced from 8 cents to 5 cents an ounce. In terms of per cent how much of a saving on the 8 cent rate does this mean? *Ans.* $37\frac{1}{2}\%$.

2. What is a salesman's rate of commission if he receives a check for \$61.34 covering the amount due him on a sale of \$368.04? *Ans.* $16\frac{2}{3}\%$.

★ **3.** Currency paper contains a substantial proportion of linen, which gives it hardness, strength and durability. Approximately 1600 tons of paper are used each year to replace the currency worn out, and of this quantity about 1200 tons consist of linen fiber. What per cent of linen fiber would you say is contained in currency paper? *Ans.* 75%.

★ **4.** If a man gains \$350.00 on an investment of \$2100.00, how much per-cent profit did he make on the principal? *Ans.* $16\frac{2}{3}\%$.

5. A house costing \$35,000 is rented for \$2800.00 a year. How much per cent per annum gross profit does the owner realize on his investment? *Ans.* 8%.

6. The total expenses of all the departments in an enterprise is \$2935.00. What per cent of this total is represented by the department whose expenses amounted to \$117.40? *Ans.* 4%.

★ **7.** When the selling price of unfrosted doughnuts is 25 cents per dozen, the cost of the ingredients, including the frying compound, is about 9 cents. This makes the gross profit on the ingredients 16 cents. Compute the per-cent rate of the gross profit on the selling price. *Ans.* 64%.

★ **8.** Of a company's 1600 employees, 300 are stockholders. Compute mentally the per cent of employees owning stock. *Ans.* $18\frac{3}{4}\%$.

* **9.** If an association having a membership of 360 on January 1 closes its books on December 31 with a membership of 390, how much per-cent increase did the new membership total represent over the total at the beginning of the year?   *Ans.* $8\frac{1}{3}\%$.

10. A bankrupt settles a debt of $2250.00 with a payment of $1735.00. What per cent of his indebtedness does his settlement represent? Compute the answer to the nearest hundredth of a per cent.   *Ans.* 77.11%.

11. Brown and Sweet enter into partnership, Brown investing $3000 and Sweet $5500. How much per cent of the total did Sweet invest? Find the answer to the nearest hundredth of a per cent.   *Ans.* 64.71%.

12. In 1896 the average weekly salary in the Chicago stockyards was $6.65. In 1946 it was approximately $45.00. How much per cent is the salary earned in 1896 of the amount received in 1946? Find the answer to the nearest hundredth of a per cent.   *Ans.* 14.77%.

13. A concern decides to appropriate a certain amount of money to advertise the products of each of its departments. The amount allotted is to be determined by the per-cent relationship between the department's sales and the company's total sales for the last fiscal year. To what per cent of the appropriation would Department A be entitled if the amount of its sales for the year is $84,000 and the total sales of all the departments combined amounted to $630,000?   *Ans.* $13\frac{1}{3}\%$.

14. A firm employs 3 salesmen. The totals of their sales in one week were, respectively, $840.00, $736.00 and $424.00. Compute the per-cent relationship to the total of the amount of business produced by each salesman.   *Ans.* 42, 36.8, and 21.2%, respectively.

15. It has been found that there is a direct relationship between the amount of brooder floor space and brooder mortality. Thus of 73,000 chicks brooded in a floor space of less than 35 square feet per 100 chicks, the mortality was approximately 20,000, while of 25,000 chicks brooded in an area of 50 square feet or over per 100 chicks, the mortality was approximately 3500. Compute to the nearest tenth of a per cent the rate of mortality in each instance.   *Ans.* 27.4% and 14%.

56. Easy Ways to Remember How to Find a Number When the Value of a Per Cent or Any Fractional Part of It Is Known. The necessity for finding information of this nature occurs quite frequently in business, and the ability to do it quickly is very serviceable.

To begin with a simple example: If 20 per cent of a number is 6, what is the number? We know that 20 per cent is one fifth.

Therefore, we reason, if one fifth equals 6, five fifths will equal five times 6, or 30. Similarly, if $33\frac{1}{3}$ per cent (which is exactly one third) of a number is 4, the number will be three times 4, or 12.

Here is a practical example whose solution will require just a little more effort. A salesman receives a check for $45.00 representing commission earned. If his commission rate is 15 per cent, how much business does the check represent? Let us see. We know that 15 per cent of the total sales is $45.00. Fifteen per cent means 15 hundredths, and if 15 hundredths equal $45.00, it is easy to see that one hundredth equals one fifteenth of $45.00, or $3.00. (If this is not clear, think of the hundredths in this example as units, and it will be seen instantly that if 15 units equal $45.00, one unit will equal one fifteenth of $45.00.) Knowing that one hundredth equals $3.00, we find without the need for further computation that 100 hundredths of the number we have set out to compute equal 100 times $3.00, or $300.00.

The reader has doubtless noticed that whereas in the illustrations in the first paragraph we reduced 20 per cent ($\frac{20}{100}$) to a number with the lowest common denominator, namely, $\frac{1}{5}$, and $33\frac{1}{3}$ per cent likewise to a number with the lowest common denominator, namely, $\frac{1}{3}$, in the solution to the problem in the succeeding paragraph we did not trouble to reduce 15 per cent ($\frac{15}{100}$) to $\frac{3}{20}$. The reason will be immediately obvious when it is observed that 15 is divisible into $45.00 exactly three times, and that it requires less effort to divide 15 into $45.00 and multiply the result ($3.00) by 100, in order to find the value of 100 hundredths, than to reduce $\frac{15}{100}$ to $\frac{3}{20}$, divide $45.00 by 3 to find the value of $\frac{1}{20}$, and then—in order to find the value of 20 twentieths—to multiply the result ($15.00) by 20.

Example 1: If 17% of a number is $34.00, what is the number?

Solution: $\frac{17}{100}$ of the number is $34.00.

Therefore $\frac{1}{100}$ (which is $\frac{1}{17}$ of $\frac{17}{100}$) of the number equals $\frac{1}{17}$ of $34.00, or $2.00.

If $\frac{1}{100}$ equals $2.00, 100 hundredths will equal 100 times $2.00, or $200.00.

Our number, therefore, is $200.00.

Example 2: If 24% of a value is $78.24, what is the value?

Solution: $\frac{24}{100}$ is equivalent to $\frac{6}{25}$.

If $\frac{6}{25}$ of a value is $78.24, $\frac{1}{25}$ (which is $\frac{1}{6}$ of $\frac{6}{25}$) of the value equals $\frac{1}{6}$ of $78.24, or $13.04.

If $\frac{1}{25}$ equals $13.04, $\frac{25}{25}$ will equal 25 times $13.04, or $326.00.

100% of the value, therefore, is $326.00.

Per-cent rates that contain a fraction and are not aliquot parts of 100 can be handled with equal facility, as will be seen in Example 3.

Example 3: Of what amount does $36\frac{1}{4}$% equal $17.30?

Solution: $36\frac{1}{4}$%, or $\dfrac{36\frac{1}{4}}{100}$, may also be written as $\dfrac{36.25}{100}$. As in the previous illustration, let us divide the fractional value $17.30 by the per-cent rate 36.25 in order to obtain the value of 1%. It is seen at a glance that 5 cancels into each number. So to simplify the process of dividing by 36.25, let us divide each number by 5; thus $17.30 is reduced to $3.46, and 36.25 is reduced to 7.25.

Our problem now is to divide $3.46 by 7.25 to find the value of 1% and then to multiply the result by 100 to find the value of the number.

We now see that in dividing $3.46 by 7.25 the answer might run into three or four figures after the decimal point, so to simplify the computation still further, let us multiply *first* and *then* divide, instead of dividing first and then multiplying as we did in the other illustrations.

$3.46 multiplied by 100 equals $346.00

$346.00 divided by 7.25 equals $47.72.

The value of our number, therefore, is $47.72.

The same technique can be used for finding the value of a number when a fraction, instead of a per cent, of it is known.

Example 4: Three nineteenths of a number equals $4.29.   Find the number.

Solution: $\frac{3}{19}$ of the number is $4.29.

Therefore $\frac{1}{19}$ (which is $\frac{1}{3}$ of $\frac{3}{19}$) of the number equals $\frac{1}{3}$ of $4.29, or $1.43.
If $\frac{1}{19}$ equals $1.43, $\frac{19}{19}$ will equal 19 times $1.43, or $27.17.
Our number, then, is $27.17.

Example 5: Four ninths of what number equals 0.64?

Solution: $\frac{4}{9}$ of the number is 0.64.

Therefore $\frac{1}{9}$ (which is $\frac{1}{4}$ of $\frac{4}{9}$) of the number equals $\frac{1}{4}$ of 0.64, or 0.16.
If $\frac{1}{9}$ equals 0.16, $\frac{9}{9}$ will equal 9 times 0.16, or 1.44.
The number, therefore, is 1.44.

PROBLEMS

1. It occurs to a businessman away from his office that he might not be carrying sufficient fire insurance on his property.   He remembers that the insurance rate is 23 cents per $100 valuation, and that the amount of the one-year premium just paid is $52.90, but does not remember the amount for which the property is insured.   If you were in a similar dilemma how would you determine the amount of insurance carried on the property?
Ans. Divide $52.90 by .23, and multiply the quotient by 100.
★ 2. Sixty cubic feet of water occupy 40% of a tank's capacity.   What is the volume of the unoccupied space in the tank?   *Ans.* 90 cubic feet.
3. A baker finds that 3 ounces of a butter-flavor sample produce the desired effect if used with 225 pounds of shortening.   Estimate the amount of shortening that could be flavored to the baker's satisfaction with the contents of a 16-ounce bottle of the product.   *Ans.* 1200 pounds.
★ 4. If 7 gallons of an asphalt protective coating will cover 28% of an area to be treated, how many gallons will be needed to cover the entire area?   *Ans.* 25 gallons.
★ 5. A prospective purchaser of property reads an advertisement inserted by an agent whose custom the reader knows it to be to request a

cash payment of 15% of the price asked. The advertisement states that the amount of the cash payment is $1200.00. What is the asked price of the property?　　　　　　　　　　　　　　　*Ans.* $8000.00.

6. If 648 cubic inches of aluminum liquid weigh 57 pounds, how much would the weight of a cubic foot of this element be? (Hint: 648 cubic inches is equivalent to $37\frac{1}{2}$% of a cubic foot.)　*Ans.* 152 pounds.

★ **7.** The total of the discount column of a Cash Receipts Book shows that in a typical month customers deducted cash discounts to the extent of $127.00. If the concern's cash discount rate is 2% and if each remittor took advantage of the cash discount and made no other deduction of any kind, what would the approximate total be of the sums entered in the Accounts Receivable column in the cash book for the month under discussion? (Hint: The amounts entered in the Accounts Receivable column are the amounts to be credited to the accounts—that is, they include the discounts deducted; in other words, each amount represents the sum of the actual amount remitted plus the amount of discount deducted.)

Ans. $6350.00.

★ **8.** An operator of a fruit and vegetable market finds that for one reason or another $16\frac{2}{3}$% of the apples he buys decays and becomes unfit for sale. If in one week he accumulates 3 bushels of decayed apples, approximately how many bushels of this fruit were sold in that time? (Hint: Only the difference between 100% of the quantity purchased and $16\frac{2}{3}$% could be sold.)　　　　　　　　　*Ans.* 15 bushels.

★ **9.** In the last 4 months of 1945 the average monthly production of steel ingots was $85\frac{5}{7}$% of the average monthly production in the first 8 months. If the monthly average for the period of September to December was 6 million tons, what was the average monthly production of steel ingots for the period of January to August? (Hint: $85\frac{5}{7}$% equals $\frac{6}{7}$.)

Ans. 7 million tons.

10. When water freezes, its volume increases by $8\frac{1}{2}$%. Estimate the space an amount of water will occupy if when frozen its volume is 1085 cubic feet. (Hint: 1085 cubic feet represents $\dfrac{108\frac{1}{2}}{100}$ or $\dfrac{217}{200}$ of the space occupied by the water.)　　　　　　　　　*Ans.* 1000 cubic feet.

57. Quick Ways to Determine the Per-Cent Equivalent of Any Fractional Part of the Pound Sterling. It is a comparatively simple matter to convert a fractional part of the pound sterling to its per-cent equivalent. There are twenty shillings to the pound. A shilling, therefore, is $\frac{1}{20}$ of a pound. And since $\frac{1}{20}$ is 5 per cent, any number of shillings can be converted to the per-cent equivalent of a pound simply by multiplying by 5. Thus 7 shillings equals 35 per cent; 11 shillings, 55 per cent; and so on.

There are twelve pennies, or pence, to the pound. Having noted that one shilling equals 5 per cent of a pound, it is easy to see that the amount of 6 pence (half a shilling) equals $2\frac{1}{2}$ per cent of a pound; that 3 pence represents $1\frac{1}{4}$ per cent; 9 pence, $3\frac{3}{4}$ per cent; and so on.

Under the breakdown method of multiplication (Chapter II) this method of determining the per-cent equivalent of any fractional part of the pound sterling is sure and simple. Here are some examples: Convert the following amounts of British currency to per-cent equivalents of the pound sterling: (a) 7 shillings and 6 pence; (b) 4 shillings and 9 pence; (c) 11 shillings and 3 pence.

$$
\begin{array}{lll}
\text{(a)} & 7 \text{ shillings (7 times } 5\%) & = 35\% \\
& 6 \text{ pence } (\tfrac{1}{2} \text{ of } 5\%) & = 2\tfrac{1}{2}\% \\
\hline
& 7 \text{ shillings and 6 pence} & = 37\tfrac{1}{2}\% \\
\\
\text{(b)} & 4 \text{ shillings (4 times } 5\%) & = 20\% \\
& 9 \text{ pence } (\tfrac{3}{4} \text{ of } 5\%) & = 3\tfrac{3}{4}\% \\
\hline
& 4 \text{ shillings and 9 pence} & = 23\tfrac{3}{4}\% \\
\\
\text{(c)} & 11 \text{ shillings (11 times } 5\%) & = 55\% \\
& 3 \text{ pence } (\tfrac{1}{4} \text{ of } 5\%) & = 1\tfrac{1}{4}\% \\
\hline
& 11 \text{ shillings and 3 pence} & = 56\tfrac{1}{4}\%
\end{array}
$$

The parts of a shilling represented by 3, 6 and 9 pence are easiest to work with, since they are equivalent, respectively, to $\frac{1}{4}$, $\frac{1}{2}$ and $\frac{3}{4}$ of 5 per cent. However, parts of the shilling, like 1, 2, 4, 5, 7, 8, 10 and 11 pence, can also be converted very easily. Thus since a shilling equals 5 per cent of a pound, 1 penny, which is $\frac{1}{12}$ of a shilling, equals $\frac{1}{12}$ of 5 per cent, or .417 per cent; 2 pence, equivalent to $\frac{1}{6}$ of a shilling, equals .833 per cent. And so on.

Here the reader should be cautioned. Although it is correct to consider 1 penny as .417 per cent of a pound, it would be incorrect to compute the per-cent equivalent of, say, 16 shillings and 8 pence, by multiplying 200 (the number of pence in 16 shillings and 8 pence) by .417, for .417 as the per-cent equivalent of a pound is correct only to the third decimal place. The per-cent equivalent of a substantially large part of a pound, such as the amount discussed in this paragraph, should be computed as follows:

$$16 \text{ shillings } (16 \text{ times } 5\%) = 80\%$$
$$6 \text{ pence } (\tfrac{1}{2} \text{ of } 5\%) \qquad = \ 2.5\%$$
$$2 \text{ pence } (\tfrac{1}{3} \text{ of } 2.5\%) \qquad = \ .83\%$$

$$16 \text{ shillings and 8 pence } \ = 83.33\% \text{ or } 83\tfrac{1}{3}\%.$$

There is another method for computing the per-cent equivalent of a fractional part of the pound sterling which may be preferred by some. It includes the entire amount in a single operation, and the procedure is easy to remember. The entire amount is converted to pence, and this is done simply by multiplying the number of shillings by 12 and adding the pence to the result. The total is then shown as the numerator of a fraction whose denominator is 240—240 being the number of pence in a pound.

Thus 6 shillings and 4 pence would be shown as $\frac{76}{240}$.

The next step is to eliminate the zero in 240, and this is done by dividing numerator and denominator by 10. So that $\frac{76}{240}$ becomes $\frac{7.6}{24}$. Now 24 as a denominator is an interesting number. Remembering that $\frac{1}{12}$ is the equivalent of $8\frac{1}{3}$ per cent, it is easy to see that if we divide $8\frac{1}{3}$ by 2 the per-cent equivalent of $\frac{1}{24}$ is obtained. Dividing $8\frac{1}{3}$ by 2 gives us $4\frac{1}{6}$. All we need do now is multiply the numerator by $4\frac{1}{6}$ and show the result as the per-cent equivalent.

The fraction $\frac{7.6}{24}$ thus becomes 7.6 times $4\frac{1}{6}$, which equals 31.67, and we know that 6 shillings and 4 pence represents 31.67 per cent of a pound.

PROBLEMS

Compute by the 5 per cent method the per-cent equivalents of the pound sterling of the following amounts. (Hint: "s." means shilling or shillings, and "d." stands for penny or pence.)

* **1.** 15s. 0d.   *Ans.* 75%.
* **2.** 3s. 6d.   *Ans.* $17\frac{1}{2}$%.
* **3.** 8s. 3d.   *Ans.* $41\frac{1}{4}$%.
* **4.** 12s. 9d.   *Ans.* $63\frac{3}{4}$%.
* **5.** 17s. 2d.   *Ans.* 85.83 or $85\frac{5}{6}$%.
* **6.** 18s. 11d.   *Ans.* 94.58 or $94\frac{7}{12}$%.

Compute the per-cent equivalents of the pound sterling of the following amounts by the fractional method, using 240 as the denominator.

7. 3s. 0d.   *Ans.* 15%.
8. 4s. 6d.   *Ans.* $22\frac{1}{2}$%.
9. 6s. 8d.   *Ans.* $33\frac{1}{3}$%.
10. 9s. 4d.   *Ans.* $46\frac{2}{3}$%.
11. 13s. 10d.   *Ans.* $69\frac{1}{6}$%.
12. 16s. 2d.   *Ans.* $80\frac{5}{6}$%.

58. How to Quickly Approximate Per-Cent Rates Without the Use of Pencil and Paper. It is frequently required to compare figures on a percentage basis. A businessman may, for instance, want to compare total overhead expenses with total sales, or the total sales of one department with that of another. Or an incongruity in the payrolls may make it desirable to compare the total office payroll with the total factory payroll.

Let us take a simple example in which the ratio is 37 to 298, figures which can stand for any number of things. Thirty-seven brings to mind the fraction $37\frac{1}{2}$, which is $\frac{3}{8}$ of 100; and 298 is so near to 300 that, for many practical purposes, it may be safely regarded as 300. Our ratio, then, becomes $37\frac{1}{2}$ to 300, which, written as a fraction, is $\dfrac{37\frac{1}{2}}{300}$. Since our objective is to determine the rate per cent, it is now necessary to change the denominator to 100, and this can be readily accomplished by reducing it (300) to one third of itself. In order to retain the value of the ratio, the numerator ($37\frac{1}{2}$) must now be reduced to one third of itself too. The ratio now is $12\frac{1}{2}$ to 100, and it is safe to assume that in the ratio 37 to 298 the first number is approximately $12\frac{1}{2}$ per cent of the latter.

The average weekly office payroll of a small manufacturer is $219.00, and the average weekly factory payroll $746.00. How much per cent of the factory payroll is the office payroll?　The ratio is 219 to 746, which, stated in fractional form, is $\frac{219}{746}$.　Since it is required to have a denominator of 100, let us increase the unit digit in each number to 10, changing 219 to 220 and 746 to 750. Now canceling the zero at the end of each number reduces the ratio to $\frac{22}{75}$.　With 75 as the denominator we need but add to this number one third of itself to bring it up to 100.　To retain the equality of the ratio we must likewise add to 22 one third of itself. One third of 22 equals $7\frac{1}{3}$; 22 plus $7\frac{1}{3}$ equals $29\frac{1}{3}$.　It is clear, therefore, that for all practical purposes the manufacturer's office payroll is approximately 29 per cent of his factory payroll.

Let us take an example from some business statistics.　The extent of retail advertising in January, 1945, was 52,841,000 lines. In October, 1945, the total number of lines was 75,072,000.　Approximately what per cent of the number of lines used in October was used in January?

The number 841,000 in the January total is well over $\frac{3}{4}$ of a million, so let us change the total from 52,841,000 to the round figure of 53 million.　In the October total, 72,000 is such a small fraction of a million that, for purposes of approximate computation, it may be disregarded; so we will change 75,072,000 to 75 million.　Our ratio now is 53 to 75, or $\frac{53}{75}$.

Here, as in the preceding illustration, our denominator is 75 and, as we have seen, the task of changing this number to 100 is quite simple—we simply add to 75 one third of itself.　Likewise we add to 53 one third of itself.　One third of 53 is $17\frac{2}{3}$; 53 plus $17\frac{2}{3}$ equals $70\frac{2}{3}$.　We may assume, therefore, that the total number of lines of retail advertising used in January, 1945, was approximately 71 per cent of the total used in October, 1945.

A news item states that the factory production of butter in the United States in June, 1946, was 68,995,000 pounds, compared with a total production of 155,905,000 pounds in July, 1945.　It is required to compare on a per-cent basis the January, 1946, figure with that of July, 1945.

Let us begin by canceling the three zeros at the end of each total, changing the figures to 68,995 and 155,905, respectively. Now 995 in the former figure is so near to 1000 that it would be

perfectly safe, for our purposes, to change the total to the round
figure of 69,000. In the other figure, 905 too is very near to 1000,
so let us also change this total, making it 156,000. We can now
eliminate another three zeros from each number, which leaves us
with the ratio 69 to 156, or $\frac{69}{156}$.

In order to find the rate per cent we must reduce the denominator of the ratio to 100. Now 156 is very near to 150, and 150 is
exactly three halves of 100, so we will reduce 156 to 100, the reduction being approximately by one third. To retain the equality of
the ratio we must likewise reduce the numerator (69) by one
third. One third of 69 equals 23, and 69 minus 23 equals 46.
Remembering that we reduced 156 by slightly *more* than one
third, we may safely assume that the factory production of butter
in January, 1946, was approximately a little over 46 per cent of
the production in July, 1945.

Problems

* **1.** An employee whose weekly salary is $48.50 asks for an increase
of $50.00 a month. By approximately how much per cent of his present
earnings does he wish his weekly salary increased?

Ans. Approximately 25%.

2. A speculator purchased a house for $38,200 and sold it for $48,750.
Approximately how much per-cent profit did he make on his investment?

Ans. Approximately 28%.

* **3.** Improvements in lighting so stepped up a company's production
that girls who had previously assembled only 21 units per day now
assembled 27½. By approximately how much per cent was production
increased?   *Ans.* Approximately 30%.

* **4.** A dealer increased the price of a rug from $99.50 to $125.75. By
approximately what rate per cent did he raise the price?

Ans. Approximately 26%.

* **5.** In 1944 there were 1,924,714 passenger vehicles and 298,376
commercial vehicles in New York State. Compute the approximate
number of commercial vehicles for each 100 passenger vehicles.

Ans. Approximately 15.

* **6.** The net profit of a dry goods store for the year in a farm community
in Michigan is $8045. If the sales volume was $79,910, approximately
how much per-cent profit was made on the sales?

Ans. Approximately 10%.

★ **7.** A firm's net profit in 1946 was $23,815. For the year 1945 the profit was $25,172. Approximately how much per cent of the profit for 1945 does the profit for 1946 constitute?   *Ans.* Approximately 96%.

★ **8.** In May, 1946, purchases of life insurance in the United States amounted to $1,956,796,000. In May of the previous year, the purchases amounted to $1,267,474,000. Approximately what per cent is the May, 1945, figure of the May, 1946, figure?   *Ans.* Approximately 63%.

★ **9.** In April, 1945, a total of 143,292 red cedar shingle squares was imported from British Columbia. The total imported in April, 1946, was 149,887. What per cent, approximately, is the smaller figure of the larger?   *Ans.* Approximately 95%.

★ **10.** The cash receipts of farmers in 1945 amounted to more than $20,000,000,000. For the first 6 months in 1946 their receipts totaled $8,710,000,000. Assume that the farmers' receipts for the first 6 months in 1945 equaled half the total for the year. Estimate to the nearest unit how much per cent of the January-to-June 1945 receipts is represented by the January-to-June 1946 receipts.   *Ans.* 87%.

CHAPTER VIII

PREPARING AND CHECKING BILLS

Since billings are the bloodstream of every business enterprise, it will not be amiss to consider a phase of business mathematics in which much time and effort can be saved by group computation.

59. The Shortest Way of Preparing a Bill When Several Items Are Subject to the Same Discount. Let us suppose we are in the hardware business and wanted to prepare a bill to cover the following sale:

$$13 \text{ gross Screws @ .54 per gross less } 57\tfrac{1}{2}\%$$
$$18 \text{ gross Screws @ .46 per gross less } 57\tfrac{1}{2}\%$$
$$10 \text{ gross Screws @ .58 per gross less } 57\tfrac{1}{2}\%$$

Should we compute the net amount of each item individually? Let us see. The discount is the same in each instance; therefore, it is unnecessary to do so. All we need do is compute the total for each item without regard to the discount, add the totals, and deduct $57\tfrac{1}{2}$ per cent, thus:

$$
\begin{aligned}
13 \text{ gross @ .54 per gross} &= \$\ 7.02 \\
18 \text{ gross @ .46 per gross} &= \ \ \ 8.28 \\
10 \text{ gross @ .58 per gross} &= \ \ \ \underline{5.80} \\
&\ \ \ \ \ \$21.10 \\
-57\tfrac{1}{2}\% \ * \ &= \ \ \ \underline{12.13} \\
&\ \ \ \$\ 8.97
\end{aligned}
$$

In the foregoing illustration the actual amount of the discount is shown. Many business houses, however, do not show the amount of the discount—the discount rate only, followed by the net amount, is indicated, thus:

$$\$21.10$$
$$\text{less } 57\tfrac{1}{2}\% \qquad \$8.97$$

* The reader's attention is directed to Art. 46, Example 6A, for alternative methods of quickly computing the net amount of a sale subject to a discount of $57\tfrac{1}{2}$ per cent.

If, however, a number of items subject to the same rate of discount were followed by a number of items subject to a different rate of discount, then, naturally, two separate extensions should be shown.

Suppose, on the other hand, that two groups of items subject to a discount of, let us say, 60 per cent were separated by a group of items subject to $57\frac{1}{2}$ per cent. In that event three separate extensions should be shown: one for the first group of 60 per cent items, one for the group of $57\frac{1}{2}$ per cent items, and one for the last group of 60 per cent items.

However, if we were the recipient of such an invoice and wished to check the extensions, we would not need to calculate separately the discount on each of the two groups of 60 per cent items; we should compute and add the gross totals of the two groups, and arrive at the net amount in one calculation. The result should equal the sum of the two net amounts shown on the invoice.

Following is an illustration of the body of an invoice showing the net totals of three groups of items as discussed in the preceding paragraphs.

8 gross	@ 1.23 per gross less 60%	$ 9.84		
11 gross	@ .28 per gross less 60%	3.08		
5 gross	@ 2.10 per gross less 60%	10.50		
6 gross	@ 1.76 per gross less 60%	10.56		
		$33.98 less 60%		$13.59
9 gross	@ 1.60 per gross less $57\frac{1}{2}$%	$14.40		
4 gross	@ .85 per gross less $57\frac{1}{2}$%	3.40		
$2\frac{1}{2}$ gross	@ .90 per gross less $57\frac{1}{2}$%	2.25		
		$20.05 less $57\frac{1}{2}$%		$8.52
3 gross	@ 2.10 per gross less 60%	$ 6.30		
4 gross	@ 1.40 per gross less 60%	5.60		
3 gross	@ 2.00 per gross less 60%	6.00		
6 gross	@ 3.20 per gross less 60%	19.20		
2 gross	@ 3.00 per gross less 60%	6.00		
		$43.10 less 60%		$17.24
				$39.35

Here is a practical bit of advice: Whenever possible, arrange the items to be billed on one invoice so that those on which the same discount is allowable are grouped together.   This will reduce the number of discount computations, as shown in the following demonstration.

Example: A clerk takes an order on the telephone, copying the items in the sequence in which they are given to him, as follows:

> 5 Paper Cutting Boards @ $6.75 each
> $2\frac{1}{2}$ gross $9'' \times 12\frac{1}{2}''$ Clip Boards @ $0.50 each
> 6 doz. 1-oz. bottles Correction Fluid @ $0.30 each
> 2 doz. Pencil Sharpeners @ $2.25 each
> 40 lb. Black Mimeograph Ink @ $2.10 lb.

The quantity discounts to which the customer is entitled are, respectively, $33\frac{1}{3}\%$, 20%, 20%, $33\frac{1}{3}\%$, and 20%.   If the entire order were invoiced at one time, how should the bill be made out?

Solution: The items subject to the same discount should be grouped together, in this manner:

5 paper Cutting Boards	@ $6.75 ea	$33.75
2 doz. Pencil Sharpeners	@ 2.25 ea	54.00
		———
		$87.75
	less $33\frac{1}{3}\%$	$58.50
$2\frac{1}{2}$ gross $9'' \times 12\frac{1}{2}''$ Clip Boards	@ $0.50 ea	$180.00
6 doz. 1-oz. bottles Correction Fluid	@ .30 ea	21.60
40 lb. Black Mimeograph Ink	@ 2.10 lb	84.00
		———
		$285.60
	less 20%	228.48
		———
		$286.98

This method of showing one net amount for a group of as many items as possible is recommended only when it is believed that the customer will not mind it.   Where the list price of an item runs into a sizable figure this practice is not advisable, for in such instances the customer might wish to see the net cost of the item in the invoice, regardless of how many other products are subject to the same discount.

PROBLEMS

Show how you would compute with a minimum of pencil-and-paper work the net value of each of the following shipments.

1. 3 cases of a sterilizing agent at $18.00 per case less 25%.
   6 drums of a sterilizing agent at $24.00 per drum less 25%.

   Ans. $148.50.

2. 20 cases Chesterfield cigarettes (200,000) at $7.38 per thousand, less 10% and 1%.
   15 cases Pall Mall cigarettes (150,000) at $7.38 per thousand, less 10% and 1%.
   2500 La Magnita cigars at $115.00 per thousand, less 8% and 2%.
   2600 Haddon Hall cigars at $138.00 per thousand, less 8% and 2%.

   Ans. $2884.16.

3. 10 A-12 rubber stamps at 45 cents each less 40%
   24 A-17 rubber stamps at 30 cents each less 50%
   8 B-4 rubber stamps at 65 cents each less 40%
   16 A-25 rubber stamps at 55 cents each less 50%

   Ans. $13.82.

4. 9 doz. glass miniature dogs at $3.00 doz. less 10%
   3 doz. glass miniature dogs (large) at $4.50 doz. less 5%
   6 doz. glass miniature ships at $5.00 doz. less 10%
   4 doz. glass miniature cows at $3.75 doz. less 5%

   Ans. $78.37.

5. 2 glass domes at $7.00 each less 20%
   3 20-watt fluorescent lamps at $0.75 each less 25%
   3 doz. #16 files at $4.30 doz. less 20%
   12 doz. #13 files at $3.70 doz. less 25%

   Ans. $56.51.

6. 12 boxes Ascorbic Acid (vitamin C) at $2.10 box less $33\frac{1}{3}$%
   3 kilograms Niacin (Nicotinic Acid U.S.P.) at $8.50 per kilogram less 20%
   6 boxes Cecalmin (Vitamin C and Calcium Gluconate) at $0.65 per box less $33\frac{1}{3}$%
   3 bottles Riboflavin U.S.P. at $25.00 each less 20%

   Ans. $99.80.

60. The Shortest Way of Computing or Checking the Amount of a Bill in Which the Prices Are Different, but the Quantities Are Alike. Here is a bill that recently came to the author's attention:

$$
\begin{array}{rl}
27 \ @ \ 2.40 & \quad 64.80 \\
27 \ @ \ 1.90 & \quad 51.30 \\
27 \ @ \ 3.45 & \quad 93.15 \\
27 \ @ \ 2.20 & \quad 59.40 \\
27 \ @ \ 4.26 & \quad 115.02 \\
\end{array}
$$

$$383.67$$

Since all the quantities are alike, it is unnecessary to check each extension separately. It is only necessary to add the unit prices and multiply the total by the number representing the quantity of each item, the number in this instance being 27. The sum of the unit prices is $14.21, which, multiplied by 27, gives us $383.67. Instead of five separate computations and an operation in addition, we have but one simple operation in addition and one operation in multiplication.

It not infrequently happens that in a bill for many different items, all quantities but one or two are alike, and the unlike quantities are a multiple of the quantity common to the rest of the items. In that event the process of checking the extensions is as simple as when all the quantities are alike.

Take, for instance, the following example in which all the quantities but one are alike:

$$
\begin{array}{rl}
37 \ @ & 2.00 \\
37 \ @ & 1.80 \\
37 \ @ & .90 \\
37 \ @ & 4.15 \\
74 \ @ & 2.35 \\
37 \ @ & .74 \\
37 \ @ & .36 \\
\end{array}
$$

Notice that the single different quantity, 74, is exactly double the quantity common to the rest of the items. So here is what we do: we imagine that instead of having one item reading 74 @ $2.35, we have two items, each reading 37 @ $2.35. Now we add the amounts in the price column, remembering to add $2.35 twice. The total is $14.65. Multiplying this by 37 we arrive at the answer, $542.05, and this is the total which the bill should show.

Suppose, however, that the unlike quantity were 39 instead of 74. In that case we should make our computation just as we would if each quantity were 37, and add to the total the product of twice $2.35—2 being the difference between 39 and 37. The computation would be as follows:

$$37 \text{ times } \$12.30 * = \$455.10$$
$$2 \text{ times } \$2.35 \quad = \quad 4.70$$
$$\overline{}$$
$$\$459.80$$

Example: What is the amount of a purchase consisting of the following:

> 3 pounds of butter at 89 cents per pound
> 3 loaves of bread at 14 cents each
> 3 pounds of oranges at 22 cents per pound

Solution: The sum of 89 cents plus 14 cents plus 22 cents is $1.25. And 3 times $1.25 is $3.75.

Problems

★ **1.** Four men whose wage rates, respectively, are $1.40, $1.00, $1.55 and $1.05 per hour put in a total of 16 hours each on a job. Estimate in a single computation the amount of their combined earnings.

Ans. $80.00 (*Art. 1-a*)

★ **2.** It is the custom of a merchant to mail a new price list monthly to his 2500 customers. If his costs per thousand price lists over a period of three months were, respectively, $6.60, $6.30 and $7.10, what did the printer's bills for the 7500 price lists amount to? *Ans.* $50.00.

★ **3.** A formula calls for the mixing in equal proportion by weight of five different ingredients. The ingredients cost, respectively, 25 cents, 31 cents, 19 cents, 18 cents and 27 cents per pound. In order to produce the desired volume of the product an order is issued for 40 pounds of each

---

*$12.30 is the total of the figures in the price column.

ingredient. Find in a single computation the amount of the purchase.
Ans. $48.00.

4. A manufacturer ships by express five sample packages, each weighing $41\frac{1}{2}$ pounds, to each of four branch offices. One branch office is in a zone to which the express rate of 12.28 cents per pound applies; another is in a zone in which the rate is 30.70 cents per pound; the rate in a third zone is 46.05 cents; and in the zone of the fourth branch office the rate is 55.26 cents. Estimate the total cost of shipping the 20 packages, without multiplying by any other digit than 2. (Since the weight of each package exceeds 41 pounds, it should be considered as 42 pounds.) *Ans.* $303.01.

★ **5.** A grocer sells 40 pounds of oleomargarine costing him $0.165 per pound, and 40 pounds of American Cheddar cheese which cost him $0.295 per pound. What is his combined total cost of the quantities sold of these products? *Ans.* $18.40. (*Art. 25*)

★ **6.** Estimate the cost of the following purchase of botanical drugs:

> 200 lb. powdered Calamine   at 37 cents per lb.
> 200 lb. whole Almond Shells at 16 cents per lb.
> 400 lb. Dragon's Blood   at 94 cents per lb.

(Hint: The product of 400 times 94 cents is equivalent to the product of 200 times $1.88.) *Ans.* $482.00.

61. The Shortest Way of Computing or Checking the Amount of a Bill in Which the Prices Are Alike, but the Quantities Are Different. In practically every business establishment occasions arise when a computation to be made resembles another computation made only a moment or so ago.

On an invoice before me, for instance, are two charges:

> 7 boxes @ .74
> 17 boxes @ .74

In both instances the price per box is the same; there is a difference only in the quantity—the quantity in the second item is exactly 10 units greater than the quantity in the first item.

Obviously, then, it would be unnecessary to compute the second item as a separate or entirely new problem. It is seen at a glance that the second extension will exceed the first extension by the product of 10 times 74 cents. So that all we need do is add $7.40

to the amount of the first extension. The computation would be
as follows:

$$7 \text{ boxes @ } .74 \qquad\qquad\qquad = \$ \; 5.18$$
$$17 \text{ boxes @ } .74 \; (\$7.40 \text{ plus } \$5.18) = \;\; 12.58$$

This technique can be applied with equally good effect—and
particularly when the computation is to be made mentally—
when there is a variation in one of the prices, as in the following
illustration:

Example: Estimate mentally the total cost of the following
lengths of fabric: 8 yards at $3.00, 3 yards at $3.00, 7 yards at
$6.00, and 5 yards at $3.00.

Solution: Seven yards at $6.00 a yard is equivalent to 14 yards
         at $3.00 a yard. Counting the 7, therefore, as 14,
         our problem, restated, becomes 30 yards at $3.00,
         and we know instantly that the answer is $90.00.

PROBLEMS

1. A dealer in typewriter supplies orders 2 gross of ribbons at $31.68
per gross. Due to a shortage of raw materials the manufacturer finds it
necessary to deliver in small quantities, and he issues an invoice to cover
the first three deliveries, as follows:

8 doz. ribbons delivered Oct. 21 @ $31.68 gross	$21.12
6 doz. ribbons delivered Nov. 8 @ 31.68 gross	15.84
4 doz. ribbons delivered Nov. 16 @ 31.68 gross	10.56
	————
	$47.52

Check the correctness of the total by a single computation in addition.
                    Ans. $1\frac{1}{2}$ gross at $31.68 per gross = $47.52.

★ **2.** A buyer purchases for the account of three principals the following
quantities of handbags, all at $38.00 per dozen: 8 dozen, 4 dozen, and 3
dozen. If his commission is 10% of the amount of the purchase, how
much commission will he have earned on the three transactions?
                              Ans. $57.00. (*Art. 1-b*)

★ **3.** A shipping company purchases for its main offices six 1-inch
20-prong Visible Binders, size $15\frac{1}{2}'' \times 10\frac{1}{2}''$, at $11.50 each, and eight

$1\frac{1}{2}$-inch 14-prong binders of the same type, size $14'' \times 7\frac{5}{8}''$, also at $11.50 each. Compute mentally the total cost of the 14 binders.

Ans. $161.00. (*Art. 1-f*)

★ **4.** A contractor hires four men to repair the wood floors of a factory building. The men work steadily 8 hours a day and complete the repairs in five days. Three are paid $1.25 an hour; the fourth receives $1.55 an hour. Compute mentally the total labor cost. (Hint: Compute the total for all four men on the basis of $1.25 an hour, then add the product of 40 times the difference between $1.55 and $1.25.)   *Ans.* $212.00.

★ **5.** The manufacturer of a time-recording machine receives the following orders:

3 machines at $125.00 each
2 machines at $129.00 each
4 machines at $125.00 each
3 machines at $129.00 each
4 machines at $125.00 each

Estimate mentally the total amount of business represented by the five orders. (Hint: Compute 16 times $125.00 and add 5 times $4.00.)

Ans. $2020.00.

★ **6.** An auctioneer disposes of a lot of chairs to six buyers, as follows:

8 chairs at $7.75 each
10 chairs at $8.25 each
9 chairs at $7.75 each
5 chairs at $7.75 each
6 chairs at $8.25 each
2 chairs at $8.25 each

Compute the total amount received for the 40 chairs. (Hint: Find the value of 40 chairs at $7.75, and add to the result the product of 18 times the difference between $8.25 and $7.75.)   *Ans.* $319.00.

CHAPTER IX

DEALING WITH PARTS OF THE GROSS, THE TON, AND THE YARD

In Chapter II, the breakdown method of multiplication was treated more or less as an introduction to the subjects that followed. In this chapter we will see how the breakdown method can be used to good advantage in solving problems which deal with the dozen and the gross; with ounces, pounds and tons; and inches, feet and yards.

Because of the frequency with which problems involving these units occur in many different industries, this chapter is of special significance. If, in the course of his business activities, the reader has frequent occasion to solve problems concerned with parts of the gross, he is urged to pay particular attention to Art. 64, in which is discussed a not very commonly known but extremely useful short-cut.

62. How to Compute Values When the Price Given Is per Dozen, and the Quantity Is Stated in Units. Most of us would have no difficulty determining how much was due the fruiterer upon a purchase of three oranges whose price was six for 35 cents. We would know that the amount was half of 35 cents, or 18 cents.

It is simple enough. Yet many individuals with an aptitude for figures forget the simplicity of such computations when confronted by a problem like 38 at $2.90 a dozen. Many experienced office workers go to the trouble, in computing problems of this nature, of ascertaining the price per unit and multiplying that figure by the quantity when the simpler thing to do would be to use the breakdown method, as follows:

$$36 \text{ at } \$2.90 \text{ a dozen (3 times } \$2.90) = \$8.70$$
$$2 \text{ } (\tfrac{1}{6} \text{ of } \$2.90) \qquad\qquad\qquad = \quad .48$$

$$38 \text{ at } \$2.90 \text{ per dozen} \qquad\qquad = \$9.18$$

If the quantity were 35 instead of 38, the solution would be just as rapid:

$$36 \text{ at } \$2.90 \text{ a dozen (3 times } \$2.90) = \$8.70$$
$$-\ 1\ (\tfrac{1}{12} \text{ of } \$2.90) \qquad\qquad\qquad = \quad .24$$

$$35 \text{ at } \$2.90 \text{ per dozen} \qquad\qquad = \$8.46$$

Let us take a problem with a larger quantity: 291 at $4.32 a dozen. Note that 291 equals $24\tfrac{3}{12}$ dozen.

$$20 \text{ dozen at } \$4.32 \text{ a dozen (twice } \$43.20) = \$\ 86.40$$
$$4 \text{ dozen } (\tfrac{1}{5} \text{ of } \$86.40) \qquad\qquad\quad = \quad 17.28$$
$$\tfrac{3}{12} \text{ dozen } (\tfrac{1}{4} \text{ of } \$4.32) \qquad\qquad\quad = \quad 1.08$$

$$24\tfrac{3}{12} \text{ dozen at } \$4.32 \text{ per dozen} \qquad = \$104.76$$

Example: A jeweler sold 34 watch bands at $0.75 each. If he purchased them at $5.50 per dozen, how much gross profit did he make on the 34 bands?

Solution: Seventy-five cents each is equivalent to $9.00 per dozen. The gross profit, therefore, is $3.50 a dozen ($9.00 minus $5.50 equals $3.50). So that on 34 watch bands the gross profit will be the product of $2\tfrac{10}{12}$ times $3.50.

$$3 \text{ times } \$3.50 \qquad\qquad\qquad = \$10.50$$
$$-\ \tfrac{2}{12} \text{ of } \$3.50\ (\tfrac{1}{6} \text{ of } \$3.50) \quad = \quad .58$$

The gross profit on the 34 bands = $\ 9.92

PROBLEMS

1. Estimate the value of 134 rubber balls at $1.10 a dozen.
Ans. $12.28.

2. What is the total cost of 16 seat cushions at the price of $37.80 a dozen? *Ans.* $50.40.

3. A manufacturer ordered 21 pen-and-pencil sets to be presented to his salesmen in appreciation of their efforts. The price of the sets was $58.20 a dozen. What did his generosity cost? *Ans.* $101.85.

4. A sweater manufacturer finds that he can turn out 77 sweaters every hour. His product sells at $15.00 a dozen and he can dispose of his entire production without difficulty. If his plant operates on a 40-hour per week basis, what is the total sales value of his weekly production?

Ans. $3850.00.

5. An inventory record shows a balance on hand of 39 plastic aprons. Compute their worth at the current price of $7.88 per dozen. *Ans.* $25.61.

6. A dealer in men's furnishings finds upon examining a delivery of neckties that 17 of them are defective. If the price at which they were billed is $7.75 a dozen, how much credit will the dealer be entitled to upon the return of the defective ties? *Ans.* $10.98.

63. How to Compute the Value of a Fraction of a Gross, When the Price or Rate Given Is per Gross. If you really enjoy working with figures you will probably find the study of this article a satisfying adventure. When the author first discovered how simple and easy it was to compute quickly any quantity at so much "per gross," he felt, to use the words of the immortal Keats, "like some watcher of the skies, when a new planet swims into his ken."

Let us open this study with a few simple examples.

Example 1: Find the cost of 24 units at $3.00 per gross.

Solution: Twenty-four is exactly two dozen. Since there are 12 dozen in a gross, 24 is exactly one sixth of a gross. One sixth of $3.00 is 50 cents, and that is our answer.

Example 2: Find the cost of 15 units at $4.20 per gross.

Solution: 12 at $4.20 a gross ($\frac{1}{12}$ of $4.20) = $.35
3 ($\frac{1}{4}$ of .35)   = .09
_____

15 units at $4.20 per gross   = $.44

Example 3: Find the cost of 18 units at $7.40 per gross.

Solution: 12 at $7.40 a gross ($\frac{1}{12}$ of $7.40) = $.62
6 ($\frac{1}{2}$ of .62)   = .31
_____

18 units at $7.40 per gross   = $.93

Example 4: Find the cost of 27 units at $6.30 per gross.

Solution: 24 at $6.30 a gross ($\frac{1}{6}$ of $6.30) = $1.05
      3 ($\frac{1}{8}$ of $1.05)   =   .13

---

    27 units at $6.30 per gross   = $1.18

Example 5: Find the cost of 40 units at $5.60 per gross.

Solution: 36 at $5.60 a gross ($\frac{1}{4}$ of $5.60) = $1.40
      4 ($\frac{1}{9}$ of $1.40)   =   .16

---

    40 units at $5.60 per gross   = $1.56

Example 6: Find the cost of 85 units at $16.20 per gross.

Solution: 72 at $16.20 a gross ($\frac{1}{2}$ of $16.20) = $8.10
    12 ($\frac{1}{6}$ of $8.10)   = 1.35
     1 ($\frac{1}{12}$ of $1.35)   =   .11

---

    85 units at $16.20 per gross   = $9.56

The reader's attention is now directed to Table VII which shows how easy it is in computing problems involving the gross and parts of the gross to break down virtually any number of units.

The following illustrations will help toward a more thorough understanding of the breakdown method and its use in solving problems dealing with price per gross.

Example 7: Find the cost of 234 units at $4.26 per gross.

Solution: When the quantity exceeds one gross, find the number of gross by dividing by 144, and make a separate series of calculations for the remainder.

    144 (1 gross) at $4.26 a gross = $4.26
     72 ($\frac{1}{2}$ of $4.26)   = 2.13
     12 ($\frac{1}{6}$ of $2.13)   =   .355
      6 ($\frac{1}{2}$ of .355)   =   .177

---

    234 units at $4.26 per gross   = $6.92

TABLE VII

Aliquot Parts and Near-Aliquot Parts of the Gross

Quantities	Relations to the Gross
12	$12(\frac{1}{12}$ of gross$)$
15	$12 + 3(\frac{1}{4}$ of 12$)$
18	$12 + 6(\frac{1}{2}$ of 12$)$
21	$24(\frac{1}{6}$ of gross$) - 3(\frac{1}{8}$ of 24$)$
24	$24(\frac{1}{6}$ of gross$)$
30	$24 + 6(\frac{1}{4}$ of 24$)$
36	$36(\frac{1}{4}$ of gross$)$
42	$36 + 6(\frac{1}{6}$ of 36$)$
48	$48(\frac{1}{3}$ of gross$)$
54	$48 + 6(\frac{1}{8}$ of 48$)$
60	$72(\frac{1}{2}$ gross$) - 12(\frac{1}{6}$ of 72$)$
72	$72(\frac{1}{2}$ gross$)$
78	$72 + 6(\frac{1}{12}$ of 72$)$
84	$72 + 12(\frac{1}{6}$ of 72$)$
90	$72 + 12(\frac{1}{6}$ of 72$) + 6(\frac{1}{2}$ of 12$)$
96	$72 + 24(\frac{1}{3}$ of 72$)$
102	$72 + 24(\frac{1}{3}$ of 72$) + 6(\frac{1}{4}$ of 24$)$
108	$72 + 36(\frac{1}{2}$ of 72$)$, or $144 - 36(\frac{1}{4}$ of 144$)$
114	$72 + 36(\frac{1}{2}$ of 72$) + 6(\frac{1}{6}$ of 36$)$
120	$144 - 24(\frac{1}{6}$ of 144$)$
126	$144 - 24(\frac{1}{6}$ of 144$) + 6(\frac{1}{4}$ of 24$)$
132	$144 - 12(\frac{1}{12}$ of 144$)$
138	$144 - 6(\frac{1}{2}$ of $\frac{1}{12}$ of 144$)$

Example 8: Find the cost of 630 units at $14.60 per gross.

Solution: 576 (4 gross) at $14.60 a gross = \$58.40

         48 ($\frac{1}{3}$ of \$14.60)   =   4.87

          6 ($\frac{1}{8}$ of \$4.87)   =   .61

630 units at \$14.60 per gross   = \$63.88

When the price per gross is but a small fraction of a dollar and the quantity is a fraction of a gross, the computation can be done mentally with relative ease, as the following illustrations show:

Example 9: Find the cost of 5 dozen at 9 cents per gross.

Solution: Nine cents per gross is $\frac{9}{12}$ cent ($\frac{3}{4}$ cent) per dozen. Five times $\frac{3}{4}$ cent equals $\frac{15}{4}$ cents, which, to the nearest penny, is 4 cents.

Example 10: Find the cost of 4 dozen at 7 cents per gross.

Solution: Four dozen is one third of a gross, and one third of 7 cents, to the nearest penny, equals 2 cents.

Example 11: Find the cost of 50 units at $1.25 per gross.

Solution: 48 at $1.25 a gross ($\frac{1}{3}$ of $1.25)   = $.42
2 times .01 ($1.25 a gross is approximately
    .01 each)   = .02
_____

50 units at $1.25 per gross   = $.44

Often a little imagination eliminates the need for calculation, as evidenced by the following:

Example 12: Find the cost of 20 units at .66 per gross.

Solution: The quantity is so small that, in view of the very low unit price, it may safely be regarded as one seventh of a gross. One seventh of 66 cents equals a little more than 9 cents. Since the quantity is not quite one seventh of a gross, our estimate of 9 cents is pretty accurate.

The use of this technique in finding the value of a fraction of a gross is also helpful in dealing with units of measurement. Since one square foot, for example, is equivalent to 144 square inches, the weight of a fraction of a square foot of any material can be quickly computed by the breakdown method, as shown in Example 13.

Example 13: If the weight of one square foot of steel, 0.22 inches thick, is 8.976 pounds, how much will 81 square inches of steel of this thickness weigh?

Solution: 72 square inches ($\frac{1}{2}$ of 8.976 pounds) = 4.488 pounds
9 square inches ($\frac{1}{8}$ of 4.488 pounds) = .561 pounds

81 square inches   = 5.049 pounds

PROBLEMS

1. A photographer purchased two gross of 8″ × 10″ photo enlarging papers at $7.00 per gross sheets. If he used 98 sheets, what is the value of the quantity that remained?   *Ans.* $9.23.

2. A dealer in cosmetics receives a shipment of lipsticks in nickel-plated containers which he purchased at $27.40 a gross, and discovers a shortage of 30 containers. How much of a credit may he expect to receive from the seller to cover the missing containers?   *Ans.* $5.71.

3. Compute to the nearest cent the value of 100 $\frac{1}{2}$-inch metal tapping screws at 41 cents per gross.   *Ans.* $0.28.

4. At the price of 95 cents a gross, what is the worth of 120 button molds? (Hint: Subtract the value of 24 molds from the value of 144.)
Ans. $0.79.

5. During the sugar shortage in 1946, the proprietor of a health food store sold in one day 57 one-pound packages of maple sugar at $1.25 each. If his cost was $108.00 per gross packages, how much gross profit did he make on the day's sales of this product?   *Ans.* $28.50.

6. A square foot of iron $\dfrac{109}{1000}$ of an inch thick weighs 4.36 pounds. Estimate to the nearest one hundredth of a pound the weight of a sheet of iron of this thickness measuring 11 inches by 9 inches. *Ans.* 3 pounds.

64. A Quick Way to Find the Cost per Unit, Given the Price or Rate per Gross. Here is a little trick which once helped the author to win $100.00 in a mathematics quiz.

To find the cost of a single article priced at so much per gross, most of us would divide the price by 144. A much shorter way is to divide by 1000 and multiply by 7.

Example 1: Find the cost of a single article, the price of which is $88.00 a gross.

Solution: Dividing $88.00 by 1000 gives us $0.088, and $0.088 multiplied by 7 gives us $0.616, or $0.62 to the nearest cent. Very little calculation was necessary, and we did not need to use pencil and paper.

The reason for the method is this: 144 is contained in 1000 just a little over seven times (7 times 144 equals 1008); and when the price per gross is less than $144.00, the small difference between 1008 and 1000 is of little or no consequence. In actual practice the price, when given per gross, is more likely than not to be less than $144.00, and the smaller the price per gross the more inconsequential will be the difference between 1008 and 1000.

Example 2: Find to the nearest cent the unit cost of a product purchased at $8.75 per gross.

Solution: $8.75 divided by 1000   = $0.00875
$0.00875 multiplied by 7 = $0.06125

Ans. $0.06.

Example 3: Find to the nearest tenth of a cent the unit cost of a product purchased at $11.60 per gross.

Solution: $11.60 divided by 1000 = $0.0116
$0.0116 multiplied by 7 = $0.0812

Ans. $0.081.

Example 4: Estimate to the nearest hundredth of a cent the value per unit of a product billed at $5.18 per gross.

Solution: $5.18 divided by 1000   = $0.00518
$0.00518 multiplied by 7 = $0.03626

Ans. $0.0363.

Example 5: A dealer purchased one gross 14-ounce cans of lye at $10.50 per gross cans. Find his cost per can to the nearest tenth of a cent.

Solution: $10.50 divided by 1000 = $0.0105
$0.0105 multiplied by 7 = $0.074

Ans. $0.074.

Find to the nearest tenth of a cent the cost per unit of the following products:

1. Small, camel's-hair pencil brushes, billed at $6.50 a gross.

Ans. $0.046.

2. Twelve-ounce containers of vegetable soap cakes, costing $11.85 per gross. *Ans.* $0.083.

3. Five-inch long single leaf holly at $6.25 a gross.   *Ans.* $0.044.

4. One-gallon empty tins, costing $7.40 a gross.   *Ans.* $0.052.

5. Tubes of household cement, billed at $21.60 per gross.

Ans. $0.151.

Compute the following problem to the nearest hundredth of a cent.

6. A girl can stamp 144 metal parts per hour. If her wage rate is 82 cents an hour, what is the unit cost of stamping these parts?

Ans. $0.0057.

65. How to Compute the Value of a Quantity Stated in Thousands, Hundreds, Tens and Units, Given the Price per Gross, or the Number of Gross in Any Quantity, Given the Rate of Production. Now that we have familiarized ourselves with the fact that seven gross equals 1008, let us explore the possibilities of another technique.

We will take the problem 4080 units at $12.64 per gross. One glance at the quantity tells us that it contains 1008 four times, with something left over. Four times 1008 (4032) deducted from 4080 leaves 48 which is $\frac{1}{3}$ of a gross. This simplifies our problem, which may be restated to read $28\frac{1}{3}$ gross at $12.64 per gross. It may now be solved quickly and easily, as follows:

$$
\begin{array}{lcr}
20 \text{ gross at } \$12.64 \text{ a gross (twice } \$126.40) & = & \$252.80 \\
8 \text{ gross at } \$12.64 & = & 101.12 \\
\tfrac{1}{3} \text{ gross at } \$12.64 & = & 4.21 \\
\hline
28\tfrac{1}{3} \text{ gross at } \$12.64 \text{ per gross} & = & \$358.13
\end{array}
$$

In the illustration that follows, the number of gross contained in the quantity is not so obvious at a glance as in the preceding illustration.   The procedure, however, is the same.   A quick glance tells us that 3852 contains 1008 (7 gross) three times, so we write down 3024 (3 times 1008).   A second glance shows that the difference between 3852 and 3024 exceeds 504 (half of 7 gross), so we write down 504.   And the process is continued until the entire quantity is accounted for.   The solution to this problem calls for a preliminary calculation to convert the quantity into gross and parts of a gross, as illustrated:

Example 1: Find the cost of 3852 units at $4.68 per gross.

Solution: 3024 (3 times 1008) = 21 gross

$$504 \ (\tfrac{1}{2} \text{ of } 1008) \quad = \quad 3\tfrac{1}{2} \text{ gross}$$
$$252 \ (\tfrac{1}{4} \text{ of } 1008) \quad = \quad 1\tfrac{3}{4} \text{ gross}$$
$$72 \ (\tfrac{1}{2} \text{ of } 144) \quad = \quad \tfrac{1}{2} \text{ gross}$$

$$3852 \qquad\qquad\qquad = 26\tfrac{3}{4} \text{ gross}$$

25 gross at $4.68 a gross ($\tfrac{1}{4}$ of $468.00) = $117.00
1 gross at $4.68   = 4.68
$\tfrac{1}{2}$ gross at $4.68   = 2.34
$\tfrac{1}{4}$ gross at $4.68   = 1.17

$26\tfrac{3}{4}$ gross at $4.68 per gross   = $125.19

Note the favorable opportunity presented by this technique when the quantity is 504; this number is exactly half of 7 gross, so that in all ordinary calculations we need but to multiply the price per gross by 7 and divide by 2.   By the same token, to find the value of 252 units (one fourth of 7 gross) we need but to multiply the price per gross by 7 and divide by 4.

Example 2: A machine fills tubes with ointment at the rate of 25 per minute.   If it is operated continuously for six hours, how many gross tubes will have been filled at the end of that time?

Solution: Six hours equals 360 minutes, and 360 times 25 equals 9000.   We know that 1008 equals 7 gross, so we proceed as follows:

9072 (which is the product of 1008
          times 9)   = 63 gross
—   72 (because 9072 exceeds 9000 by
          72)   = $\frac{1}{2}$ gross

9000   = $62\frac{1}{2}$ gross

Problems

1. If nursing bottles cost \$14.26 per gross, what would be the value of 252 bottles? *Ans.* \$24.96.

★ 2. Compute the number of gross in a lot of 960 screws. *Ans.* $6\frac{2}{3}$ gross.

★ 3. How many complete 1-gross packages can be made up from 1600 coffee filters? *Ans.* 11 complete 1-gross packages.

★ 4. If a manufacturer can produce 6048 clock bases in 6 hours, how long would it take him to make up 14 gross? *Ans.* 2 hours.

★ 5. A manufacturer can produce 936 large hard-rubber carving knife handles in 4 hours. How much time would he require to produce 13 gross? *Ans.* 8 hours.

6. If 320 complete lady's dressing combs can be manufactured in one hour, how many gross can be made in three $7\frac{1}{2}$-hour days? *Ans.* 50 gross.

7. The feeding of carbon pencils into a tamping machine is a finishing operation in the production of battery bobbins. If 5600 pencils can be fed into such a machine in one hour, how many complete gross bobbins will be finished in 4 hours? *Ans.* 155 complete gross.

8. A manufacturer, wanting to determine an average rate of speed in terms of gross per hour for hole-punching shoe bags, three holes to a bag, assigns three girls to do this work for one hour. One girl completes 864 bags; another, 828; and the third, 900. What average rate of speed per hour might be determined from these figures? (Hint: Find the total number of shoe bags completed by the three girls, divide by 3, then reduce to gross.) *Ans.* 6 gross per hour.

66. A Good Way to Recognize Instantly Whether a Computation Based on a Price per Gross is Approximately Correct. Proving a computation to insure its accuracy is always advisable. It is often very helpful, however, to make also what the author likes to call a "visual check." This consists of nothing more than a comparison between the exact answer and the approximate answer determined by a mental picture of the problem.

The answer to virtually every problem in business mathematics may be approximated by visual checking, and this practice is particularly recommended when solving problems in which the quantity is stated in units and the price given is per gross.

Take for instance the problem 200 units at 50 cents per gross. A quick visual check would be as follows:

$$1000 \text{ (7 times 50 cents)} = \$3.50$$

$$200 \ (\tfrac{1}{5} \text{ of } \$3.50) \qquad = \$ .70$$

An exact computation would show that the answer is $69\tfrac{1}{2}$ cents, or half a cent less than the approximated answer.

Naturally, the larger the quantity and the higher the price per gross, the greater will be the difference between the exact and the approximate computations. Thus the exact answer to the problem 250 units at $1.90 per gross is $3.30, while the quickly computed approximate answer, obtained by taking one fourth of 7 times $1.90, is $3.33—a difference of 3 cents, compared with the difference of only half a cent in the preceding problem.

A good illustration of the rapidity with which the approximate answer to a more or less time-consuming problem of this nature may be figured by the method indicated would be the problem discussed in Art. 65, namely: 3852 units at $4.68 per gross. The exact computation called for several little calculations. A visual check, however, tells us at a glance that the quantity is very close to 27 gross. (Four thousand is approximately 28 gross, so 3852, which is 148 short of 4000, is approximately 27 gross.) All we need to do now is compute 27 times $4.68, the price per gross, and we have the "approximate" answer, $126.36. This figure exceeds the exact answer by only $1.17, which is a pretty good indication that our original computation was about right.

It should be noted here that in approximating answers to problems dealing with the gross, the amount should always exceed the amount in the exact answer, the reason being that in the approximate computation 1000 units are counted as 7 gross, whereas the true equivalent of 7 gross is 1008 units. An approximate computation by the indicated method is, therefore, slightly less than 1 per cent in excess of the exact computation. So if we take **99** per cent of the approximate computation we come pretty close to the exact figure.

It would be well to be always on the lookout for quantities which, in whole or in part, are aliquot parts of the gross. Thus 7200 is the equivalent of 100 times $\frac{1}{2}$ gross; 3600 equals 100 times $\frac{1}{4}$ gross; 1836 can be broken down to the sum of 100 times $\frac{1}{8}$ gross plus $\frac{1}{2}$ gross, which equals 13 gross; and so on.

Example: Make a quick, approximate computation of the value of 7700 erasers at $4.30 per gross.

Solution: 7200 at $4.30 per gross (100 times $\frac{1}{2}$ gross
　　　　　 or 100 times $2.15)　　　　　　　= $215.00
　　　　 500 at $4.30 per gross ($3\frac{1}{2}$ times $4.30 or
　　　　　 7 times $2.15)　　　　　　　　 = 　15.05

_____

　　　 7700 at $4.30 per gross　　　　　　 = $230.05

Problems

Coupling your knowledge of the breakdown method of multiplication with the fact that for purposes of approximate computation 1000 equals 7 gross, find the approximate value—or the exact value if that is just as easy—of each of the following lots of merchandise.

1. 9800 hexagonal nuts at 32 cents a gross. 　　　*Ans.* $21.79.

2. 1200 prescription bottles at $2.57 per gross. (Hint: 1200 is the equivalent of 100 times $\frac{1}{12}$ gross, or $8\frac{1}{3}$ gross.) 　　*Ans.* $21.42.

3. 1600 magazine clips at $3.00 per gross. (Hint: 1600 is equivalent to 2000 minus $\frac{1}{5}$ of 2000.) 　　　　　　　*Ans.* $33.60.

4. 5400 manuscript pens at $3.15 per gross. (Hint: 3600 equals 100 times $\frac{1}{4}$ gross; and 1800 equals 100 times $\frac{1}{8}$ gross.) 　*Ans.* $118.13.

5. 900 brushes at $7.30 a gross. (Hint: 900 equals 1008 minus 108, and 108 is $\frac{3}{4}$ of a gross.) 　　　　　　　*Ans.* $45.62.

6. 750 jewelry novelties at $23.00 a gross. (Hint: Since the higher the price, the more significant is the difference between the *actual* and the *approximate* computations, it would be better in this instance to add the value of 720, which is 10 times $\frac{1}{2}$ gross, to the value of 30 units than to take $\frac{3}{4}$ of 7 gross.) 　　　　　　　*Ans.* $119.79.

67. How to Compute Charges When the Price Given Is per Ton, and the Quantity Is Stated in Pounds. A simple and practical way of computing problems of this nature is to convert the price per ton to the price per thousand pounds, and to proceed with the computation by the breakdown method. (Since there are 2000 pounds to the ton, the value per thousand pounds will be half of the price per ton.)

Example 1: Find the cost of 1150 pounds at $23.60 per ton.

Solution: Note that the cost per 1000 pounds is $11.80.

$$
\begin{array}{lll}
1000 \text{ pounds} & = & \$11.80 \\
100 \text{ pounds } (\tfrac{1}{10} \text{ of } \$11.80) & = & 1.18 \\
50 \text{ pounds } (\tfrac{1}{2} \text{ of } \$1.18) & = & .59 \\
\hline
\end{array}
$$

1150 pounds at $23.60 per ton = $13.57

Example 2: Find the cost of 2762 pounds at $134.50 per ton.

Solution: Note that the cost per 1000 pounds is $67.25.

$$
\begin{array}{lll}
2000 \text{ pounds (1 ton)} & = & \$134.50 \\
500 \text{ pounds } (\tfrac{1}{2} \text{ of } \$67.25) & = & 33.625 \\
250 \text{ pounds } (\tfrac{1}{2} \text{ of } \$33.625) & = & 16.812 \\
10 \text{ pounds } (\tfrac{1}{100} \text{ of } \$67.25) & = & .672 \\
2 \text{ pounds } (\tfrac{1}{5} \text{ of } \$0.672) & = & .134 \\
\hline
\end{array}
$$

2762 pounds at $134.50 per ton = $185.74

Example 3: Find the cost of 67 pounds at $142.28 per ton.

Solution: The cost per 1000 pounds is $71.14; therefore, the cost per 100 pounds is $7.114.

$$
\begin{array}{lll}
50 \text{ pounds } (\tfrac{1}{2} \text{ of } \$7.114) & = & \$3.557 \\
10 \text{ pounds } (\tfrac{1}{10} \text{ of } \$7.114) & = & .711 \\
5 \text{ pounds } (\tfrac{1}{2} \text{ of } .711) & = & .355 \\
2 \text{ pounds } (\tfrac{1}{5} \text{ of } .711) & = & .142 \\
\hline
\end{array}
$$

67 pounds at $142.28 per ton = $4.77

Example 4: What is the value of 6735 pounds of pig iron at the market quotation of $28.50 per ton?

Solution: 6000 pounds at $28.50 per ton (3 times

$28.50) = $85.50

700 pounds (7 times $\frac{1}{20}$ of $28.50 or 7

times $1.425) = 9.975

35 pounds ($\frac{1}{20}$ of $9.975) = .498

6735 pounds at $28.50 per ton = $95.97

Note how simple it is, once the price per ton has been reduced to the price per 1000 pounds, to find the price per 100 pounds, per 10 pounds, or per single pound. It is merely a matter of moving the decimal point to the left one, two, or three places, respectively.

PROBLEMS

In the following problems a ton is to be taken to mean a short ton— that is, 2000 pounds.

1. Using the average net weight of 364 pounds per barrel, estimate the cost of the contents of 7 barrels of borax at $58.60 per ton.

Ans. $74.66.

2. The net weight of a barrel of barium chloride is 412 pounds. At $73.00 per ton how much would 11 barrels of this chemical cost?

Ans. $165.42. (*Art. 13*)

3. Compute the total cost of 5 bags of sulphate ammonia weighing 188, 197, 175, 176 and 196 pounds, respectively, at the market quotation of $30.50 a ton. *Ans.* $14.21.

4. How much is 1342 pounds of solid calcium chloride worth at $19.75 a ton? *Ans.* $13.25. (*Art. 13*)

5. A paper house finds at the end of its fiscal year that it has an inventory of 3816 pounds of chip paperboard. If the value of this product is $58.00 a ton, how much is the inventory worth? *Ans.* $110.66. (*Art. 13*)

6. What is the value of 2640 pounds of book paper at $260.00 a ton?

Ans. $343.20. (*Art. 13*)

7. Round plate washers are packed in kegs of 200 to 250 pounds. Assuming an average of 225 pounds per keg, how much would 7 kegs of this material be worth at $110.00 a ton? *Ans.* $86.63. (*Art. 13*)

8. What is the cost of 3 barrels of pipe elbows having a total net weight of 1624 pounds at $240.00 a ton?   *Ans.* $194.88. (*Art. 13*)

68. How to Compute Quickly the Value of Any Number of Ounces When the Price Given Is per Pound. Since the technique to be demonstrated here is based upon the breakdown method of multiplication (Chapter II), we will confine ourselves in this article to a study of the solution of problems.

We will consider here the avoirdupois pound, which is the equivalent of 16 ounces. This is the common system in English-speaking countries for weighing all commodities except precious stones, precious metals, and drugs (when used for compounding prescriptions).

Example 1: Find the value of 9 ounces at $1.38 per pound.

Solution: 8 ounces ($\frac{1}{2}$ pound)   = $.69
         1 ounce ($\frac{1}{8}$ of .69)   = .09
___

9 ounces at $1.38 per pound = $.78

Example 2: Find the value of $13\frac{1}{4}$ ounces at $24.25 per pound.

Solution: 8 ounces ($\frac{1}{2}$ pound)   = $12.125
         4 ounces ($\frac{1}{2}$ of $12.125)   =   6.062
         1 ounce ($\frac{1}{4}$ of $6.062)   =   1.515
         $\frac{1}{4}$ ounce ($\frac{1}{4}$ of $1.515)   =   .379
___

$13\frac{1}{4}$ ounces at $24.25 per pound = $20.08

Example 3: Find the value of $15\frac{1}{2}$ ounces at $4.72 per pound.

Solution: 16 ounces (1 pound)   = $4.72
  — $\frac{1}{2}$ ounce *   =   .15
___

$15\frac{1}{2}$ ounces at $4.72 per pound = $4.57

* Compute the value of $\frac{1}{2}$ ounce mentally this way: A half ounce is the equivalent of one eighth of 4 ounces, or one eighth of $1.18.

Example 4: What is the value of $12\frac{3}{4}$ ounces of cinnamon bark oil purchased at $34.60 a pound?

Solution: 8 ounces at $34.60 a pound ($\frac{1}{2}$ of $34.60) = $17.30
4 ounces ($\frac{1}{2}$ of $17.30)   = 8.65
$\frac{1}{2}$ ounce ($\frac{1}{8}$ of $8.65)   = 1.08
$\frac{1}{4}$ ounce ($\frac{1}{2}$ of $1.08)   = .54

$12\frac{3}{4}$ ounces at $34.60 a pound   = $27.57

PROBLEMS

1. How much should a dealer charge for 14 ounces of dried raspberries selling at $4.75 a pound?   *Ans.* $4.16.

2. At $1.50 a pound, what is the value of $10\frac{1}{2}$ ounces of camphor?
Ans. $0.99.

3. If the market price of zirconium metal, a substance used in the manufacture of vacuum tubes, is $15.60 a pound, how much is $7\frac{1}{4}$ ounces worth?   *Ans.* $7.07.

4. If the market price of gold bronze, put up in ounce packages, is $1.75 a pound, what is a dealer's inventory of 5 packages of this product worth?   *Ans.* $0.55.

Compute the worth of the following quantities of essential oils to the nearest whole cent.

5. $3\frac{1}{4}$ ounces of angelica root at $136.00 a pound.   *Ans.* $27.63.

6. 11 ounces of ginger at $11.25 a pound.   *Ans.* $7.73.

7. $14\frac{1}{2}$ ounces of lemongrass at $3.95 a pound.   *Ans.* $3.58.

8. $2\frac{1}{8}$ ounces of calamus at $24.00 a pound.   *Ans.* $3.19.

69. How to Compute the Value of a Length of Material, Given the Price per Yard. Bearing in mind that there are 12 inches to the foot and three feet to the yard, observe the simplicity of the solutions in the following illustrations:

Example 1: Estimate the value of 24 inches of material at $3.24 per yard.

Solution: 12 inches ($\frac{1}{3}$ of $3.24) = $1.08

24 inches (twice $1.08) = $2.16

Example 2: Estimate the value of 11 inches of material at $10.62 per yard.

Solution: 12 inches ($\frac{1}{3}$ of $10.62)   = $3.54
 − 1 inch ($\frac{1}{12}$ of $3.54)   =   .29
_____

11 inches at $10.62 per yard = $3.25

Example 3: Estimate the value of 17 inches of material at $7.48 per yard.

Solution: 12 inches ($\frac{1}{3}$ of $7.48)   = $2.49
4 inches ($\frac{1}{3}$ of $2.49)   =   .83
1 inch ($\frac{1}{4}$ of .83)   =   .21
_____

17 inches at $7.48 per yard = $3.53

Example 4: Estimate the value of 63 inches of material at $4.82 per yard.

Solution: 36 inches (1 yard)   = $4.82
18 inches ($\frac{1}{2}$ of $4.82)   =   2.41
9 inches ($\frac{1}{2}$ of $2.41)   =   1.21
_____

63 inches at $4.82 per yard = $8.44

Example 5: Estimate the value of 14 yards 2 feet 4 inches of material at $6.24 per yard.

Solution: 10 yards (10 times $6.24)   = $62.40
4 yards (4 times $6.24)   =   24.96
2 feet ($\frac{1}{6}$ of $24.96)   =   4.16
4 inches ($\frac{1}{9}$ of $6.24)   =   .69
_____

14 yds. 2 ft. 4 in. at $6.24 per yard = $92.21

Example 6: Vicuña is an expensive fabric used in the clothing industry.   At $110.00 per yard, how much would 3 yards 7 inches of this material cost?

Solution: 3 yards at $110.00 a yard   = $330.00
6 inches ($\frac{1}{6}$ of $110.00)   =   18.33
1 inch ($\frac{1}{6}$ of $18.33)   =   3.06

3 yards 7 inches at $110.00 a yard = $351.39

PROBLEMS

1. At $26.00 a yard, what would the cost be of 3 yards 11 inches of worsted overcoating?   *Ans.* $85.94.

2. A guanaco-and-wool fabric is quoted at $89.00 a yard. Estimate the cost of 6 yards 19 inches of this material.   *Ans.* $580.97.

3. What would the cost be of 9 yards 13 inches of a tweed cloth at $6.50 a yard?   *Ans.* $60.85.

4. Compute the worth of 4 yards 7 inches of upholstery fabric at $18.50 a yard.   *Ans.* $77.60.

5. What would be the correct charge for 3 yards $8\frac{1}{2}$ inches of lampshade cloth at $13.50 a yard?   *Ans.* $43.69.

6. A brocade fabric used for making slippers and evening bags sells for $22.00 a yard. How much would 2 yards 5 inches of this material cost?   *Ans.* $47.06.

CHAPTER X

CHECKING RESULTS IN MULTIPLICATION

It is probably no exaggeration to say that failure to check computations is the cause of nine tenths of the errors in business mathematics.

Just as the expert speller, after spelling the word "embarrass" correctly all his life, may suddenly forget himself and spell this word with only one r, the experienced mathematician may at a particular moment—due to haste, or hunger, or any other reason— compute the product of 7 times 9 as 53 instead of 63. And it not infrequently happens that the same error is repeated in the checking operation, particularly if the interval between the two computations is short-spaced.

It is suggested, therefore, that the reader develop the habit of checking his computations, and of using in the checking operations different methods from the ones used to obtain the answer the first time. Employers are urged to emphasize the importance of this phase of office routine to their billing clerks and other employees who work with figures. Prevention is better than cure, and this aid to accuracy may help to avoid costly errors and embarrassing moments.

70. Even Simple Multiplication Problems Can Be Computed in Several Different Ways. There are many ways of checking a calculation. Even the simplest problem may be computed in half a dozen ways or more. Take, for example, the problem 37 times 24. Observe how, in the following illustration, this can be computed by at least six different methods.

	Transposing Multiplicand
The Conventional Method	*and Multiplier*

37		24
× 24		× 37
148		168
74		72
888		888

	Multiplying and Dividing the
	Two Factors, Respectively,
The Double-and-Halve Method	*By Some Other Value Than 2*
74 (37 multiplied by 2)	148 (37 multiplied by 4)
× 12 (24 divided by 2)	× 6 (24 divided by 4)
888	888

The Breakdown Method

37 times 25 (3700 divided by 4)	= 925
− 37 times 1	= 37
37 times 24	= 888

The Method Discussed in Art. 13

37 times 20	= 740
37 times 4 ($\frac{1}{5}$ of 740)	= 148
37 times 24	= 888

PROBLEMS

Without calculating the answers show, by restatements of the factors, three different methods, exclusive of the conventional method, of computing or checking the answer to each of the following problems. For example, the restatements of the factors in the five illustrations, exclusive of the conventional method, given in this article would read: 24 times 37; 74 times 12; 148 times 6; 37 times 25, minus 37; and 37 times 20, plus one fifth of the result.

1. The value of 576 machine parts at $3\frac{1}{2}$ cents each.

> *Ans.* $2.88 times 7; $1.44 times 14; $5.76 times $2\frac{1}{2}$, plus $5.76.

2. The exchange value of 400 Colombian gold pesos at $58\frac{1}{2}$ cents per peso.

> *Ans.* 4 times $58.50; 200 times $1.17; 400 times $57\frac{1}{2}$ cents, plus $4.00.

3. The area in square inches of a sheet of plywood panel measuring 49 inches by 62 inches.

> *Ans.* 50 times 62, minus 62; 98 times 31; 49 times 2, plus 30 times the result.

4. The cost of 48 clocks at $3.20 each.

> *Ans.* 50 times $3.20, minus 2 times $3.20; 24 times $6.40; 4 times the product of 12 times $3.20.

5. The total weight of 27 barrels of cement, each weighing 376 pounds.

> *Ans.* 30 times 376, minus one tenth of the result; 9 times the product of 3 times 376; 400 times 27, minus $\frac{6}{100}$ of the result.

6. The area in square feet of a loft 120 feet long by 39 feet wide.

> *Ans.* 12 times 390; 6 times 780; 100 times 39, plus one fifth of the result.

7. The total number of ironing-board covers that can be produced in 40 hours by a girl whose rate of speed is 98 covers per hour.

> *Ans.* 4 times 980; 8 times 490; 100 times 40, minus 2 times 40.

8. The value of 2 gross of buckles costing 73 cents a dozen.

> *Ans.* 24 times 75 cents, minus 24 times 2 cents; 12 times $1.46; 6 times $2.92.

9. The amount of pay due an employee for $7\frac{1}{2}$ hours at $1.16 per hour.

> *Ans.* 10 times $1.16, minus one fourth of the result; 15 times $0.58; 30 times $0.29.

10. The weight of 84 cubic inches of iron. (One cubic inch of iron weighs .26 pounds.)

> *Ans.* 84 times .25, plus .84; 12 times the product of 7 times .26; 4 times .26, plus 20 times the result.

11. The total number of cocoa beans roasted in a revolving drum in 8 hours at the rate of 720 every 40 minutes.

> *Ans.* 12 times 720; 6 times 1440; 4 times the product of 3 times 720.

12. The tax due on property assessed at $126,000 at the rate of $2.70 on each $100.

> *Ans.* $1260 times 2.7; 9 times the product of 1260 times .3; $1260 times 3, minus one tenth of the result.

13. The cost of 120 shares of stock at $38\frac{1}{2}$—that is, at $38.50 each.

Ans. 120 at $37.50, plus $120.00; 100 times $38.50, plus one fifth of the result; 12 times $385.00.

14. The value of 2750 pounds of cottonseed oil at $17\frac{1}{2}$ cents a pound.

Ans. 5500 times $0.0875; 275 times $1.75; $1\frac{3}{4}$ times $275.00.

15. The amount due on the purchase of 34 dresses at $13.50 each.

Ans. $\frac{1}{8}$ of $3400.00, plus $34.00; 17 times $27.00; 15 times $27.00, plus 2 times $27.00.

16. The cost of $89\frac{1}{2}$ yards of fabric at 92 cents a yard.

Ans. 90 times 92 cents, minus one half of 92 cents; 100 times 92 cents, minus $10\frac{1}{2}$ times 92 cents; $89\frac{1}{2}$ times $1.00, minus $89\frac{1}{2}$ times 8 cents.

17. The number of gross pencils that can be produced in a $36\frac{1}{4}$-hour week at the rate of 64 gross an hour.

Ans. 8 times the product of 8 times $36\frac{1}{4}$; 9 times the product of 4 times 64, plus one quarter of 64; 145 times 16.

18. The weight of 28 cubic feet of water. (One cubic foot of water weighs $62\frac{1}{2}$ pounds.)

Ans. 14 times 125; 7 times 250; 50 times 28, plus one quarter of the result.

19. The number of feet in 22 rods. (One rod equals $16\frac{1}{2}$ feet.)

Ans. 11 times 33; $5\frac{1}{2}$ times 66; $8\frac{1}{4}$ times 44.

20. The total amount of dry hay yielded by 96 acres at the rate of $7\frac{3}{4}$ tons per acre.

Ans. 100 times 7.75, minus 4 times 7.75; 31 times 24; 31 times 25, minus 31.

71. Checking Results When the Multiplier Is a Single Digit.

The ease and simplicity of checking results in multiplication is not limited to problems in which one of the factors contains two or more digits. Problems in which one of the factors is a single digit can also be calculated in several different ways. Whether the single digit is an odd number or an even number, the double-and-halve method of multiplication (Chapter III) can be used to good effect. Multiplying by 10 and subtracting the product of the multiplicand times the difference is another good method. In the illustrations that follow, Method A in each solution is by the double-and-halve technique, and Method B by the other technique.

Example 1: Multiply 873 by 6.

Solution:

Method A: 873 times 6 (1746 times 3) = 5238

Method B: 873 times 10   = 8730
        −   873 times 4   = 3492
        ─────────────────────────────────
            873 times 6   = 5238

Example 2: Multiply 732 by 7.

Solution:

Method A: 1464 times 3   = 4392
            1464 times $\frac{1}{2}$ = 732
        ───────────────────────────────────────
            1464 times $3\frac{1}{2}$ (732 times 7) = 5124

Method B: 732 times 10   = 7320
        −   732 times 3   = 2196
        ────────────────────────────────
            732 times 7   = 5124

Example 3: Find the product of 1364 times 8.

Solution:

Method A: 2728 times 4   = 10912

Method B: 1364 times 10 = 13640
        −   1364 times 2   = 2728
        ──────────────────────────
            1364 times 8   = 10912

Example 4: Find the product of 2731 times 9.

Solution:

Method A: 5462 times 4   = 21848
            5462 times $\frac{1}{2}$ = 2731
        ───────────────────────────────────────
            5462 times $4\frac{1}{2}$ (2731 times 9) = 24579

Method B: 2731 times 10   = 27310
        −   2731   = 2731
        ─────────────────────────────────
            2731 times 9   = 24579

The breakdown method of multiplication (Chapter II) can also be used as a check if it is necessary or advisable. And the multiplier can be broken up in any way desired. Thus to prove the product of any number times 6, one may add the product of the multiplicand times 4 to the product of the multiplicand times 2; the product of any number times 7 equals the product of the multiplicand times 5 plus the product of the multiplicand times 2, or the product of the multiplicand times 4 plus the product of the multiplicand times 3; the multiplier 8 can be broken up into the numbers 6 and 2, 5 and 3; and 9 can be broken up into 7 and 2, 6 and 3, 5 and 4.

Example 5: Prove, by adding the results of two partial products, that the cost of shipping a 7-pound package by air express from Los Angeles to Esmeraldas, Ecuador, at the rate of $1.38 a pound, is $9.66.

Solution: 5 times $1.38 = $6.90
2 times $1.38 = 2.76
_____
7 times $1.38 = $9.66

PROBLEMS

1. Prove by the double-and-halve method that the value of six men's overcoats at $48.50 each is $291.00.   *Ans.* 3 times $97.00.

2. The most valuable beef by-product is the hide, which is approximately 7 per cent of the live weight. Compute by the breakdown method the approximate amount of hide obtained from the slaughter of animals whose total live weight was 2742 pounds.   *Ans.* 192 pounds.

3. Prove by Method B in the foregoing illustrations that the amount earned by a workman for 8 hours labor at $1.48 an hour is $11.84.

4. Prove by Method B, also, that the cost of nine tons of 6-inch cast iron water pipe at $70.33 a ton is $632.97.

72. Checking Results When the Difference Between the Multiplier and a Particular Multiple of 10 Is a Multiple of One of the Digits in the Multiplier. One of the simplest and most interesting time-saving methods of checking calculations is the technique of using a partial product obtained in the first computation. The following illustrations will make this clear perhaps better than a word-explanation.

Example 1: Multiply 173 by 68.

Solution:

$$
\begin{array}{r}
173 \\
68 \\
\hline
1384 \\
1038 \\
\hline
11764
\end{array}
$$

Proof: Sixty-eight is the difference between 100 and 32. So that the product of 173 times 68 is equivalent to the product of 173 times 100 minus the product of 173 times 32. We have already obtained the product of 8 times 173 in the first computation, so (since 32 is the product of 4 times 8) to obtain the product of 32 times 173 we need but multiply 1384 (the product of 8 times 173) by 4. Our proof, therefore, consists of nothing more than the deduction of 4 times 1384 from the product of 100 times 173.

$$
\begin{array}{lr}
100 \text{ times } 173 & = 17300 \\
-\quad 32 \text{ times } 173 \text{ (4 times 1384)} = & 5536 \\
\hline
68 \text{ times } 173 & = 11764
\end{array}
$$

Example 2: Find the product of 249 times 73.

Solution:

$$
\begin{array}{r}
249 \\
73 \\
\hline
747 \\
1743 \\
\hline
18177
\end{array}
$$

Proof: Seventy-three is the difference between 100 and 27. The product of 249 times 73, then, is equivalent to the product of 249 times 100 minus the product of 249 times 27. Since we already know what 3 times 249 equals, we need but multiply that equivalent by 9, thus:

$$
\begin{aligned}
100 \text{ times } 249 &= 24900 \\
-\ \ 27 \text{ times } 249 \ (9 \text{ times } 747) &= \ \ 6723 \\
\hline
73 \text{ times } 249 &= 18177
\end{aligned}
$$

Note the interesting result of finding the answer to the next problem by multiplying by factors rather than by the actual digits of the multiplier.

Example 3: Multiply 237 by 64.

Solution:

$$
\begin{array}{r}
237 \\
8 \\
\hline
1896 \\
8 \\
\hline
15168
\end{array}
$$

Proof: In proving the answer to this problem, we have the choice of two multiples of 10: 80 and 40. Sixty-four equals 80 minus 16, and 16 equals the product of 2 times 8; sixty-four also equals 40 plus 24, and 24 equals 3 times 8. Let us use the number 40 in our proving operation.

$$
\begin{aligned}
40 \text{ times } 237 \ (4 \text{ times } 2370) &= \ \ 9480 \\
24 \text{ times } 237 \ (3 \text{ times } 1896) &= \ \ 5688 \\
\hline
64 \text{ times } 237 &= 15168
\end{aligned}
$$

Results of products in which the multiplier is a three-digit number can be proved just as easily as when the multiplier is a two-digit number, as will be seen in the following demonstration.

Example 4: Compute the product of 843 times 628.

Solution:

$$
\begin{array}{r}
843 \\
628 \\
\hline
6744 \\
1686 \\
5058 \\
\hline
529404 \\
\end{array}
$$

Proof: The number 628 is equivalent to 700 minus 72, and 72 equals 9 times 8. The proving procedure, then, is as follows.

$$
\begin{array}{ll}
700 \text{ times } 843 \ (7 \text{ times } 84300) = 590100 \\
- \quad 72 \text{ times } 843 \ (9 \text{ times } 6744) \ \ = \ \ 60696 \\
\hline
628 \text{ times } 843 \qquad\qquad\qquad = 529404 \\
\end{array}
$$

Example 5: Find the exchange value of 2846 francs at the rate of .84 cents, and prove your answer. (Note that .84 cents means $\frac{84}{100}$ of a cent.)

Solution:

$$
\begin{array}{r}
2846 \\
84 \\
\hline
11384 \\
22768 \\
\hline
239064 \\
\end{array}
$$

239064 hundredths of a cent equals $23.91.

Proof:

$$
\begin{array}{ll}
100 \text{ times } 2846 & = 284600 \\
- \quad 16 \text{ times } 2846 \ (4 \text{ times } 11384 \text{ or } 2 \\
\qquad \text{times } 22768) & = \ \ 45536 \\
\hline
84 \text{ times } 2846 & = 239064 \\
\end{array}
$$

1. Find the cost of 136 gallons of turpentine at 84 cents per gallon, and prove the answer.   *Ans.* $114.24.

2. A bushel of rye weighs 56 pounds. Compute the weight of 67 bushels of this product, and prove the answer. (Hint: 56 equals 80 minus 24.)   *Ans.* 3752 pounds.

3. Compute the value of 974 pounds of zinc at the market quotation of $0.0828 per pound, and prove the answer. (Hint: .0828 equals .09 minus .0072.)   *Ans.* $80.65.

4. One horsepower equals 746 watts. Estimate the number of watts represented by 836 horsepower, and prove the answer. (Hint: 746 equals 800 minus 54.)   *Ans.* 623,656 watts.

5. A cubic inch of steel weighs 0.284 pounds. Find the weight of 378 cubic inches of steel, and prove the answer. (Hint: 284 equals 300 minus 16.)   *Ans.* 107.352 pounds.

6. The oke is a Greek unit of measurement equivalent to 2.82 pounds. Compute the weight in pounds of 167 okes, and prove the answer. (Hint: 2.82 equals 3 minus .18.)   *Ans.* 470.94 pounds.

Assume that you have before you the scratch-pad computation of each of the following problems worked by the conventional method, which you are to check. Without working the problem itself, explain how you would take advantage of one of the partial products in each computation in proving the answer. Assume in each case that the multiplier is the number with the asterisk.

7. Compute the number of inches in 73.86 meters. One meter equals 39.37* inches.

        Ans. Since 39.37 equals 40 minus .63, multiply 73.86 by 40 and
          subtract 9 times the product of .07 times 73.86.

8. What would be the approximate weight of 387 cubic feet of limestone and marbles, if the average weight of this material is 168* pounds per cubic foot?

        Ans. Since 168 equals 200 minus 32, multiply 387 by 200 and
          subtract 4 times the product of 8 times 387.

9. If the average production of butter fat per cow is 346* pounds per year, approximately how much butter fat might be obtained in a year from 473 cows?

        Ans. Since 346 equals 400 minus 54, multiply 473 by 400 and
          subtract 9 times the product of 6 times 473.

10. Estimate the total weight of 283 barrels of cement, using the average weight of 376* pounds per barrel.

> *Ans.* Since 376 equals 400 minus 24, multiply 283 by 400 and subtract 4 times the product of 6 times 283.

11. If cream containing 28% butter fat weighs 8.37* pounds per gallon, how much would 46.75 gallons weigh?

> *Ans.* Since 8.37 equals 9 minus .63, multiply 46.75 by 9 and subtract 9 times the product of .07 times 46.75.

12. Estimate the cost of 3785 feet of hot-rolled boiler tubes at $24.68* per 100 feet.

> *Ans.* Since 24.68 equals 25 minus .32, multiply 37.85 by 25 and subtract 4 times the product of .08 times 37.85.

73. Checking Results When in Several Different Problems the Multiplicands Are Represented by the Same Number or Value, e.g., 673 times 51, 673 times 35, 673 times 89. A group of problems of this nature affords an excellent opportunity to prove the accuracy of the individual answers in a way uniquely different from anything discussed in this book thus far.   No matter how many problems are involved, only three simple computations are necessary: two in addition, and one in multiplication.   Let us compute the answers to the three problems cited in the heading of this article, by the short-cut methods with which we are now familiar, then proceed with the checking operations, which will be explained as we go along.

First Problem: To multiply 673 by 51.

$$673 \text{ times } 50 \ (\tfrac{1}{2} \text{ of } 67300) = 33650$$
$$673 \text{ taken once} \qquad\qquad = \quad 673$$

$$673 \text{ times } 51 \qquad\qquad\quad = 34323$$

Second Problem: To multiply 673 by 35.

$$673 \text{ times } 25 \ (\tfrac{1}{4} \text{ of } 67300) = 16825$$
$$673 \text{ times } 10 \qquad\qquad = \quad 6730$$

$$673 \text{ times } 35 \qquad\qquad\quad = 23555$$

Third Problem: To multiply 673 by 89.

673 times 100	= 67300
— 673 times 11	= 7403

673 times 89   = 59897

Proof:

Step No. 1. Add the multipliers.

Multiplier in first problem	= 51
Multiplier in second problem	= 35
Multiplier in third problem	= 89

The sum of the three multipliers = 175

Step No. 2. Compute the product of the multiplicand (the number common to each problem) times the sum of the multipliers—the sum of the multipliers having been obtained in Step. No. 1. In other words, multiply 673 by 175.

673 times 100	= 67300
673 times 50 ($\frac{1}{2}$ of 67300)	= 33650
673 times 25 ($\frac{1}{2}$ of 33650)	= 16825

673 times 175   = 117775

Step No. 3. Now add the individual answers obtained by computing each problem separately.

Answer to first problem	= 34323
Answer to second problem	= 23555
Answer to third problem	= 59897

The sum of the three answers = 117775

The totals obtained in Steps 2 and 3 are alike, and so we may be reasonably sure that the answers arrived at in the separate computations of the three problems are correct.

It should be noted that no matter how many problems are involved, the checking procedure is not varied one bit. Whether it is required to prove the answers to 3 problems or to 300 problems, only the three indicated steps are necessary.

The value and importance of this technique cannot be overestimated. It can be used to excellent advantage in billing departments—particularly if the billings are heavy and the number of products is not very large. Payroll clerks can use it profitably to check the amounts earned by employees paid at the same rate per hour. And the technique can be used by engineers and production men in an endless variety of ways.

PROBLEMS

1. Five men are employed at the rate of $1.23 an hour. In one week they put in 40, 38, 39, 37 and $38\frac{1}{2}$ hours, respectively. Compute the individual amounts earned, then check the amounts by the method discussed. *Ans.* $49.20, $46.74, $47.97, $45.51, $47.36; total, $236.78.

2. A bottle distributor advertises a special creation at the price of $4.15 per gross bottles and sells, as a result, the following quantities: 12, 14, 15, 8 and 24 dozen respectively. Compute the amount of each individual purchase, then check your figures by the group computation method.   *Ans.* $4.15, $4.84, $5.19, $2.77, $8.30; total, $25.25.

3. The ratio of labor costs to selling prices in a commercial printing concern is $37\frac{1}{2}\%$. The company's monthly sales for July through December in one year were, respectively, $4780, $5362, $4490, $5146, $3620 and $4350. Compute the approximate labor costs for each of the six months on the basis of the aforestated ratio, and check your figures by the group method.
    Ans. $1792.50, $2010.75, $1683.75, $1929.75, $1357.50, $1631.25; total, $10,405.50.

4. A dealer in fabrics makes six sales of three different materials, as follows:

3 yards @ $12.75	$2\frac{1}{2}$ yards @ $ 3.20	8 yards @ $16.10
4 yards @ 3.20	4 yards @ 16.10	5 yards @ 12.75
5 yards @ 16.10	6 yards @ 12.75	3 yards @ 3.20
19 yards @ $ 3.20	11 yards @ $12.75	5 yards @ $16.10
7 yards @ 12.75	3 yards @ 16.10	3 yards @ 3.20

Show the total amount for each of the six sales, and check these amounts by group computation.

    Ans. $131.55, $148.90, $202.15, $150.05, $188.55, $90.10; total, $911.30.

74. A Quick Way of Checking Computations of 25 Per Cent and $33\frac{1}{3}$ Per Cent. The per-cent rates of 25 and $33\frac{1}{3}$ are two of the most frequently used per-cent rates in modern business. There is scarcely an enterprise in which occasion does not arise at one time or another when it is necessary to make a computation involving one or the other of these rates.

Let us take as an example a sale amounting to $87.48 subject to a discount of 25 per cent. The net amount would be arrived at as follows:

Amount of sale.............. $87.48
Less 25%................. 21.87
Net amount due............ $65.61

Now 25 per cent is an interesting rate: it is exactly one fourth, and a very easy number to work with mentally. Thus if we deduct one fourth from anything, we know that what is left over is exactly equal to three times the amount deducted. So that instead of checking a discount deduction by repeating the original process of computation, it is better to see if the net amount arrived at is exactly equal to three times the amount of discount deducted. Thus to use the figures in the foregoing illustration, we should multiply $21.87 by 3, and seeing that the product equals $65.61, we should know beyond any question of doubt that our computation is correct.

The same holds true for the discount rate of $33\frac{1}{3}$ per cent. The figures on a sale to a jobber amounting to $364.20 subject to the jobber's commission of $33\frac{1}{3}$ per cent would be as follows:

Amount of sale............. $364.20
Less $33\frac{1}{3}$%............... 121.40
Net amount due........... $242.80

Here, too, it is plain that if the discount is one third of the original amount, the net amount should equal two thirds of the original amount. All we need do, then, is see whether $242.80 equals twice $121.40. We see that it does, and are safe in assuming that the figures in the computation are correct.

It goes without saying, of course, that in every subtraction problem, the answer should be checked mentally by adding it to the amount subtracted: the sum should equal the original amount.

PROBLEMS

The answers to the following problems should be proved by the processes of multiplication and addition. Thus to prove that 16 less 25% equals 12, write: ''This figure equals 3 times 4; and 12 plus 4 equals 16.''

1. A man buys a house for $27,500, of which 25% is payable in cash. Compute the amount that will be due after this payment has been made, and prove your answer.

> *Ans.* $20,625. This figure equals 3 times $6875, and $20,625 plus $6875 equals $27,500.

2. A businessman purchases a rebuilt typewriter for $85.00, from which amount 25% is deducted as a trade-in allowance for his old typewriter. Compute the net cost of the new machine and prove your answer.

> *Ans.* $63.75. This figure equals 3 times $21.25, and $63.75 plus $21.25 equals $85.00.

3. An error in a production process entitled a dealer to an allowance of $33\frac{1}{3}\%$ on a purchase of merchandise amounting to $729.00. Calculate the amount that the dealer will be expected to pay in full settlement, and prove your answer.

> *Ans.* $486.00. This figure equals twice $243.00, and $486.00 plus $243.00 equals $729.00.

4. A manufacturer is informed by his production manager that three orders—amounting to $290, $628 and $342, respectively—are "going out today." Having in mind that each shipment is to be billed "less $33\frac{1}{3}\%$," compute the net total of the three amounts, using the technique discussed in the preceding article, and prove your answer.

> *Ans.* $840.00. This figure equals twice $420.00, and $840.00 plus $420.00 equals $1260.00.

75. Checking Computations of Charges When the Price Is Subject to a Discount. A simple way of checking computations of this nature, e.g., 7 times $18.00 less 20 per cent, is to reverse the order in which the discount is deducted. Thus if in the original computation we first calculated $18.00 less 20 per cent and then multiplied the net unit price by 7 we might, in checking the computation, first calculate 7 times $18.00 and then deduct 20 per cent from the total. Both methods are shown in the following illustration. (Note that $18.00 less 20 per cent is equivalent to 80 per cent of $18.00.)

Method A: 80% of $18.00 (8 times $1.80)   = $ 14.40
_____

7 times $14.40   = $100.80

Method B: 7 times $18.00   = $126.00
_____

80% of $126.00 (8 times $12.60) = $100.80

If necessary, the answer may be checked in still other ways, as explained in Art. 70. The product of 7 times $18.00, for instance, might be checked by finding the product of 14 times $9.00, or 21 times $6.00. And the result obtained by computing 80 per cent of $126.00 might be proved by the double-and-halve method—that is, by taking 40 per cent of $252.00 (40 per cent being half of 80 per cent; and $252.00, twice $126.00).

PROBLEMS

Each of the following problems is to be worked by the two methods discussed in the text.

1. 540 mattress covers at $1.60 each less 20%.   *Ans.* $691.20.
2. 12 dozen paint brushes at $36.50 per dozen less 10 %. *Ans.* $394.20.
★ 3. 6 dozen surgical needles at $6.00 per dozen less 25%. *Ans.* $27.00.
4. 8 dozen hunting knives at $12.80 per dozen less 15%. *Ans.* $87.04.
5. 18 duplicators at $18.50 each less $27\frac{1}{2}$%. *Ans.* $241.42.

76. Checking Computations of Charges When the Price Is Subject to a Discount and One of the Factors Is Divisible by the Denominator of the Discount Rate Written as a Fraction. Many computations which, to the uninitiated, might seem to be unsolvable without pencil and paper, can be computed mentally with virtually no expenditure of effort, or in one simple operation on paper. Here is a simple short-cut seldom taken advantage of even by the mathematically inclined.

In computing the problem 5 times $16.12 less 20 per cent ($\frac{1}{5}$), we see at a glance that 5, which we will call the multiplier, is divisible by 5 in the denominator of the discount rate. All that is necessary, then, is to reduce the multiplier by the indicated per cent rate and proceed with the rest of the computation. Five minus one fifth of 5 equals 4; 4 times $16.12 equals $64.48.

The problem 15 times $23.84 less 20 per cent can be computed in exactly the same way. Fifteen minus 20 per cent equals 12; 12 times $23.84 equals $286.08. The only figures that need to be written down in working the problem are the figures in the answer.

Another interesting example is 8 times $7.40 less $37\frac{1}{2}$ per cent. This discount rate is equivalent to $\frac{3}{8}$. Eight minus three eighths of 8 equals 5; 5 times $7.40 equals $37.00. A perfectly simple problem in mental arithmetic!

Example: Compute mentally the cost of 16 dozen leather compacts at $28.50 per dozen less $37\frac{1}{2}\%$.

Solution: 16 dozen less $37\frac{1}{2}\%$ equals 10 dozen.

10 dozen at $28.50 per dozen equals $285.00.

PROBLEMS

These problems are to be worked mentally. Only the answers are to be written down.

★ **1.** 8 electric table stoves at $14.75 each less $12\frac{1}{2}\%$.   *Ans.* $103.25.
★ **2.** 40 steel files at $15.50 each less 25%.   *Ans.* $465.00.
★ **3.** 300 radio headphone cords at $18.00 per 100 less $33\frac{1}{3}\%$.
Ans. $36.00.
★ **4.** 36 doll carriages at $5.00 each less $16\frac{2}{3}\%$.   *Ans.* $150.00.
★ **5.** 10,000 yards of elastic binding at $5.86 per 100 yards less 20%.
Ans. $468.80.

77. Checking Multiplication by Casting Out the Nines. Here is a useful method for checking multiplication when one or both factors contain three or more digits. (It may also be used, with a slight modification, for checking addition, subtraction and division, as we shall see later—the process is substantially the same in all four operations.) It is simple and interesting, and is not practiced as commonly as it might be.

The method entails the addition of the digits of each factor and the product, the division of each sum by 9, and the setting down of the remainder, which we will call the check number. Thus to prove that the product of 786 times 89 equals 69,954, we proceed as follows:

```
  786  7 + 8 + 6            = 21. Casting out the 9's leaves   3
× 89   8 + 9               = 17. Casting out the 9 leaves     8
  ─────
69954  6 + 9 + 9 + 5 + 4 = 33. Casting out the 9's leaves   6
```

This being a problem in multiplication, we multiply the check number of the multiplicand (check number 3) by the check number of the multiplier (check number 8), which gives us 24. The sum of the digits in 24 is 6. We find that this is the check number for the answer to our problem, and so we may presume our answer (69954) to be correct.

Note that we only "presume" the answer to be correct. Checking multiplication by casting out the nines is not 100 per cent proof. If, by a mischance, digits in the answer had been transposed, or if a nine or a zero had been added or omitted, the error would not show up in the proof. For instance, if the answer to the problem illustrated were incorrectly shown as 96954, 60954 or 699054, the final check number, after casting out the nines, would still be 6.

A word of caution should be added here. When the sum of the digits in any factor in a multiplication problem adds up to an exact multiple of 9, the check number is shown as 9; in other words, all the nines but one are cast out. Note that this rule applies only to the factors; it does not apply to the product. One illustration will make this clear:

```
  666  6 + 6 + 6       = 18. Casting out one 9 leaves     9
× 3    3              = 3. No 9's to cast out leaves     3
 ────
 1998  1 + 9 + 9 + 8 = 27. Casting out the 9's leaves    0
```

PROBLEMS

Prove by casting out the nines that the answers to the following multiplication problems are correct.

1. 136 times 8 equals 1088.
2. 432 times 17 equals 7344.
3. 613 times 38 equals 23294.
4. 274 times 126 equals 34524.
5. 246 times 324 equals 79704.

CHAPTER XI

SIMPLE INTEREST

The computation of interest is a needlessly distressing and time-consuming experience for a surprisingly large number of businessmen and office workers.

Here, as in the many other types of problems discussed in the preceding chapters, a knowledge of decimals, aliquot parts and the breakdown method of multiplication comes to the rescue. A study of the articles and tables in this chapter should enable the reader to compute interest problems quickly and accurately, regardless of the interest rate or number of days.

78. The Difference Between Ordinary and Exact Interest. *Ordinary* interest is computed on the basis of 360 days in the year. This is the universally accepted method, used particularly when short periods or small sums are involved. *Exact* interest is computed on the basis of 365 days in the year. This is the method used by the Federal Government. It is used by banks and by state and city governments when large sums are involved.

Here the reader's attention is directed to Table VIII, which is an interesting study in the variations between ordinary interest and exact interest on $1000 at 1 per cent for any number of days from 1 to 360. It is especially interesting to observe that the difference between ordinary and exact interest on $1000 at 1 per cent for 360 days is less than 14 cents.

79. The Cancellation Method of Computing Interest. The conventional method of finding interest is the cancellation method, with the rate and period shown as common fractions. Thus in computing ordinary interest, 38 days would be shown as $\frac{38}{360}$; in computing exact interest, the same period would be indicated by the fraction $\frac{38}{365}$. The rate of 5 per cent would be shown as

TABLE VIII

Showing the Ordinary and Exact Simple Interest on $1000 at 1 Per Cent for the Number of Days Indicated

Days	Ordinary Interest	Exact Interest	Days	Ordinary Interest	Exact Interest
1	0.0277778	0.0273973	150	4.1666667	4.1095890
2	0.0555556	0.0547945	160	4.4444444	4.3835616
3	0.0833333	0.0821918	170	4.7222222	4.6575342
4	0.1111111	0.1095890	180	5.0000000	4.9315068
5	0.1388889	0.1369863	190	5.2777778	5.2054795
6	0.1666667	0.1643836	200	5.5555556	5.4794521
7	0.1944444	0.1917808	210	5.8333333	5.7534247
8	0.2222222	0.2191781	220	6.1111111	6.0273973
9	0.2500000	0.2465753	230	6.3888889	6.3013699
10	0.2777778	0.2739726	240	6.6666667	6.5753425
20	0.5555556	0.5479452	250	6.9444444	6.8493151
30	0.8333333	0.8219178	260	7.2222222	7.1232877
40	1.1111111	1.0958904	270	7.5000000	7.3972603
50	1.3888889	1.3698630	280	7.7777778	7.6712329
60	1.6666667	1.6438356	290	8.0555556	7.9452055
70	1.9444444	1.9178082	300	8.3333333	8.2191781
80	2.2222222	2.1917808	310	8.6111111	8.4931507
90	2.5000000	2.4657534	320	8.8888889	8.7671233
100	2.7777778	2.7397260	330	9.1666667	9.0410959
110	3.0555556	3.0136986	340	9.4444444	9.3150685
120	3.3333333	3.2876712	350	9.7222222	9.5890411
130	3.6111111	3.5616438	360	10.0000000	9.8630137
140	3.8888889	3.8356164			

$\frac{5}{100}$, $3\frac{1}{2}$ per cent as $\frac{7}{200}$, and so on. (The principle of interest computation is, of course, the same, regardless of the method used. A simple formula is: Principal times period times rate.)

Since most readers are probably more or less familiar with cancellation procedure, it is considered unnecessary to accompany the solutions in the following illustrations by explanations. Readers who are not thoroughly conversant with this phase of mathematics are advised to study the article entitled "Cancellation and How It Simplifies the Process of Multiplying Fractions," in the last chapter, before proceeding further.

Example 1: Find ordinary interest on $320.00 for the period July 1 to September 1 at 4 per cent.

Solution:

$$\frac{32\cancel{0} \times \cancel{6\cancel{0}} \times \overset{2}{\cancel{4}}}{\underset{3}{\cancel{36\cancel{0}}} \times \underset{5}{\cancel{10\cancel{0}}}} = \frac{32}{15} = \$2.13$$

Example 2: Find exact interest on $146,000.00 for the period July 8 to September 11 at $3\frac{1}{2}$ per cent.

Solution: Note that the exact number of days in the interest period is 65.

$$\frac{\overset{10}{\underset{73\cancel{0}}{\cancel{146000}}} \times \overset{13}{\cancel{65}} \times 7}{\underset{73}{\cancel{365}} \times \cancel{200}} = \frac{910}{1} = \$910.00$$

It is interesting to note that if, in Example 2, ordinary, rather than exact, interest was to be computed, the amount would be $922.64 instead of $910.00.

80. Simplification of the Cancellation Method. Under the cancellation method, as discussed in the preceding article, the last figure in the denominator of the fraction representing the interest period (360) is a zero, and the last two figures of the denominator of the fraction representing the per cent rate are also zeros. It is obvious, therefore, that time would be saved by cancelling the three zeros into the principal mentally, before the problem in fractional form is written down. The cancellation is effected by simply pointing off the decimal in the principal three places to the left, that is, one place for each zero.

Thus in Example 1 in the preceding article, in which we were to find the ordinary interest on $320.00 for the period July 1 to September 1 at 4 per cent, the solution would be simplified by writing the fractional form as follows:

$$\frac{.32 \times 60 \times 4}{36}$$

Notice that under the simplified method only one simple paper cancellation is necessary (12 into 60, and 12 into 36), whereas the solution by the conventional method required at least four paper cancellations.

PROBLEMS

Without working them to a finish, show how you would reduce the following problems to fractional form after having canceled the zeros in the denominators into the principal mentally.

1. Find the ordinary interest on $746.00 at 3% for 24 days.

$$Ans. \ \frac{.746 \times 3 \times 24}{36}.$$

2. Find the ordinary interest on an 80-day note of $1364.00 bearing interest at $3\frac{1}{2}\%$.

$$Ans. \ \frac{13.64 \times 7 \times 8}{72}.$$

3. What will the ordinary interest amount to on a 45-day note of $2300.00 bearing interest at $3\frac{1}{4}\%$?

$$Ans. \ \frac{2.3 \times 13 \times 45}{144}.$$

4. At the ordinary interest rate of 4% what would it cost to borrow $850.00 for 75 days?

$$Ans. \ \frac{.85 \times 4 \times 75}{36}.$$

5. What would it cost to borrow $1125.00 at the ordinary interest rate of $4\frac{1}{2}\%$ for 95 days?

$$Ans. \ \frac{1.125 \times 9 \times 95}{72}.$$

81. The 60-Day, 6 Per Cent Method of Computing Ordinary Interest, and How It Lends Itself to a Basically Valuable Short-Cut. Readers who enjoy working with figures will probably find the study of this article a stimulating experience. Let us take a simple problem and learn why many *ordinary* interest computations can be made speedily and accurately by simply pointing off the decimal in the principal two or three places, as the case may be.

Problem: Find ordinary interest on $378.00 for 60 days at 6 per cent. Setting down the problem for solution by the cancellation method, we have

$$\frac{378 \times 60 \times 6}{360 \times 100}$$

Observe the interesting picture presented by the two fractions— the one representing the interest period, the other the interest rate. Notice that the product of the numerators (60 and 6) equals 360, which is also one of the denominators and may, therefore, be canceled into it. This leaves us with the fraction $\frac{378}{100}$, and we know immediately that our answer is $3.78.

We, therefore, arrive at the following conclusions:

1. To find ordinary interest for 60 days at 6 per cent, it is but necessary to point off the decimal in the principal two places to the left.

2. To find ordinary interest for 6 days at 6 per cent, it is but necessary to point off the decimal in the principal *three* places to the left.

PROBLEMS

Compute mentally, to the nearest cent, the ordinary interest due on the following amounts loaned at 6% for 60 days.

* 1.	$145.00	*Ans.* $1.45.
* 2.	$237.40	*Ans.* $2.37.
* 3.	$897.60	*Ans.* $8.98.
* 4.	$364.10	*Ans.* $3.64.
* 5.	$920.50	*Ans.* $9.21.
* 6.	$756.20	*Ans.* $7.56.
* 7.	$193.67	*Ans.* $1.94.
* 8.	$324.62	*Ans.* $3.25.
* 9.	$613.56	*Ans.* $6.14.
* 10.	$1162.38	*Ans.* $11.62.

82. A Quick Way of Computing Ordinary Interest for Any Number of Days When the Rate Is 6 Per Cent. Here we will make another experiment with the breakdown method of multiplication, and readers who have familiarized themselves with the two aliquot tables (Table VI in Chapter II, and Table VII in Chapter IX) will find the study in these pages easy to follow. In this article a third aliquot table is introduced—Table IX, which deals with aliquot, near-aliquot and fractional parts of 60 days, and an examination of its contents should help in a quick understanding of the illustrations given here. This table presents an interesting picture of the exact relation to 60 days of any number of days from 1 to 30. No attempt should be made to memorize the relations shown; an understanding of the procedure in determining the relations will be of infinitely greater value.

By way of diversion, the following illustrations will be accompanied by little comment. Bear in mind, please, the conclusion arrived at in the preceding article: To find ordinary interest for 60 days at 6 per cent, we need but to point off the decimal in the principal two places to the left.

Example 1: Find the ordinary interest on $194.00 for 80 days at 6%.

Solution: Interest for 60 days is $\qquad$ = \$1.94
Interest for 20 days ($\frac{1}{3}$ of \$1.94) = .65

Interest for 80 days $\qquad$ = \$2.59

Example 2: Find the ordinary interest on $325.00 for 36 days at 6%.

Solution: Interest for 30 days ($\frac{1}{2}$ of \$3.25) = \$1.625
Interest for 6 days ($\frac{1}{5}$ of \$1.625) = .325

Interest for 36 days $\qquad$ = \$1.95

Example 3: Find the ordinary interest on $821.50 for 7 days at 6%.

Solution: Interest for 6 days ($\frac{1}{10}$ of \$8.21) = \$.821
Interest for 1 day ($\frac{1}{6}$ of .821) $\qquad$ = .137

Interest for 7 days $\qquad$ = \$.96

TABLE IX

ALIQUOT, NEAR-ALIQUOT AND FRACTIONAL PARTS OF 60 DAYS

Number of Days	Relation to 60 Days
1	$\frac{1}{6}$ of $\frac{1}{10}$ of 60
2	$\frac{1}{3}$ of $\frac{1}{10}$ of 60
3	$\frac{1}{2}$ of $\frac{1}{10}$ of 60
4	($\frac{1}{3}$ of $\frac{1}{10}$ of 60) multiplied by 2
5	$\frac{1}{12}$ of 60
6	$\frac{1}{10}$ of 60
7	($\frac{1}{10}$ of 60) plus $\frac{1}{6}$ of result
8	($\frac{1}{10}$ of 60) plus $\frac{1}{3}$ of result
9	($\frac{1}{10}$ of 60) plus $\frac{1}{2}$ of result
10	$\frac{1}{6}$ of 60
11	($\frac{1}{6}$ of 60) plus $\frac{1}{10}$ of result
12	$\frac{1}{5}$ of 60
13	($\frac{1}{5}$ of 60) plus $\frac{1}{12}$ of result
14	($\frac{1}{5}$ of 60) plus $\frac{1}{6}$ of result
15	$\frac{1}{4}$ of 60
16	($\frac{1}{5}$ of 60) plus $\frac{1}{3}$ of result
17	($\frac{3}{10}$ of 60) minus ($\frac{1}{6}$ of $\frac{1}{10}$ of 60)
18	$\frac{3}{10}$ of 60
19	($\frac{1}{3}$ of 60) minus $\frac{1}{20}$ of result
20	$\frac{1}{3}$ of 60
21	($\frac{1}{3}$ of 60) plus $\frac{1}{20}$ of result
22	($\frac{1}{3}$ of 60) plus $\frac{1}{10}$ of result
23	($\frac{2}{5}$ of 60) minus ($\frac{1}{12}$ of $\frac{1}{5}$ of 60)
24	$\frac{2}{5}$ of 60
25	$\frac{5}{12}$ of 60
26	($\frac{2}{5}$ of 60) plus ($\frac{1}{6}$ of $\frac{1}{5}$ of 60)
27	($\frac{1}{2}$ of 60) minus $\frac{1}{10}$ of result
28	($\frac{2}{5}$ of 60) plus $\frac{1}{6}$ of result
29	($\frac{1}{2}$ of 60) minus ($\frac{1}{3}$ of $\frac{1}{10}$ of result)
30	$\frac{1}{2}$ of 60
Over 30	$\frac{1}{2}$ of 60, plus equivalent of the number of days remaining. Thus a 35-day period equals $\frac{1}{2}$ of 60, plus $\frac{1}{12}$ of 60; $\frac{1}{2}$ of 60 plus $\frac{1}{6}$ of the result; or 7 times $\frac{1}{12}$ of 60.

Example 4: Find the ordinary interest on $218.00 for 7 months at 6%.

Solution: Interest for 2 months   = $2.18

Interest for 4 months (twice $2.18) =   4.36

Interest for 1 month ($\frac{1}{2}$ of $2.18)   =   1.09

Interest for 7 months   = $7.63

Example 5: Find the ordinary interest on $381.00 for 1 year 9 months and 15 days at 6%.

Solution: Note that the period may be restated as 21 months and 15 days.

Interest for 20 months (10 times $3.81) = $38.10

Interest for 1 month ($\frac{1}{2}$ of $3.81)   =   1.905

Interest for 15 days ($\frac{1}{2}$ of $1.905)   =   .952

Interest for 21 months and 15 days   = $40.96

Example 6: Find the ordinary interest on $243.00 for 85 days at 6%.

Solution: Interest for 60 days   = $2.43

Interest for 20 days ($\frac{1}{3}$ of $2.43) =   .81

Interest for 5 days ($\frac{1}{4}$ of .81)   =   .20

Interest for 85 days   = $3.44

There is no definite rule for breaking down the number of days. In the solution to the last example, for instance, we might just as well have added the interest for 30 days to the interest for 60 days, deducting from the total one sixth of the interest for 30 days.

PROBLEMS

Compute to the nearest cent the ordinary interest due on the following loans at 6%.

* **1.** $165.00 for 120 days.   *Ans.* $3.30.
  2. $843.00 for 150 days.   *Ans.* $21.08.

  ★ **3.** $326.00 for 180 days.   *Ans.* $9.78.

  ★ **4.** $619.60 for 20 days.   *Ans.* $2.07.

    5. $437.54 for 40 days.   *Ans.* $2.92.

    6. $1233.40 for 100 days.   *Ans.* $20.56.

    7. $1476.64 for 50 days.   *Ans.* $12.31.

    8. $1348.00 for 84 days.   *Ans.* $18.87.

    9. $1520.00 for 77 days.   *Ans.* $19.51.

  10. $1054.00 for 68 days.   *Ans.* $11.95.

83. How to Compute Ordinary Interest Quickly When the Rate Is Other Than 6 Per Cent. Here is another interesting study in aliquot parts. In the preceding article we learned how to compute interest when the rate is 6 per cent. With this information at our finger tips it is a comparatively simple matter to find the interest at 5 per cent, $4\frac{1}{2}\%$, or any other rate, as shown in Table X.

The following illustrations will help to fix this process in mind:

Example 1: Find the ordinary interest on $528.00 for 48 days at $5\frac{1}{2}\%$.

Solution: Interest for 60 days at 6%   = $5.28

            Interest for 60 days at $5\frac{1}{2}\%$ ($\frac{1}{12}$ of $5.28) = $4.84

  − Interest for 12 days at $5\frac{1}{2}\%$ ($\frac{1}{5}$ of $4.84) =   .97

            Interest for 48 days at $5\frac{1}{2}\%$ = $3.87

Example 2: Find the ordinary interest on $342.00 for 110 days at $6\frac{1}{2}\%$.

Solution: Interest for 120 days at 6% (twice $3.42) = $6.84

  − Interest for   10 days at 6% ($\frac{1}{12}$ of $6.84) =   .57

            Interest for 110 days at 6%   = $6.27

            Interest for 110 days at $\frac{1}{2}\%$ ($\frac{1}{12}$ of $6.27) =   .52

            Interest for 110 days at $6\frac{1}{2}\%$ = $6.79

PROBLEMS

Find by the breakdown method, as illustrated in the text, the ordinary interest in the following problems.

1. $508.00 for 54 days at 5%.   *Ans.* $3.81.
2. $276.40 for 80 days at 2%.   *Ans.* $1.23.
3. $1475.00 for 93 days at 3%.   *Ans.* $11.43.
4. $2394.80 for 110 days at $4\frac{1}{2}$%.   *Ans.* $32.93.
5. $1676.25 for 124 days at $2\frac{1}{2}$%.   *Ans.* $14.43.
6. $322.42 for 115 days at 4%.   *Ans.* $4.12.
7. $6781.90 for 140 days at $1\frac{1}{2}$%.   *Ans.* $39.56.
8. $793.34 for 45 days at 7%.   *Ans.* $6.94.
9. $426.57 for 44 days at $3\frac{1}{2}$%.   *Ans.* $1.82.
10. $2043.93 for 82 days at $5\frac{1}{2}$%.   *Ans.* $25.60.

TABLE X

APPLICATION OF THE BREAKDOWN METHOD TO THE COMPUTATION OF INTEREST
AT VARIOUS RATES

To Find Interest at	Find the Interest at 6%, and Complete the Computation as Indicated
5%	Deduct $\frac{1}{6}$
$5\frac{1}{2}$%	Deduct $\frac{1}{12}$
4%	Deduct $\frac{1}{3}$
$4\frac{1}{2}$%	Deduct $\frac{1}{4}$
3%	Deduct $\frac{1}{2}$
$3\frac{1}{2}$%	Deduct $\frac{1}{2}$, and add $\frac{1}{6}$ of the result
2%	Divide by 3
$2\frac{1}{2}$%	Divide by 3, and add $\frac{1}{4}$ of the result
1%	Divide by 6
$1\frac{1}{2}$%	Divide by 4

When the interest rate is higher than 6%, the
process of computation is exactly the same, except
that instead of *subtracting* the difference between
6% and the exact rate, the difference is *added*.

**84. Changing the Principal to Facilitate Calculation of Interest
by the 60-Day, 6 Per Cent Method.** If you were asked to compute
the ordinary interest on $6000.00 for 17 days at 6 per cent, could
you do it mentally and quickly? It is really as simple as A B C.

The finding of interest is nothing more than a process of multiplication. By the cancellation method this problem would be set down as

$$\frac{6000 \times 17 \times 6}{360 \times 100}$$

Now here is a situation which may bring to the reader's mind an interesting fact touched upon in preceding chapters: The product of the factors in any multiplication problem is not affected by the order in which the factors are written down. Thus the product of 48 times 18 is exactly the same as the product of 18 times 48, and 120 times 14 produces exactly the same result as 12 times 10 times 14.

Having this fact in mind, observe how conveniently the aforestated problem may be changed: $6000 multiplied by $\frac{17}{360}$ is equivalent to $60 multiplied by 100 multiplied by $\frac{17}{360}$; and the result will be exactly the same if we restated the problem as $17 multiplied by 100 multiplied by $\frac{60}{360}$, or as $1700 multiplied by $\frac{60}{360}$. Let us use the last form and see how simple the problem has become.

$$\frac{1700 \times 60 \times 6}{360 \times 100}$$

This is now a 60-day, 6 per cent problem, pure and simple. And observe how beautifully it solves itself: The product of the numerators 60 and 6 cancels itself into the denominator 360; and all we need to do now is to divide the only remaining numerator (1700) by the only remaining denominator (100), and we see instantly that the answer is 17, or $17.00.

Let us study the following examples and their solutions:

Example 1: Find the ordinary interest on $12,000.00 for 71 days at 6%.

Solution: Interchanging principal and time, we have a principal amounting to $7100.00 and an interest period of 120 days. Since the period is exactly twice 60 days, the interest will be exactly twice what it would be for 60 days. The answer, therefore, is twice $71.00, or $142.00.

Example 2: Find the ordinary interest on $1500.00 for 11 days at 6%.

Solution: Interchanging principal and time, the principal becomes $1100.00 and the interest period 15 days. Here the situation is reversed: instead of the interest period being a *multiple* of 60 days, it is a *fraction*—exactly one fourth of 60 days. We know, then, that the interest will be one fourth of $11.00, or $2.75.

Obviously, this method of changing the principal to facilitate calculation of interest is used most conveniently when the figures lend themselves easily to the process, that is, when the last two figures in the principal are zeros and the preceding figures are a multiple or aliquot part of 60. However, this interchange of the number of days with a part of the principal may always be made. And the method may be used to excellent advantage as a check on computations made by a different method.

PROBLEMS

Find the ordinary interest in each of the following problems, assuming an interest rate of 6% in each case.

  * **1.** $3000 for 85 days.   *Ans.* $42.50.
  * **2.** $4500 for 38 days.   *Ans.* $28.50.
  * **3.** $6600 for 54 days.   *Ans.* $59.50.
  * **4.** $900 for 100 days.   *Ans.* $15.00.
  * **5.** $3600 for 25 days.   *Ans.* $15.00.
     6. $5400 for 105 days.   *Ans.* $94.50.
  * **7.** $8000 for 48 days.   *Ans.* $64.00.
     8. $7200 for 36 days.   *Ans.* $43.20.
     9. $4800 for 23 days.   *Ans.* $18.40.
 * **10.** $1200 for 64 days.   *Ans.* $12.80.

85. Calculations by the 60-Day, 6 Per Cent Method Can Be Easily Proved. Because of its flexibility, the breakdown method of multiplication is an ideal means of proving answers to ordinary interest problems. Note, in the following illustration, the different

ways in which this method may be used to compute the ordinary
interest on $1798.00 for 140 days at 6 per cent.

Method A: Interest for 120 days (twice $17.98)   = $35.96
              Interest for 20 days ($\frac{1}{6}$ of $35.96)   =   5.99
              _____
              Interest for 140 days   = $41.95

Method B: Interest for 60 days   = $17.98
              Interest for 15 days ($\frac{1}{4}$ of $17.98)   =   4.495
              Interest for 75 days ($17.98 plus $4.495)   =   22.475
              _____
              Interest for 150 days   = $44.95
            — Interest for 10 days ($\frac{1}{6}$ of $17.98)   =   3.00
              _____
              Interest for 140 days   = $41.95

Problems

Compute the ordinary interest in each of the following problems by
two different breakdowns, as shown in the text. Assume an interest rate
of 6% in each instance.

1. $1430.00 for 40 days.	*Ans.* $9.53.
★ **2.** $2826.30 for 90 days.	*Ans.* $42.39.
3. $3748.60 for 25 days.	*Ans.* $15.62.
4. $1685.20 for 24 days.	*Ans.* $6.74.
5. $854.70 for 150 days.	*Ans.* $21.37.
6. $1232.40 for 160 days.	*Ans.* $32.86.
7. $763.80 for 135 days.	*Ans.* $17.19.
8. $3046.24 for 85 days.	*Ans.* $43.16.
★ **9.** $4010.00 for 12 days.	*Ans.* $8.02.
10. $6200.00 for 18 days.	*Ans.* $18.60.

**86. A Simple Way to Find the Number of Days in Any Interest
Period.** A quick way to find the number of days in an interest
period is to list the number of days in each month separately, and
total them. The number of days in the interest period May 4 to
September 17 would, therefore, be found as follows:

May	=	27 days
June	=	30 days
July	=	31 days
August	=	31 days
September	=	17 days

136 days

However, there is a table which, when available for ready reference, facilitates such computations. Table XI shows the number of each day of the year counting from January 1, and, as will be readily apparent, the computation by the use of this table of the number of days in any interest period resolves itself into a simple problem in subtraction. The number of days in the interest period in the preceding illustration would, for example, be computed by subtracting 124 (May 4 being the 124th day of the year) from 260 (September 17 being the 260th day of the year), and we know immediately that there are 136 days in this period. Note that this checks with our month-by-month calculation.

PROBLEMS

Show how you would compute by the month-by-month method the number of days in the following interest periods.

1. March 6 to May 19.   *Ans.* 25 + 30 + 19 = 74.
2. April 22 to June 5.   *Ans.* 8 + 31 + 5 = 44.
3. May 27 to July 20.   *Ans.* 4 + 30 + 20 = 54.
4. May 16 to August 31.   *Ans.* 15 + 30 + 31 + 31 = 107.
5. June 20 to September 15.   *Ans.* 10 + 31 + 31 + 15 = 87.
6. August 6 to November 10.   *Ans.* 25 + 30 + 31 + 10 = 96.

Compute the number of days in the following interest periods, using Table XI as your guide.

7. April 6 to July 9.   *Ans.* 94 days.
8. September 22 to December 20.   *Ans.* 89 days.
9. August 11 to November 3.   *Ans.* 84 days.
10. March 8 to September 14.   *Ans.* 190 days.
11. July 17 to October 25.   *Ans.* 100 days.
12. April 10 to August 17.   *Ans.* 129 days.
13. January 15 to March 6 in a leap year. *Ans.* 51 days.
14. January 17 to April 18 in a non-leap year. *Ans.* 91 days.

tation at the bank on which it was drawn, the amount would automatically be charged to Walpole's account by his bank.

Some interesting facts should be noted in connection with this transaction. The amount advanced by the bank was calculated not on the face value of the note nor on the amount advanced, but on the *maturity* value of the note. Also, the bank discount (really the interest charge) was *deducted at the time the money was advanced*. In other words, in having the note discounted, Walpole not only lost the equivalent of 1 per cent on the maturity value of the note (1 per cent because the bank charged him 4 per cent and the note called for an interest payment of 3 per cent), but he also lost the use of $51.85, the bank charge, for 110 days; so that he actually paid slightly more than the 4 per cent charged by the bank. This difference between simple interest and bank discount is discussed further in the article that follows.

Example: A 90-day note is issued on April 2 for $4500.00 with interest at 2% per annum. The note was discounted on April 12 at 3%. Calculate the net proceeds.

Solution: Principal............................... $4500.00

Plus interest at 2% for 90 days (2% for 1
year would be $90.00; 2% for 90 days
= $\frac{1}{4}$ of $90.00)........................ 22.50

Maturity value of note.................. $4522.50

Less bank discount at 3% for 80 days *
(90 days minus the period that elapsed
from April 2 to April 12)............... 30.16

Net proceeds............................ $4492.34

* Note how simple this computation becomes by the 60-day 6 per cent method:

$4522.50 for 60 days at 6%　　　　　　　= $45.23
$4522.50 for 20 days at 6% ($\frac{1}{3}$ of $45.23) = 15.08

$4522.50 for 80 days at 6%　　　　　　　= $60.31

$4522.50 for 80 days at 3% ($\frac{1}{2}$ of $60.31) = $30.16

PROBLEMS

Calculate the net proceeds for each of the following notes.

Date of Note	Date Discounted	Term	Face Value	Interest Rate	Discount Rate
1. Mar. 11	Mar. 26	60 days	$3000	3%	4%
					Ans. $2999.92.
2. May 8	May 28	90 days	$8000	$2\frac{1}{2}$%	3%
					Ans. $8003.04.
3. June 21	July 21	120 days	$2400	3%	$3\frac{1}{2}$%
					Ans. $2402.79.
4. July 1	July 16	30 days	$4200	2%	3%
					Ans. $4201.74.
5. Sept. 14	Sept. 24	60 days	$3460	0	3%
					Ans. $3445.58.
6. Oct. 21	Nov. 10	120 days	$12900	1%	$3\frac{1}{2}$%
					Ans. $12,817.17.

88. A Simple Explanation of the Difference Between Simple Interest and Bank Discount. It was pointed out in the preceding article that when Walpole discounted his note he paid actually more than the 4 per cent charged him as "bank discount." Let us see why.

In having the note discounted Walpole, in effect, borrowed a sum of money—he borrowed $4190.15 for 110 days, for which privilege he paid the bank $51.85. Now if he had otherwise secured a loan of $4190.15 at the simple interest rate of 4 per cent or, let us say, if he owed someone $4190.15 and had given the creditor a note for this amount, payable in 110 days, with 4 per cent simple interest, Walpole would have had to pay *less* than $51.85. In other words, at the end of 110 days he would owe, in addition to the principal, $\frac{4}{100}$ of $\frac{110}{360}$ of $4190.15 which, reduced to fractional form, equals $\dfrac{4190.15 \times 4 \times 110}{100 \times 360}$ or $51.21, which amount is $0.64 less than was charged him as "bank discount."

PROBLEMS

Using the figures obtained in working the problems in Art. 87, compute the amount of interest which the note-holder in each instance would have to pay if, instead of discounting the note, he borrowed for the unexpired period of the note a sum of money equal to the net proceeds, at a rate of interest equal to the discount rate charged by the bank.

    Ans. (1) $15.00; (2) $46.68; (3) $21.02; (4) $5.25; (5) $14.36; (6) $124.61.

89. How to Determine the Present Value of a Sum of Money Due at a Future Date at Simple Interest. Suppose Henry Branred invested $100.00 at 4 per cent per annum. Assuming that the interest is paid annually, his investment would be worth, at the end of one year, $104.00. Let us now take the transaction in reverse. Suppose Branred had $104.00 coming to him a year hence, and he wanted to know the present value of this sum, assuming the prevailing rate of interest to be 4 per cent. Obviously, the present value of this debt is $100.00.

Let us now do a little reasoning together. Henry Branred's investment of $100.00 at the rate of 4 per cent would be worth, as we have seen, $104.00 at the end of one year. It is clear, then, that his investment at the beginning of the year is equal to $\frac{100}{104}$ of its value at the end of the year. From this we can conclude that *any* principal at 4 per cent per annum is equivalent at the beginning of a one-year period to $\frac{100}{104}$ of what it will amount to at the end of the one-year period. Similarly, any principal at 3 per cent per annum is equivalent at the beginning of a one-year period to $\frac{100}{103}$ of what it will amount to at the end of the one-year period. And so on. The denominator of the ratio, in other words, is the sum of 100 plus the interest rate.

Example 1: What is the present value of an investment that will be worth $468.00 a year hence? Assume the interest rate to be 4% payable annually.

Solution: The present value of the investment equals $\frac{100}{104}$ of the future value.

          $\frac{1}{104}$ of $468.00   = $ 4.50

          $\frac{100}{104}$ of $468.00 (100 times $4.50) = $450.00

Proof: 4% of $450.00   = $ 18.00

          $18.00 plus $450.00   = $468.00

Example 2: Find the present worth of an investment whose value six months hence will be $252.50. Assume the interest rate to be 2% per annum, payable semiannually.

Solution: An annual interest rate of 2% payable semiannually is equivalent to an interest rate of 1% for six months. So that the present value of this investment equals $\frac{100}{101}$ of the future value.

$\frac{1}{101}$ of $252.50 $\qquad\qquad$ = $ 2.50
$\frac{100}{101}$ of $252.50 (100 times $2.50) = $250.00

Proof: $\quad$ 1% of $250.00 $\qquad\qquad$ = $ 2.50
$\qquad\quad$ $2.50 plus $250.00 $\qquad$ = $252.50

Example 3: A manufacturer sold a bill of goods amounting to $3800.00 on net terms of 90 days. A few weeks after the shipment is billed he finds himself in need of cash. If money is worth 3%, how much should the manufacturer be willing to accept in full payment 60 days before payment is due?

Solution: The problem resolves itself into the question: What is the present worth of $3800.00 due two months hence at 3% per annum?

Two months at 3% per annum is equivalent to one year at $\frac{1}{2}$ of 1%. The present value of $3800.00 due two months hence is therefore $\dfrac{100}{100\frac{1}{2}}$ or $\frac{200}{201}$ of $3800.00.

$$\frac{200}{201} \text{ of } \$3800 = \frac{200 \times 3800}{201} = \frac{\$760,000}{201} \text{ or } \$3781.09$$

A word of explanation might be added here. In Examples 1 and 2 we computed $\frac{100}{104}$ and $\frac{100}{101}$, respectively, by first dividing by the denominator, and multiplying by the numerator *afterward*. The computations were made in that order principally to emphasize the convenience of this method of procedure; it is obviously easier to divide $468.00 by 104 and then multiply the result by 100 than to multiply $468.00 by 100 and divide by 104 afterward, because $468.00 divided by 104 gives us exactly $4.50. More often than not, however, the process of division is not complete with the determination of the cent digits, and it may be a good plan for the reader to make it a rule to calculate the product of the numerators first, and divide the result by the denominator—as we did in Example 3.

Problems

Find the present worth of the following sums, at the prevailing rates of interest indicated.

1. A sum worth $2200 one year hence—$3\frac{1}{2}\%$.   *Ans.* $2125.60.
2. A sum worth $3460 six months hence—$3\%$.   *Ans.* $3408.86.
3. A sum worth $8200 nine months hence—$4\%$.   *Ans.* $7961.16.
4. A sum worth $12,000 three months hence—2%.   *Ans.* $11,940.30.
5. A sum worth $9600 eight months hence—$3\%$.   *Ans.* $9411.76.
6. A sum worth $5000 four months hence—$1\frac{1}{2}\%$.   *Ans.* $4975.12.

CHAPTER XII

AVOIDING ERRORS IN ADDITION

The reader may have always taken it for granted that the process of addition is very simple, and there is no doubt that for a great many people this process of computation never presents any difficulty. It is, nonetheless, a fact that errors occur in addition just as frequently as in the other mathematical operations. Moreover, anyone is likely to make an error in addition. Only recently a certified public accountant, who enjoys an enviable practice, said to the author, "I hate to add figures, because I often catch myself making mistakes at it."

The reader will do well to acquaint himself with the various methods of addition discussed in this chapter. He is advised to pay particular attention to the methods described in Arts. 92 and 94; they are interesting as well as important. And a little diversion may even be found in studying the article, "Checking Addition by Casting Out the Nines."

90. The Most Practical Method of Reading Combinations of Figures. Many of us fall into the habit of injecting "and" when adding figures. There is really no need for this, and the practice is time-wasting and tends to confuse. Instead of saying, "6 and 9 are 15, and 4 are 19, and 6 are 25," it is better to say (silently, of course) "15, 19, 25," and so on.

Incidentally, it would be well to adopt the habit of leaving out the "and" when reading figures. Instead of reading 798 as "seven hundred and ninety-eight," just read, "seven hundred ninety-eight." Similarly, 1654 should be read "sixteen hundred fifty-four."

91. Mental Addition Without Carrying. What makes mental addition so difficult for some individuals is the "carrying" part of it. The need for carrying is eliminated when, instead of adding from right to left, we add from left to right.

231

In adding 3163 and 234, for instance, mentally, it is better to add, first 200, then 30, and lastly 4. The process would, therefore, consist of three simple steps which produce the two partial totals 3363 and 3393, and the final total 3397. Similarly, to add 7847 and 342 mentally, the process would comprise the two partial sums 8147 (7847 plus 300) and 8187 (8147 plus 40), and the final total 8189 (8187 plus 2).

When adding mentally numbers ending in 7, 8 or 9, it is sometimes more convenient to increase the value of the last digit to 10, complete the process of addition, then subtract from the answer the value by which the original number had been increased. Thus in adding 84 and 99, say "84 plus 100 equals 184, minus 1 equals 183." In adding 136 and 68, say "136 plus 70 equals 206, minus 2 equals 204."

The technique will be found most useful when adding numbers the sum of whose unit digits is 10 or more, as in the examples given. This procedure is not necessary, however, when adding numbers the sum of whose unit digits is less than 10; for example, in adding 241 to 358, there would be no point in changing 358 to 360.

EXERCISES

Add the following pairs of numbers mentally, then check your answers by adding them by the conventional method.

★ **1.**	572 and 216.	*Ans.* 788.
★ **2.**	613 and 324.	*Ans.* 937.
★ **3.**	735 and 152.	*Ans.* 887.
★ **4.**	944 and 361.	*Ans.* 1305.
★ **5.**	245 and 57.	*Ans.* 302.
★ **6.**	354 and 38.	*Ans.* 392.
★ **7.**	$8.23 and $4.29.	*Ans.* $12.52.
★ **8.**	$12.66 and $5.48.	*Ans.* $18.14.
★ **9.**	$14.75 and $3.42.	*Ans.* $18.17.
★ **10.**	$16.36 and $15.63.	*Ans.* $31.99.

PROBLEMS

Using Table XII as your guide, estimate the time in the following countries when it is 10:50 A.M. in New York. (See hint following the problems.)

TABLE XII

SHOWING THE NUMBER OF HOURS AND MINUTES TO BE ADDED TO EASTERN
STANDARD TIME TO DETERMINE THE TIME IN FOREIGN COUNTRIES

Country	Hours	Minutes	Country	Hours	Minutes
Aden..............	8	0	Calcutta...........	10	30
Algeria.............	5	0	Canary Islands.....	4	0
Argentina..........	1	0	Cape Colony.......	7	0
Azores.............	3	0	Cape Verde Is......	3	0
Batavia............	12	30	France............	5	0
Belgium............	5	0	Greece............	7	0
Bolivia.............	1	0	India..............	10	30
Bombay............	10	30	Netherlands........	5	20
British Borneo......	13	0	New Zealand.......	16	30
Brazil.............	2	0	United Kingdom....	5	0
Bulgaria............	7	0	Moscow (U.S.S.R.).	8	0
Burma.............	11	30	Yugoslavia.........	6	0

    1. Brazil   *Ans.* 12:50 P.M.

    2. United Kingdom   *Ans.* 3:50 P.M.

    3. Moscow, U.S.S.R.   *Ans.* 6:50 P.M.

    4. British Borneo   *Ans.* 11:50 P.M.

    5. Batavia.   *Ans.* 11:20 P.M.

    6. New Zealand.   *Ans.* 3:20 A.M.

(Hint: Add the hours and minutes separately, convert the minutes in
the total to hours, and make any necessary adjustment in the answer
from A.M. to P.M., or from P.M. to A.M., by eliminating the 12's. Thus to
find the time in Bombay when it is 8:40 A.M. in New York, we would
proceed as follows:

	Hours	*Minutes*	
Time in New York....................	8	40	A.M.
Add 10 hours 30 minutes to determine the			
time in Bombay......................	10	30	
Total............................	18	70	
Converting the minutes to hours, we obtain	19	10	
Eliminating the 12 from the total number			
of hours, gives us.....................	7	10	

The time in Bombay is therefore 7:10, and we know without the need for
any further computation that this means 7:10 P.M., not 7:10 A.M.)

92. Speeding Addition by Combining Figures. It is always a good plan when adding a column of figures, to combine digits that follow each other and add up to 10 because 10 is added so easily. Thus when 7 is followed by 3, or 3 by 7, instead of adding each digit separately, their *sum* (10) is added. This, of course, applies to any combination—1 and 9, 2 and 8, 4 and 6, and so on.

EXERCISES

Add by the technique discussed in the text the following groups of numbers:

1. 23	**2.** 13	**3.** 149	**4.** 64
47	28	31	128
44	42	74	32
56	53	186	53
12	17	29	324
38	36	140	16

Ans. (1) 220; (2) 189; (3) 609; (4) 617.

93. Adding Two or Three Columns of Figures at One Time. Here is an interesting short-cut that is often overlooked. Note, in the following problem, that the sum of the figures in the tens and units columns is less than 100, and that the digits in the hundreds column are easy to add. Rather than add each column separately, it is easier to take in at a glance the digits in the hundreds column and say "1400," then run your eye up the tens and units columns saying, "1427, 1449, 1458."

309
422
408
319
―――

Another illustration will suffice to make this clear:

224
132
108
321
402
―――

Say "1100, 1123, 1131, 1163, 1187." No need for carrying, and no need for pencil and paper.

Add mentally by the technique discussed the numbers in the following groups:

★ 1. 211	★ 2. 125	★ 3. 843	★ 4. 931
324	432	124	129
403	513	308	723
630	707	422	612

Ans. (1) 1568; (2) 1777; (3) 1697; (4) 2395.

94. Addition by Grouping. When the columns of figures are very long—that is, when they consist of about twenty numbers or more—a very practical way to add them is to separate the numbers into groups, drawing a line under every five or six numbers, and total each group separately. The sum of the sub-totals supplies the answer. An illustration follows:

142	
84	
256	
138	
29	649
236	
55	
198	
71	
562	1122
784	
32	
109	
128	
875	1928
543	
852	
106	
25	
481	2007
	5706

The convenience of grouping will be readily appreciated. Instead of adding all twenty numbers in the preceding illustration at one time, only five at a time were added to arrive at a sub-total. And it was necessary to add only four sub-totals to obtain the total. Groups may, of course, be arranged according to one's aptitude for figures—some may find it more convenient to add but four numbers at a time, others may have no difficulty adding six or seven numbers at one time.

PROBLEMS

Add the following sets of figures by the sub-total method, grouping the numbers in Problems 1 and 2 in 4's, and the numbers in Problems 4 and 5 in 5's. Show in your answers the sub-totals as well as the totals.

1. $ 21.41	2. $ 91.20	3. $217.45	4. $139.37
12.83	12.44	82.30	4.13
4.75	137.26	6.17	9.26
18.90	93.12	19.23	11.41
2.06	4.88	4.11	19.19
134.14	17.25	7.14	126.04
25.23	131.60	18.28	32.07
41.17	18.32	.32	4.93
9.18	24.67	12.44	2.16
12.05	130.13	190.26	15.82
7.23	19.24	11.17	72.14
135.64	6.16	4.60	13.06
		29.32	28.18
		15.25	142.02
		23.45	8.23

Ans.

1. Sub-totals: 57.89, 202.60, 164.10. Total: $424.59.
2. Sub-totals: 334.02, 172.05, 180.20. Total: $686.27.
3. Sub-totals: 329.26, 228.44, 83.79. Total: $641.49.
4. Sub-totals: 183.36, 181.02, 263.63. Total: $628.01.

95. Addition by Casting Out the Tens. This is another method of adding long columns of figures. It consists simply of putting

down a dot each time the sum of the digits reaches 10. When a
column of figures has been added, the number in excess of the last
10 is written down on the answer line, and the sum of the dots is
added to the figures in the next column. The procedure is the same
with each column. Let us take the example illustrated:

```
          3 4 2
          7·3·6
          8·5 2·
          6 1 7
          4·2 4·
          8 9·2
          6·5·3
          7·1 8·
          9·1 5
          ─────────
          6 1 4 9
```

Starting with the units and beginning at the top of the column,
we reach 10 on the third line, so we insert a dot alongside of the 2.
Continuing, we have another 10 on the fifth line (7 plus 4 equals
11), so we insert a dot alongside of the 4 and carry 1. On the eighth
line our sum is 14, so we insert a dot alongside of the 8 and carry 4.
Four plus 5 equals 9, so we write down 9 in the unit column of the
answer.

We have three dots alongside of the units, so we carry the 3 to
the tens column. Starting at the top of the tens column, our sum
on the second line is 10, so we insert a dot alongside of the 3. And
so on all the way down the column.

Alongside of the tens column we have three dots, so we carry
the 3 to the hundreds column and continue in exactly the same
way as we did with the tens column. Completing the addition
of the digits in the hundreds column, we find that there are six
dots to be accounted for, so we simply write 6 in the thousands
column of the answer, which gives us 6149.

Add the following groups of numbers by the conventional method, then check your answers by casting out the tens.

1. 419	**2.** 175	**3.** 2483	**4.** 3617
236	482	7646	1342
705	367	9218	9076
864	279	4709	4835
381	520	3167	8314
275	965	9345	2538
463	854	8752	1743
192	312	1345	5808
	768		1482

96. Addition by the Two-Line Method. Many who are not unaccustomed to working with figures are sometimes exasperated by the variety of answers obtained when adding long columns of figures or a series of numbers which run into six or more figures. Physical interruptions and thought interruptions are common causes of errors in addition.

A conventional method of addition—one which makes it possible to go over a column once more without having to start all over again—might best be described as the "two-line" method. By this method each column is added separately, the unit figure of the total being put down directly under the figures totaled, while the tens figure is put down on the line below, one space to the left. The addition of the two lines of figures supplies the answer. Note the explanation which accompanies the following illustration in which four rows of figures are added by this method.

$$
\begin{array}{r}
3426724 \\
6213816 \\
4167482 \\
2389156 \\
\hline
5075068 \\
1112211 \\
\hline
16197178
\end{array}
$$

The sum of the digits in the unit column is 18, so we put down the 8 in the unit column of the first partial total, and 1 on the line below, one space to the left.   The sum of the digits in the tens column is 16, so we put down the 6 in the tens column of the first partial total, and 1 on the line below, one space to the left.   And so on.   Adding the two partial totals, we arrive at the answer, 16,197,178.

PROBLEMS

Add the following sums by the two-line method.

1. $ 473.56	2. $2612.15	3. $7109.23	4. $2581.17
6235.18	923.81	218.14	1024.83
1920.71	1617.57	3106.27	2151.72
4364.16	2328.18	1934.85	3042.93
		2075.63	4672.57

Ans. (1) $12993.61; (2) $7481.71; (3) $14444.12; (4) $13473.22.

97. Addition by the "Angular" Method.   Another helpful device might be aptly described as the "angular" method.   Here, as in the two-line method described in Art. 96, the sum of each column of figures is written down as a separate total, but in a different form, the various totals forming an "angle" with the answer. Thus, in the example illustrated, the sum of the units is 22, the sum of the tens 21, and the sum of the hundreds 14.

428	22
743	21
285	14
176	—
—	1632

Note the angle that these sums form with the total.   In setting them down care should, of course, be taken to write each sum in the correct place: the last figure in the sum of the tens should be in the tens column, the last figure in the sum of the hundreds in the hundreds column, and so on.

Add the following sums by the "angular" method, and check your answers by the two-line method.

1. $1.89	2. $52.60	3. 102.46	4. $244.27
3.42	84.73	273.91	183.46
5.86	91.26	91.82	701.50
8.27	15.92	146.73	236.41
		51.20	238.56

Ans. (1) $19.44; (2) $244.51; (3) $666.12; (4) $1604.20.

98. Checking Addition by Adding in Reverse Order. As in the other mathematical processes, it is a good plan always to prove the answer to a problem in addition by adding the figures a second time. The second time, however, the figures should be added in reverse order. Thus, if the total is obtained the first time by starting at the top, it should be obtained in the proving operation by starting at the bottom.

The reason for this is that often when a series of numbers is added in a hurry a wrong total may be applied to a combination of certain digits, and if the addition is done again in exactly the same way the same mistake is likely to be repeated.

This system of proving addition is perfectly applicable to sums obtained by the method of casting out the tens, discussed in Art. 73. It is advisable, however, to make the dots set down in the proving operation distinguishable from the first dots. A pencil of a different color might be used; or ink, if a pencil was used for the first series of dots, or vice versa; or dashes, checks or circles might be substituted for dots.

In proving totals obtained by the "angular" method, discussed in Art. 95, the same principle may be applied, but with a slight modification: the columns are added from left to right instead of from right to left; and the figures are added in the opposite direction, that is, starting from the top instead of from the bottom, and vice versa.

Taking the example illustrated in Art. 97, our scratch pad would show the two processes (the original computation and the proving operation) as follows:

Problem in Addition	First Process	Second Process
428	22	14
743	21	21
285	14	22
176	—	—
—	1632	1632

PROBLEMS

Add the sums in the following groups in any way you wish, then check your answers by the "angular" method—first from right to left, then from left to right, as illustrated in the text.

1. $25.47	2. $17.63	3. $46.35	4. $55.23
18.72	4.22	14.89	91.28
34.66	27.60	29.62	76.45
19.25	9.24	57.18	83.20
		15.90	4.06

Ans. (1) $98.10; (2) $58.69; (3) $163.94; (4) $310.22.

99. Checking Addition by Multiplication. It often happens that an interesting group of numbers like the following is to be added: 24, 48, 12, 8, 16. Notice that each number is a multiple of 4. A good way to find the total of such a group of numbers or prove the answer is to add the multiples and multiply their sum by 4. The multiples are 6, 12, 3, 2 and 4 respectively; their sum is 27, which, multiplied by 4, gives us 108.

PROBLEMS

Add the gollowing groups of numbers by the method discussed in the text, and show your method of procedure.

1. 9, 15, 21, 27, 39.	*Ans.* 111.
2. 12, 18, 36, 42, 54.	*Ans.* 162.
3. 8, 24, 40, 56, 64.	*Ans.* 192.
4. 14, 21, 35, 49, 56.	*Ans.* 175.
5. 36, 63, 45, 18, 27, 54.	*Ans.* 243.

100. Checking Addition by Casting Out the Nines. This method, the principle of which is the same in all four mathematical operations, entails nothing more than the addition of the digits of each number including the answer, dividing each total by 9, and setting down the remainder.

Thus to prove the sum of 4562, 3895 and 4263 we proceed as follows:

4562	$4 + 5 + 6 + 2 = 17.$	Casting out the 9 leaves	8
3895	$3 + 8 + 9 + 5 = 25.$	Casting out the 9's leaves	7
4263	$4 + 2 + 6 + 3 = 15.$	Casting out the 9 leaves	6
			—
12720	$1 + 2 + 7 + 2 = 12.$	Casting out the 9 leaves	3

Having set down the "remainders" for the four numbers (8, 7, 6 and 3), we proceed to check them, and this too is done by casting out the nines. The sum of 8, 7 and 6 is 21, and casting out the nines leaves 3. Since 3 is the check number ("remainder") for the answer to our problem, we may presume the answer (12720) to be correct. But as explained in Art. 77, "Checking Multiplication by Casting Out the Nines," this method of calculation by casting out the nines is not infallible.

PROBLEMS

Prove by casting out the nines that the answers to the following problems in addition are correct.

1. 374 plus 296 plus 570 equals 1240.

2. 912 plus 485 plus 366 plus 281 equals 2044.

3. 2468 plus 1767 plus 45 plus 197 equals 4477.

4. 95 plus 2076 plus 853 plus 124 equals 3148.

5. 184 plus 236 plus 8745 plus 14 plus 296 equals 9475.

CHAPTER XIII

AVOIDING ERRORS IN SUBTRACTION

Subtraction is a comparatively simple operation, for problems in subtraction involve but three values: the number from which we are to subtract, the number to be subtracted, and the difference.

However, one is more subject to err in subtraction than in a simple problem in addition; therefore, the former operation calls for more concentrated attention than the latter.

A study of Art. 101 should enable the reader to perform mentally a larger variety of problems in subtraction than seemed possible heretofore. And readers who hitherto have not used it very commonly are urged to familiarize themselves with the method of checking subtraction by addition, discussed in Art. 102.

101. A Simple Method of Mental Subtraction. Suppose you made a purchase amounting to $2.95 and tendered a $10.00 bill in payment. You doubtless would have no difficulty determining mentally just how much change to expect: you would subtract $3.00 from $10.00 and add 5 cents to the difference.

It is really very simple. Yet many individuals find it difficult to subtract 43 cents from 97 cents mentally.

A very practical procedure is to take the number to be subtracted and increase it mentally to the nearest multiple of 10, then to mentally increase the other quantity by the same value. Restated, then, the foregoing problem, 97 cents minus 43 cents, would be $1.04 minus 50 cents, and we should know instantly that the answer is 54 cents.

In subtracting 348 from 624 we should find it more practical to increase the number to be subtracted to the nearest hundred. Thus 348 becomes 400, and 624 becomes 676. And we see at a glance that 400 subtracted from 676 leaves 276.

The solution to the problem 6420 minus 5865 may require just a little more effort to obtain the answer mentally. Here we increase the number to be subtracted to 6000. Since we have added 135 to 5865, we must likewise add 135 to 6420. Our problem has thus been changed to read 6555 minus 6000. And without giving it another thought we know that the answer is 555.

The principle of this method is, of course, based on the fact that it is easier to add than to subtract.

PROBLEMS

The answers to these problems should be computed mentally.

★ 1. What is the difference between the capacities of two tanks, one of which holds 365,000 gallons of water, the other 328,000?

Ans. 37,000 gallons.

★ 2. The distance from New York City to Boston, Massachusetts, via Cape Cod Canal and Long Island Sound is 234 nautical miles. From New York City to Fall River, Massachusetts, via Long Island Sound, the distance is 159 nautical miles. By how many nautical miles is Boston more distant from New York than Fall River?   *Ans.* 75 nautical miles.

★ 3. A home was purchased for $29,750 and sold for $33,500. How much profit was made on the sale?   *Ans.* $3750.

★ 4. If it costs $3.64 to ship a 77-pound package by express to Omaha, Nebraska, and $1.36 to ship a package of the same weight and by the same means to Bridgewater, Massachusetts, how much more costly is the transportation expense of the one package than that of the other?

Ans. $2.28.

★ 5. A cubic foot of Portland cement weighs 183 pounds. A cubic foot of concrete weighs 144 pounds. What is the difference in weight per cubic foot between the two substances?   *Ans.* 39 pounds.

★ 6. The automobile touring distance from Nashville, Tennessee, to Atlanta, Georgia, is 258 miles. From Nashville to Columbia, South Carolina, the distance is 479 miles. How much greater is the latter road distance than the former?   *Ans.* 221 miles.

★ 7. When the flying time from Los Angeles to Buenos Aires was 107 hours and 50 minutes a route was proposed that would reduce the flying time to 28 hours and 15 minutes. How much of a saving in time did the new route constitute?   *Ans.* 79 hours and 35 minutes.

★ **8.** The horsepower range of a heavy-duty Diesel engine is from $16\frac{1}{2}$ to 55. By how many horsepower does the latter figure exceed the former?

Ans. $38\frac{1}{2}$ horsepower.

★ **9.** A man borrows a sum of money on May 27 and repays it on October 19. Using Table XI as your guide, estimate the number of days covered by the loan period.   *Ans.* 145 days.

★ **10.** How much is $5.60 less 15%?   *Ans.* $4.76.

102. Checking Subtraction by Addition.   The method of checking subtraction by addition is undoubtedly the simplest of all checking methods.   In the subtraction problem that follows, for instance, all we need do to check the answer is add it mentally to 2964 (the subtrahend), and if the sum equals 4573 (the minuend) we may be sure that 1609 is the correct answer.

$$4573$$
$$-\ 2964$$
$$\overline{}$$
$$1609$$

PROBLEMS

Check your answers to the following subtraction problems by addition.

1. A firm's net profit in 1946 was $183,423.   Its net profit in 1945 was $142,893.   How much more did the firm earn in 1946 than in the previous year?   *Ans.* $40,530.

2. The land areas of North Carolina and South Carolina are 49,142 and 30,594 square miles, respectively.   By how many square miles is the area of North Carolina greater than the area of South Carolina?

Ans. 18,548 square miles.

3. A tank filled with milk weighs 7456 pounds.   If the tank when empty weighs 2463 pounds, how many pounds of milk does it contain?

Ans. 4993 pounds.

4. A highway system of 33,129 miles is made up of 4,837 miles of primary road and the remainder of secondary road.   Estimate the total number of miles represented by the secondary roadway.

Ans. 28,292 miles.

5. A survey revealed that of the 2,251,059 dwelling units in New York City as of January 1, 1946, only 359,488 were built since January 1, 1930.

According to this survey, how many dwelling units in New York City would you say were more than 16 years old on January 1, 1946?

Ans. 1,891,571.

★ 6. A yard of No. 5, 36-inch, Wide Duck fabric weighs 22.91 ounces. A yard of No. 6, 40-inch, Wide Duck fabric weighs 23.64 ounces. By what fraction of an ounce is the latter fabric heavier than the former?

Ans. .73 ounces.

7. The water distance in winter from New York City to Bombay, India, via the Suez Canal, is 8,174 nautical miles, while the distance to Calcutta, India, in the same season and via the same route, is 9,816 nautical miles. How much farther from New York City is Calcutta than Bombay? *Ans.* 1,642 nautical miles.

★ 8. One hundred feet of $2\frac{1}{2}$-inch diameter 3-strand Manila rope weigh 167 pounds. The same length of the same rope in $2\frac{5}{8}$-inch diameter weighs 191 pounds. How much heavier per 100 feet is the $2\frac{5}{8}$-inch rope than the $2\frac{1}{2}$-inch? *Ans.* 24 pounds.

9. The dimensions of two wall openings are, respectively, 13 feet by 17 feet and 15 feet by 19 feet. What is the difference in square feet between the areas of the two openings? *Ans.* 64 square feet. (*Arts. 1, 16*)

★ 10. A cubic centimeter of nickel weighs 8.8 grams. The same volume of solid tin weighs 7.184 grams. How much heavier per cubic centimeter is nickel than solid tin? *Ans.* 1.616 grams.

103. Checking Subtraction by Casting Out the Nines. The use of this method of checking subtraction is essentially the same as in checking multiplication and addition (see Arts. 77 and 100). The only difference is that the check numbers ("remainders"), instead of being multiplied or added, are subtracted.

Thus to prove that 5368 minus 3982 equals 1386, we proceed as follows:

$$5368 \quad 5 + 3 + 6 + 8 = 22. \quad \text{Casting out the 9's leaves} \quad 4$$
$$- 3982 \quad 3 + 9 + 8 + 2 = 22. \quad \text{Casting out the 9's leaves} \quad 4$$
$$\overline{} \qquad\qquad\qquad\qquad\qquad\qquad\qquad\qquad\qquad \overline{}$$
$$1386 \quad 1 + 3 + 8 + 6 = 18. \quad \text{Casting out the 9's leaves} \quad 0$$

Since the "remainder" in the answer, after casting out the nines, is 0, and the difference between the "remainder" in the minuend and the "remainder" in the subtrahend is also zero, we may presume our answer (1386) to be correct.

The following illustration is of special interest for the reason that the "remainder" in the minuend (4734) in this problem is 0. When this is the case, we insert as the check number not 0, but 9.

4734	$4 + 7 + 3 + 4 = 18.$	Casting out one 9 leaves 9
$- 2562$	$2 + 5 + 6 + 2 = 15.$	Casting out the 9 leaves 6
		$-$
2172	$2 + 1 + 7 + 2 = 12.$	Casting out the 9 leaves 3

As explained in the aforementioned Arts. 77 and 100, this method of calculation is not infallible. It is described here mainly for the interest it may have for many who are mathematically inclined. It is not recommended as a substitute for the simpler and surer method of checking subtraction by addition, as discussed in the preceding article.

PROBLEMS

Compute the answers to the following subtraction problems, and check them by casting out the nines.

1. Subtract $64,235.40 from $127,486.28.   *Ans.* $63,250.88.

2. In the fall a farmer put 3960 bushels of corn into his cribs. When he sold the corn in the spring he found that it had shrunk to 3482 pounds. Estimate the amount of the shrinkage.   *Ans.* 478 pounds.

3. One thousand board feet of Southern Cypress weigh 2670 pounds. An equal number of board feet of American Elm weighs 2920 pounds. How much heavier is 1000 board feet of the latter wood than the former?   *Ans.* 250 pounds.

4. In May, 1946, the average hourly wage earned by workers in the electrical machinery industry was $1.138. The average in the men's clothing industry for the same period was $0.997. What is the difference between the two figures?   *Ans.* $0.141.

5. The weight of a finished 6-inch thick wall of hollow clay tile is 3190 pounds per 100 square feet. The weight of a finished 10-inch thick wall of the same material is 4580 pounds per 100 square feet. How much heavier per 100 square feet is the 10-inch thick wall than the 6-inch thick wall?   *Ans.* 1390 pounds.

6. A manufacturer wishing to expand his facilities considers renting a loft of 6380 square feet. His present loft measures 103 feet by 58 feet. How much additional floor space would he have if he moved from the one loft to the other?   *Ans.* 406 square feet. (*Art. 3*)

7. Cream containing 28% of butter fat has a weight of 8.37 pounds a gallon. Cream containing 40% of butter fat weighs 8.28 pounds a gallon. What would be the difference in weight between 36 gallons of cream of the higher fat content and 32 gallons of cream of the lower fat content?

Ans. 30.24 pounds. (*Arts. 5, 6*)

8. A grower of flaxseed obtained an average of $6\frac{1}{2}$ bushels per acre from his 250 acres of land. A more fortunate grower secured 11 bushels per acre from his 420 acres. By how much did the total production of one grower exceed that of the other? *Ans.* 2995 bushels. (*Art. 1-f*)

9. The highest altitude in the state of Oregon is Mount Hood, reputed to be 11,245 feet high. The highest altitude in the state of Washington is Mount Rainier, whose height is 14,408 feet. How much higher is Mount Rainier than Mount Hood? *Ans.* 3163 feet.

10. Compute the difference in weight between 16 carcasses having an average weight of 603 pounds and 18 carcasses whose average weight is 618 pounds. *Ans.* 1476 pounds. (*Arts. 22, 25*)

CHAPTER XIV

DIVISION CAN BE AS SIMPLE AS MULTIPLICATION

No other mathematical operation is disliked so much by so many as division. Yet the truth is that in a great many instances division can be as simple as multiplication.

It is hoped that most readers will find this chapter of special interest and significance. The articles contained herein will point—perhaps more than any other chapter in this book—to the fact that many difficult-looking problems can be solved with fascinating ease and speed, and quite often without recourse to pencil and paper.

104. How to Divide Quickly and Easily by 5, 15, $7\frac{1}{2}$, $12\frac{1}{2}$, $37\frac{1}{2}$, $62\frac{1}{2}$, $112\frac{1}{2}$. The reader's interest in the study of this article may be considerably enhanced if he will first review Art. 1, which deals with the subject of multiplying by some of these numbers. The text that follows is in a way a continuation of that article, and for this reason is accompanied by little explanatory detail.

104a. To divide by 5, multiply by 2 and divide by 10.

Example: Divide 175 by 5.

Solution: 175 times 2 = 350 which, divided by 10, equals 35.

104b. To divide by 15, multiply by 2 and divide by 30.

Example: Divide 135 by 15.

Solution: 135 times 2 = 270 which, divided by 30, equals 9.

104c. To divide by $7\frac{1}{2}$, multiply by 4 and divide by 30.

Example: Divide 390 by $7\frac{1}{2}$.

Solution: 390 times 4 = 1560 which, divided by 30, equals 52.

104d. To divide by $12\frac{1}{2}$, multiply by 8 and divide by 100.

Example: Divide 175 by $12\frac{1}{2}$.

Solution: 175 times 8 = 1400 which, divided by 100, equals 14.

104e. To divide by $112\frac{1}{2}$, multiply by 8 and divide by 900.

Example: Divide $1912\frac{1}{2}$ by $112\frac{1}{2}$.

Solution: $1912\frac{1}{2}$ times 8 = 15300 which, divided by 900, equals 17.

104f. To divide by $37\frac{1}{2}$, multiply by 8 and divide by 300.

Example: Divide 675 by $37\frac{1}{2}$.

Solution: 675 times 8 = 5400 which, divided by 300, equals 18.

104g. To divide by $62\frac{1}{2}$, multiply by 8 and divide by 500.

Example: Divide $812\frac{1}{2}$ by $62\frac{1}{2}$.

Solution: $812\frac{1}{2}$ times 8 = 6500 which, divided by 500, equals 13.

The reader will do well to familiarize himself with the reason why the divisor in each of the foregoing illustrations was converted to a multiple of 10 or 100, and with the method by which the divisors were changed to multiples of 100.

The reason will be readily apparent. Changing the divisor to a multiple of 10 or 100 simplifies the problem. It is easier to multiply by 2 and divide by 10 than to divide by 5; to multiply by 2 and divide by 30 than to divide by 15; to multiply by 4 and divide by 30 than to divide by $7\frac{1}{2}$. And with regard to the last four illustrations (104d, e, f and g), it is obviously easier to multiply by a single digit and divide the result by another single digit than to divide by a number which comprises two digits and a fraction. We need not be unduly concerned with the fact that the digit in the new divisor is followed by one or two zeros, for dividing by 10 or 100 requires nothing more than moving the decimal point to the left one or two places, as the case may be.

In Chapters VI and VII ("Aliquot Parts" and "Percentages and Discounts"), the method of converting numbers to multiples of 100 was explained in detail. We know, for instance, that since $12\frac{1}{2}$ is one eighth of 100 ($\frac{100}{8}$), multiplying a number by 8 and dividing the result by 100 produces precisely the same result as dividing the number by $12\frac{1}{2}$.

It may be well, for the benefit of those who have found some difficulty with division, to introduce here an important principle concerning this operation. When we multiply by a fraction we multiply by the numerator and divide by the denominator; thus 60 multiplied by $\frac{3}{5}$ is equivalent to 180 divided by 5, which equals 36. To *divide* by a fraction the process is reversed: we multiply by the denominator and divide by the numerator; thus 60 divided by $\frac{3}{5}$ becomes 60 multiplied by $\frac{5}{3}$, which equals 300 divided by 3, or 100.

The method of converting $37\frac{1}{2}$ and $62\frac{1}{2}$ into multiples of 100 is based on exactly the same principle as converting $12\frac{1}{2}$ into a multiple of 100. The number $37\frac{1}{2}$ is equivalent to $\frac{3}{8}$ of 100, or $\frac{300}{8}$; therefore, when we divide by $37\frac{1}{2}$ all we need do is multiply by 8 and divide by 300. Similarly, $62\frac{1}{2}$ is equivalent to $\frac{5}{8}$ of 100, or $\frac{500}{8}$, and therefore to divide by $62\frac{1}{2}$ we multiply by 8 and divide by 500.

The number $112\frac{1}{2}$, however, is not an aliquot part of 1000, but a quick glance reveals that it is $\frac{1}{8}$ of 900 ($\frac{900}{8}$), so that division by $112\frac{1}{2}$ may be effected by multiplying by 8 and dividing by 900.

A rereading of this article may be found well worth while. It will help the reader to appreciate the practicability of extending the application of this short-cut method of division to such numbers as $33\frac{1}{3}$, $16\frac{2}{3}$, $66\frac{2}{3}$, etc.

Problems

★ 1. A practical way of packing mince meat for consumer distribution is to put it up in 5-pound wood pails. Estimate the number of pails of this size that can be filled from 3400 pounds of this product. *Ans.* 680.

* **2.** How many 5-ounce packages can be packed from 2000 pounds of dehydrated eggs?   *Ans.* 6400.

* **3.** What quantity of stone will be crushed in 12 minutes by a stone-crushing machine having a capacity of 275 tons per hour?   (Hint: 12 minutes equals one fifth of an hour.)   *Ans.* 55 tons.

4. If it takes 15 squares of shingles to roof a house, how many houses can be roofed with 435 squares of shingles?   *Ans.* 29.

5. A food producer finds it profitable to put up maraschino cherries in brandy syrup in 15-ounce jars.   If he can produce the finished product in batches of 1125 pounds per week, how many dozen jars would he use weekly in packing his product?   *Ans.* 100 dozen. (*Art. 22*)

* **6.** If a pound of oyster shell (a widely fed source of calcium carbonate for laying-hens) contains sufficient lime for the shells of $7\frac{1}{2}$ dozen eggs, how many pounds of oyster shell would be needed to supply the required quantity of lime for an estimated production of 60 cases of eggs, packed 30 dozen eggs to the case?   *Ans.* 240 pounds.

7. If the net weight of a container of oysters is $7\frac{1}{2}$ ounces, how many dozen containers can be filled from 450 pounds of this food product?

Ans. 80 dozen.

* **8.** How long would it take to plow 175 acres of ground at a speed of $12\frac{1}{2}$ acres per day?   *Ans.* 14 days.

9. Compute in square feet the area of the bottom of a ditch $12\frac{1}{2}$ feet deep, from which 25 cubic yards of dirt is to be removed.   (Hint: Convert 25 cubic yards to cubic feet by multiplying by 27.)   *Ans.* 54 square feet.

10. A manufacturer uses a wood tank to furnish his daily requirement of $37\frac{1}{2}$ gallons of water.   If the tank is filled to its capacity of 3225 gallons, for how long will the daily requirement be satisfied?   *Ans.* 86 days.

11. If the cost of constructing $37\frac{1}{2}$ miles of road was $874,320, what was the average cost per mile?   *Ans.* $23,315.20.

* **12.** If a dealer's gross profit on a 1-pound container of a food specialty is $62\frac{1}{2}$ cents, how many units would he have to sell to make a gross profit of $200.00?   *Ans.* 320.

13. If an oil burner, consuming $112\frac{1}{2}$ gallons of oil per hour, is in operation for 10 hours each day, how many days would a supply of 16,000 gallons of oil last?   *Ans.* $14\frac{2}{9}$ days.

14. The price of a $112\frac{1}{2}$-acre farm offered for sale is $24,075.   How much does that average per acre?   *Ans.* $214.00.

105. A Short Way of Dividing by Numbers Which Can Be Factored, Such as 24, 32, 56, 64, 121.   In Art. 5 we learned how to *multiply* by numbers which can be factored; namely, to break up the multiplier into factors and multiply separately by each factor. We learned, for instance, that 24 might be broken up into the factors 8 and 3 (the product of 8 multiplied by 3 being 24); or into the factors 6 and 4, or 12 and 2.

In dealing with factors in division the method is the same as with multiplication, except that we divide instead of multiply.

Example 1: Divide 4488 by 24.

Solution: 4488 divided by 4 = 1122
      1122 divided by 6 =   187

Example 2: Divide 5824 by 64.

Solution: 5824 divided by 8 = 728
       728 divided by 8 =   91

The foregoing illustrations will suffice to convince the reader of the time-saving advantage of dividing by factors whenever it is possible to do so. A word of caution, however, should be noted. Whereas, in multiplying by factors, it makes little difference by which factor we multiply first, in *division* it may be simpler to divide by one factor first than by the other.

Let us consider the problem of dividing 378 by 56. The most practical factors of 56 are 7 and 8. But it is obvious that if 378 is divided by 8 there will be a fraction in the quotient ($47\frac{1}{4}$). However, if we divide first by 7, the quotient (54) is a whole number. And it goes without saying that it is easier to divide 54 by 8 than $47\frac{1}{4}$ by 7.

A good practice to adopt when one factor of the divisor is an odd number and the other factor an even number is to divide by the odd number first if the unit digit of the dividend or the numerator in the fraction is an odd number, and to divide by the even factor first if the unit digit of the dividend or the numerator in the fraction is an even number; unless, of course, a quick glance reveals that the reverse procedure would be better, or that the order of division is immaterial.

* 7. A perfume manufacturer receives, C.O.D. for $15.20, a package containing 32 ounces of an essential oil that he ordered. What is his cost per ounce?   *Ans.* 47½ cents.

* 8. A research engineer put in 32 hours of his time on an assignment for which he earned a fee of $280.00. How much does this average per hour?   *Ans.* $8.75 per hour.

* 9. Compute the number of bushels represented by 1344 dry pints. (One bushel equals 64 dry pints.)   *Ans.* 21 bushels.

* 10. A food products company offers a 5-gallon can (640 fluid ounces) of a butter flavor for $108.80. How much is that per ounce? (Hint: 640 ounces for $108.80 is equivalent to 64 ounces for $10.88.)

Ans. 17 cents.

* 11. Estimate the number of cords in 1408 cubic feet of wood. (One cord of wood equals 128 cubic feet.)   *Ans.* 11 cords.

* 12. How many 128-ounce packages can be made up from a batch of material weighing 9088 ounces?   *Ans.* 71 packages.

108. How to Divide Quickly by 14, 16, 18, 20, 22, 24. If the reader has had occasion to refer to the last chapter in this book—the chapter dealing with decimals and fractions—he may have paused to contemplate the article on the subject of cancellation. A moment's reflection will reveal the interesting fact that just as cancellation is a process of division, division is a process of cancellation. In studying the subject of simple interest, for example, it was seen how important a part cancellation played with the denominators 360 and 100; and just a few pages back—in Art. 106—the advantage of factoring divisors was demonstrated.

Now we turn to a relatively simple technique—a technique which simplifies problems in division by first reducing dividend and divisor by half. Thus to divide 56 by 14 we need but to re-state the problem to read 28 divided by 7 to see instantly that the answer is 4. Similarly, the division of 128 by 16 can be accomplished mentally and effortlessly by changing the problem to 64 divided by 8. In fact, the labor of dividing by any even number can be reduced to a greater or lesser degree by first dividing dividend and divisor by 2.

Example 1: Divide 3114 by 18.

Solution: 1557 (½ of 3114) divided by 9 (½ of 18) = 173

Example 2: Divide 5256 by 24.

Solution: 2628 ($\frac{1}{2}$ of 5256) divided by 12 ($\frac{1}{2}$ of 24) = 219

The ease of dividing any number by 2 mentally makes this an especially valuable technique. Taking the foregoing illustration, for instance, compare the speed with which the answer was obtained by this method with the process of division by the conventional method:

$$
\begin{array}{r}
219 \\
24\overline{)5256} \\
48 \\
\hline
45 \\
24 \\
\hline
216
\end{array}
$$

Observe that by the conventional method it was necessary to write down no fewer than 18 figures, whereas by the technique under consideration we needed to write down no more than the seven figures in 2628 and 219, to say nothing of the expenditure of effort and energy and the greater possibility of error connected with the solution of the problem by the conventional method.

The eagle-eyed reader may have noticed that the divisor 24, discussed here, was also under consideration in Art. 105. But this should be no cause for confusion. While the result of dividing by 24 in different ways is the same, one method may be more practical in a particular instance than another. Thus to divide 4488 by 24 (the illustration given in Art. 105) it is obviously better to break up the divisor into the factors 4 and 6, for one quick glance shows that 4488 can be divided by 4 in a flash. On the other hand, in the problem 5256 divided by 24 (the illustration given in this article), the divisibility of 5256 by 4 is not effected quite so speedily. It is all a matter of choice. The net result is the important thing, and familiarity with the different techniques of accomplishing the same result will help establish a confidence in the reader that should enable him to perform these and other problems in division with incredible ease.

The divisor 20 is, of course, the simplest of all of the numbers mentioned in this article heading. For to divide by 20 it is only necessary to take one half of one tenth of the dividend. Thus 2460 divided by 20 is equivalent to 246 divided by 2, which equals 123; and 187 divided by 20 is equivalent to 18.7 divided by 2, which gives us 9.35.

Example 3: The expected result of the careful cultivation of sorghum is a yield of 14 bushels per acre. If this is accomplished, how many acres should produce a total of 1500 bushels of sorghum?

Solution: 750 ($\frac{1}{2}$ of 1500) divided by 7 ($\frac{1}{2}$ of 14) = 107$\frac{1}{7}$.

Ans. 107$\frac{1}{7}$ acres.

PROBLEMS

1. A roll of 12-inch wide asphalt-saturated mesh fabric (a material used in the building industry as a reinforcing agent) weighs approximately 14 pounds. If the net weight of a shipment of this material is 252 pounds, how many rolls might the shipment be presumed to contain?

Ans. 18 rolls.

2. Compressed nitrogen (a gas supplied for the protection of material susceptible to oxidation) is available in cylinders containing 244 cubic feet each. If 14 cubic feet of this gas are used every five business days, in how many business days will the contents of one cylinder be consumed? Estimate your answer to the nearest whole day. *Ans.* 87 days.

3. If a cow gives 16 pounds of milk a day, how many cows of this average production capacity would be needed to supply a daily requirement of 272 pounds of milk? *Ans.* 17 cows.

4. How long would it take to obtain 432 feet of finished white prints from a reproduction machine synchronized to print and develop 16 feet of these prints per minute? *Ans.* 27 minutes.

5. Assuming that there is no waste in cutting, how many castings each weighing 18 ounces can be obtained from 720 pounds of metal? (Hint: Instead of multiplying 720 pounds by 16 to obtain the total number of ounces, and then dividing by 18, it is better to multiply 720 by 8, which is half of 16, and divide the result by 9, which is half of 18.) *Ans.* 640 castings.

6. The approximate acreage used for growing strawberries in the United States is 180,000 acres, and the crop value is about $35,000,000.

What would you say is the value of the average production per acre? (Hint: By canceling the zeros, the problem resolves itself into dividing $3500 by 18.)   *Ans.* $194⅓.

★ **7.** Twenty years after its purchase the value of a house exceeded the sum of its original cost and total maintenance by approximately $28,000. Approximately how much was the average gain per year?   *Ans.* $1400.

8. How many bottles can be filled with 200 tablets each from the production of a tablet machine operated for 4 hours at a speed of 350 tablets a minute.   *Ans.* 420 bottles. (*Art.* 23)

★ **9.** A regulation of the United States Department of Agriculture states that on ships carrying livestock there shall be one attendant to each 22 head. On this basis how many attendants should be found on a ship carrying 198 head of livestock?   *Ans.* 9 attendants.

10. It takes about 22 months for a pineapple plant to yield its first crop. If an acre produces 60,000 pounds of this fruit, how much would you say is the average production per month? Estimate your answer to the nearest pound.   *Ans.* 2727 pounds.

11. If the profit on a yard of fabric is 24 cents, how many yards would have to be sold to produce a total profit of $75.00?   *Ans.* 312½ yards.

★ **12.** A variety of felt slippers is made in a 60-inch wide felt weighing 24 ounces per yard. If the net weight of a shipment of this material is 840 pounds, how many yards may it be expected to contain? (Hint: Instead of multiplying by 16 and dividing by 24, multiply by 2 and divide by 3.)   *Ans.* 560 yards.

109. How to Divide Quickly by Multiples of 11, Like 33, 44, 55, 66, etc. The procedure in dividing by these numbers is fundamentally the same as that discussed in the preceding article. The only difference is that instead of dividing dividend and divisor by 2, we divide by 3, if the divisor is 33; by 4, if the divisor is 44; and so on.

Example 1: Divide 429 by 33.

Solution: 143 (⅓ of 429) divided by 11 (⅓ of 33) = 13

Example 2: Divide 1276 by 44.

Solution: 319 (¼ of 1276) divided by 11 (¼ of 44) = 29

This technique is used to the best advantage when the dividend is exactly divisible by the respective multiple of 11—namely, by 3, 4, etc.—because it is so much easier to divide a whole number by 11 than a number containing a fraction, as for example $106\frac{2}{3}$. The question now arises, how can one know quickly whether a number is exactly divisible by 3 or 4, etc.? This question is answered by Table XIII, which explains that a number is divisible by 3 if the sum of its digits is divisible by 3; that a number is divisible by 4, if its last two figures are zeros, or if the last two figures are divisible by 4; and so on.

Example 3: Divide $16,146.57 by 33.

Solution: The sum of the digits 1, 6, 1, 4, 6, 5 and 7, is 30. And 30 is exactly divisible by 3. So the problem resolves itself into dividing $5,382.19 (which is one third of $16,146.57) by 11 (which is one third of 33).

$5,382.19 divided by 11 = $489.29

Example 4: Divide $8,671.08 by 44.

Solution: The last two figures (.08) are exactly divisible by 4. So we proceed as follows:

$2,167.77 ($\frac{1}{4}$ of $8,671.08) divided by 11
($\frac{1}{4}$ of 44)   = $197.07

It is obvious that a number is exactly divisible by 5 if the last figure is 5 or a zero. So let us continue with an illustration in which the divisor is 66.

Example 5: Divide 29832 by 66.

Solution: Table XIII tells us that a number is divisible by 6 if it is an even number and the sum of its digits is divisible by 3. We find that the sum of the digits 2, 9, 8, 3 and 2 is divisible by 3. So we may be sure, as we were in the preceding illustrations, that when we come to divide by 11, the dividend will be a whole number.

4972 ($\frac{1}{6}$ of 29832) divided by 11 ($\frac{1}{6}$ of 66) = 452

Although the technique operates beautifully when the original dividend is exactly divisible by the original divisor, that is, when

TABLE XIII

How to Determine Whether a Number Is Divisible by 3, 6, 9, 4, 8, 11

A Number Is Divisible by	If
3	the sum of its digits is divisible by 3. Thus 4605 is divisible by 3 because 15, the sum of its digits, is divisible by 3.
6	it is an even number and the sum of its digits is divisible by 3.
9	the sum of its digits is divisible by 9.
4	its last two figures are zeros, or if the last two figures are divisible by 4. Thus 924 is divisible by 4 because 24 is divisible by 4.
8	the last three figures are divisible by 8. Thus 7144 is divisible by 8 because 144 is divisible by 8.
11	the difference between the sum of the figures in the even places and the sum of the figures in the odd places is 0 or 11. Thus 53031 may be recognized as a number divisible by 11 because 1 plus 0 plus 5 equals 6, and 3 plus 3 equals 6, and 6 minus 6 equals 0. The number 162679 is divisible by 11 because 9 plus 6 plus 6 equals 21; 7 plus 2 plus 1 equals 10; and 21 minus 10 equals 11.

the final result is a whole number, it is just as practical to use when the result in the final answer contains a fraction, as will be seen in the following illustration:

Example 6: Divide 19216 by 88.

Solution: The last three figures (216) are divisible by 8, so we know that the entire number is divisible by 8. Note, also, that in this instance we took the last three digits as a *whole number*, not the *sum* of the digits as when dividing by 3, 4 and 6.

2402 ($\frac{1}{8}$ of 19216) divided by 11 ($\frac{1}{8}$ of 88) = $218\frac{4}{11}$

Example 7: Glass asbestos in the 36-inch width is available in rolls of approximately 33 square feet. If 4176 square feet are required, and if the product can be purchased only in whole rolls, how many rolls will be needed?

Solution: 1392 ($\frac{1}{3}$ of 4176) divided by 11 ($\frac{1}{3}$ of 33) = $126\frac{6}{11}$

Ans. 127 rolls.

PROBLEMS

1. A contractor wishes to estimate the number of boxes of panes, 12 by 18 inches, required in the construction of a building. The panes, of which 1404 will be needed, are packed 33 to a box. How many boxes of the glass will be used on the job? Estimate your answer to the nearest whole box. *Ans.* 43 boxes.

2. At a speed of 3300 bobbins per hour, how long would it take a machine to clean 39,000 bobbins. Compute the answer to the nearest tenth of an hour. (Hint: Dividing 39,000 by 3300 is equivalent to dividing 390 by 33.) *Ans.* 11.8 hours, or 11 hours and 48 minutes.

★ 3. If 44 feet of $\frac{1}{4}$-inch diameter sash cord weigh approximately one pound, what should be the approximate net weight of a package containing 572 feet of this cord? *Ans.* 13 pounds.

4. A store's total receipts for the day were $598.40. If this represented 440 sales, what was the average amount per sale? *Ans.* $1.36.

★ 5. A rigidly mounted tool cuts yellow brass $\frac{5}{32}$ of an inch deep at 550 feet per minute. Estimate the time required to cut 15,400 feet of this metal to the aforementioned depth. *Ans.* 28 minutes.

6. If it takes .55 hours to punch three holes in 1000 sheets of a heavy weight paper $8\frac{1}{2}$ by 11 inches, how many sheets could be punched in 8 hours? Compute your answer to the nearest half a thousand sheets. (Hint: Dividing 8 by .55 is equivalent to dividing 800 by 55.) *Ans.* 14,500 sheets.

7. The cost of the labor and material to paint a building exterior was $384.00. If the painted surface comprised an area of 6600 square feet, what was the cost per square foot? Compute your answer to the nearest cent. *Ans.* 6 cents per square foot.

8. A square foot of asbestos mill board, $\frac{3}{32}$ inch thick, weighs 6.6 ounces. Compute the approximate number of square feet in a stack of this board weighing $239\frac{1}{4}$ pounds. *Ans.* 580 square feet.

9. A printer finds that it takes 7.7 hours to trim the pages of one thousand 880-page books. If his plant operates on an $8\frac{3}{4}$-hour-day basis, how many books could be completed in five days? *Ans.* 5682 books.

10. If a turret lathe cuts annealed tool steel at a speed of 77 feet per minute, how long would it take to cut 6300 feet of this material? Compute the answer to the nearest minute.

Ans. 82 minutes, or 1 hour 22 minutes.

11. A pharmaceutical manufacturer finds that he can market a quality product by using 88 ounces of a special ingredient to every one gross bottles. If he purchased 125 pounds of the ingredient, for approximately how many gross bottles will the material suffice? Estimate the total to the nearest gross. *Ans.* 23 gross.

12. If the net weight of 120 tin plate sheets, 14 by $19\frac{1}{4}$ inches, is 88 pounds, how many sheets would be represented by an inventory of 1496 pounds of this material? *Ans.* 2040 sheets.

13. Of $2\frac{1}{4}$-inch plain washers there are approximately 121 to the pound. If a counting scale indicates an inventory of approximately 4050 of these parts, how many pounds should this inventory weigh? State the answer to the nearest half pound. *Ans.* $33\frac{1}{2}$ pounds.

14. If a foot of $2\frac{3}{4}$-inch diameter hoisting rope weighs approximately 12.1 pounds, how many feet of this material would be contained in a net weight of 1331 pounds? *Ans.* 110 feet.

110. How to Shorten the Process of Dividing by Three- and Four-Figure Numbers Which Can Be Factored, Such as 284, 428, 945, 1664, 2418, 5409, 6416, 8127. Some of the preceding articles in this chapter gave us a background for a quick appreciation of another little short-cut we are about to consider. We saw in Art. 105 how easy it is to divide by two-figure numbers which can be factored; in Art. 106, how conveniently we can divide by two-figure numbers which are divisible by 9; in Art. 108, the simple technique of dividing by some two-figure even numbers; and in Art. 109 we learned a time-saving method of dividing by two-figure, and some three-figure, numbers which are multiples of 11. Let us now advance a step and see how the principle governing the aforementioned processes can be expanded to three- and four-figure numbers.

Let us begin with the simple problem of dividing 38908 by 284. With our now mathematically trained eye we see at once that the divisor (284) is divisible by 4; and as regards the dividend (38908), we know from our study in the preceding article that a number is divisible by 4 if the last two figures are zeros, or if the last two figures are divisible by 4. The last two figures in

38908 are divisible by 4, so we can reduce our problem to read, 9727 (which is one fourth of 38908) divided by 71 (which is one fourth of 284).   Now see how easy and effortless it is to divide 9727 by 71 compared with the division of 38908 by 284.

$$
\begin{array}{r}
137 \\
284)\overline{38908} \\
284 \\
\hline
1050 \\
852 \\
\hline
1988
\end{array}
\qquad
\begin{array}{r}
137 \\
71)\overline{9727} \\
71 \\
\hline
262 \\
213 \\
\hline
497
\end{array}
$$

Ans. 137.

It is hardly necessary to comment on the greater ease of dividing by 71 than by 284.   Worthy of special note is the fact that whereas division by the original numbers required the writing down of 25 figures in the computation, the process of dividing by the reduced numbers called for only 20 figures.   (As we shall see in the next article, even this number can be reduced by an interesting technique.)

If our problem had been to divide 82604 by 428, the division of both numbers by 4 first would have been no less interesting.   The problem would then be reduced to read, 20651 divided by 107. See how the two methods of computation compare here:

$$
\begin{array}{r}
193 \\
428)\overline{82604} \\
428 \\
\hline
3980 \\
3852 \\
\hline
1284
\end{array}
\qquad
\begin{array}{r}
193 \\
107)\overline{20651} \\
107 \\
\hline
995 \\
963 \\
\hline
321
\end{array}
$$

Ans. 193.

In the foregoing illustration, the difference between the number of figures written down in one computation and the number written down in the other is not so great as in the first illustration. But is it not much easier to divide by 107 than by 428? What better figures can one wish for in a divisor than 1 and 0? And, as we shall see in a few moments, the 1 in the divisor appears not by accident but by design.

Since one of the objectives in this book is to develop in the reader a mathematical consciousness, it will be found profitable to refresh the memory with the contents of three tables in Chapter I—Tables II, III and IV—and to observe the interesting extent and variety of three- and four-figure numbers in which the relationship between one part of a number and the rest of the number helps considerably to simplify a problem in multiplication. If the reader will then couple the knowledge gained by a study of this group of tables with the information contained in Table XIII in the preceding article, he will recognize the amazing ease with which it is possible to solve many a problem in division which, to the uninitiated, would appear virtually unsolvable without the use of pencil and paper.

It might be emphasized here that exact divisibility of the dividend by one of the factors of the divisor is not essential; when exact divisibility in the dividend is possible, it is merely an added advantage as we will see by the variety in the following illustrations:

Example 1: Divide 78,435 by 945.

Solution: Since the last digit in the dividend as well as in the divisor is 5, we know that both numbers are divisible by 5; and to divide each number by 5 would, of course, shorten the process of computation. A quick glance, however, tells us that the divisor is also divisible by 9, which would give us the very desirable number 109. All we need to do to find out whether the dividend is divisible by 9 is to see if the sum of its digits is divisible by 9. We find that it is. So we will divide both numbers by 9.

78,435 divided by 9 equals 8715
945 divided by 9 equals 105

$$\begin{array}{r} 83 \\ 105\overline{)8715} \\ 840 \\ \hline 315 \end{array}$$

Ans. 83.

Example 2: Divide 4800 by 1664, and state the answer to the nearest hundredth of a unit.

Solution: Sixteen (the first two digits in the divisor) is exactly divisible into 64 (the last two digits), and dividing 1664 by 16 gives us 104. Sixteen goes into 4800 exactly 300 times. So our problem has been reduced to read, 300 divided by 104. We see instantly that both new numbers are also divisible by 4, so our problem can be further reduced to dividing 75 by 26.

$$\begin{array}{r} 2.884 \\ 26\overline{)75} \\ 52 \\ \hline 230 \\ 208 \\ \hline 220 \\ 208 \\ \hline 120 \end{array}$$

Ans. 2.88.

Example 3: Divide 307,086 by 2418.

Solution: We see at a glance that the divisor is divisible by 6. The dividend is an even number and the sum of its digits is divisible by 3; hence it, too, is divisible by 6. So let us reduce both numbers accordingly.

307086 divided by 6 equals 51181
2418 divided by 6 equals 403

$$\begin{array}{r} 127 \\ \overline{403)51181} \\ 403 \\ \hline 1088 \\ 806 \\ \hline 2821 \end{array}$$

Ans. 127.

Example 4: Divide $5400.00 by 8127, and state your answer to the nearest cent.

Solution: We see instantly that 8127 is divisible by 27, for 27 goes exactly three times into 81. And 27 goes exactly 200 times into 5400. So here is how we proceed.

5400 divided by 27 equals 200
8127 divided by 27 equals 301

$$\begin{array}{r} .664 \\ \overline{301)200} \\ 1806 \\ \hline 1940 \\ 1806 \\ \hline 1340 \end{array}$$

Ans. 66 cents.

Example 5: If 306 feet of fuse wire weigh one pound, and if the wire is wound ½ pound to the spool, how many spools would be necessary to furnish 6000 feet of this material? In computing the answer, a fraction of a spool is to be considered a whole unit.

Solution: One spool contains 153 feet. Since 3 cancels into 153 and also into 6000, let us reduce the problem to read 2000 feet divided by 51 feet.

$$
\begin{array}{r}
39.2 \\
51\overline{)2000} \\
153 \\
\hline
470 \\
459 \\
\hline
110
\end{array}
$$

Ans. 40 spools.

It is interesting to observe that the process of dividing by numbers in which one part is a multiple of the other, as for instance 945 (Example 1), calls for just a little more effort than in multiplying by such numbers. To multiply by 945 it is but necessary to multiply by 900 and add one twentieth (that is $\frac{1}{2}$ of $\frac{1}{10}$) of the result to itself. In dividing by 945 the procedure is a little different, for in division we cannot add or subtract as we can in multiplication. Thus to divide by 945, we had to divide first by one factor, and then—to complete the process—we had to divide the result (or quotient, as it is called in division) by the other factor.

PROBLEMS

1. If one square foot of $\frac{1}{4}$-inch thick polished plate glass, 124 by 170 inches, weighs about 3.27 pounds, approximately how many square feet would there by in 98.1 pounds of this glass?   *Ans.* 30 square feet.

2. A jobber's records show that he sold over a 12-month period a total of 2406 units of a particular product. The total amount billed for this merchandise was \$6905.22. What was the average amount for which each unit was billed?   *Ans.* \$2.87.

3. How long would it take to handle 45,000 yards of material on a warping machine at a speed of 918 yards a minute?   *Ans.* 49 minutes.

4. When cotton yarn is put into a winding machine, it consists of a continuous strand of about 60,000 yards. What is the equivalent of this length in miles? One mile equals 1760 yards. Compute the answer to the nearest mile.   *Ans.* 34 miles.

5. A manufacturer wishes to estimate the hourly average of his labor costs over a 6-month period. His payroll records indicate that in the last 6 months he paid the total sum of $5331.68 for 5672 man-hours of work. What was this manufacturer's average labor cost per hour?

Ans. 94 cents.

6. If 112 cows produce in 2 weeks a total of 25,536 pounds of milk, what is the average production for each cow per week? (Hint: Divide half of 25,536 by 112.) *Ans.* 114 pounds.

7. Estimate the number of square feet in one plate of wire glass 60 by 110 inches. (Hint: One square foot equals 144 square inches; so instead of finding the product of 60 times 110 and dividing the result by 144, find the product of 5 times 110 and divide the result by 12.)

Ans. $45\frac{5}{6}$ square feet.

8. If it requires about 4000 coconuts to produce one metric ton of copra, approximately how many nuts would be needed to produce 5 short tons of copra? A metric ton equals 2205 pounds, and a short ton equals 2000 pounds. (Hint: In computing the number of times 2205 goes into 10,000, obtain the result to the nearest thousandth of a unit, as the result will have to be multiplied by 4000.)

Ans. Approximately 18,140 coconuts.

9. Compute the equivalent in gallons of 792 cubic feet of water. One gallon equals 231 cubic inches, and one cubic foot equals 1728 cubic inches. (Hint: This problem resolves itself into converting cubic feet to cubic inches, and dividing by 231. However, each of the factors 11 and 3 is divisible into 231 and 792, which reduces these numbers to 7 and 24, respectively. So that the problem is simply one of multiplying 1728 by 24 and dividing the result by 7.) *Ans.* $5924\frac{4}{7}$ gallons.

10. The British thermal unit (Btu) is a unit of heat. It is defined as the quantity of heat required to raise one pound of water through a temperature of one degree Fahrenheit. Thus the heat required to raise 200 pounds of water through 25° F. equals 200 times 25, or 5000 Btu. Compute in pounds the approximate amount of water whose temperature in one hour could be raised 147° F. with a heater having a 35,000 Btu output per hour. Obtain your answer to the nearest pound.

Ans. 238 pounds.

111. Division by the Short Continental Method. This method of division is another valuable little short-cut seldom taken advantage of in the business world. By this method the partial products are subtracted mentally, and only the remainders are written down.

Example: Find the cost per unit of 37 like radios, the total cost of which is $793.65.

Conventional Method	*Short Continental Method*
21.45	21.45
37)793.65	37)793.65
74	53
——	166
53	185
37	
——	
166	
148	
——	
185	
185	

The step-by-step procedure in performing this problem by the short Continental method is as follows: The divisor is contained in 79 twice, so we write 2 in the quotient just as we would if the problem were worked by the conventional method. Now 37 times 2 equals 74, so we deduct 74 *mentally* from 79; the remainder is 5, so we write 5 under the 9.

Now 3 is brought down from the dividend, making the next number to be divided, 53. Thirty-seven goes into 53 once, so 1 is written into the quotient; and subtracting 37 from 53 mentally, only the difference, 16, is written down.

The next figure to be brought down from the dividend is 6, making the number now to be divided, 166. Thirty-seven into 166 goes 4 times with 18 left over, so 4 is written down as the next figure in the quotient, and 18 is shown as the remainder.

Now the 5 is brought down, making the last number to be divided, 185. Thirty-seven goes into 185 exactly five times, so 5 is inserted as the next and last figure in the quotient. The insertion of the decimal point completes the answer, which is $21.45.

Note that not only does the short Continental method of division reduce the amount of pencil-and-paper work, but the process of computation is speeded up too.

While this method may be applied regardless of the number of figures in the divisor, it is used to the best advantage when the divisor contains fewer than four figures, and when there is a zero or low digit in the divisor. Some excellent examples of problems which contain the latter type of divisor can be taken from the illustrations in the preceding article. Let us take the five problems whose solutions were demonstrated in that article, using the reduced equivalents of the dividends and divisors as they appear in the solutions, and observe the rapidity and ease with which the answers are obtained by this time-saving method of mental subtraction.

Example 1: Divide 8715 by 105.

Solution:

$$\begin{array}{r} 83 \\ \hline 105\overline{)8715} \\ \hline 315 \end{array}$$

Ans. 83.

There was really no need to write down 840 (the product of 8 times 105), for it is so easy to subtract 840 from 871 mentally.

Example 2: Divide 75 by 26, and state the answer to the nearest hundredth of a unit.

Solution:

$$\begin{array}{r} 2.884 \\ \hline 26\overline{)75} \\ \hline 230 \\ \hline 220 \\ \hline 120 \end{array}$$

Ans. 2.88.

Here, too, there was no necessity for writing down the product of twice 26, for 52, the product, can be subtracted from 75 without any effort at all. Similarly, the product of 8 times 26 (which, by the breakdown method, is computed by adding the product of 8 times 25 to 8 times 1) can be subtracted from 230 with less effort than it takes to write down 208. And the same applies to the rest of the problem.

Example 3: Divide 51181 by 403.

Solution:

$$
\begin{array}{r}
127 \\
403\overline{)51181} \\
\hline
1088 \\
\hline
2821
\end{array}
$$

Ans. 127.

The relative ease with which 403 can be subtracted from 511 and 806 from 1088 should make it an unforgivable offense for the reader to solve a problem of this nature by the conventional method after reading this article.

Example 4: Divide \$200.00 by 301, and state your answer to the nearest cent.

Solution:

$$
\begin{array}{r}
.664 \\
301\overline{)200} \\
\hline
1940 \\
\hline
1340
\end{array}
$$

Ans. 66 cents.

Notice how the presence of a zero in the divisor makes this method so easy. Six times 301 equals 1806; 1800 subtracted from 2000 equals 200, and 6 subtracted from 200 equals 194.

Example 5: Divide 2000 by 51, and state the answer to the nearest whole unit.

Solution:

$$
\begin{array}{r}
39.2 \\
51\overline{)2000} \\
\hline
470 \\
\hline
110
\end{array}
$$

Ans. 39.

Here, as in the preceding illustration, the presence of a 1 in the divisor makes the method very practical. Note, also, that even when the divisor is multiplied by a high digit like 9, the task of subtracting the product mentally is very simple.

PROBLEMS

1. If a glassblower can turn out 23 dozen units in a day, in how many days will he be able to produce 300 dozen units?   Compute the answer to the nearest whole day.   *Ans.* 13 days.

2. If a cubic foot of loose coal weighs 31 pounds, how many cubic feet would be occupied by 4123 pounds of this coal?   *Ans.* 133 cubic feet.

3. Lumber is measured in terms of board feet.   For example, a board 1 foot long, 1 foot wide, and 1 inch thick is said to contain one board foot of lumber; and a board 26 feet long, 3 inches wide, and 2 inches thick contains 13 board feet of lumber.   How many boards of the latter dimensions should be supplied to equal a total of 4056 board feet?

Ans. 312 boards.

4. If a bolt of lace contains 105 yards, how many whole bolts can be made up with 25,000 yards of this material?   (Hint: Dividing 25,000 by 105 is equivalent to dividing 5000 by 21.)   *Ans.* 238 bolts.

5. A salesman's commissions for the year total $5902.00.   How much does that average per week?   *Ans.* $113.50.

6. Estimate the number of 34-ounce containers of boned turkey that can be filled from a total of 435 pounds of this product.   (Hint: Remember to convert the pounds to ounces before dividing by 34.)

Ans. 204 containers.

7. If three million barrels of oil are obtained from 17,000 wells, what is the average number of barrels obtained from each well?

Ans. 176 barrels.

8. How many 19-ounce tins of tomatoes can be filled from a net quantity of 2300 pounds of tomatoes?   *Ans.* 1936 tins.

9. It is sometimes necessary in radio practice to convert meters to kilocycles.   To obtain the approximate equivalent, 300,000 is divided by the number of meters.   Find the approximate equivalent in kilocycles of 114 meters, computing the answer to the nearest whole unit.   (Hint: Notice that both numbers are divisible by 6.)   *Ans.* 2631 kilocycles.

10. How many 117-pound bales of a spice can be packed from 14,000 pounds of this food product?   *Ans.* 119 bales.

112. A Quick Way to Determine How Many Gross Are Contained in a Quantity Which Runs into Five or More Figures. For anyone who deals constantly with gross quantities the cardinal fact brought out in Art. 64—that 1008 equals 7 gross—is worth keeping in mind. The number 1008 is not only easy to remember, but also a convenient number to divide by—much more convenient than 144. A quick glance at any 4- or 5-figure number reveals instantly how many times 1008 goes into it. Into 7056, for instance, 1008 goes exactly 7 times, so we know that 7056 equals 49 gross; into 9147, 1008 goes 9 times with something left over; into 12098, 12 times with something left over; and so on. To complete the computation it is but necessary to multiply by 7 the exact number of times that 1008 goes into the number, and to divide the remainder by 12 to determine how many dozens and parts of a dozen are represented by the rest of the number.

To divide by 1008 is a very simple matter. First we determine how many times 1000 goes into the thousands; thus into 6000, 1000 goes 6 times; into 8000, 8 times; into 14,000, 14 times. The next step is to find out whether 8 (the last figure in 1008) goes into the last three figures of the number as many times as 1000 is contained in the total number of thousands. If it does, well and good; if it does not, the quotient is simply reduced by 1. A few examples will make this clear.

Example 1: How many gross are contained in 9084?

Solution: 1000 goes into 9000 nine times. So
we write down the product: 9
times 1000 $= 9000$
The next step is to see whether 8
goes 9 times into the rest of the
number (that is, into 84). It
does. So we write down the
product: 9 times 8 $=\quad 72$

1008 times 9	$= 9072$ or 63 gross
9084 minus 9072	$=\quad 12$ or 1 dozen
9072 plus 12	$= 9084$

Ans. 63 gross and 1 dozen equals $63\frac{1}{12}$ gross.

The "1008" method of estimating the number of gross contained in a 4- or 5-figure quantity has much to recommend it—not only for the ease of computation, but also because of the fewness of the figures to be written down. Having determined that 1008 goes into a number 34 times, for example, we need but to write 34 in the thousands columns, and the result of 34 times 8 in the hundreds, tens and units columns, to complete the first step of the computation. The calculation entails two simple products: 1000 times a number, and 8 times that number.

Example 2: Compute the number of gross, dozens and fraction of a dozen contained in 34,480.

Solution: 1000 goes into 34,000, 34 times.

34 times 1000	$= 34000$
Does 8 go 34 times into 480?	
Yes, it does. 34 times 8	$=$ 272
1008 times 34	$= 34272$ or 238 gross
34480 minus 34272	$=$ 208 or $17\frac{4}{12}$ dozen
34272 plus 208	$= 34480$

Ans. $17\frac{4}{12}$ dozen equals 1 gross $5\frac{4}{12}$ dozen; 238 gross plus 1 gross $5\frac{4}{12}$ dozen equals 239 gross $5\frac{4}{12}$ dozen.

Example 3: How many gross are contained in 12,046?

Solution: 1000 goes into 12,000, 12 times.

12 times 1000	$= 12000$
Does 8 go 12 times into 46?	
No, it does not. So let us try 11.	
11 times 1000	$= 11000$
11 times 8	$=$ 88
11 times 1008	$= 11088$ or 77 gross
12046 minus 11088	$=$ 958 or $79\frac{10}{12}$ dozen
11088 plus 958	$= 12046$

Ans. $79\frac{10}{12}$ dozen equals 6 gross $7\frac{10}{12}$ dozen; 77 gross plus 6 gross $7\frac{10}{12}$ dozen equals 83 gross $7\frac{10}{12}$ dozen.

The reader's attention is called to the fact that since the product of 1008 times 12 (which is 12096) exceeded 12046 (the figure in the foregoing illustration) by exactly 50 (which is $4\frac{2}{12}$ dozen), we might have shortened the process of computation by deducting $4\frac{2}{12}$ dozen from 84 gross (84 gross being the equivalent of 1008 times 12). This would give us 83 gross $7\frac{10}{12}$ dozen, which agrees with the figure obtained in the other solution. However, this shorter method should be applied only after the principle is thoroughly understood.

With a little practice the reader will find it a very simple matter to determine just how many whole gross are contained in a 5-figure number. At a glance he will recognize, for instance, that a number like 28124 cannot possibly contain 1008 twenty-eight times, because 28 times 8 equals more than 124 (the last three figures in the dividend). With experience he will be able to reduce the computation to a very few figures, as shown in the following illustration.

Example 4: Compute the number of gross in 21,246 drapery rings.

Solution:

1008 times 21	= 21168 or 147 gross
21246 minus 21168	= 78 or $6\frac{1}{2}$ dozen
21168 plus 78	= 21246

Ans. 147 gross $6\frac{1}{2}$ dozen.

PROBLEMS

In stating the answers to the following problems, fractions of a gross are to be shown as dozens and parts of a dozen, e.g., $3\frac{7}{12}$ dozen, $8\frac{10}{12}$ dozen, etc.

★ **1.** Estimate mentally the number of gross in 9072 bottles.

Ans. 63 gross.

2. Compute the number of gross pounds in 10 long tons. A long ton equals 2240 pounds. *Ans.* 155 gross $6\frac{8}{12}$ dozen.

3. If there are 309 6d nails to the pound, how many gross would be represented by 100 pounds of these nails? *Ans.* 214 gross 7 dozen.

4. What is the gross equivalent of 14,250 round-head stove bolts? *Ans.* 98 gross $11\frac{1}{2}$ dozen.

5. State the gross equivalent of 25,400 nickel-plated nuts.

Ans. 176 gross $4\frac{8}{12}$ dozen.

6. A counting scale shows that the present stock of $\frac{8}{32} \times \frac{1}{2}$ flat-head, steel, nickel-plated screws is approximately 8600. How many gross does that equal? *Ans.* 59 gross $8\frac{8}{12}$ dozen.

7. How many gross are there in 4087 radio volume controls?
Ans. 28 gross $4\frac{7}{12}$ dozen.

8. How many gross are contained in an inventory of 12,250 radio sockets? *Ans.* 85 gross $\frac{10}{12}$ dozen.

9. A manufacturer has a stock of round brass rods $2\frac{7}{8}$ inch long, $1\frac{5}{16}$ inch in diameter, which weighs 4368 pounds. If 1000 of these rods weigh 1248 pounds, how many gross rods does he have in all?
Ans. 24 gross $3\frac{8}{12}$ dozen. (*Art. 110*)

10. If 24,191 feet of steel wire 0.177 inch in diameter weigh 2000 pounds, how many gross feet would there be in 4000 pounds? Compute the answer to the nearest whole dozen feet. *Ans.* 336 gross feet.

113. How to Determine the Weekly Salary of an Employee Hired at So Much per Month. The simplest way to convert a monthly salary to a weekly salary is to find the annual equivalent of the monthly amount and divide the result by 52, since there are 52 weeks in a year.

Example 1: Compute the weekly salary of an employee hired at \$200.00 a month.

Solution: \$200.00 a month equals \$2400.00 a year.

\$2400.00 divided by 52* (\$600.00 divided by 13)
= \$46.15

$$
\begin{array}{r}
46.153 \\
13\overline{)600.00} \\
\hline
80 \\[2pt]
20 \\
\hline
70 \\
\hline
50
\end{array}
$$

* Note the advantage taken in these computations of two techniques discussed in preceding articles: first, 52 is divisible by 4, and 4 is also divisible into \$2400.00, as it would be into a salary of virtually any amount; second, the simple divisor 13 lends itself perfectly to the application of the short Continental method of division (Art. 112).

by another, we simply refer to the table of multiples where it is
seen at a glance that the desired product is 3283 and that the corresponding multiple is 7. So we write down 7 as the first figure in
the quotient, and 3283 as the first partial product, as shown in the
illustration.

*To obtain the second partial product and the corresponding figure
in the quotient:* Proceeding in exactly the same way, we find by
the taole that the desired partial product is 2814 and that the
corresponding multiple is 6.

*To obtain the third partial product and the corresponding figure
in the quotient:* And here, to our pleasure, the table tells us that
2345 is exactly five times the divisor, and so 5 is written down as
the last figure in the quotient.

$$\begin{array}{r} 765 \\ \hline 469)\overline{358785} \end{array}$$

First partial product 3283

$$\begin{array}{r} \hline 3048 \end{array}$$

Second partial product...... 2814

$$\begin{array}{r} \hline 2345 \end{array}$$

Third partial product....... 2345

In the example illustrated, divisibility happens to be exact. If
the last dividend had been 2348 instead of 2345, we would of
course have had a remainder of $\frac{3}{469}$ which, if the answer was
required to the nearest whole unit or to the nearest tenth, would
be simply disregarded.

One example of the usefulness of a table of multiples can be
found in the subject treated in the preceding article, where we
learned to compute the weekly equivalent of a monthly salary.
Another example might be that of a manufacturing plant where it
is necessary to take frequent inventory and where it would be
helpful for the stock clerk or other individual responsible for the
computation, to be able to quickly determine just how many
units are contained in a certain number of pounds, once it is
known how many parts are contained in one pound.

It is worth noting that the use of tables of multiples saves not only time and effort, but reduces the possibility of error. And the larger the divisor the more serviceable is the table.

As the problems that follow indicate, tables of multiples can be used to advantage in a limitless variety of ways.

PROBLEMS

Set up a table of multiples for each divisor in these problems, and use the tables to compute the answers.

1. Find the number of cubic yards in 6426 cubic feet.   One cubic yard equals 27 cubic feet.   *Ans.* 238 cubic yards.

2. A manufacturer wishes to compare his production records with the payroll figures. If the established average production is 34 units per hour, approximately how many man-hours should the payroll records call for on each of the following days: Monday, total production 816 units; Tuesday, total production 712 units; Wednesday, total production 956 units?

>   *Ans.* Monday, 24 man-hours; Tuesday, 21 man-hours; Wednesday, 28 man-hours.

3. Compute the equivalent in gallons of 2932 pounds of tar. A gallon of tar weighs 8.4 pounds. Estimate the answer to the nearest gallon. (Hint: Dividing 2932 by 8.4 is equivalent to dividing 29320 by 84.)

>   *Ans.* 349 gallons.

4. What is the amount earned weekly by an employee engaged at a salary of $285.00 per month?   *Ans.* $65.77. (*Art. 113*)

5. At a speed of 97 miles an hour how much flying time would be consumed on trips of the following distances, 243, 879, 1260, 1723 and 680 miles? Compute the answer to the nearest tenth of an hour. (Hint: Divide the total of the five distances by 97.)

>   *Ans.* 49.3 hours, or 49 hours 18 minutes.

6. How many square feet are there in 9360 square inches?   One square foot equals 144 square inches.   *Ans.* 65 square feet.

7. How long would it take a coal-crushing machine having a capacity of 364 tons per hour to pulverize 31,668 tons of coal?   *Ans.* 87 hours.

8. What is the horsepower equivalent of 69,378 watts?   One horsepower equals 746 watts.   *Ans.* 93 horsepower.

9. Estimate the number of cubic feet that would be occupied by 2875 pounds of lumber of the Norway Pine, if one cubic foot of this

Multiplying the check number of the quotient (check number 6) by the check number of the divisor (check number 7) gives us 42; and the sum of the digits in 42 is 6. This agrees with the check number of the dividend, and so we may presume our answer to be correct.

In the foregoing illustration the quotient happens to be a whole number. However, in division there is often a remainder; for example, 3483 divided by 13 equals 267 and 12 left over, 12 being the remainder. In that event we simply add the sum of the digits in the remainder to the product of the check numbers of quotient and divisor, and proceed in the usual manner. Thus to prove the answer to the aforestated problem, we proceed in the following manner. (Note that when the sum of the digits in the dividend or divisor is an exact multiple of 9, we show 9 as the check number.)

(Dividend)	3483	$3 + 4 + 8 + 3 = 18.$	Casting out one 9 leaves	9
(Divisor)	13	$1 + 3 = 4.$	There is no 9 to cast out, so we write down	4
(Quotient)	267	$2 + 6 + 7 = 15.$	Casting out the 9 leaves	6
(Left over)	12	$1 + 2 = 3.$	See explanation above	

Multiplying the check number of the whole number in the quotient (check number 6) by the check number of the divisor (check number 4) gives us 24; the sum of the digits in the remainder (the quantity left over in the operation of division) is 3 which, added to 24, equals 27; and the sum of the digits in 27 is 9. This agrees with the check number of the dividend, and we may presume our answer, 267 with 12 left over, to be correct.

Here, as with the other operations—addition, subtraction and multiplication—the reader is reminded that this method of proving division is not always error-proof.

PROBLEMS

Prove your answers to these problems by the method of casting out the nines.

★ 1. A man's "take-home" pay for 5 days is $48.65. How much does that average per day?   *Ans.* $9.73. (*Art. 104*)

2. A cotton batting and felt combination—a product used in the upholstery industry—is put up in rolls averaging about 15 pounds to the roll. How many rolls can be made up from 4320 pounds of this material?   *Ans.* 288 rolls. (*Art. 104*)

3. How many bushels are contained in 1500 quarts?   (One bushel equals 32 quarts.)   Give your answer to the nearest whole unit.
                              Ans. 47 bushels. (*Art. 105*)

4. If it cost $22.56 to dig a trench 36 feet long, 3 feet wide and 6 feet deep, what was the average cost per cubic yard?   (Hint: Instead of computing the product of 36 times 3 times 6, and dividing the result by 27 to obtain the total number of cubic yards, cancel 9 into the length, and 3 into the width or depth, and consider the product of the reduced dimensions as cubic yards.)   *Ans.* 94 cents per cubic yard. (*Art. 105*)

5. A combination of asphalt emulsion and asbestos fiber for troweling on insulation surfaces has a covering capacity of 9 square feet per gallon. How many gallons would be necessary to cover an area of 585 square feet of insulation surface?   *Ans.* 65 gallons.

6. If a loft 72 feet long has an area of 2232 square feet, what is its width?   *Ans.* 31 feet. (*Art. 106*)

7. If olive oil weighs .033 pounds per cubic inch, how many full gallons can be obtained from 132 pounds of this food product?   One gallon equals 231 cubic inches.   *Ans.* 17 full gallons. (*Art. 109*)

8. How many return trips would a businessman have to make between Boston, Massachusetts, and Columbia, South Carolina—a distance of 693 miles—to travel a total of 19,200 miles?   Compute the answer to the nearest whole number.   *Ans.* 14 return trips. (*Art. 110*)

9. If a sheet of asbestos ebony 42 by 96 inches weighs 257.6 pounds, how much would one square foot of this material weigh?   (Hint: Instead of multiplying 42 by 96 and dividing the result by 144 to obtain the number of square feet, cancel 12 into 42 and 96, and consider the product of the reduced dimensions as square feet.)
                              Ans. 9.2 pounds per square foot. (*Art. 111*)

10. If a gas engine consumes one gallon of lubricating oil for 19,000 horsepower hours, how many gallons would it consume in producing 361,000 horsepower hours?   *Ans.* 19 gallons. (*Art. 111*)

CHAPTER XV

THE "DOUBLE-AND-DOUBLE" METHOD OF DIVISION

There is an interesting similarity between the technique introduced in this chapter and the method discussed in Chapter III (The "Double-and-Halve" Method of Multiplication). These are sister chapters in the real sense of the term. The principle of the method in Chapter III is based on the fact that when two factors in a multiplication problem are multiplied and divided, respectively, by the same value, the product is not affected. In this chapter we will discuss a process based on the fact that when both the dividend and the divisor in any problem are multiplied or divided by the same value the quotient is not affected.

The four articles in the present chapter are among the most important in this book, and the reader is advised to give them his special attention. They should help deepen his insight into the remarkable speed and accuracy with which many problems in division can be worked mentally or with surprisingly little use of pencil and paper.

117. How to Divide Mentally and Quickly by $1\frac{1}{2}$, $2\frac{1}{2}$, $3\frac{1}{2}$, $4\frac{1}{2}$, $5\frac{1}{2}$ and $7\frac{1}{2}$. To divide by any of these numbers, simply double the dividend and double the divisor, and proceed with the problem. Thus to divide 36 by $1\frac{1}{2}$ we would change the dividend to 72 and the divisor to 3, which revision would enable us to see at once that the answer is 24. Similarly, $37\frac{1}{2}$ divided by $2\frac{1}{2}$ is equivalent to 75 divided by 5, and, without having to write down a single figure, we see that the answer is 15.

Problems in which the divisor is $3\frac{1}{2}$, $4\frac{1}{2}$ or $5\frac{1}{2}$ would be revised in exactly the same way. Thus to divide 28 by $3\frac{1}{2}$ we would divide 56 by 7; and the division of 315 by $4\frac{1}{2}$ is equivalent to the division of 630 by 9. By keeping this principle in mind, the answer to the problem of dividing $247\frac{1}{2}$ by $5\frac{1}{2}$ is immediately apparent; $247\frac{1}{2}$ divided by $5\frac{1}{2}$ is equivalent to 495 divided by 11, and without going a step farther we know, from our experience with the multiplier 11 (Art. 1-f), that 495 is the product of 45 times 11. So that our answer to this problem is 45.

Here, as in any other problem in division, it should be remembered that if we double the dividend we must also double the divisor, and vice versa, in order that the quotient may not be affected. In this connection it might be well to review Art. 20, which deals with the subject of multiplying by some of the numbers discussed here, and to observe the difference between the procedure in multiplying and the procedure in dividing. In multiplying by $2\frac{1}{2}$, if we double the multiplier we must *halve* the multiplicand, or vice versa—that is, if we double the multiplicand we must halve the multiplier. In dividing by $2\frac{1}{2}$, if we double the divisor we must also *double* the dividend, or vice versa.

The term "double-and-double" method of division—as the term "double-and-halve" method of multiplication (Chapter III)—was chosen for its descriptive value. And here, as with the double-and-halve method of multiplication, the value by which the two numbers are increased need not be limited to 2. To divide by $2\frac{1}{2}$, for instance, it is often more convenient to multiply the dividend and divisor by 4 rather than by 2. In revising figures for quick mental computation it is easier, for example, to restate the problem $42\frac{1}{2}$ divided by $2\frac{1}{2}$ as 170 divided by 10, rather than as 85 divided by 5. Similarly, to divide by $7\frac{1}{2}$ it is very convenient to multiply dividend and divisor by 4; thus the problem 420 divided by $7\frac{1}{2}$ becomes solvable mentally simply by changing it to read 1680 divided by 30; or, to simplify the problem still further, 420 can be divided by 30, and the quotient (that is, 14) multiplied by 4.

The divisor $7\frac{1}{2}$, incidentally, was previously discussed in Art. 104. Mention of the technique is repeated here to underscore the ease with which it is possible to divide by this number mentally.

Example: A paint product reputed to protect building exteriors against the ravages of weather and having a covering capacity of 100 square feet per gallon is sold in units of $7\frac{1}{2}$ gallons. Compute mentally the number of units of this material needed to treat an area of 21,000 square feet.

Solution: At 100 square feet per gallon, 210 gallons would be needed to treat 21,000 square feet.

210 gallons divided by $7\frac{1}{2}$ gallons is equivalent to 840 divided by 30, or 84 divided by 3.

And it is seen at a glance that the answer is 28 units.

Oftentimes it is easier to work problems of this type by performing the processes of multiplication and division in the following order rather than in the order discussed so far:

1. Increase the divisor.
2. Divide the dividend by the increased divisor.
3. Multiply the quotient.

For example, suppose we wished to divide 273 by $1\frac{1}{2}$. Multiplying the divisor by 2 changes it to 3. We see at a glance that 3 goes into 273 exactly 91 times; so instead of multiplying 273 by 2 and dividing the result by 3, we divide 273 by 3 and multiply the quotient by 2. The following illustration will give a clear picture of the advantage of the second method over the first.

Method A		Method B	
2 times 273	= 546	2 times $1\frac{1}{2}$	= 3
2 times $1\frac{1}{2}$	= 3	273 divided by 3 (mentally)	= 91
546 divided by 3	= 182	91 multiplied by 2 (mentally)	= 182

Another good example would be 459 divided by $4\frac{1}{2}$ which, by Method B, is solvable mentally quick as a flash. Multiplying $4\frac{1}{2}$ by 2 gives us 9; 459 divided by 9 equals 51; and 51 multiplied by 2 equals 102.

PROBLEMS

★ 1. A liquid preparation for making concrete water-resistant is used in the proportion of $1\frac{1}{2}$ gallons per cubic yard of 1:2:4 concrete. What quantity of 1:2:4 concrete would be indicated by a consumption of $25\frac{1}{2}$ gallons of this product?   *Ans.* 17 cubic yards.

 * 2. Glass wool, a fibrous material made from glass slag and used for insulation, weighs $1\frac{1}{2}$ pounds per cubic foot. Compute the number of cubic feet represented by 63 pounds of glass wool.   *Ans.* 42 cubic feet.

 * 3. If a tractor consumes an average of $2\frac{1}{2}$ quarts of oil per day, how many days would a 60-gallon drum of oil last?   *Ans.* 96 days.

 * 4. Ascorbic acid, used by apple juice packers, is put up in $2\frac{1}{2}$ kilo drums. How many drums of this size can be filled from a quantity of 460 kilos?   *Ans.* 184 drums.

 * 5. If one bushel of flaxseed yields $2\frac{1}{2}$ gallons of oil, how many bushels would be necessary to obtain 420 gallons?   *Ans.* 168 bushels.

 * 6. The daily average of pedestrians over 12 years of age passing a store between the hours of 11 A.M. and 2:30 P.M. is 2450. How many pedestrians does that average per hour?   *Ans.* 700.

 * 7. How many $3\frac{1}{2}$-yard lengths can be cut from a 40-yard bolt of cloth?   *Ans.* $11\frac{3}{7}$ lengths.

 * 8. How many times would it be necessary to fill a 14-quart bucket to empty a tank containing 28 gallons of water? (One gallon equals 4 quarts.)   *Ans.* 8 times.

 * 9. A formula for a decorative coating calls for the use of $4\frac{1}{2}$ pounds of a pigment known as titanium barium, per gallon. Estimate the number of pounds of this pigment that should be used to produce 180 gallons of the coating.   *Ans.* 40 pounds.

 * 10. If $4\frac{1}{2}$ acres of land produce $85\frac{1}{2}$ bushels of wheat, what is the average production per acre?   *Ans.* 19 bushels.

 * 11. A government regulation requires that an adult-size, cork life-preserver shall contain a minimum of $5\frac{1}{2}$ pounds of cork. On this basis how many life-preservers can be made with 1870 pounds of cork?

Ans. 340.

 * 12. If a polo ball weighs $5\frac{1}{2}$ ounces, how many polo balls would be contained in a shipment whose net weight was 1320 pounds?

Ans. 240 polo balls.

 * 13. In the tanning industry a series of vats are used so that the tanning liquid comes from the bottom of one vat and overflows into the top of the next. If the cubic capacity of each of these vats is 264 cubic feet and one of the dimensions $5\frac{1}{2}$ feet, what is the product of the other two dimensions?   *Ans.* 48.

 * 14. A manufacturer contemplates the installation of a tank to hold 800 gallons of a liquid. How many cubic feet of space would a tank of this capacity occupy? (One cubic foot equals $7\frac{1}{2}$ gallons.)

Ans. $106\frac{2}{3}$ cubic feet.

* 15. The result of an experiment shows that $7\frac{1}{2}$ ounces of a special ingredient used along with other materials will produce 135 ounces of a desirable product. How many ounces of the finished product would contain one ounce of the special ingredient?   *Ans.* 18 ounces.

118. How to Speed Up Division by Any Number Containing the Fraction $\frac{1}{2}$, e.g., $8\frac{1}{2}$, $15\frac{1}{2}$, $21\frac{1}{2}$. The process of dividing by any number containing the fraction $\frac{1}{2}$ is exactly the same as that of dividing mentally by any of the numbers discussed in the preceding article. The only difference is that the computation may have to be completed on paper.

Example 1: Divide 204 by $8\frac{1}{2}$.

Solution: Changing the problem to 408 divided by 17, and completing the computation by the short Continental method (Art. 111), we proceed as follows:

$$
\begin{array}{r}
24 \\
\hline
17)\overline{408} \\
\hline
68 \\
\hline
\end{array}
$$

Ans. 24.

Example 2: Divide 6696 by $15\frac{1}{2}$.

Solution: Revising the problem to read 13392 divided by 31, the answer is obtained as follows:

$$
\begin{array}{r}
432 \\
\hline
31)\overline{13392} \\
\hline
99 \\
\hline
62 \\
\hline
\end{array}
$$

Ans. 432.

Example 3: Divide $313.90 by $21\frac{1}{2}$.

Solution: This problem is equivalent to $627.80 divided by 43.

$$
\begin{array}{r}
14.60 \\
43\overline{)627.80} \\
\hline
197 \\
\hline
258 \\
\end{array}
$$

Ans. $14.60.

PROBLEMS

1. One of the uses of wood skewers is for the application of insulation layers. If 1000 skewers, $5\frac{1}{2}$ inches by $\frac{1}{4}$ inch, weigh $6\frac{1}{2}$ pounds, how many pins of this size would comprise a total weight of 221 pounds? *Ans.* 34,000 pins.

2. If $9\frac{1}{2}$ ounces of flour are used to bake a loaf of bread, how many loaves can be baked with 1900 pounds of flour? *Ans.* 3200 loaves.

★ 3. Without considering the brokerage fees, etc., connected with the purchase, estimate the number of shares quoted at $11\frac{1}{2}$—that is, at $11.50 —that can be purchased for $460.00. *Ans.* 40 shares.

4. If a dumping truck has a payload capacity of $13\frac{1}{2}$ cubic yards, how many loads would be necessary to clear 324 cubic yards? *Ans.* 24 loads.

5. How many $15\frac{1}{2}$-ounce tins of smoked shad can be packed from 600 pounds of this food product? Estimate the total to the nearest unit. *Ans.* 619 tins.

6. How many $31\frac{1}{2}$-gallon barrels would be necessary to dispose of 756 gallons of liquid? *Ans.* 24 barrels.

119. How to Divide Quickly by Numbers Containing Fractions Other Than $\frac{1}{2}$, e.g., $2\frac{1}{3}$, $28\frac{3}{4}$, $45\frac{5}{9}$. The process of "doubling" dividend and divisor is never more useful than when dealing with divisors which contain fractions. And here, as in Arts. 117 and 118, we will observe that while for the purpose of explanation the technique is referred to as "doubling," actually it makes no difference whether dividends and divisors in any problem are multiplied by 2, 3, 4, 5 or any other number, for when the dividend and the divisor are multiplied by the same value the quotient is not affected.

Example 1: Divide 133 by $2\frac{1}{3}$.

Solution: As in the preceding two articles, our objective is to eliminate the fraction from the divisor, so let us multiply both numbers by 3 (3 being the denominator of the fraction).

133 multiplied by 3 = 399
$2\frac{1}{3}$ multiplied by 3 =　　7
399 divided by 7　　= 57

Example 2: Divide 1961 by $13\frac{1}{4}$.

Solution: Here the denominator in the fraction is 4, so let us multiply both numbers by 4. This changes the problem to 7844 divided by 53, which is readily computed by the short Continental method:

$$
\begin{array}{r}
148 \\
53\overline{)7844} \\
\hline
254 \\
\hline
424
\end{array}
$$

Ans. 148.

Example 3: Divide 9940 by $28\frac{2}{5}$.

Solution: Note that the numerator in the fraction here is 2, so in converting the divisor to a whole number we must remember to add 2 to the product of 28 times 5.

9940 multiplied by 5 = 49700
$28\frac{2}{5}$ multiplied by 5 =　　142

$$
\begin{array}{r}
350 \\
142\overline{)49700} \\
\hline
710
\end{array}
$$

Ans. 350.

Example 4: Divide 230 by $28\frac{3}{4}$.

Solution:

> 230 multiplied by 4 = 920
> $28\frac{3}{4}$ multiplied by 4 = 115
> 920 divided by 115 =   8

Example 5: Divide 410 by $45\frac{5}{9}$.

Solution: Multiplying each number by 9, our problem is 3690 divided by 410, and the briefest glance tells us that the answer is 9.

Example 6: Divide $711\frac{3}{4}$ by $31\frac{1}{3}$, and give the answer to the nearest whole unit.

Solution: To convert the divisor in this problem to a whole number we must multiply it by 3. This changes our problem to $2135\frac{1}{4}$ (or 2135.25) divided by 94.

$$\begin{array}{r} 22.7 \\ 94\overline{)2135.25} \\ \hline 255 \\ \hline 672 \end{array}$$

Ans. 23.

Let us pause here to see if we understand the reason for the procedure in the foregoing illustration. In each of the other examples, the dividend was automatically changed to a whole number along with the divisor. However, the essential consideration in this technique is to eliminate the fraction from the divisor. In solving the problem in Example 6 we might easily have multiplied both numbers by 12, thus eliminating the fraction from the dividend as well as from the divisor, but this would have resulted in a divisor having three digits, and it is certainly easier to divide 2135.25 by the two-digit number 94 than 8541 by the three-digit number 376.

The ease of dividing by numbers containing decimal fractions which are aliquot numbers is surprisingly overlooked by many. To divide by numbers which contain such decimal fractions as .125 and .625, for example, there is no need to burden oneself with the task of dividing by each of the three digits in these fractions—for .125 is an aliquot part of 1 (it is $\frac{1}{8}$); so that a divisor like 5.125 can be conveniently considered as $5\frac{1}{8}$. Similarly, since .625 is equivalent to $\frac{5}{8}$, the divisor 7.625 can be readily changed to $7\frac{5}{8}$.

As often as not the reader will find that the elimination of decimal fractions from a divisor not only shortens the process of computation, but may completely eliminate the need for further calculation.

Example 7: Divide \$20.50 by 5.125.

Solution: 5.125 is the same as $5\frac{1}{8}$, and \$20.50 divided by $5\frac{1}{8}$ is equivalent to \$164.00 divided by 41. Without the need for further computation, it is seen that the answer is \$4.00.

Having discussed decimal fractions which are aliquot parts, we will now consider mixed numbers that are aliquot parts, and note the interesting results of converting these numbers.

Let us begin with the number $1\frac{1}{4}$. To divide by $1\frac{1}{4}$ should one multiply dividend and divisor by 4? Multiplied by 4, the number $1\frac{1}{4}$ becomes 5, and as we learned in another place in this book, division by 5 can be simplified by multiplying dividend and divisor by 2. But, instead of multiplying first by 4 and then by 2, we can just as easily multiply by 8 in one operation (8 being the product of 4 times 2). Thus 45 divided by $1\frac{1}{4}$ becomes 360 (which is 8 times 45) divided by 10 (which is 8 times $1\frac{1}{4}$), and quick as a flash we see that the answer is 36.

To divide by $1\frac{2}{3}$ we would proceed in the same manner. Instead of multiplying $1\frac{2}{3}$ by 3, which would give us 5, we multiply by 6, which equals 10. In this way, division by $1\frac{2}{3}$ is made as easy as ABC. Thus the problem \$80.85 divided by $1\frac{2}{3}$ becomes \$485.10 divided by 10, and in a split second we know that the answer is \$48.51.

Note the method of procedure in the following illustration where the mixed-number divisor, when multiplied by the figure in the denominator, is a commonly known aliquot part of 100.

Example 8: Divide \$396.00 by $8\frac{1}{3}$.

Solution: If we multiplied these numbers by 3, the divisor would be 25. However, since it is so much easier to divide by 100 than by 25, let us multiply the numbers by 4 times 3, since 25 is contained in 100 four times.

12 times \$396.00   = \$4752.00
12 times $8\frac{1}{3}$ = 100
\$4752.00 divided by 100 = \$47.52

Here we can use with excellent effect the technique mentioned at the end of Art. 117—namely, that it is sometimes easier to multiply the quotient rather than the dividend. Thus in working the problem 560 divided by $2\frac{1}{3}$, we see at a glance that 7 (the product of 3 times $2\frac{1}{3}$) goes exactly 80 times into 560; so instead of multiplying 560 by 3 and dividing the result by 7, we divide 560 by 7 and multiply the quotient by 3. Similarly, in dividing 34 by $4\frac{1}{4}$, instead of dividing 136 (the product of 4 times 34) by 17 (the product of 4 times $4\frac{1}{4}$), we would divide 34 by 17 and multiply the quotient (2) by 4.

EXERCISES

Perform the following problems in division by the procedure indicated.

	Multiply the dividend by	And divide the result by	
★ 1. Divide 960 by $3\frac{1}{3}$.	3	10	*Ans.* 288.
2. Divide $787\frac{1}{2}$ by $3\frac{3}{4}$.	8	30	*Ans.* 210.
3. Divide 6225 by $6\frac{1}{4}$.	16	100	*Ans.* 996.
4. Divide 6775 by $8\frac{1}{3}$.	12	100	*Ans.* 813.
5. Divide 1716 by $9\frac{1}{11}$.	11	100	*Ans.* 188.76.
6. Divide \$517.00 by $11\frac{1}{9}$.	9	100	*Ans.* \$46.53.
7. Divide \$1295.00 by $14\frac{2}{7}$.	7	100	*Ans.* \$90.65.
8. Divide \$1842.00 by $16\frac{2}{3}$.	6	100	*Ans.* \$110.52.
9. Divide \$7437.50 by $31\frac{1}{4}$.	16	500	*Ans.* \$238.00.
10. Divide \$936.00 by $33\frac{1}{3}$.	3	100	*Ans.* \$28.08.

PROBLEMS

1. It is reported that in a single year no less than 42,000 bushels of sea-stars (a class of starfish very destructive to mussels and oysters) have been removed from the oyster beds of Connecticut. If a bushel is equivalent to approximately $1\frac{1}{4}$ cubic feet, how many cubic feet of space would be occupied by the aforementioned quantity of sea-stars, assuming that it were possible to pack them all together?   *Ans.* 33,600 cubic feet.

★ **2.** A good yield of fiber flax is about $2\frac{1}{4}$ tons of air-dried straw per acre. On this basis how many acres would be required to produce 270 tons of this product?   *Ans.* 120 acres.

★ **3.** A tailor's inventory shows that he has three bolts of cloth suitable for men's suits, totaling 91 yards. If the average suit length is $3\frac{1}{4}$ yards, how many suits could be made from the three bolts?   *Ans.* 28 suits.

★ **4.** How many $3\frac{1}{4}$-inch strips can be cut from a sheet of zinc 39 inches wide?   *Ans.* 12 strips.

5. Toluol, a product used in the manufacture of lacquers, weighs approximately $7\frac{1}{4}$ pounds per gallon. Compute the equivalent in gallons of 406 pounds of this product.   *Ans.* 56 gallons.

6. What should the net weight be of 133 yards of four-leaf twill fabric, if $1\frac{3}{4}$ yards of this material weighs one pound?   *Ans.* 76 pounds.

★ **7.** If a one-foot bar of steel weighs $2\frac{3}{4}$ pounds, how many feet would be contained in 374 pounds of this steel?   *Ans.* 136 feet.

★ **8.** If a truck averages $4\frac{3}{4}$ cubic yards of dirt to the load, how many trips must it make to haul 190 cubic yards of dirt?   *Ans.* 40 trips.

9. A job lot of $5\frac{3}{4}$ gross metal parts is offered at \$20.70 for the lot. How much does this average per gross parts?   *Ans.* \$3.60.

10. In lumbermen's boots there is usually a heavy felt sole, stitched just above the leather sole. This felt material is made in sheets weighing $7\frac{3}{4}$ pounds and measuring 40 by 60 inches by $\frac{5}{16}$-inch. How many square feet of this material would be contained in a total weight of 1860 pounds?   *Ans.* 4000 square feet.

11. If a roll of 48-inch building paper contains 666 square feet, what is the length of the roll? (Hint: 48 inches equals $1\frac{1}{3}$ feet.) *Ans.* $499\frac{1}{2}$ feet.

12. How many ivory billiard balls, each weighing $4\frac{2}{3}$ ounces, may be expected to be found in a total net weight of 42 pounds?   *Ans.* 144.

13. Insulating wool blankets, approximately 23 inches wide and 2 inches thick, are packed in lengths of $44\frac{1}{3}$ feet to the carton. If a total of 665 feet of this material is required, how many cartons should be purchased?   *Ans.* 15 cartons.

14. A manufacturer purchased bolts of cloth whose total yardage was 1323 yards. He planned to make aprons requiring $1\frac{1}{8}$ yards of this material per apron. If no material is wasted in production, how many aprons should he be able to make? *Ans.* 1176 aprons.

15. How many bricks $2\frac{1}{8}$ inches thick would make 8 stacks, each 5 feet 8 inches high? *Ans.* 256 bricks.

120. Speeding Up Division by Whole Numbers Like 35, 75, 125, 135, 165, 175, 250, 350, 750, 850, 1450, etc. Having in mind the thought that it is easier to divide by a single digit than by a two-digit number, and by a two-digit than by a three-digit number, let us look into the interesting possibilities of speeding by the double-and-double method the solution of problems in which the divisor is a whole number.

The number 35 contains two digits. By doubling it, however, a single-digit number is obtained. So that the answer to a problem like 420 divided by 35 becomes obvious at a glance: 840 divided by 70 is equivalent to 84 divided by 7, which equals 12.

When 75 is doubled we still have a two-digit number—namely, 150. But when 75 is multiplied by 4 a single-digit number is obtained. Thus the problem 1200 divided by 75 can be quickly worked mentally when the numbers are changed to 4800 and 300, respectively, for all we need do is divide 48 by 3, which equals 16.

Example 1: Divide 510 by 15.

Solution: Twice 510 = 1020
Twice 15 = 30

1020 divided by 30 equals 102 divided by 3.
102 divided by 3 equals 34.

The same principle, without any variation, can be applied to numbers ending in 5. Thus three-digit numbers, e.g., 135 and 165, when multiplied by 2, become two-digit numbers—namely, 270 and 330. And it is obviously easier to divide by 270 than by 135, and by 330 than by 165. If a number ends with 50, it does not make one bit of difference; thus the divisor 850 can be as conveniently changed to 1700 as 85 to 170.

Example 2: A plot of land 25 by 100 feet is offered for sale at a price of $80,000. How much does this average per square foot?

Solution: The area of the plot is 2500 square feet. Canceling the two ciphers in 2500 and the last two ciphers in 80,000, we have the equivalent of 25 square feet costing $800. Since 25 is one fourth of 100, let us multiply both numbers by 4; 100 square feet (4 times 25) equals $3200 (4 times 800). And we see at once that the cost is $32 per square foot.

PROBLEMS

1. If the net weight of a case of frozen eggs is 35 pounds, how many cases can be filled from 2695 pounds of this food product?

Ans. 77 cases.

2. The covering capacity of a waterproof cement for applying cork covering and lagging is 35 square feet per gallon. Estimate the number of gallons that would be required to cover 5740 square feet.

Ans. 164 gallons.

★ 3. An electrically operated mimeograph can produce 125 letters a minute. At this rate of speed how long would it take to produce 45,000 copies of a letter? Assume that the machine runs smoothly from start to finish, and without any loss of time.   *Ans.* 6 hours. (*Art. 2-c*)

★ 4. How many cubic feet of space would be occupied by 7125 pounds of a medium quality brickwork having a weight of 125 pounds per cubic foot?   *Ans.* 57. (*Art. 2-c*)

5. How many bars of electrolytic copper, each weighing 135 pounds, would be contained in 2835 pounds of this material?   *Ans.* 21 bars.

6. To seed his wheat field of 175 acres, a farmer used 306 bushels of seed. How much seed did this average per acre? Compute the answer to the nearest quarter of a bushel.   *Ans.* $1\frac{3}{4}$ bushels.

7. It costs a manufacturer $416.25 to assemble 185 units. How much is that per unit?   *Ans.* $2.25.

★ 8. A trailer body, loading frozen products at around 0° F., requires 250 pounds of dry ice for each day that the load is to be in transit. At this rate of consumption, for how many days will 4250 pounds of dry ice suffice?   *Ans.* 17 days.

★ 9. A pound of green lake printing ink will cover approximately 250,000 square inches on Enamel No. 1 stock. If the estimated number of square inches to be printed in this color on the mentioned stock is 23,687,000, how many pounds of ink will be used on the job? Compute the answer to the nearest pound. *Ans.* 95 pounds.

★ **10.** How many 350-pound barrels of sugar can be filled from seven short tons of this food product? (Hint: A short ton equals 2000 pounds.)
Ans. 40 barrels.

★ **11.** At the rate of 350 acres per hour, how long would it take to dust 8400 acres by airplane? *Ans.* 24 hours.

12. One pound of commercially pure aluminum, .001 inches thick, can cover an area of 10,250 square inches. What quantity of this material would be needed to cover an area of 2 million square inches? Compute the answer to the nearest pound. *Ans.* 195 pounds.

CHAPTER XVI

SHORT-CUTTING THE SHORT-CUTS: OR HOW TO SAVE PENCIL-AND-PAPER WORK EVEN WITH SHORT-CUTS

It is not at all unlikely that the reader who has made an earnest attempt to master the techniques discussed in the preceding chapters will by this time have developed a visual "figure-sense." This figure consciousness may have suggested to him other short-cuts, including many that are particularly applicable to the industry in which he may happen to be engaged, for there is virtually no limit to the number of mathematical short-cuts that can be developed by one whose interest has been stimulated along these lines.

The techniques described in the articles that follow may help the reader to cultivate ability in this direction and perhaps free his mind from any remaining shackles of conventional mathematics.

121. Eliminating Superfluous Zeros. This practical little short-cut has always been a source of pleasure to the author in his mathematical adventures. It consists of nothing more than the simple elimination from partial products of meaningless zeros occurring after the decimal point.

Let us take some examples which we worked by the breakdown method in Art. 16, and observe how the breakdown method can be expanded by the process of eliminating superfluous zeros. One of these problems reads: Multiply 28 cents by 35. And reference to the solution will show that we wrote down $7.00 to represent the partial product of 25 times 28 cents, $2.80 as the product of 10 times 28 cents, and the total of $9.80. In all, nine figures were written down. By eliminating superfluous zeros, a simple problem

304

like this does not require the writing down of more than five figures, as shown by the following:

$$25 \text{ times } 28 \text{ cents} = 7.$$
$$10 \text{ times } 28 \text{ cents} = 2.8$$

$$35 \text{ times } 28 \text{ cents} = 9.8$$

We know that we are dealing with dollars and cents, so there is no point in writing down the two meaningless zeros in 7.00 and the zero in 2.80. In fact, there is even no need to write the total on the scratch pad, for the mental addition of $7.00 and $2.80 requires no effort whatever.

Another typical example is 76 times 44 cents. In the solution by the breakdown method illustrated in Art. 16, ten figures were used. By the process of eliminating superfluous zeros and the total, only four figures are necessary:

$$75 \text{ times } 44 \text{ cents} = 33.$$
$$1 \text{ times } 44 \text{ cents} = \quad .44$$

It would be pure folly to add on paper the partial products in the foregoing computation, for there is really nothing to add. In fact, this problem, because of the nature of the factors, can be worked mentally without any additional effort.

A third example, which is even more interesting because the solution involves three partial products, is the one worked in Art. 30—namely, 36 times $1.0275. By the short method illustrated in that article, the solution calls for the writing down of 12 figures. With visual "figure-sense," this problem—which at first glance may appear to require quite a bit of calculating—can be solved with as few as five—or even four—figures, as follows:

$$36 \text{ times } \$1.00 \qquad\qquad = 36.$$
$$36 \text{ times } .025 \ (18 \text{ times } .05) = \quad .9$$
$$36 \text{ times } .0025 \ (\tfrac{1}{10} \text{ of } .9) \quad = \quad .09$$

And here, too, there is no adding to be done. Automatically, the answer will be read as $36.99.

A good source of additional examples will be found in several articles in Chapter V. One problem in Art. 35, for instance, calls for the multiplication of 86 by 84. By the short-cut method indicated in that article, we wrote down: first the partial product 7200, then the partial product 24, and lastly the total. By eliminating superfluous zeros and the total, however, we could obtain the answer by writing down no more than four figures, as follows:

$$72$$
$$24$$

There is no need to draw a line across and write the total, for the total is obvious—it is 7224.

It is very interesting to note that by the technique by which the foregoing problem and others like it are worked, the first partial product always has two or three zeros at the end, and the second partial product (which constitutes the last figures in the answer) never contains more than two figures. In other words, the figures in one partial product are really filled in in spaces that are virtually reserved for them by the first partial product. Thus the answer is obtained automatically in a single line.

PROBLEMS

Problems 1 to 6 in the following group are to be worked mentally.

* **1.** Find the square of 65.   *Ans.* 4225. (*Art. 32*)
* **2.** Find the square of 85.   *Ans.* 7225. (*Art. 32*)
* **3.** Multiply 38 by 32.   *Ans.* 1216. (*Art. 35*)
* **4.** Multiply 67 by 63.   *Ans.* 4221. (*Art. 35*)
* **5.** Multiply 88 cents by 26.   *Ans.* $22.88.
* **6.** Multiply 42 cents by 55.   *Ans.* $23.10.

   7. Show how you would compute the product of $3\frac{5}{8}$ times $14.00 without writing down more than 6 figures. (Hint: The answer itself need not be written down, for it will be obvious at a glance.)

Ans. 42.
7.
1.75 (*Art. 17*)

8. Show how you would compute the product of $5\frac{1}{4}$ times $13.40 without writing down more than 5 figures. (Hint: Here, too, the answer itself need not be written down, for it will be seen at a glance.)

Ans. 67.
3.35

9. Show how you would write the partial products in computing the answer to 826 times $1.37\frac{1}{2}$. *Ans.* 826.
206.5
103.25

10. Remembering that $33\frac{1}{3}$ is one third of 100, how would you write the partial products for $35\frac{1}{3}$ times $18.00? *Ans.* 600.
36.

122. How to Compute the Answers in a Series of Multiplication Problems in Which One Factor Is Constant, and the Other Varies in a Co-operative Way, e.g., 162 times $1.46, 158 times $1.46, 1540 times $1.46. It often happens that in a series of problems one factor (which we will call the multiplicand) is constant, and the other factor (which we will call the multiplier) varies in a minor degree. Let us say, for instance, that the computation of the problem 162 times $1.46 was followed by the problem 158 times $1.46. The first problem could be calculated very conveniently as follows:

2 times $1.46   = $ 2.92
160 times $1.46 (80 times $2.92) = 233.6 *

162 times $1.46   = $236.52

Now the answer to the problem 158 times $1.46 can be obtained from the figures in the foregoing calculation without having to compute a single product, thus:

160 times $1.46 (as already computed) = $233.6
 —   2 times $1.46 (as already computed) =   2.92

158 times $1.46   = $230.68

* The zero was omitted in accordance with the discussion in the preceding article.

If a third product called for the computation of 1540 times $1.46, we could use the partial products obtained in the preceding problems, as follows:

160 times $1.46 (as already computed)	= $ 233.6
— 6 times $1.46 (3 times $2.92)	= 8.76
154 times $1.46	= $ 224.84
1540 times $1.46 (10 times $224.84)	= $2248.40

Let us now take the two problems 829 times 257 and 829 times 253, and observe how conveniently the computation of the first problem speeds the computation of the second.

250 times 829 ($\frac{1}{4}$ of 829000)	= 207250
7 times 829	= 5803
257 times 829	= 213053
257 times 829 (as already computed)	= 213053
— 4 times 829	= 3316
253 times 829	= 209737

Note the interesting method of procedure in the solutions to the following problems, in which the unit digits are alike, but the hundreds and tens digits are different: Multiply 426 by 217, and 426 by 337.

$$426$$
$$217$$

7 times 426..............	2982
210 times 426 (30 times 2982)	8946
	92442

426 times 217 (as already computed)	=	92442
426 times 120 (12 times 4260)	=	51120
426 times 337	=	143562

Problems

* 1. If 75 times 85 cents equals $63.75, how much does 73 times 85 cents equal? (Mentally, please.) *Ans.* $62.05.

2. Compute on paper (a) the product of 240 times $3.18; then compute mentally (b) the product of 243 times $3.18.

Ans. (a) $763.20; (b) $772.74.

3. An agent is given two orders for fabric—one for 280 yards, the other for 320 yards. If his commission is 12 cents a yard, how much does he earn on each order? The commission on the second order is to be computed mentally. *Ans.* $33.60, $38.40.

* 4. A food products company packs figs in 17-ounce tins. One day it had a batch of 7344 ounces, from which 3 gross tins were packed. Compute mentally the number of tins that could be packed from the next batch of 7684 ounces. *Ans.* 3 gross $1\frac{8}{12}$ dozen.

* 5. A device produces 85 gallons of 95 per cent ethyl alcohol from 34 bushels of corn, which is at the rate of $2\frac{1}{2}$ gallons per bushel. Estimate mentally the quantity of the aforementioned alcohol that could be obtained from 37 bushels of corn. *Ans.* $92\frac{1}{2}$ gallons.

* 6. In $2\frac{1}{2}$ hours a total of 2625 gallons of water was obtained from a well, which averages $17\frac{1}{2}$ gallons per minute. Compute mentally the total number of gallons that would be obtained at this rate in 2 hours, 40 minutes. *Ans.* 2800 gallons.

* 7. A machine turns out 8400 kilos of kapok in 10 days. Without putting pencil to paper, calculate the number of kilos of this material that could be turned out in $11\frac{1}{4}$ days. *Ans.* 9450 kilos. (*Art. 91*)

* 8. If 450 gallons of gasoline were used by a plane on a 600-mile trip, how many gallons would be used on a trip of 660 miles? (Only two seconds should be taken to do this problem mentally.) *Ans.* 495 gallons.

* 9. A Baltimore manufacturer purchased 6 tons of chemically bonded magnesite at $65.00 a ton, so that his purchase cost him $390.00. The next day he purchased 6 tons of standard magnesite, the price of which was $76.00 a ton. Compute in two different ways the total cost of the second purchase. *Ans.* $456.00. (*Art. 91*)

10. A linear foot of flat bar steel, $2\frac{1}{4}$ inches wide and $\frac{3}{8}$ inch thick, weighs 2.87 pounds. Compute (a) the net weight of a box containing $11\frac{1}{4}$ feet of this steel and, using the figures in this calculation, compute (b) the net weight of a box containing $13\frac{1}{4}$ feet of the same steel. Estimate the total weight in each instance to the nearest hundredth of a pound.

Ans. (a) 32.29 pounds; (b) 38.03 pounds.

* **11.** If the capacity of a tank 4 inches in diameter and 6 feet deep is 564 gallons, what would be the capacity of a tank 4 inches in diameter and 9 feet deep? *Ans.* 846 gallons. (*Art. 91*)

* **12.** One coal-crushing machine has a capacity of 244 tons an hour; another, 264 tons. If the total amount of coal crushed by the first machine in $2\frac{1}{4}$ hours is 549 tons, what quantity could be expected to be pulverized by the other machine in the same length of time? Compute the answer mentally, and without multiplying 264 by $2\frac{1}{4}$. *Ans.* 594 tons.

123. How to Speed the Process of Estimating Areas in Square Feet or Square Yards, and Volumes in Cubic Feet or Cubic Yards. In finding areas or volumes, computations can often by speeded by canceling into one or more of the dimensions, the factors of the unit of measurement in which the answer is desired.

Suppose, for instance, it is desired to obtain the area in square yards of a room 18 feet long by 14 feet wide. Ordinarily, one would multiply 18 by 14 and then divide the result by 9, since there are 9 square feet in a square yard. This procedure, however, is unnecessarily laborious. Since it is necessary to divide by 9 eventually anyway, it would be simpler to cancel 9 into 18, which gives us 2, then to multiply 14 by 2 and consider the result as square yards. In this way, not only is time saved in the computation, but the calculation becomes one which can be done mentally.

Example 1: Find the area in square yards of a room 36 feet long by 13 feet wide.

Solution: 36 divided by 9 = 4
4 times 13 = 52

Ans. 52 square yards.

Note in the next example that while 9 cannot be canceled into one dimension, one factor can be canceled into one dimension and the other factor into the other dimension.

Example 2: Find the area in square yards of a room 24 feet long by 12 feet wide.

Solution: 24 divided by 3 =   8

12 divided by 3 =   4
4 times 8   = 32

Ans. 32 square yards.

It will be interesting to observe the two methods of procedure in the following examples in which one factor of 9 is not exactly divisible into one of the dimensions.

Example 3: Find the area of a floor 19 feet long by 15 feet wide.

Solution:

Method A: 19 divided by 3 = $6\frac{1}{3}$
           15 divided by 3 =   5
            5 times $6\frac{1}{3}$ = $31\frac{2}{3}$

Method B: 15 divided by 3 =   5
           19 times 5   = 95
           95 divided by 3 = $31\frac{2}{3}$

Ans. $31\frac{2}{3}$ square yards.

There are 27 cubic feet in a cubic yard. But the cancellation of 27 is just as easy as the cancellation of 9, as will be seen in the following demonstrations.

Example 4: Find the number of cubic yards of space in an excavation 45 feet long, by 33 feet wide, by 6 feet deep.

Solution: 45 divided by 3   =   15
         33 divided by 3   =   11
          6 divided by 3   =   2
        15 times 11 times 2 = 330

Ans. 330 cubic yards.

Computation of the problem that follows is simplified still further by the fact that the entire number 27 cancels into one of the dimensions.

Example 5: Find the capacity in cubic yards of a room **27 feet** long, 14 feet wide, and 16 feet high.

Solution: 27 divided by 27   =   1
14 times 16 times 1 = 224

Ans. 224 cubic yards.

One square foot equals 144 square inches, and 144 can be factored in several ways; 144 is divisible by 2, 3, 4, 6, 8, 9, 12, 16. Observe in the following illustrations the interesting results which this divisor helps to obtain.

Example 6: Find the area in square feet of a sheet 24 inches by 96 inches.

Solution: Since one of the dimensions is 24, let us cancel 144 into the dimensions with the factors 6 and 24.

24 divided by 24 =   1
96 divided by   6 = 16
16 times 1   = 16

Ans. 16 square feet.

Example 7: Estimate the area in square feet of a sheet 46 inches long by 32 inches wide.

Solution: Sixteen cancels into 32, so let us use the factors 16 and 9, since the product of these numbers equals 144.

32 divided by 16 =   2
46 divided by 9 = $5\frac{1}{9}$
2 times $5\frac{1}{9}$ = $10\frac{2}{9}$

Ans. $10\frac{2}{9}$ square feet.

If the reader has made a page-by-page study of the chapters that have been covered thus far, he may recall seeing now and then, in connection with problems dealing with areas and cubic capacities, a parenthesized hint to use the short method of computation discussed here. The author considers the subject of wide-enough importance, nonetheless, to discuss it fully, and it is hoped that readers will have gained something from the detailed explanations of the technique in this article.

PROBLEMS

There are two parts to each of the following problems: (a) Show how you would reduce the dimensions, in accordance with the technique discussed in the text, by writing down the revised dimensions; (b) Write the answer, which is to be computed mentally.

★ **1.** Find in square yards the area of a room 21 feet long by 18 feet wide. *Ans.* (a) 21 by 2; (b) 42 square yards.

★ **2.** How many square yards of rock lath would be needed to cover a ceiling 24 feet long by 15 feet wide? *Ans.* (a) 8 by 5; (b) 40 square yards.

★ **3.** Estimate the equivalent in square yards of the area of a floor 54 feet long by 20 feet 4 inches wide. (Hint: 4 inches equals one third of a foot, so consider the width as $20\frac{1}{3}$ feet.)
Ans. (a) 6 by $20\frac{1}{3}$; (b) 122 square yards.

★ **4.** Wire lath usually comes in rolls 150 feet long by 36 inches wide. What is the area in square yards of a roll of this material?
Ans. (a) 50 times 1; (b) 50 square yards.

★ **5.** The standard dimensions of insulation corkboard blocks are 12 inches by 36 inches. Compute the number of square yards that can be covered with 24 blocks of this product.
Ans. (a) 8 times 1; (b) 8 square yards.

★ **6.** How many cubic yards of concrete would be used in placing a 4-inch thick concrete floor 36 feet long by 18 feet wide?
Ans. (a) $\frac{1}{3}$ times 4 times 6; (b) 8 cubic yards.

★ **7.** Estimate in cubic yards the capacity of an excavation 44 feet long, 36 feet wide, and having an average depth of 6 feet.
Ans. (a) 44 times 4 times 2; (b) 352 cubic yards.

★ **8.** What is the area in square feet of a piece of plywood panel 48 inches by 84 inches? *Ans.* (a) 4 by 7; (b) 28 square feet.

★ **9.** What is the area in square feet of a piece of phenolic fiber panel 36 inches by 66 inches? *Ans.* (a) 3 by $5\frac{1}{2}$; (b) $16\frac{1}{2}$ square feet.

★ **10.** Compute the area in square feet of a sheet of plate glass 180 inches by 56 inches. *Ans.* (a) $1\frac{1}{4}$ times 56; (b) 70 square feet.

CHAPTER XVII

SLIDE RULES AND CALCULATING MACHINES: THEY ARE INGENIOUS AND NECESSARY DEVICES, BUT WHY BE A SLAVE TO THEM?

No attempt is made here to depreciate the importance of slide rules and calculating machines. The very extensive use of both devices in the business and professional world is sufficient evidence of their immense value. But the fact remains that a large variety of mathematical problems can be worked mentally more quickly and, in many instances where the slide rule is involved, more accurately, by the use of an appropriate short-cut.

124. A Word About Slide Rules. The slide rule is a mathematical instrument widely used by engineers, architects, shopmen and others. Its advantage lies in the fact that it saves time and energy in calculations involving multiplication, division, squares and square roots, cubes and cube roots, logarithms, sines and tangents. In fact, any calculation except addition and subtraction can be made with the slide rule.

It is truly a remarkable device. But, unfortunately, many individuals become slaves to the slide rule, depending upon the instrument for the solution of every little problem.

The slide rule, undoubtedly, is the quickest means of solving a problem like

$$\frac{384 \times 48 \times 98}{264 \times 60 \times 246}$$

But there is no need to use the slide rule to multiply 18 by $3\frac{1}{2}$, or 75 by 14, or to obtain the answer to many problems which can be computed mentally in less time than it takes to pick up the slide rule and make the necessary adjustment of its parts. By the double-and-halve method, for instance, the product of 18 times $3\frac{1}{2}$ can be obtained quick as a flash by multiplying mentally 9 by 7; 75 times 14 is equivalent to 150 times 7 which, in turn, equals the sum of 700 and 350; and so on.

Nevertheless, the slide rule is an invaluable instrument, and readers who have not yet been initiated into its "mysteries" will find it a satisfying experience to learn at least the elementary principles governing its use. Although it is not the intent of this book to explain fully the use of the slide rule, it is hoped that by presenting a few pertinent facts many readers unfamiliar with this device may be stimulated to study its many interesting possibilities.

There are three things about the slide rule which might indicate to one seeing such an instrument for the first time that it is very different from a measuring rule. First, there are the markings which, unlike the markings of a measuring rule, are not even. Second, there is a movable strip (the "slide") inside the main or fixed part (the "stock"). And third, the rule includes a transparent attachment known as the "runner" or "indicator," with a hairline in the center.

Despite the many improvements over the years, the slide rule in common use today is essentially the same as it was originally designed by its inventor, a French lieutenant named Mannheim, in 1850.

The standard slide rule is 10 inches long, and this is the length of the specially adapted rules for use by electrical engineers, surveyors, radio technicians, etc. There is a Mannheim slide rule 20 inches long, specially designed for use in business offices. And another, designed for pocket use and only 5 inches long, weighs "no more than a fountain pen."

Suffice to say that the greatest advantage of the slide rule is the saving it affords in time and labor. And although this strange-looking device, to quote from Don Herold's admirable little book *How to Choose a Slide Rule*, "looks like something a magician might use to take rabbits out of a hat," it is an instrument with which every person who enjoys working with figures should strike up an acquaintance. At the time that this book goes to press, there is a students' popular slide rule on the market that costs only one dollar; and another (manufactured by the Lawrence Engineering Service, Peru, Indiana) sells for as little as 25 cents.

125. A Word About Calculating Machines. The part played by the calculating machine in modern business and industry is very different from that of the slide rule. With the slide rule countless problems can be solved in but a fraction of the time it would take on a calculating machine. Other problems, involving scientific formulas, roots, powers, logarithms, etc., would be well-nigh unsolvable or too time-consuming to compute on calculating machines. The fact is, however, that calculating machines, such as those manufactured by Felt & Tarrant, Marchand, Monroe, Burroughs, and others, do wonders. Every phase of business computation—multiplication and division as well as addition and subtraction—can be done rapidly and efficiently on one or another of these machines. Visible dials preclude the possibility of error in multiplication and division; and in the case of subtraction and division, totals and quotients obtained on machines equipped with tape rolls can be readily proved.

Aside from all this, some of the latest models are truly a feast for the eyes—a pleasure to look at and an incentive to any office worker who spends much time with figures. But just as in the case of the slide rule, there is such a thing as becoming a slave to the calculating machine. It may be an unfair exaggeration to call it mental laziness when one turns to the calculating machine to compute a problem like 9 times 37, when all one needs to do is subtract 37 from 370 mentally. It seems so easy to obtain the answer by depressing a few keys and a bar on the machine; but consider the energy-consuming and fatiguing motions that must be made—the shifting of the eyes from the work-sheet to the keyboard, and from the keyboard to the work-sheet—and you will readily appreciate that much time and energy might be saved by acquiring the habit of computing a large variety of problems mentally by the methods explained in this book, even when a calculating machine is accessible.

CHAPTER XVIII

AVERAGES AND PROPORTIONS

If the reader finds it pleasurable as well as useful to know how to cut time and ensure accuracy in mathematical computations, another delightful adventure is in store for him here. One of the techniques in the opening article is a particularly interesting study which, apart from the subject discussed, might happily expand the reader's mathematical horizon.

126. A Simple Way to Find the Average Due Date of Several Bills. For any of a number of reasons a businessman may wish to pay at one time several bills which fall due on different dates. He may be unable to pay the first bill on its due date, or he may have a special reason for wanting to pay all the bills from a certain creditor—including some bills that are not yet due—in one lump sum.

Let us suppose that on February 24 a man decides to pay at one time on the average due date a creditor's two bills—one for $340.00 due on March 9, and another for $460.00 due on March 20. On what date could he cancel his indebtedness with a payment of $800.00, the sum of the two amounts?

A good method of procedure is based on the fact that the interest earned, let us say, on $100 in 8 days is equivalent to the interest earned on $200 in 4 days, or on $400 in 2 days, or on $800 in 1 day. The method is as follows: Start with the last day of the month preceding the earliest due date. Take each bill separately and calculate the amount of the principal which, for one day, would earn as much interest as the amount of the bill would earn for the number of days indicated by the due date. The total of the principal amounts divided by the total amount of the bills equals

317

the average due date. Taking the aforementioned two bills, here are the actual figures:

$340 due March 9. $340 for 9 days = $ 3,060 for 1 day
460 due March 20. $460 for 20 days =   9,200 for 1 day
___   _____
$800 $12,260 for 1 day

This computation indicates that if the debtor had paid the sum of $800 on the last day of February, instead of paying the two bills, each on its due date, the amount of interest of which he would have deprived himself would be equal to the interest on $12,260 for 1 day. So what we do is this: We divide $12,260 by $800, which gives us 15, and it is on the 15th day of March that the entire debt may be canceled by a payment of $800.

The same method would be applied to an account consisting of any number of bills, as will be seen in the following demonstration.

Example 1: Find the average due date of three bills: one for $100 due April 11, one for $150 due April 20, and one for $150 due April 26.

Solution:

$100 due April 11. $100 for 11 days = $1100 for 1 day
150 due April 20.   150 for 20 days = 3000 for 1 day
150 due April 26.   150 for 26 days = 3900 for 1 day
___   _____
$400 $8000 for 1 day

$8000 divided by $400 equals 20. So that the entire account may be canceled by a payment of $400 on April 20.

It may be noticed that an interesting relation between the amounts and due dates of the bills exists in the foregoing illustration. The first bill is due *9 days ahead* of the second bill, and the third bill is due *6 days after* the second bill. On the other hand, the amount of the first bill is $100, and the amount of the third bill $150. One period (6 days) is two thirds of the other (9 days); and likewise, one amount ($100) is two thirds of the other ($150).

Thus if we use the bill due on April 20 as a pivotal point, we see without the need for further calculation that by advancing the due date of the first bill to April 20, and by anticipating payment of the third bill on April 20, the interest lost in the one instance is offset by the interest gained in the other instance, for the interest on $100 for 9 days (April 11 to 20) is equivalent to the interest on $150 for 6 days (April 20 to 26); which is another way of saying that 100 times 9 is equivalent to 150 times 6.

This technique of offsetting one bill against another will perhaps be better understood from a study of the following illustration in which only two bills are involved.

Example 2: Estimate the average due date of two bills: one for $400 due May 6, the other for $800 due May 18.

Solution: The briefest glance shows that one amount is exactly half of the other or, conversely, that one amount is twice as large as the other. Now since the interest on $2.00 for 1 day is exactly double the interest on $1.00 for 1 day, it is logical to suppose that the effect of holding up payment of the $400 bill for two days would be offset by the effect of advancing payment of the $800 bill one day.

Is it not clear, then, that since we are dealing in 3's (2 days plus 1 day equals 3 days, and 2 times $400 plus 1 times $400 equals 3 times $400), if we took the number of days between the one date and the other (May 6 to May 18 equals 12 days) and apportioned two thirds of that many days to the small bill and one third to the large bill, we will have arrived at the average due date? Here are the actual figures:

$\frac{1}{3}$ of 12 = 4. $\frac{2}{3}$ of 12 = 8.

May 6 (due date of bill for $400) plus 8 = 14.
May 18 (due date of bill for $800) minus 4 = 14.
So that the debt of $1200 (the sum of both bills) would be discharged by a payment of $1200 on May 14.

Example 3: Find the average due date of a bill for $360 due May 10, and a bill for $90 due May 25.

Solution: $90 is exactly one fourth of $360. So that the interest lost in advancing payment of the bill for $90 four days is equivalent to the interest gained in holding up payment of the bill for $360 one day. Notice that here we are dealing in 5's (4 days plus 1 day equals 5 days). Dividing 15 (the number of days from May 10 to May 25) by 5, gives us 3. And apportioning four times 3 days to the bill for $90, and one time 3 days to the bill for $360, we arrive at the average due date. Thus:

May 25 (due date of bill for $90) minus 12 = 13.
May 10 (due date of bill for $360) plus 3 = 13.
So that May 13 is the date on which a payment of $450 would liquidate the indebtedness of the two bills under consideration.

Notice that in the example just worked the situation was somewhat different from that in Example 2—the bill for the large amount was due ahead of the bill for the small amount. But this did not make one bit of difference in the method of procedure.

The following illustrations reflect the ease with which many problems of this nature can be solved instantly, even when three bills are involved. Such problems occur far more frequently than one might suppose.

Example 4: Find the average due date of three bills: $300.00 due July 9; $119.40 due July 17; $200.00 due July 29.

Solution: An interesting relation between the amounts and due dates of the first and last bills makes the amount of the second bill of no importance as far as the average due date is concerned. Taking the due date of the second bill as a pivotal point, we see that the number of days from July 9 (the due date of the first bill)

to July 17 (the due date of the second bill) is exactly
two thirds of the number of days from July 17 (the
due date of the second bill) to July 29 (the due date
of the third bill).   Now this relation of two thirds
between the two periods is a happy one, for $200
(the amount of the third bill) is two thirds of $300
(the amount of the first bill).

The interest gained on $300 for 8 days (300 times 8)
is exactly the same as the interest lost on $200 for
12 days (200 times 12).   The entire debt may,
therefore, be canceled by a payment equivalent to
the sum of the amounts of the three bills, on July
17, which is the due date of the second bill.

Example 5: Find the average due date of three bills: $175.00 due
September 4; $326.23 due September 18; $350.00 due September 25.

Solution: Here, too, there is an interesting relation between the
due dates.   There are exactly twice as many days
between September 4 (the due date of the first bill)
and September 18 (the due date of the second bill) as
there are between September 18 and September 25
(the due date of the third bill).   And, as in the
previous illustration, the amounts of the first and
third bills are in the same proportion.   The amount
of the bill that is due 14 days ahead of the second
bill is exactly half of the amount of the bill due 7
days later than the second bill.   The amount of
the second bill is, therefore, immaterial, and we are
safe in assuming that the entire indebtedness may
be canceled on September 18 (the due date of the
second bill) by a payment equivalent to the sum of
the three bills.

Example 6: Find the average due date of three bills: $660.00 due
November 15; $180.00 due November 23; and $880.00 due November 29.

Solution: From November 15 to November 23 is 8 days. And
from November 23 to November 29 is 6 days. Does
this ratio, in reverse, apply to the amounts of the
first and last bills? Yes, it does. The interest on
$660 for 8 days is equivalent to the interest on $880
for 6 days. (Proof: 660 times 8 = 5280, and
880 times 6 = 5280.) We see at once, therefore,
that the average due date of this account is November 23 (the due date of the second bill).

In any problem similar to the foregoing, is it necessary, in planning to pay all three bills on the due date of the second bill, that
the product of the amount of the first bill times the difference in
days be exactly equal to the product of the amount of the last bill
times the difference in days? Not at all.

Suppose, for instance, that in Example 6 the first product
instead of being 5280 were 5232, which would be the case if the
amount of the bill were $654.00 instead of $660.00. The significance of this difference would be that if the first bill and the last
bill were paid on November 23 (the due date of the second bill),
the debtor would be depriving himself of the use of $48.00 (5280
minus 5232 equals 48) for one day. Just how much is it worth to
use $48.00 for one day? At the arbitrary interest rate of 4 per
cent, it would be worth the insignificant amount of a little more
than half of one cent.

In computing average due dates, then, a difference of a few
dollars one way or the other is not important. And, by the same
token, it is not necessary to consider fractions of a dollar in making
such computations, it being only necessary to increase or decrease
the number of dollars according to whether the fraction is greater
or less than half a dollar.

Furthermore, even if the amount in each of the three bills in
Example 6 were multiplied by the number of days, as illustrated
in the solution to Example 1, we should find that the average due
date would be November 23 (the due date of the second bill)
regardless of whether the amount of the bill under discussion was

$660.00 or $654.00, for it is obvious that when the total of the equivalent amounts for one day is divided by the total of the bills the quotient may include a fraction; and just as in the case of a sum which includes a fraction of a cent we show the answer to the nearest cent, so in the case of a fraction of a day we show the answer to the nearest whole day.

In order to make this clear, let us refer back to Example 1, changing the amount of the bill for $100.00 to $105.00, and see whether this addition of $5.00 makes any difference in the average due date of the account.

$105 due April 11. $105 for 11 days = $1155 for 1 day
150 due April 20.   150 for 20 days = 3000 for 1 day
150 due April 26.   150 for 26 days = 3900 for 1 day
_____   _____
$405 $8055 for 1 day

$8055 divided by 405 equals 19.9, or 20, which gives us exactly the same due date as when the first bill was for $100.00 rather than for $105.00.

The reader might be wondering by this time, what would be the procedure when more than three bills are involved. This would, of course, depend upon the amounts and due dates of the bills. If there is no relation between these factors, as there was in Examples 2 to 6, the simplest way would be to take each bill separately and compute the equivalent amount for one day, and so on. If, on the other hand, in a group of four bills there is such a relation between three of the bills, it would be necessary to compute the average due date of the three bills only, and then continue the process in relation to the fourth bill. To illustrate, let us consider the amounts and dates in Example 6 in this light, adding a fourth bill for $1280.00 due on November 5. The account would be equivalent to the following:

$1280 due November 5
1720 due November 23

All we need do is proceed as we did in solving the problem in Example 1:

$1280 for 5 days = $ 6,400 for 1 day
1720 for 23 days =   39,560 for 1 day

————   ——————————

3000 $45,960 for 1 day

$45,960 divided by 3000 equals 15.32, or 15, which means that the entire debt could be liquidated by paying all four bills on November 15.

The habit of observing relations between numbers is a mighty helpful tool in solving mathematical problems of all kinds. In the last illustration, for instance, it will readily be seen that in multiplying $1280 by 5, $660 by 15, $180 by 23, and $880 by 29, to add the products and divide their total by the sum of the amounts involved would be an unnecessary waste of time and energy, to say nothing of the advantage gained from being able to make computations of this nature mentally.

PROBLEMS

Find the average due date of each of the following accounts. The due dates in the first three problems are to be determined by the technique indicated in the solution to Example 1 in the text. The due dates in Problems 4 and 5 are to be computed mentally.

1. $100.00 due February 6, $250.00 due February 22, and $150.00 due February 26.   *Ans.* February 20.

2. $375.00 due March 4, $125.00 due March 8, and $204.00 due March 25.   *Ans.* March 11.

3. $75.00 due May 3, $250.00 due May 8, $250.00 due May 9, $125.00 due May 10, and $425.00 due May 13.   *Ans.* May 10.

★ 4. $212.50 due July 11, $347.00 due July 14, and $106.25 due July 20.
Ans. July 14.

★ 5. $312.31 due September 10, $219.43 due September 20, and $624.62 due September 25.   *Ans.* September 20.

127. Three Good Ways of Dividing Profits Among Partners.
There are three commonly accepted ways of dividing profits among partners.

1. In the ratio of capitals. This method is the simplest of all. If Smith, for example, has $10,000 invested, and his partner Brown $5000, Smith (whose investment constitutes two thirds of the total capital) receives two thirds of the profit, and Brown (whose investment represents one third of the total capital) receives one third of the profit.

2. In an agreed-upon ratio after interest has been credited to each partner's capital account. In some partnerships there is an agreement by which the partners share alike, even though the individual investments are unequal. There may be any number of reasons for such an arrangement. The partner with the smaller investment may, for instance, have special abilities or be more active in the business. In such circumstances it is sometimes also agreed that before the profits are divided, interest at a specified rate be credited to each partner's capital account. Let us say that the gentlemen mentioned under the first arrangement agreed to divide profits equally, and that interest at the rate of 4 per cent be credited to their respective capital accounts before the profit is divided. Assuming that the profit amounted to $35,000, the amounts received by each would be as follows:

Smith would receive 4 per cent interest on his $10,000 investment, or $400.

Brown would receive 4 per cent interest on his $5000 investment, or $200.

The profit of $35,000 has been reduced by these interest credits to $34,400, and since the profit is to be divided equally, each partner will receive half of $34,400, or $17,200.

Smith will therefore be credited with $400 plus $17,200, or $17,600.

And Brown will be credited with $200 plus $17,200, or $17,400.

It should be remembered that when the agreement provides that interest be credited to each partner's capital account, the interest is credited regardless of whether there is a profit or a loss, and regardless of whether the profit does or does not exceed the total of the interest credits. If, for instance, the profit, before the interest is credited, amounted to only $500, the net loss, too, would be shared equally. In that event the amounts credited to the individual partners would be as follows:

Smith would be credited with $400 interest, less
$50 (half of the loss),* or $350.
Brown would be credited with $200 interest less
$50 (half of the loss),* or $150.

If, instead of a profit of $500, the business sustained a loss of $900, the interest would still be credited to the partners' capital accounts, and then the total loss would be shared equally. By total loss is meant, of course, the net loss after interest has been credited. Since the interest credits amount to $600, the total loss would be $1500 ($900 plus $600). Here is how the partners' capital accounts would be affected:

Smith would be credited with $400 interest, and debited with
$750 (half of the loss of $1500), resulting in a net debit to his
account of $350.
Brown would be credited with $200 interest, and debited with
$750 (half of the loss of $1500), resulting in a net debit to his
account of $550.

3. In the ratio of average capital. An agreement of this nature might be in effect when the partners are in the habit of making withdrawals or additions to their capital during the business year. Let us suppose that Smith and Brown, instead of leaving their respective investments untouched during the entire year, made withdrawals and additions as follows:

Smith			*Brown*		
Jan. 1		$10,000	Jan. 1		$5,000
Mar. 1	Withdrew	1,000	Apr. 1	Added	1,500
Aug. 1	Added	2,500	July 1	Withdrew	500
Nov. 1	Withdrew	2,000			

* A profit of $500 becomes a loss of $100 after a total of $600 in interest has been credited to the partners' capital accounts.

The logic of a profit-sharing arrangement based on average capital will be appreciated when it is observed that while Smith withdrew during the year $500 more than he added, Brown added $1000 more than he withdrew; and further, that the additions and withdrawals were made on widely varying dates.

The procedure here is somewhat similar to that followed in the preceding article, where we learned how to find the average due date of several bills. Our object here will be to determine how many months each partner's capital remains unchanged, then to compute the equivalent amount for one month. Taking each partner's capital account separately, here is how the equivalents are computed:

Smith's Investment

Capital for 2 months (Jan. 1 to Mar. 1),	$10,000 =	$ 20,000 for 1 month
Capital for 5 months (Mar. 1 to Aug. 1),	9,000 =	45,000 for 1 month
Capital for 3 months (Aug. 1 to Nov. 1),	11,500 =	34,500 for 1 month
Capital for 2 months (Nov. 1 to Dec. 31),	9,500 =	19,000 for 1 month

12 months $118,500 for 1 month

Brown's Investment

Capital for 3 months (Jan. 1 to Apr. 1),	$5,000 =	$15,000 for 1 month
Capital for 3 months (Apr. 1 to July 1),	6,500 =	19,500 for 1 month
Capital for 6 months (July 1 to Dec. 31),	6,000 =	36,000 for 1 month

12 months $70,500 for 1 month

We have, in effect, reduced the individual capital accounts of Smith and Brown to a common basis. Smith's investment for the year is the equivalent of $118,500 for one month, and Brown's investment for the year is the equivalent of $70,500 for one month.

Since the sum of these equivalent investments is $189,000, it is clear that Smith's investment constitutes $\frac{118,500}{189,000}$ (or $\frac{1185}{1890}$) of the total amount invested in the business by both partners, and that Brown's investment constitutes $\frac{70,500}{189,000}$ (or $\frac{705}{1890}$) of the total.

If the profit for the year amounted to $11,340, it would therefore be shared as follows:

Smith would receive $\frac{1185}{1890}$ of $11,340, or $7110.
Brown would receive $\frac{705}{1890}$ of $11,340, or $4230.

Let us now take a slightly more difficult example—a partnership between Kent and Stern, whose respective capital accounts for the year show the following additions and withdrawals:

Kent		*Stern*	
Jan. 1	$7,000	Jan. 1	$4,000
June 16 Added	1,000	Apr. 10 Withdrew	1,000
Aug. 23 Withdrew	2,000	Oct. 14 Added	1,000

Since in this instance the changes were made *during* the month rather than on the first day of the month, it will be necessary to take the averages for one day. And since the round number 360 is used so conveniently in interest computations to represent the number of days in a year, let us use this number here too.

Kent's Investment

Capital for 166 days (Jan. 1 to June 16),	$7,000 =	$1,162,000 for 1 day
Capital for 67 days (June 16 to Aug. 23),	8,000 =	536,000 for 1 day
Capital for 127 days (Aug. 23 to Dec. 31),	6,000 =	762,000 for 1 day
360 days		$2,460,000 for 1 day

Stern's Investment

Capital for 100 days (Jan. 1 to April 10),	$4,000 = $	400,000 for 1 day
Capital for 184 days (Apr. 10 to Oct. 14),	3,000 =	552,000 for 1 day
Capital for 76 days (Oct. 14 to Dec. 31),	4,000 =	304,000 for 1 day
360 days		$1,256,000 for 1 day

The sum of the equivalent investments of Kent and Stern for one day is the sum of $2,460,000 and $1,256,000, or $3,716,000.

So that Kent's share of the profit will be $\dfrac{2,460,000}{3,716,000}$ or $\frac{2460}{3716}$, and Stern's share will be $\dfrac{1,256,000}{3,716,000}$ or $\frac{1256}{3716}$.

If the profit for the year was $13,006, it would be shared as follows:

> Kent would receive $\frac{2460}{3716}$ of $13,006, or $8610.
> Stern would receive $\frac{1256}{3716}$ of $13,006, or $4396.

When Profits Are to Be Shared Among More Than Two Partners.
The method of dividing profits when there are more than two partners is substantially the same as when only two partners are involved. Thus under the first method—by which profits are shared in the ratio of capitals—if along with Smith who had $10,000 invested, and Brown who had $5000 invested, there was a third partner Kane, who invested $5000, the ratios would be as follows:

Smith's investment of $5000 would constitute $\frac{5000}{20000}$, or one fourth.

Brown's investment of $10,000 would constitute $\frac{10000}{20000}$, or one half.

Kane's investment of $5000 would constitute $\frac{5000}{20000}$, or one fourth.

Note that the denominator represents the sum of the individual investments; and, conversely, that the sum of the numerators equals the amount, or number, in the denominator.

Under the second method—by which partners share alike after interest has been credited to their accounts—each partner would be credited or debited (according to whether there was a profit or a loss) on the basis of the number of partners. Each of three partners would share a third; each of four partners a fourth; and so on.

And if, under the third method—that of sharing in the ratio of average capital—Smith and Brown had a third partner, Morrison, the procedure would not be altered one bit. The monthly equivalents would be computed for each of the three partners, the equivalent investments would be totaled, and then each partner would share in the ratio of his monthly equivalent to the total.

Thus, if Morrison's monthly equivalent was $41,000, the sum of the three equivalents (Smith's $118,500, Brown's $70,500, and

Morrison's $41,000) would be $230,000.   Each would therefore share as follows:

Smith would receive $\dfrac{118,500}{230,000}$ of the total profit.

Brown would receive $\dfrac{70,500}{230,000}$ of the total profit.

Morrison would receive $\dfrac{41,000}{230,000}$ of the total profit.

Problems

1. Three partners agree to share profits in the ratio of capital. Wilson's capital is $6000, Lewis invested $4000, and Field $5000.   If the total profit is $12,000, how much will each receive as his share of the profit?   *Ans.* Wilson $4800, Lewis $3200, Field $4000.

2. What would each partner's share be in Problem 1 if all shared equally and each was credited with 3% interest on his investment before the profit was divided?   The word "share" is used here to mean profit plus interest.   *Ans.* Wilson $4030, Lewis $3970, Field $4000.

3. Assume that the partners in the foregoing problems made the following additions and withdrawals from their respective capital accounts and that the profit was shared in the ratio of average capital.   What would each receive if the total profit was $12,000?   Assume that the capital of each partner was invested on January 1.

Wilson withdrew $500 on July 1.
Lewis added $1000 on May 1, and withdrew $500 on July 1.
Field withdrew $2000 on May 1 and added $1000 on September 1.

Ans. Wilson $4870.59, Lewis $3741.18, Field $3388.23.

128. How to Find Average Cost or Selling Price.   When a product is made by the mixing of different materials it is necessary, if the selling price is to be determined, to know the average cost. A manufacturer of pharmaceuticals, for instance, may produce a preparation by mixing so many gallons of one ingredient with so many gallons of another, and in order to have a definite figure on which to base the selling price, he must know what the mixture costs him per gallon, quart or pint.   Similarly, a company, contemplating the combination of different wools, may want to determine the average cost per pound of the mixture. The procedure is simple: The total cost of the mixture is divided by the total quantity of the materials used.

Example 1: A mill owner desires to know the average cost per pound of a mixture formed by the combination of the following lots of wools:

179 lb. @ $1.12 per lb.   188 lb. @ $1.07 per lb.
346 lb. @ 1.04 per lb.   411 lb. @ 1.16 per lb.

Estimate the average cost to the nearest cent.

Solution: 179 lb. @ $1.12 per lb. = $200.48
346 lb. @ 1.04 per lb. =   359.84
188 lb. @ 1.07 per lb. =   201.16
411 lb. @ ·1.16 per lb. =   476.76
                                             _____
1124 lb.   = $1238.24

$1238.24 divided by 1124 equals $1.10, which is the average cost per pound of the mixture.

Exactly the same procedure is followed when it is desired to obtain the average selling price, as demonstrated in the solution to the following problem.

Example 2: A farmer made the following sales of cotton during the gathering season, for which he received the amounts shown:

Number of Bales	Weight in Pounds	Price Per Lb. (in cents)	Total
31	14,320	31.25	$4,475.00
16	15,168	31.55	4,785.50
12	11,026	31.60	3,484.22
24	23,872	30.95	7,388.38

Compute to the nearest hundredth of a cent the average price per pound received by the farmer.

Solution: The total number of pounds of cotton sold is 64,386, and the total amount received is \$20,133.10. \$20,133.10 divided by 64,386 equals 31.27 cents.

The farmer received, therefore, an average price of 31.27 cents per pound.

PROBLEMS

1. A food company makes a coffee mixture by mixing 112 pounds of one grade of coffee costing $26\frac{1}{2}$ cents a pound with 35 pounds of another grade costing 23 cents a pound. Estimate the average cost per pound of the mixture to the nearest hundredth of a cent.

Ans. 25.67 cents per pound. (*Art. 16*)

2. A retail nut shop mixes the following nuts: 25 pounds costing 17 cents a pound, 30 pounds costing 22 cents a pound, and 50 pounds costing 25 cents a pound. Compute the average cost per pound to the nearest cent.   *Ans.* 22 cents per pound. (*Art. 111*)

3. A druggist prepared a laxative from the following formula, using the quantities specified:

> 1 gallon Cascara   costing \$2.50 per gallon
> 2 gallons Rhubarb and Soda costing   1.75 per gallon
> $\frac{3}{4}$ gallon Milk of Magnesia   costing   1.10 per gallon
> $1\frac{1}{4}$ gallon Syrup of Licorice   costing   1.50 per gallon

Estimate to the nearest quarter of a cent his average cost per pint. (Hint: 8 pints equals one gallon.)   *Ans.* $21\frac{3}{4}$ cents per pint.

4. A candy manufacturer decides to offer a mixture which he made from the following:

> 128 lb. of a quality sold for \$0.35 per lb.
> 85 lb. of a quality sold for   .28 per lb.
> 114 lb. of a quality sold for   .24 per lb.
> 23 lb. of a quality sold for   .40 per lb.

At how much per pound should he sell the mixture if he is to receive for the entire quantity the same amount that he would have received if he sold the four different qualities separately at the indicated prices?

Ans. 30 cents per pound. (*Arts. 2-b, 16, 120*)

5. A baker sold the following cookies: 32 pounds at \$1.10 a pound, 48 pounds at 90 cents a pound, and 70 pounds at 70 cents a pound. Compute to the nearest cent the average selling price per pound.

Ans. 85 cents per pound. (*Arts. 1-d, 111, 120*)

6. The records of a cafeteria showed that the following sales were made in one day:

43 @ $0.10	206 @ $0.40	96 @ $0.70
56 @ .15	240 @ .45	84 @ .75
84 @ .20	320 @ .50	80 @ .80
90 @ .25	310 @ .55	62 @ .85
164 @ .30	262 @ .60	33 @ .90
140 @ .35	130 @ .65	

Estimate to the nearest cent the amount of the average sale for the day.
Ans. 50 cents. (*Arts. 1-b, 1-d, 2-a, 2-b, 16, 105*)

129. How to Determine the Exact Quantity Necessary of Each of a Number of Variously Priced Materials to Produce a Mixture at a Specified Cost. Manufacturers frequently find it necessary to determine the exact proportion in which to mix a number of different materials in order to produce a mixture to cost a specified amount. It is usual in such circumstances to mix one or more materials whose cost per unit of measurement is *less* than that of the desired mixture, with one or more materials costing *more*. In some instances, as in Example 1, no particular proportion is specified; in others, as in Example 2, the formulation provides for the consumption of a specified quantity of one of the materials; and in still others, as in Examples 3 and 4, the proportion in which two of the materials are to be mixed is predetermined.

We will study four different types of mixtures. In each case the solution to the problem entails three steps. In the first step we will deal (a) with materials costing *less* per unit of measurement than the desired mixture, when there is no specified proportion, or (b) with the material of which a specified quantity is to be used. In the second step we will deal (a) with materials whose cost per unit of measurement *exceeds* that of the desired mixture, when there is no specified proportion, or (b) with materials which are to be used in a specified proportion, regardless of cost. It will be noted that in one step (it may be the first step and it may be the second) we find what is called the *gain*; and in the other step the *loss*—that is, a key figure which will enable us, in the third step, to determine how much of each of the materials dealt with in the second step is to be used with the materials dealt with in the first step.

A careful study of the subject matter that follows, including the summary at the end of the article, will make this clear.

WHEN IT IS DESIRED TO DETERMINE THE PROPORTION IN
WHICH TO USE THREE MATERIALS—TWO COSTING "LESS"
PER UNIT OF MEASUREMENT THAN THE DESIRED MIXTURE,
AND ONE COSTING "MORE":

Example 1: A manufacturer of textile products has on hand three lots of wool, of which he wishes to make a mixture at a material cost of $1.18 per pound. The cost per pound of the three lots is $1.03, $1.14 and $1.24, respectively. In what proportion should the materials be used to produce the desired mixture?

Solution:

First step: $1.18 minus $1.03 = .15; 15 times 1 (1 lb.) = 15
1.18 minus 1.14 = .04; 4 times 1 (1 lb.) = 4
                                                    ——
                                              Gain = 19

Second step: $1.18 minus $1.24 = minus .06.   Loss = 6

Third step: 19 (gain) divided by 6 (loss)   = $3\frac{1}{6}$

Conclusion: A mixture costing $1.18 a pound could therefore be produced by mixing the materials as follows:

1 lb. of the material costing $1.03 lb. = $1.03
1 lb. of the material costing $1.14 lb. = 1.14
$3\frac{1}{6}$ lb. of the material costing $1.24 lb. = 3.93
                                           ————
$5\frac{1}{6}$ lb.   = $6.10

Proof: $6.10 divided by $5\frac{1}{6}$ = $1.18.

WHEN A SPECIFIED QUANTITY OF MATERIAL COSTING
"MORE" PER UNIT OF MEASUREMENT THAN THE DESIRED
MIXTURE IS TO BE USED WITH AN UNDETERMINED QUAN-
TITY OF A MATERIAL COSTING "LESS" THAN THE DESIRED
MIXTURE:

Example 2: A manufacturer wishes to use 374 pounds of material costing $1.16 a pound to produce a mixture costing $1.12 a pound.

To be used in the mixture is a material of which several hundred pounds are available, the cost of which is $1.02 a pound. How much of the latter material will be needed to produce the mixture?

Solution:

First step: $1.12 minus $1.16 = minus .04.
                Minus 4 times 374 (374 lb.)
                     = minus 1496.   Loss = 1496

Second step: $1.12 minus $1.02 = .10.   Gain =   10

Third step: 1496 (loss) divided by 10 (gain)   = $149\frac{6}{10}$

Conclusion: A mixture costing $1.12 a pound
                 could therefore be produced by
                 mixing the materials as follows:

                 374 lb. of the material costing $1.16 lb. = $433.84
                 $149\frac{6}{10}$ lb. of the material costing $1.02 lb. =   152.59

                 $523\frac{6}{10}$ lb.   = $586.43
Proof: $586.43 divided by 523.6 = $1.12.

WHEN A SPECIFIED QUANTITY OF MATERIAL COSTING "LESS" PER UNIT OF MEASUREMENT THAN THE DESIRED MIXTURE IS TO BE USED WITH TWO MATERIALS COSTING "MORE" THAN THE DESIRED MIXTURE, AND IN EQUAL PROPORTION:

Example 3: A manufacturer has 120 pounds of material costing 70 cents a pound, which he plans to use in a mixture, the materials of which are to cost him $1.00 a pound. Along with the 70-cent material are to be used, in equal quantities, a material costing $1.15 a pound and a material costing $1.05 a pound. How many pounds of each of the last-mentioned materials will be used in the mixture?

Solution:

First step: $1.00 minus $0.70 = .30; 30 times 120 (120 lb.)
                     = 3600.   Gain = 3600.

Second step: $1.00 minus $1.15 = minus .15;
$1.00 minus $1.05 = minus .05;
Minus 15 plus minus 5 = minus 20.

Total loss = 20
Average loss = 10

Third step: 3600 (gain) divided by 10 (average loss) = 360.
The loss of 360 must now be equally divided
between the two products—that is, the one
costing $1.15 a pound, and the other costing
$1.05 a pound. In other words, it will be
necessary to use 180 pounds of each of the two
materials.

Conclusion: A mixture costing $1.00 a pound could therefore
be produced by mixing the materials as fol-
lows:

120 lb. of the material costing $0.70 lb. = $ 84.00
180 lb. of the material costing 1.15 lb. = 207.00
180 lb. of the material costing 1.05 lb. = 189.00
_____   _____
480 lb.   = $480.00

Proof: $480.00 divided by 480 = $1.00.

WHEN A SPECIFIED QUANTITY OF MATERIAL COSTING
"LESS" PER UNIT OF MEASUREMENT THAN THE DESIRED
MIXTURE, IS TO BE USED WITH TWO MATERIALS COSTING
"MORE" THAN THE DESIRED MIXTURE, AND IN THE PRO-
PORTION OF 3 TO 1:

Example 4: One hundred pounds of a material costing $2.00 a
pound are to be used along with 3 parts of a material costing $2.35
a pound to 1 part of a material costing $2.70 a pound, to produce a
mixture costing $2.30 a pound. What quantities of the 3 to 1
materials will need to be used?

Solution:

First step: $2.30 minus $2.00 = .30; 30 times 100 (100
lb.) = 3000.   Gain = 3000

Second step: $2.30 minus $2.70 = minus .40;
     minus 40 times 1 (1 lb.)   = minus 40
    $2.30 minus $2.35 = minus .05;
     minus 5 times 3 (3 lb.)   = minus 15

          Total loss =   55
        Average loss = $13\frac{3}{4}$ *

Third step: 3000 (gain) divided by $13\frac{3}{4}$ (average loss) = 218. Since two of the materials are to be used in the proportion of 3 parts of the $2.35 quality to 1 part of the $2.70 quality, we now divide 218 by 4, which gives us $54\frac{1}{2}$. And it is clear that we will need to use $163\frac{1}{2}$ lb. of the $2.35 material with $54\frac{1}{2}$ lb. of the $2.70 material.

Conclusion: The mixture will therefore be as follows:

   100 lb. of the material costing $2.00
    lb.   = $200.00
   $163\frac{1}{2}$ lb. of the material costing $2.35
    lb.   = 384.22
   $54\frac{1}{2}$ lb. of the material costing $2.70
    lb.   = 147.15

   318 lb.   = $731.37

Proof: $731.37 divided by 318 = $2.30.

SUMMARY

Example 1: The step-by-step procedure was comparatively simple. Neither of the two conditions common to the other problems obtained here. That is, no specified quantity of any material was to be used, and no materials were to be used in any particular proportion. So under the first step to the solution, we dealt with

---

* The "loss" on one pound of the $2.70 material is 40, and the loss on three pounds of the $2.35 material is 15; therefore, the loss on four pounds of both materials used in the specified proportion is 55, or $13\frac{3}{4}$ per pound.

the materials costing *less* per unit of measurement than the desired mixture; and under the second step, with the material costing *more* than the desired mixture.

Also, since none of the materials was to be used in a specified quantity, we used, under the first step, one pound as the basis of computation.

Example 2: A definite quantity of material was specified. Since the second step to the solution is used as a guide for computing under the third step the *unknown* quantities, it is understandable that the *known* quantities should be disposed of under the first step.

Example 3: Here, too, a definite quantity of material was to be used in the mixture. So, as in Problem 2, the known quantity was dealt with under the first step, and the unknown quantities under the second step. It is important to observe that under the third step, in dividing the gain by the loss, we arrived at the *total* weight of the two materials dealt with under the second step. Since the two materials were to be used in equal proportion, 360 (the total) was divided by 2.

Example 4: This problem is similar to that in Example 3. A specified quantity of material was to be used, and two other materials were to be mixed in a certain proportion. The only difference is that, instead of being in equal proportion, the two materials in this instance were to be used in the ratio of 3 to 1.

Thus, while in Example 3, where the materials are used in equal proportion, we divided the total loss by 2 to obtain the average loss, here, the ratio being 3 to 1, we divided the total loss by 4 (since 3 plus 1 equals 4) to obtain the average loss.

And, while in Example 3, where the proportion was equal, we divided 360 (the figure obtained under the third step) by 2, here, the ratio being 3 to 1, we divided 218 (the figure obtained under the third step) by 4, apportioning three fourths of 218 to the one material and one fourth to the other.

It is interesting to note that it makes no difference whether the gain is determined in the first step and the loss in the second, or vice versa. It should be remembered, however, that the larger number is always divided by the smaller number; thus, while in Examples 1, 3 and 4, the gain was divided by the loss, in Example 2 the loss was divided by the gain.

It is a fascinating study—this subject of mixtures—and a re-reading of this article will make it seem not nearly so difficult as it may appear after the first reading.

PROBLEMS

1. It is desired to make a mixture of two materials—one costing $3.40 a pound, the other $3.95 a pound. If the cost of the materials used in the mixture is to be $3.75 a pound, in what proportion should the materials be mixed?

Ans. 1 pound of the $3.40 material to $1\frac{3}{4}$ pounds of the $3.95 material.

2. A mixture is to be made of three materials which cost, respectively, $2.00, $2.40 and $2.85 a pound. If the cost of the finished product is to be $2.60 a pound, in what proportion should the three materials be used?

Ans. One pound of the $2.00 material, one pound of the $2.40 material, and $3\frac{1}{5}$ pounds of the $2.85 material.

3. A manufacturer has 226 pounds of a product costing $1.84 a pound. He wishes to use this entire quantity along with another product to make a mixture costing $2.20 a pound. If the other material costs $2.35 a pound, how many pounds of it should be used? *Ans.* 542.4 pounds.

4. If the situation in the preceding problem were reversed, the 226 pounds costing $2.35 a pound and the other material $1.84 a pound, how many pounds of the $1.84 material should be used with the 226 pounds? *Ans.* $94\frac{1}{8}$ pounds.

5. Two materials—one weighing 83 pounds and costing $2.10 a pound, the other weighing 120 pounds and costing $1.30 a pound—are to be used with a third material costing $4.20 a pound, to produce a mixture costing $2.80 a pound. How many pounds of the $4.20 material will be needed to produce the desired mixture? *Ans.* 170 pounds.

6. Two materials—one weighing 125 pounds and costing $2.00 a pound, the other weighing 64 pounds and costing $5.00 a pound—are to be mixed with a third material costing $4.00 a pound, to produce a mixture costing $3.50 a pound. How much of the third material should be used? (Hint: Even though one of the materials to be used in a specified quantity —the one costing $5.00 a pound—exceeds the price of the mixture, it may be included along with the material costing $2.00 a pound under the first step; in other words, the minus quantity representing the $5.00 material will be deducted from the plus quantity representing the $2.00 material, and the difference will represent the gain.) *Ans.* 183 pounds.

7. Three pounds of a material costing $3.00 a pound are to be used with two pounds of a material costing $4.00 a pound, along with a third material costing $8.00 a pound and in a quantity to be determined, to make a mixture costing $6.50 a pound. How many pounds of the third material should be used to produce the desired mixture? *Ans.* 10⅓ pounds.

8. Two hundred pounds of a material costing $1.80 a pound are to be part of a mixture costing $2.40 a pound. Two other materials are to be used in the following proportion: 5 pounds of a material costing $3.00 a pound for every 3 pounds of a material costing $2.60 a pound. What quantities of the last-mentioned products will be needed?

> *Ans.* 166⅔ pounds of the $3.00 material and 100 pounds of the $2.60 material.

9. Sixty pounds of a product costing $2.30 a pound are to be used with two other materials to produce a mixture costing $3.00 a pound. How many pounds of each of these other materials will be required if they are to be used in the proportion of 2 to 1 and cost, respectively, $3.60 and $3.90 a pound?

> *Ans.* 40 pounds of the $3.60 material and 20 pounds of the $3.90 material.

10. Eighty pounds of a material costing 90 cents a pound and 40 pounds of a material costing $1.00 a pound are to be mixed with three other materials to form a product costing $1.40 a pound. The other three materials, which are to be mixed in the proportion of 3, 2 and 1, cost, respectively, $1.70, $1.60 and $1.50 a pound. How many pounds of each will be required to produce the desired mixture?

> *Ans.* 120 pounds of the $1.70 material, 80 pounds of the $1.60 material, and 40 pounds of the $1.50 material.

130. How to Determine Proportionate Values, Dimensions of Reductions and Enlargements, etc. One of the commonest sources of headaches to many businessmen is the subject of proportion. A merchant, for example, receiving an offer of a piece of property in exchange for his present property, may want to make a comparison on a square-foot basis. A manufacturer who has purchased a casting which weighs 160 pounds may want to know the exact cost of another casting weighing 288 pounds. Or a farmer, finding that 223 pounds of milk produced 7 pounds of butter fat, may want to determine the quantity of milk required to produce, let us say, 44 pounds of butter fat. These are just a few of virtually countless kinds of problems which can be solved easily and quickly by simple proportion.

Proportion means the relation of one to another. And when we speak of the relation which the value of one number has to another, we are referring to the ratio of the two numbers. Thus the relation of 50 to 100 can be expressed by the ratio of 1 to 2 (written 1:2), because 50 is $\frac{1}{2}$ of 100. Similarly, the relation of 25 to 100 can be expressed by the ratio of 1 to 4, or 1:4; the relation of 7 to 21 by the ratio 1 to 3, or 1:3; the relation of 6 to 9 by the ratio 2 to 3, or 2:3.

As will be seen from the foregoing, the ratio of two numbers consists of the fraction which results from the division of one number by the other. Thus the relation of 50 to 100 is represented by the ratio 1:2 because, as has been pointed out, $\frac{50}{100}$ is equivalent to $\frac{1}{2}$. Similarly, the relation of $\frac{25}{100}$ is expressed by the ratio 1:4 because $\frac{25}{100}$ is equivalent to $\frac{1}{4}$. And the relation of 160 to 288 (the weights of the two castings referred to in the first paragraph) can be expressed by the ratio 5:9, since $\frac{5}{9}$ is the fraction obtained from $\frac{160}{288}$ by cancellation.

When we speak of the relation between two equal ratios we speak of them as being in proportion. Thus $\frac{50}{100}$ is in proportion or is equivalent to $\frac{200}{400}$. Reason? 50 divided by 100 equals $\frac{1}{2}$, and 200 divided by 400 equals $\frac{1}{2}$. It is clear, then, that 50:100 equals 200:400, which is read "50 is to 100 as 200 is to 400."

Example 1: A businessman owning 3 lofts of 2500 square feet each is offered a plant of 12,000 square feet in exchange. What is the ratio of the sum of the areas of the three lofts to the area of the plant?

Solution: The sum of the areas of the 3 lofts is 7500 square feet. The ratio, therefore, is $\frac{7500}{12,000}$, which is equivalent to $\frac{5}{8}$.

Ans. 7500:12,000 = 5:8.

In the example just worked, the equivalent ratio was obtained automatically and with very little effort, because it was simply a matter of canceling one number into the other. Frequently, however, one of the values in the equivalent ratio is predetermined, and it is necessary to calculate the fourth value. Thus, to use a simple illustration, if we were to solve the problem: What ratio having 10 as the denominator is equal to the fraction $\frac{2}{4}$, we would write, using x as the unknown quantity, $2:4 = x:10$, or $\dfrac{2}{4} = \dfrac{x}{10}$.

Attention is now called to a very interesting rule in connection with ratios and proportion, which reads, "In any fractional equation the product of the means equals the product of the extremes." This has already been discussed in Art. 55 ("How To Find the Rate Per Cent"), to which the reader is urged to refer for further study. It is interesting to observe that "the product of the means equals the product of the extremes" is another way of saying that in any equation (e.g., $\frac{2}{4} = \frac{5}{10}$), the numerator of the first fraction multiplied by the denominator of the second fraction (2 times 10 in the example just cited) equals the product of the denominator of the first fraction multiplied by the numerator of the second fraction (4 times 5 in the same example). So that to solve the problem in the preceding paragraph, we would simply divide 20 (the product of 2 times 10) by $4x$ (4 times x) to find the value of one x which, of course, is 5. In other words, $2:4 = 5:10$, or $\frac{2}{4} = \frac{5}{10}$.

The process of finding proportionate values is similar to that of finding the rate per cent (see Art. 55). The only difference is that instead of finding the new value in relation to 100, it is found in relation to the number indicated. Thus in the case of the manufacturer who wanted to know the cost of a casting weighing 288 pounds, the fourth value would be 288; and in the case of the farmer who wished to determine the number of pounds of milk that would be required to produce 44 pounds of butter fat, the fourth value would be 44.

Example 2: A manufacturer pays $11.25 for a casting weighing 160 pounds. He wishes to purchase another casting weighing 288 pounds. What will the cost be of the larger casting?

Solution: $\dfrac{\$11.25}{160} = \dfrac{x}{288}$

160 times x (the product of the means) $= 160x$

288 times \$11.25 (the product of the ex-
tremes) $= \$3240$

Since the product of the means equals the
product of the extremes, $160x$ equals
\$3240.

Therefore, $1x$ equals \$3240 divided by 160.

\$3240 divided by 160 $= \$20.25$

Ans. \$20.25.

Example 3: If 223 pounds of milk produce 7 pounds of butter
fat, how many pounds of milk may be expected to produce 44
pounds of butter fat?

Solution: $\dfrac{223}{7} = \dfrac{x}{44}$

7 times x (the product of the means) $= 7x$

223 times 44 (the product of the extremes) $= 9812$

$7x$ equals 9812. Therefore $1x$ $= 1401\frac{5}{7}$

Ans. $1401\frac{5}{7}$ pounds.

A type of proportion which is a little different from that discussed thus far is one in which several parts have definite relations
to each other. A man, for instance, bequeaths his estate to four
sons—Walter, John, Henry and Bill—stipulating that their por-
tions be in the relation of 1, 2, 3 and 4, respectively. The net
amount of his estate, after all taxes, etc., have been paid, is \$20,000.
What is the exact amount received by each son?

It is but necessary to add the relative parts of the estate, and
then to compute the fractional part to which each son is entitled.

The sum of the relative parts is the sum of 1, 2, 3 and 4, which is 10. The part received by each son will, therefore, be as follows:

$$
\begin{array}{llll}
\text{Walter} & \tfrac{1}{10} \text{ of } \$20,000 = & \$ & 2000 \\
\text{John} & \tfrac{2}{10} \text{ of } 20,000 = & & 4000 \\
\text{Henry} & \tfrac{3}{10} \text{ of } 20,000 = & & 6000 \\
\text{Bill} & \tfrac{4}{10} \text{ of } 20,000 = & & 8000 \\
\end{array}
$$

$$\tfrac{10}{10} \text{ of } \$20,000 = \$20000$$

Example 4: A product weighing 272 pounds is to be divided into 4 parts in the proportion of 1, 3, 5 and 8. Compute the weight of each of the 4 parts.

Solution: The sum of the relative parts is 17. The 4 divisions will, therefore, be as follows:

$$
\begin{array}{lll}
\text{First part} & \tfrac{1}{17} \text{ of } 272 \text{ pounds} = & 16 \text{ pounds} \\
\text{Second part} & \tfrac{3}{17} \text{ of } 272 \text{ pounds} = & 48 \text{ pounds} \\
\text{Third part} & \tfrac{5}{17} \text{ of } 272 \text{ pounds} = & 80 \text{ pounds} \\
\text{Fourth part} & \tfrac{8}{17} \text{ of } 272 \text{ pounds} = & 128 \text{ pounds} \\
\end{array}
$$

$$\tfrac{17}{17} \text{ of } 272 \text{ pounds} = 272 \text{ pounds}$$

Estimating Dimensions of Reductions. It is sometimes necessary to estimate the dimensions to which a picture or photograph should be reduced for the purpose of ordering a photo-engraving or otherwise providing a specified space in an advertisement or other printed matter. In reducing small surfaces, like pictures, the procedure is very simple. A sheet of paper is cut to the size of the picture, or the space occupied by the picture is ruled off on a sheet of paper. A diagonal line is then drawn from the top left hand corner to the bottom right hand corner. Now the required width is marked off on the top line, from left to right, or the required length is marked off on the horizontal line at the left— according to which of the two dimensions is more important. A line is then drawn from the point thus marked (vertically or horizontally, as the case may be) to the opposite border. This will result in an intersection of the diagonal line. A line is now drawn from this point of intersection in the other direction (horizontally to the left, or vertically to the top, as the case may be). A new figure has now been formed representing the desired reduction. A reduction of a picture 3 inches wide by 2 inches high to a width of $2\frac{1}{4}$ inches would, therefore, be indicated by the following markings.

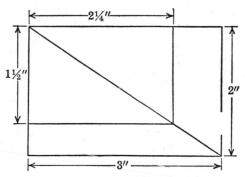

Note that the height of the reduction is $1\frac{1}{2}$ inches. This figure could have been easily determined by the equation $2:3 = x:2\frac{1}{4}$. However, it is not always practical to determine reductions of pictures and photographs mathematically, as dimensions often include cumbersome fractions of an inch. The simplest and quickest way for all practical purposes, and the way which is least subject to error, is to use the diagonal-line method.

The subject of proportion plays a very important part in the business of sign making. An artist, for example, is asked to make up a panel 8 feet high by 16 inches wide. It obviously would be unwise to start off by sketching on a sheet of these dimensions. A more practical way would be to "reduce to scale." The scale is determined by the minimum amount of paper needed to make a miniature which, other requirements being satisfied, would serve as a guide in the preparation of the final design.

One important fact should always be borne in mind in reducing the size of any square-cornered surface: the width must be reduced in exactly the same proportion as the height, and vice versa. Thus if it is desired to reduce the aforementioned 8-feet panel to 8 inches, which is equivalent to reducing it to one twelfth, the width, too, should be reduced to one twelfth—namely, to $1\frac{1}{3}$ inches.

Estimating Dimensions of Enlargements. To estimate the dimensions of an enlargement, the procedure is the reverse of that explained in the preceding paragraphs.

Suppose, for instance, it is desired to know what space would be occupied in an advertisement by an enlargement to a width of $3\frac{1}{4}$ inches of a photograph $1\frac{1}{4}$ inches wide by 1 inch high.

A rectangle, as illustrated, would be drawn, $1\frac{3}{4}$ inches wide by 1 inch high, with an extended top horizontal line, an extended left vertical line, and an extended diagonal line. The line at the top is then marked off at $3\frac{1}{4}$ inches, and a vertical line drawn from that point to intersect the diagonal line. Now a horizontal line is drawn from the intersection of the diagonal line to the left vertical line. Measuring the height of this enlarged line at the left (that is, from the top to the point of intersection made by the bottom horizontal line) we find that it is just about $1\frac{7}{8}$ inches, which approximate figure, for practical purposes, would in all probability be good enough.

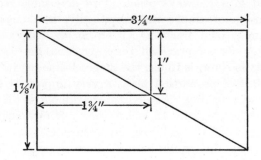

PROBLEMS

★ **1.** What is the ratio of 12 quarts to 18 gallons? *Ans.* 1:6.

★ **2.** If the scale to a map is $\frac{3}{8}$ of an inch to 25 miles, how many miles would be represented by $1\frac{1}{2}$ inches? *Ans.* 100 miles.

3. When water freezes it expands 9% of its volume. Compute the number of cubic feet of water needed to make $381\frac{1}{2}$ cubic feet of ice. (Hint: Start with the ratio $381\frac{1}{2}:109$.) *Ans.* 350 cubic feet.

4. If broken rock occupies 80% more space than solid rock, approximately how many cubic yards of solid rock will, when broken, occupy a space of 432 cubic yards? (Hint: Start with the ratio $100:180$.)

Ans. Approximately 240 cubic yards.

5. The space occupied by a motor truck completely knocked down is 188 cubic feet, which is 65% of the space occupied by the truck when completely assembled. On this basis how many cubic feet would be occupied by 10 similar motor trucks completely assembled? Compute the answer to the nearest whole cubic foot.

Ans. 2892 cubic feet. (*Arts. 120, 111*)

6. Carbon dioxide is made up of 3 parts of carbon to 8 parts of oxygen by weight. Estimate the relative weights of these elements in $38\frac{1}{2}$ grams of the gas. *Ans.* $10\frac{1}{2}$ grams of carbon and 28 grams of oxygen.

7. A feed mixture of 40 pounds bone meal, 40 pounds ground limestone and 20 pounds common salt is a good source of calcium and phosphorus for livestock. How many pounds of bone meal would be required to make 360 pounds of this feed mixture? *Ans.* 144 pounds.

8. Five men enter into partnership as follows: A invests $3000, B $2000, C $4000, D $5000, and E $6000. If the profit is to be shared in the ratio of capitals, what will be each partner's share of a profit amounting to $16,820?

Ans. A will receive $2523, B $1682, C $3364, D $4205, and E $5046.

★ 9. Seven men are put to work assembling instruments. Four are skilled and can produce 4 units each per hour. Each of the other 3 men can produce 3 units per hour. How many hours would it take the 7 men working together to produce 1000 units? *Ans.* 40 hours.

★ 10. An advertising man planning a series of advertisements for a client orders a photo-engraving to be made of a photograph 6 inches wide by 8 inches deep, the width to be reduced to $4\frac{1}{2}$ inches. Compute mentally the depth of the reduction. *Ans.* 6 inches.

131. Proportion in Reverse. A type of proportion problem different from those discussed in the preceding article, and one which can be quickly worked by simple reasoning, is the following: If a certain quantity of work can be done by 7 girls in 30 hours, in how many hours could the same amount of work be done by 10 girls?

It is obvious that we cannot proceed by the method outlined in Art. 130. But the problem is really very simple. Let us see.

It is understandable that 7 girls will do 7 times as much work in 30 hours as one girl. So that 7 girls in 30 hours will do the equivalent of 210 man-hours of work. Using this figure as a basis, and assuming that each girl works independently of the others, it is easy to compute the number of hours in which the same work can be done by virtually any number of girls, simply by dividing the number of girls into 210 hours. Thus 4 girls can do the same work in $\frac{210}{4}$ hours, or $52\frac{1}{2}$ hours; 5 girls, in $\frac{210}{5}$ hours, or 42 hours; 6 girls, in $\frac{210}{6}$ hours, or 35 hours; and 10 girls, in $\frac{210}{10}$ hours, or 21 hours.

Example: A contractor agrees to do a job in 80 working days, and hires 6 men to work on the project five days a week. At the end of the fourth week he finds that the men have done only one sixth of the job. How many additional men will the contractor need to hire in order that the work may be completed in the agreed-upon time?

Solution: Six men in 20 days do one sixth of the job.

Therefore, the remaining five sixths of the job will take six men 5 times 20 days, or 100 days.

So that the remaining five sixths of the job represents 600 man-days of work (6 men working 100 days equals 600 man-days).

The question now is, how many men will be needed to do 600 man-days of work in 60 days (60 days being the remainder of the contract period).

And the answer is obtained simply by dividing 600 (the number of man-days) by 60 (the number of days), which gives us 10.

Ten men will be required to complete the work in the remaining 60 days, and it will therefore be necessary for the contractor to hire 4 additional men.

Problems

★ **1.** If a supply of feed will last 25 days for 40 hens, how long would it last if the number of hens was increased to 50? (Hint: Divide the product of 40 times 25 by 50.) *Ans.* 20 days.

2. An airplane flying at a speed of 220 miles an hour can cover a specified distance in 5 hours. How long would it take another plane flying at a speed of 185 miles an hour to cover the same distance? Compute the answer to the nearest quarter of an hour.

Ans. 6 hours. (*Art. 111*)

3. A contractor agrees to do a job in 30 days. After 6 days he finds that the 8 men assigned to the work have done one third of the job. How many men can he afford to assign to other work with the assurance that the job will be completed on time by the remaining men?

Ans. Four men can be assigned to other work.

132. The Difference Between "Reduce by" and "Reduce to." These are two of the most misunderstood terms in the English language. Since they are directly connected with the subject of proportion, a word to clarify their meaning will not be amiss.

To reduce *by* one third means to subtract *one third*. To reduce *to* one third means that only one third is to remain; in other words, to subtract *two* thirds. The following examples will serve to illustrate.

6 inches reduced *by* one third means 6 inches minus 2 inches, or 4 inches.

6 inches reduced *to* one third means one third of 6 inches, or 2 inches.

8 inches reduced *to* one fourth means one fourth of 8 inches, or 2 inches.

12 feet reduced *by* one fourth means 12 feet minus 3 feet, or 9 feet.

15 feet reduced *to* one fifth means one fifth of 15 feet, or 3 feet.

24 reduced *by* one sixth means 24 minus 4, or 20.

50 reduced *by* two fifths means 50 minus 20, or 30.

63 reduced *to* four ninths, means four ninths of 63, or 28.

PROBLEMS

★ **1.** Reduce 36 by one ninth.	*Ans.* 32.
★ **2.** Reduce 45 by one fifth.	*Ans.* 36.
★ **3.** Reduce 720 to one sixth.	*Ans.* 120.
★ **4.** Reduce 330 to two elevenths.	*Ans.* 60.
★ **5.** Reduce 560 by three eighths.	*Ans.* 350.

* **6.** Reduce $24.60 to two thirds.   *Ans.* $16.40.

* **7.** Reduce $96.00 by two thirds.   *Ans.* $32.00.

* **8.** Reduce 4.27 by one seventh.   *Ans.* 3.66.

* **9.** Reduce 88.4 to one fourth.   *Ans.* 22.1.

* **10.** Reduce 1.2 to one tenth.   *Ans.* .12.

* **11.** A catalogue states, "Illustrations $\frac{7}{8}$ actual size." Does this mean that the actual size was reduced *by* $\frac{1}{8}$ or *to* $\frac{1}{8}$?   *Ans. By* $\frac{1}{8}$.

* **12.** If the price of a fabric which formerly sold at $4.00 a yard now sells at $3.50 a yard, by what fraction was the former price reduced?
        Ans. By $\frac{1}{8}$.

* **13.** A company's imports in one year were valued at $10,000. Its imports the following year amounted to $2000. To what fraction of its imports in the former year were the imports reduced in the year that followed?   *Ans. To* $\frac{1}{5}$.

* **14.** As a result of time lost by striking, a workman's earnings one month were reduced to one third of that in the preceding month, in which he earned $240.00. How much did he earn during the strike month?
        Ans. $80.00.

* **15.** A company reduced the size of one of its packages to 14 ounces. If this constitutes a reduction by one eighth of the previous size, what was the previous size?   *Ans.* 16 ounces.

* **16.** A peanut harvester reduces by seven eighths the labor required to harvest peanuts. How long would it take with the aid of this machine to do the work which formerly required 56 man-hours of labor?
        Ans. 7 hours.

CHAPTER XIX

PROFIT RATIOS

With a mental conception of the mathematical relation of profit to cost price and profit to selling price, the subject of profit ratios becomes uniquely simple. It will be our objective in this chapter to gain an acquaintance with the method that will provide us with this mental conception. To this end two tables are included which, besides helping toward a quick perception of the relations under discussion, will add interest and pleasure to the study of this important subject.

133. How to Determine Instantly the Ratio of Profit to Selling Price, Given the Ratio of Profit to Cost Price. The matter of determining profit ratios would not seem nearly so difficult if we thought of it as simple addition or subtraction. If we add $1.00 to $2.00, the $1.00 added constitutes one third of the total. Let us now look upon these amounts as cost price and profit, respectively—the $2.00 representing cost, and the $1.00 representing profit. It is clear that the profit of $1.00 is one third of the selling price. In other words, the ratio of profit to selling price is 1 to 3.

This may seem very simple. But could the reader say without hesitation what is the ratio to the selling price of a profit of $\frac{2}{5}$ of the cost price? This, admittedly, calls for a little more concentration. By a very simple method, however, any ratio of this nature can be determined in a matter of seconds.

When we speak of a $\frac{2}{5}$ profit on the cost price we mean, of course, two parts profit for every five parts of cost. Thus if an item costs $5.00, a $\frac{2}{5}$ profit on the cost would be $2.00, and the selling price would be $7.00. Notice the interesting relation between the selling price and the numbers in the fraction representing the profit on the cost. The profit of $\frac{2}{5}$ on the cost price becomes $\frac{2}{7}$ of the selling price because 2 (the numerator in the

351

fraction representing the profit on the cost price) plus 5 (the denominator) equals 7. In the same way, a $\frac{3}{5}$ profit on the cost price equals a profit of $\frac{3}{8}$ of the selling price. And a profit of $\frac{1}{7}$ on the cost price is equivalent to a profit of $\frac{1}{8}$ of the selling price.

The following graphic illustration of what we have just discussed will help toward a thorough understanding of this principle.

TABLE XIV

A Step-by-Step Explanation of the Proof That the Second Term in the Ratio of the Profit to the Selling Price Equals the *Sum* of Both Terms in the Ratio of the Profit to the Cost Price; and That the First Term Is the Same as It Is in the Ratio of the Profit to the Cost Price

When the Ratio of Profit to Cost Price Is	The Ratio of Profit to Selling Price Is	Explanation			
		A	B	C	
		The Cost Price Is	Profit on the Cost Price Is	Selling Price Is A Plus B	The Ratio of Profit to Selling Price Is Therefore B to C
$\frac{1}{2}$	$\frac{1}{3}$	$\frac{2}{2}$	$\frac{1}{2}$	$\frac{3}{2}$	$\frac{1}{2}$ to $\frac{3}{2}$, or 1 to 3, or $\frac{1}{3}$
$\frac{1}{3}$	$\frac{1}{4}$	$\frac{3}{3}$	$\frac{1}{3}$	$\frac{4}{3}$	$\frac{1}{3}$ to $\frac{4}{3}$, or 1 to 4, or $\frac{1}{4}$
$\frac{1}{4}$	$\frac{1}{5}$	$\frac{4}{4}$	$\frac{1}{4}$	$\frac{5}{4}$	$\frac{1}{4}$ to $\frac{5}{4}$, or 1 to 5, or $\frac{1}{5}$
$\frac{1}{5}$	$\frac{1}{6}$	$\frac{5}{5}$	$\frac{1}{5}$	$\frac{6}{5}$	$\frac{1}{5}$ to $\frac{6}{5}$, or 1 to 6, or $\frac{1}{6}$
$\frac{1}{6}$	$\frac{1}{7}$	$\frac{6}{6}$	$\frac{1}{6}$	$\frac{7}{6}$	$\frac{1}{6}$ to $\frac{7}{6}$, or 1 to 7, or $\frac{1}{7}$
$\frac{1}{7}$	$\frac{1}{8}$	$\frac{7}{7}$	$\frac{1}{7}$	$\frac{8}{7}$	$\frac{1}{7}$ to $\frac{8}{7}$, or 1 to 8, or $\frac{1}{8}$
$\frac{1}{8}$	$\frac{1}{9}$	$\frac{8}{8}$	$\frac{1}{8}$	$\frac{9}{8}$	$\frac{1}{8}$ to $\frac{9}{8}$, or 1 to 9, or $\frac{1}{9}$
$\frac{1}{9}$	$\frac{1}{10}$	$\frac{9}{9}$	$\frac{1}{9}$	$\frac{10}{9}$	$\frac{1}{9}$ to $\frac{10}{9}$, or 1 to 10, or $\frac{1}{10}$
$\frac{2}{3}$	$\frac{2}{5}$	$\frac{3}{3}$	$\frac{2}{3}$	$\frac{5}{3}$	$\frac{2}{3}$ to $\frac{5}{3}$, or 2 to 5, or $\frac{2}{5}$
$\frac{2}{5}$	$\frac{2}{7}$	$\frac{5}{5}$	$\frac{2}{5}$	$\frac{7}{5}$	$\frac{2}{5}$ to $\frac{7}{5}$, or 2 to 7, or $\frac{2}{7}$
$\frac{2}{7}$	$\frac{2}{9}$	$\frac{7}{7}$	$\frac{2}{7}$	$\frac{9}{7}$	$\frac{2}{7}$ to $\frac{9}{7}$, or 2 to 9, or $\frac{2}{9}$
$\frac{3}{5}$	$\frac{3}{8}$	$\frac{5}{5}$	$\frac{3}{5}$	$\frac{8}{5}$	$\frac{3}{5}$ to $\frac{8}{5}$, or 3 to 8, or $\frac{3}{8}$
$\frac{4}{5}$	$\frac{4}{9}$	$\frac{5}{5}$	$\frac{4}{5}$	$\frac{9}{5}$	$\frac{4}{5}$ to $\frac{9}{5}$, or 4 to 9, or $\frac{4}{9}$
$\frac{5}{6}$	$\frac{5}{11}$	$\frac{6}{6}$	$\frac{5}{6}$	$\frac{11}{6}$	$\frac{5}{6}$ to $\frac{11}{6}$, or 5 to 11, or $\frac{5}{11}$

Ratio of Profit to Cost Price	Ratio of Profit to Selling Price
$\dfrac{2}{5}$	$\dfrac{2}{5 \text{ plus } 2} = \dfrac{2}{7}$
$\dfrac{3}{5}$	$\dfrac{3}{5 \text{ plus } 3} = \dfrac{3}{8}$
$\dfrac{1}{7}$	$\dfrac{1}{7 \text{ plus } 1} = \dfrac{1}{8}$

A study of Table XIV, a step-by-step explanation of this method of computation, will be found interesting and instructive. No attempt should be made to memorize the ratios, as a clear understanding of the explanation will make this entirely unnecessary.

134. How to Determine Instantly the Ratio of Profit to Cost Price, Given the Ratio of Profit to Selling Price. The method of procedure here is exactly the reverse of that in the preceding article. Here, instead of going forward, from cost price to selling price, we move backward, from selling price to cost price. In other words, instead of increasing the second term in the ratio of the profit to the selling price, it is reduced; it is reduced by subtracting the value representing the first term, as will be seen in the following illustration:

Ratio of Profit to Selling Price	Ratio of Profit to Cost Price
$\dfrac{2}{7}$	$\dfrac{2}{7 \text{ minus } 2} = \dfrac{2}{5}$
$\dfrac{3}{8}$	$\dfrac{3}{8 \text{ minus } 3} = \dfrac{3}{5}$
$\dfrac{1}{8}$	$\dfrac{1}{8 \text{ minus } 1} = \dfrac{1}{7}$

Table XV will help clarify this process of subtraction.

Tables XIV and XV are complementary to each other, and it will be a profitable and worth-while study to compare the explanation in one with that of the other.

TABLE XV

A STEP-BY-STEP EXPLANATION OF THE PROOF THAT THE SECOND TERM IN THE RATIO OF THE PROFIT TO THE COST PRICE EQUALS THE *Difference* BETWEEN THE TERMS IN THE RATIO OF THE PROFIT TO THE SELLING PRICE; AND THAT THE FIRST TERM IS THE SAME AS IT IS IN THE RATIO OF THE PROFIT TO THE SELLING PRICE

When the Ratio of Profit to Selling Price Is	The Ratio of Profit to Cost Price Is	Explanation			
		A — The Selling Price Is	B — Profit on Selling Price Is	C — Cost Price Is A minus B	The Ratio of Profit to Cost Price Is Therefore B to C
$\frac{1}{3}$	$\frac{1}{2}$	$\frac{3}{3}$	$\frac{1}{3}$	$\frac{2}{3}$	$\frac{1}{3}$ to $\frac{2}{3}$, or 1 to 2, or $\frac{1}{2}$
$\frac{1}{4}$	$\frac{1}{3}$	$\frac{4}{4}$	$\frac{1}{4}$	$\frac{3}{4}$	$\frac{1}{4}$ to $\frac{3}{4}$, or 1 to 3, or $\frac{1}{3}$
$\frac{1}{5}$	$\frac{1}{4}$	$\frac{5}{5}$	$\frac{1}{5}$	$\frac{4}{5}$	$\frac{1}{5}$ to $\frac{4}{5}$, or 1 to 4, or $\frac{1}{4}$
$\frac{1}{6}$	$\frac{1}{5}$	$\frac{6}{6}$	$\frac{1}{6}$	$\frac{5}{6}$	$\frac{1}{6}$ to $\frac{5}{6}$, or 1 to 5, or $\frac{1}{5}$
$\frac{1}{7}$	$\frac{1}{6}$	$\frac{7}{7}$	$\frac{1}{7}$	$\frac{6}{7}$	$\frac{1}{7}$ to $\frac{6}{7}$, or 1 to 6, or $\frac{1}{6}$
$\frac{1}{8}$	$\frac{1}{7}$	$\frac{8}{8}$	$\frac{1}{8}$	$\frac{7}{8}$	$\frac{1}{8}$ to $\frac{7}{8}$, or 1 to 7, or $\frac{1}{7}$
$\frac{1}{9}$	$\frac{1}{8}$	$\frac{9}{9}$	$\frac{1}{9}$	$\frac{8}{9}$	$\frac{1}{9}$ to $\frac{8}{9}$, or 1 to 8, or $\frac{1}{8}$
$\frac{1}{10}$	$\frac{1}{9}$	$\frac{10}{10}$	$\frac{1}{10}$	$\frac{9}{10}$	$\frac{1}{10}$ to $\frac{9}{10}$, or 1 to 9, or $\frac{1}{9}$
$\frac{2}{5}$	$\frac{2}{3}$	$\frac{5}{5}$	$\frac{2}{5}$	$\frac{3}{5}$	$\frac{2}{5}$ to $\frac{3}{5}$, or 2 to 3, or $\frac{2}{3}$
$\frac{2}{7}$	$\frac{2}{5}$	$\frac{7}{7}$	$\frac{2}{7}$	$\frac{5}{7}$	$\frac{2}{7}$ to $\frac{5}{7}$, or 2 to 5, or $\frac{2}{5}$
$\frac{2}{9}$	$\frac{2}{7}$	$\frac{9}{9}$	$\frac{2}{9}$	$\frac{7}{9}$	$\frac{2}{9}$ to $\frac{7}{9}$, or 2 to 7, or $\frac{2}{7}$
$\frac{3}{8}$	$\frac{3}{5}$	$\frac{8}{8}$	$\frac{3}{8}$	$\frac{5}{8}$	$\frac{3}{8}$ to $\frac{5}{8}$, or 3 to 5, or $\frac{3}{5}$
$\frac{4}{9}$	$\frac{4}{5}$	$\frac{9}{9}$	$\frac{4}{9}$	$\frac{5}{9}$	$\frac{4}{9}$ to $\frac{5}{9}$, or 4 to 5, or $\frac{4}{5}$
$\frac{5}{11}$	$\frac{5}{6}$	$\frac{11}{11}$	$\frac{5}{11}$	$\frac{6}{11}$	$\frac{5}{11}$ to $\frac{6}{11}$, or 5 to 6, or $\frac{5}{6}$

135. How to Find the Selling Price, Given the Cost Price and the Per Cent of Profit on the Selling Price. When the cost price is $80.00, and the profit 20 per cent of the selling price, what is the selling price? A brief glance at these figures tells us that the selling price is $100.00. But why is it $100.00? Let us see.

We are told that the profit is 20 per cent of the selling price. Now, since the selling price is made up of two things—cost price and profit—it is clear that if the profit is 20 per cent of the selling price, the cost inevitably constitutes the rest of the selling price— namely, 80 per cent, for 100 per cent minus 20 per cent equals 80 per cent.

Knowing the exact amount of the cost, and knowing also that this amount represents 80 per cent of the selling price, we need but to find the relative value of 20 per cent and add it to the cost price, to determine the selling price.

Example 1: The cost price of a product is $60.00. If it is desired to make a profit of 25% on the selling price, what should the selling price be?

Solution: If the profit is to be 25% of the selling price, the cost price ($60.00) will represent 75% of the selling price.

$$75\% \text{ of selling price} = \$60.00$$
$$25\% \text{ of selling price } (\tfrac{2}{7}\tfrac{5}{5}, \text{ or } \tfrac{1}{3}, \text{ of } \$60.00) = \quad 20.00$$

$$100\% \text{ of selling price} = \$80.00$$

Ans. Selling price is $80.00.

Example 2: If the cost price is $84.00 and the profit is to be 30% of the selling price, what should the selling price be?

Solution: If the profit is to be 30% of the selling price, the cost price ($84.00) will represent 70% of the selling price.

$$70\% \text{ of selling price} = \$ 84.00$$
$$30\% \text{ of selling price } (\tfrac{3}{7} \text{ of } \$84.00) = \quad 36.00$$

$$100\% \text{ of selling price} = \$120.00$$

Ans. Selling price is $120.00.

Example 3: The profit on an item is to be 32% of the selling price. If the cost is $140.25, what will the selling price be?

Solution: If the profit is to be 32% of the selling price, the cost will be 68% of the selling price.

68% of selling price	= $140.25
32% of selling price ($\frac{32}{68}$, or $\frac{8}{17}$, of $140.25) =	66.00

100% of selling price	= $206.25

Ans. Selling price is $206.25.

PROBLEMS

* 1. A jobber plans to dispose of miscellaneous products which cost him a total of $280.00. If he is to make a profit of 20% of the selling price, for how much should this merchandise be sold?   *Ans.* $350.00.

2. A dealer pays $126.00 for a rug. He decides to make a profit of 30% of the selling price. For how much should he sell the rug?

Ans. $180.00.

3. A grocer sells a food specialty costing him $180.00 per gross packages, and makes a profit of 25% of the selling price. How much does he receive per gross packages?   *Ans.* $240.00.

4. A toy manufacturer makes an average profit of 38% of his sales. If his costs in a month amount to $1550.00, what is the sales value of the toys produced in that period?   *Ans.* $2400.00.

* 5. An electrical device costing $27.50 is to bring a profit of $33\frac{1}{3}$% of the selling price. What should the selling price be?   *Ans.* $41.25.

136. How to Find the Cost Price, Given the Selling Price and the Per Cent of Profit on the Selling Price. If an article sells for $100.00 at a profit of 25 per cent of the selling price, what is the cost price?

Since the selling price is made up of two things—cost price and profit—and since the profit is 25 per cent of the selling price, it is obvious that the cost price will be 75 per cent of the selling price, for 100 per cent minus 25 per cent equals 75 per cent. Seventy-five per cent of $100.00 equals $75.00. So that the cost price is $75.00.

Example 1: An item sells for $90.00, and the profit is $33\frac{1}{3}$% of the selling price. What is the cost?

Solution: If the profit is $33\frac{1}{3}\%$ of the selling price, the cost represents $66\frac{2}{3}\%$ of the selling price.

$66\frac{2}{3}\%$ of $90.00 = $60.00.

Ans. Cost price is $60.00.

Example 2: If a product is sold for $175.00 and the profit is 35% of the selling price, how much is the cost price?

Solution: The cost price is 65% of the selling price.

65% of $175.00 = $113.75

Ans. Cost price is $113.75.

Example 3: An item sells for $73.50 and the profit is 28% of the selling price. What does the item cost?

Solution: The cost is 72% of the selling price.

72% of $73.50 = $52.92

Ans. Cost price is $52.92.

PROBLEMS

★ **1.** A manufacturer of a stationery specialty makes a profit of 30% of the selling price. If he sells the product for $1.60, what does it cost him?
Ans. $1.12.

2. If the total amount realized from the sale of a job lot of merchandise was $300.00, and the profit was 18% of this amount, how much did the merchandise cost? *Ans.* $246.00. (*Art. 50*)

3. An importer makes an average profit of $37\frac{1}{2}\%$ of his sales. If his sales for the year amounted to $14,248.00, approximately how much did he pay for the merchandise sold? *Ans.* $8,905.00. (*Art. 46*)

4. A woolens dealer's total sales for the day amounted to $620.00. If his average profit is 36% of the selling price, what was the approximate cost of the merchandise sold? *Ans.* $396.80. (*Art. 5*)

5. A building was sold for $27,500, on which amount a profit of 28% was made. How much did the building cost? *Ans.* $19,800. (*Art. 50*)

137. How to Find the Per-Cent Equivalent of a Specified Profit, Given the Cost or Selling Price. If a profit of $10.00 is made on a sale of $100.00, how much is the per cent of profit on the selling price? We know instantly that the answer is 10 per cent, for $10.00 is one tenth of $100.00, and one tenth is equivalent to 10 per cent.

But suppose the sale amounted to $168.00, and the profit to $21.00, how much per cent of the selling price would the profit be then? It is really very simple. Just as we divided $100.00 by $10.00 in the preceding problem, we would divide $168.00 by $21.00. This gives us 8. The profit is, therefore, one eighth of the selling price. And one eighth, as we learned in the study of aliquot parts, is equivalent to $12\frac{1}{2}$ per cent.

Not all problems of this nature, however, are solved quite so easily. For example, to determine the per-cent equivalent of a profit of $40.20 made on a sale of $268.00 calls for a little extra effort. Nonetheless, this problem resolves itself simply into finding the equivalent ratio of $40.20 to $268.00, in which the second term is 100. The problem, in other words, is one of proportion, which subject we studied in Art. 130. Let us take this as our first example and follow through the solution.

Example 1: How much per cent of the sale is represented by a profit of $40.20 made on a sale of $268.00?

Solution: $40.20 is to $268.00 as x is to 100.

Since the product of the means equals the product of the extremes (Art. 55), 40.20 times 100 (the product of the extremes) equals 268 times x (the product of the means).

40.20 times 100 = 4020
268 times x = $268x$

$268x$ equals 4020.
Therefore, $1x$ equals 4020 divided by 268, which equals 15.
The profit of $40.20 therefore represents 15% of the selling price.

Example 2: A profit of $55.68 is made on a sale amounting to $174.00. How much per cent profit is that on the selling price?

Solution: $55.68 is to $174.00 as x is to 100.

> 55.68 times 100 = 5568
> 174 times x = $174x$
>
> $174x$ equals 5568.
> Therefore, $1x$ equals 5568 divided by 174, which
> equals 32.
> The profit of $55.68 therefore represents 32% of the
> selling price.

Exactly the same method of procedure is applied when the profit is based on the cost rather than on the selling price. Thus:

Example 3: If it is desired to sell an item costing $21.00 for $27.00, how much per cent of the cost price is represented by the profit?

Solution: $6.00 (the profit) is to $21.00 as x is to 100.

> 6 times 100 = 600
> 21 times x = $21x$
>
> $21x$ equals 600.
> Therefore, $1x$ equals 600 divided by 21, which equals
> 28.57.
> The profit of $6.00 therefore represents 28.57% of the
> cost price.

Example 4: A product costs $216.00, and it is planned to make a profit of $50.00 on the sale. How much per cent of the cost price would this profit represent?

Solution: $50.00 is to $216.00 as x is to 100.

> 50 times 100 = 5000
> 216 times x = $216x$
>
> $216x$ equals 5000.
> Therefore, $1x$ equals 5000 divided by 216, which equals
> 23.15.
> The profit of $50.00 therefore represents 23.15% of
> the cost price.

Problems

Estimate in the following problems the rates per cent represented by the profit on the cost price or the profit on the selling price, as the case may be:

★ **1.** A profit of $13.00 on a cost of $52.00. (Hint: 52 is exactly divisible by 13.)   *Ans.* 25%.

     2. A profit of $63.00 on a cost of $180.00.   *Ans.* 35%. (*Art. 110*)

     3. A profit of $78.20 on a cost of $340.00.   *Ans.* 23%.

     4. A profit of $38.13 on a cost of $93.00.   *Ans.* 41%.

     5. A profit of $77.14 on a cost of $203.00.   *Ans.* 38%. (*Art. 111*)

     6. A profit of $36.12 on a sale of $84.00.   *Ans.* 43%.

     7. A profit of $57.77 on a sale of $218.00.   *Ans.* $26\frac{1}{2}$%.

     8. A profit of $40.95 on a sale of $126.00.   *Ans.* $32\frac{1}{2}$%.

     9. A profit of $143.35 on a sale of $305.00.   *Ans.* 47%. (*Art. 111*)

     10. A profit of $30.78 on a sale of $76.00.   *Ans.* $40\frac{1}{2}$%.

138. A Quick Way to Find the Per-Cent Equivalent of a Specified Profit, When the Cost or Selling Price, as the Case May Be, Is an Aliquot Part of $100. When the cost or selling price is an amount like $25.00, $50.00, or $75.00, there is no need to calculate the per-cent equivalent of the profit by the method described in the preceding article. A shorter way is to increase the amount of the cost or selling price, as the case may be, to $100, and to increase the amount of the profit in the same proportion. The resulting figures supply the answer. Thus:

Example 1: A profit of $5.25 is made on a sale of $25.00. How much per cent profit on the sale is this?

Solution: $25.00 is exactly one fourth of $100.00. So we will multiply the amount of the sale and the amount of the profit by 4.

     $25.00 multiplied by 4 = $100.00

     $ 5.25 multiplied by 4 =   21.00

A profit of $5.25 on a sale of $25.00 is therefore equivalent to a profit of $21.00 on a sale of $100.00. And we know without the need for further calculation that the profit on this transaction is 21% of the amount of the sale.

It will be noted that when the dividend and the divisor are each multiplied by the same number, the quotient remains the same. Thus, in the problem just worked, in multiplying $25.00 (the divisor) by 4, and $5.25 (the dividend) by 4, the quotient is not affected.

Example 2: If a profit of $29.50 is made on a sale amounting to $50.00, how much per cent profit is that on the sale?

Solution: $50.00 multiplied by 2 = $100.00
$29.50 multiplied by 2 =   59.00

A profit of $29.50 on a sale of $50.00 is therefore equivalent to a profit of $59.00 on a sale of $100.00. So that the profit is 59% of the amount of the sale.

In dealing with profit on the cost price, the procedure is exactly the same. Thus:

Example 3: It is planned to make a profit of $12.00 on an item costing $25.00. How much per cent profit would that be on the cost price?

Solution: $25.00 multiplied by 4 = $100.00
$12.00 multiplied by 4 =   48.00

A profit of $12.00 on an item costing $25.00 therefore represents 48% of the cost price.

The solution in the illustration that follows calls for just a trifle more attention.

Example 4: If an article costs $75.00 and the profit is $27.00, how much per cent is the profit of the cost price?

Solution: Note that to increase $75.00 to $100.00, we must multiply by $1\frac{1}{3}$.

$75.00 times $1\frac{1}{3}$ = $100.00
$27.00 times $1\frac{1}{3}$ =   36.00

A profit of $27.00 on an item costing $75.00 therefore represents 36% of the cost price.

Example 5: A profit of $3.00 is what per cent of the cost price of $12.50?

Solution: $12.50 times 8 = $100.00
$ 3.00 times 8 =   24.00

Ans. 24%.

Up to this point we have been *multiplying* dividend and divisor. However, multiplication is nothing more nor less than a process of addition. So that when we *add* a value to the dividend and to the divisor in the same proportion, the ratio (or quotient) is not changed one bit. For example, if to each of the terms in the fraction $\frac{4}{12}$ we add one fourth of the term, the result is the same. Proof:

4 plus 1 (1 being one fourth of 4) = 5
12 plus 3 (3 being one fourth of 12) = 15

We now have a fraction $\frac{5}{15}$, which is exactly equivalent to $\frac{4}{12}$. Having this principle in mind, let us proceed with some additional per cent problems.

Example 6: On a sale amounting to $62.50 a profit is made of $20.00. How much per cent profit is this on the selling price?

Solution:

Method A: Note that the difference between $100.00 and $62.50 is $37.50. $62.50 is $\frac{5}{8}$ of $100.00, and $37.50 is $\frac{3}{8}$ of $100.00. Therefore, $37.50 is $\frac{3}{5}$ of $62.50.

$62.50 plus $\frac{3}{5}$ of $62.50 = $100.00
$20.00 plus $\frac{3}{5}$ of $20.00 =   32.00

The profit is therefore 32% of the selling price.

Method B: $62.50 multiplied by 2 equals $125.00, and $100.00
is $\frac{4}{5}$ of $125.00.

$62.50 multiplied by 2 equals $125.00.
$\frac{4}{5}$ of $125.00 = $100.00

$20.00 multiplied by 2 equals $40.00.
$\frac{4}{5}$ of $40.00   =   32.00

The answer is the same as that obtained by
Method A—namely, 32%.

Example 7: On an article costing $87.50 a profit was made of
$24.50. How much per cent profit is that on the cost price?

Solution: $87.50 is $\frac{7}{8}$ of $100.00, and $12.50 (the difference
between $100.00 and $87.50) is $\frac{1}{8}$ of $100.00. There-
fore, $12.50 equals $\frac{1}{7}$ of $87.50.

$87.50 plus $\frac{1}{7}$ of $87.50 = $100.00
$24.50 plus $\frac{1}{7}$ of $24.50 =   28.00

The profit is therefore 28% of the cost price.

This technique, as the article heading indicates, is recommended
when the cost or selling price is an aliquot part of $100.00. It
may, however, be used with equally good effect when the cost or
selling price exceeds $100.00, e.g., $112.50 and $150.00. Thus:

Example 8: An article for which $112.50 was paid is sold at a
profit of $36.00. How much per cent profit is this on the cost price?

Solution: Note that here we will *deduct* instead of add. $112.50
is the sum of $100.00 and $12.50. $12.50 is $\frac{1}{8}$ of
$100.00; but it is $\frac{1}{9}$ of $112.50. So we will deduct $\frac{1}{9}$
from each of the two values.

$112.50 minus $\frac{1}{9}$ of $112.50 = $100.00
$ 36.00 minus $\frac{1}{9}$ of $ 36.00 =   32.00

The profit is therefore 32% of the cost price.

Problems

Estimate in these problems the rates per cent represented by the profit on the cost price or the profit on the selling price, as the case may be, using the short-cut technique discussed in the text.

* 1. A profit of $6.50 on a cost of $25.00.   *Ans.* 26%.

* 2. A profit of $16.00 on a cost of $40.00.   (Hint: Multiply by $2\frac{1}{2}$.)
                                                          Ans. 40%.

* 3. A profit of $22.00 on a cost of $80.00.   (Hint: Increase by one fourth.)   *Ans.* $27\frac{1}{2}$%.

* 4. A profit of $28.35 on a cost of $70.00.   (Hint: Increase by three sevenths.)   *Ans.* $40\frac{1}{2}$%.

* 5. A profit of $21.00 on a cost of $75.00.   *Ans.* 28%.

* 6. A profit of $18.00 on a sale of $37.50.   (Hint: Reduce by one third, and multiply the results by 4.)   *Ans.* 48%.

* 7. A profit of $30.00 on a sale of $62.50.   (Hint: Multiply by 2 and subtract from the result one fifth of itself.)   *Ans.* 48%.

* 8. A profit of $16.50 on a sale of $55.00.   (Hint: Multiply by 2 and subtract from the result one eleventh of itself.)   *Ans.* 30%.

9. A profit of $20.25 on a sale of $45.00.   (Hint: Multiply by 2 and add one ninth to the result.)   *Ans.* 45%.

* 10. A profit of $57.00 on a sale of $150.00.   (Hint: Reduce by one third.)   *Ans.* 38%.

139. The Meaning of Mark-Up and Mark-Down.   Mark-up is the difference between the cost price of an article and its selling price. Thus the mark-up of a dress that costs $5.00 and is placed on sale for $8.00 is $3.00.

The term mark-up is used extensively in the retail trade. Its use is confined practically entirely to articles sold in the same condition as purchased—that is, without anything substantial having been added or removed from them. Furniture, hardware, groceries, drug supplies are just a few examples. Clothing, even when it undergoes alterations to fit the wearer, is included.

As illogical as it may seem to the reader unfamiliar with the subject, it is preferable and customary to calculate the mark-up percentage on the selling price rather than on the cost price. The reason is that the expenses of running a business are provided by the sales. In most retail businesses the difference between the gross profit and the net profit constitutes a percentage which is more or less constant. Rent, salaries and wages, and commissions earned by salesmen are some of the principal expenses of running a business, and it is the relation between the sum of these expenses and the total sales which must be kept in mind in determining merchandise mark-ups.

Mark-down, on the other hand, has an entirely different meaning. This term is used to denote a reduction in the selling price. When, for example, the selling price of an article has been reduced from $8.50 to $8.00, it is said to have been marked down.

Mark-up, then, refers to the difference between the cost price and the selling price. Mark-down refers to the difference between the reduced selling price and the previous selling price.

140. Calculating Mark-Ups and Mark-Downs. Once the percent rate of the desired profit on the selling price has been determined, it is a comparatively simple matter to calculate the equivalent value of the profit in dollars and cents.

In a large degree this subject has already been covered in Art. 135, "How To Find the Selling Price, Given the Cost Price and the Per Cent of Profit on the Selling Price." However, a very useful little table is included with the present article—Table XVI, "Showing Mark-Up Per-Cent Equivalents"—which, when it can be conveniently referred to, facilitates the process of computation. Note, for example, that when, in connection with mark-ups, it is desired to obtain 20 per cent profit on the selling price, it is only necessary to add to the cost 25 per cent of the cost; to obtain 30 per cent profit on the selling price, we would add to the cost 42.8571 per cent; and so on.

Example 1: If a product costs $18.00 how much should it be marked up to allow a profit of 25% on the selling price?

Solution: A 25% profit on the selling price is equivalent to 33.3333% ($33\frac{1}{3}$) on the cost.

$33\frac{1}{3}$% (one third) of $18.00 = $6.00

Ans. The mark-up should be $6.00.

TABLE XVI

Showing Mark-Up Per-Cent Equivalents

To Obtain This Per Cent Profit on the Selling Price	Mark Up This Per Cent on the Cost	To Obtain This Per Cent Profit on the Selling Price	Mark Up This Per Cent on the Cost
1%	1.0101%	26%	35.1351%
2	2.0408	27	36.9863
3	3.0928	28	38.8889
4	4.1667	29	40.8451
5	5.2632	30	42.8571
6	6.383	31	44.9275
7	7.5269	32	47.0588
8	8.6957	33	49.2537
9	9.8901	34	51.5151
10	11.1111	35	53.8462
11	12.3596	36	56.25
12	13.6364	37	58.7302
13	14.9425	38	61.2903
14	16.2791	39	63.9344
15	17.6471	40	66.6667
16	19.0476	41	69.4915
17	20.4819	42	72.4138
18	21.9512	43	75.4386
19	23.4568	44	78.5714
20	25.	45	81.8181
21	26.5823	46	85.1852
22	28.2051	47	88.6792
23	29.8701	48	92.3077
24	31.5789	49	96.0784
25	33.3333	50	100.

Example 2: How much of a mark-up should be given to a product costing $125.00 to allow a profit of 15% on the selling price?

Solution: Table XVI shows that a profit of 15% on the selling price is equivalent to 17.6471% on the cost.

17.6471% of $125.00
(125% of $17.6471) = $22.06

Ans. The mark-up should be $22.06.

Mark-downs are always calculated on the selling price. A 15% mark-down, for instance, on a product selling for $5.00 would bring the selling price down to $4.25.

Example 3: An article costing $60.00 was marked up 20%, and then marked down 10%, and sold. How much was received for the article?

Solution: A 20% mark-up is equivalent to 25% of the cost.

Cost	= $60.00
Plus 25%	= 15.00
Original selling price	= 75.00
Less 10% mark-down	= 7.50

Price received on the sale = $67.50

Example 4: A machinery dealer's principal expenses of doing business are: an overhead expense of 20% of the selling price, and a salesman's commission of 10%. If it is desired to make a profit of 8% on the selling price, how much should the mark-up be on a machine costing $150.00? Compute the answer to the nearest whole dollar.

Solution: A 20% overhead expense, plus 10% commission, and an 8% profit on the selling price adds up to 38%. And 38% on the selling price is equivalent to 61.2903 on the cost price.

61.2903% of $150.00
(150% of $61.2903) = $91.94

Ans. The mark-up should be $92.00.

Note the interesting method of procedure in the following illustration of the solution to a problem which is really two problems in one.

Example 5: A dealer pays $50.00 for a garment on which he wishes to make a profit of 35% on the selling price after making an allowance of 15% to the purchaser. What price should the tag on this garment show?

Solution:

First step: A profit of 35% on the selling price is equivalent to 53.8462% of the cost price.

Cost	= $50.00
Plus 53.8462% of $50.00 (50% of $53.8462)	= 26.92

The amount to be received from the purchaser	= $76.92

Second step: If $76.92 is the amount to be received from the purchaser after a 15% allowance has been made him, $76.92 must be increased by the equivalent of that percentage. To facilitate computation, the amount of $76.92 may conveniently be considered as the cost price, and the 15% a profit on the selling price. Thus: 15% on the selling price is equivalent to 17.6471% of the cost price.

Cost	= $76.92
17.6471% of $76.92	= 13.57

Price on tag	= $90.49

Proof:

Price on tag	= $90.49
Less 15% allowance to purchaser	= 13.57

Amount to be received from purchaser	= $76.92

Compute the answers to the following problems using Table XVI as a guide, when necessary, in determining the equivalent per-cent rates on the cost.

★ **1.** What should the mark-up be on an overcoat costing $36.00, if it is to represent 40% of the selling price? *Ans.* $24.00.

★ **2.** If a proprietary medicine costing 24 cents is to have a mark-up placed on it of 25%, what should the selling price be? *Ans.* 32 cents.

3. A box of cigars costing $2.50 is to be marked up 15%. How much will the mark-up amount to? (Hint: Multiply 17.6471 cents by $2\frac{1}{2}$.)
Ans. 44 cents. (*Art. 20*)

4. A merchant's inventory is valued at $7500.00. If the average mark-up in his business is 35%, how much profit may be expected on the sale of this merchandise? (Hint: Multiply $53.8462 by 75.)
Ans. $4038.46. (*Art. 50*)

5. A man contemplating the purchase of a retail business is informed that the inventory value is $12,460.00. If the expense of operating the business is 32% of the sales, and if it is desired that the sales yield a profit of 5%, at how much per cent on the cost should the merchandise be marked up? (Hint: Determine the total per-cent profit on the selling price by adding the per-cent rate represented by the operating expenses to the per-cent rate of the desired profit.) *Ans.* 58.7301%.

★ **6.** What would a 10% mark-down amount to on an article whose price tag reads $15.00? *Ans.* $1.50.

★ **7.** The asking price of a rebuilt typewriter on which a mark-up of $23.00 was placed was $85.00. If the machine sold at a mark-down of 5%, what was the amount of the sale? (Hint: The mark-up amount in this problem may be disregarded.) *Ans.* $80.75.

★ **8.** A couch costing $84.00 was marked up 40%. Subsequently the selling price was marked down 20% and the couch was sold at the reduced price. What was the mark-down price? *Ans.* $112.00.

9. A merchant bought a set of pictures for $132.00. His selling price, based on a 36% mark-up, was later revised by a $12\frac{1}{2}$% mark-down. What was the revised selling price of the pictures? Compute the answer to the nearest dollar. *Ans.* $180.00. (*Art. 42*)

10. A manufacturer's cost of a desk is $210.00. The desired profit is 40% of the amount to be received from the purchaser after allowing him a discount of 10%. What should the asking price of the desk be? Compute the answer to the nearest dollar. (Hint: This problem is similar to the one in Example 5 in the text.) *Ans.* $389.00.

141. How to Find the Rate Per Cent of a Mark-Up, Given the Selling Price and the Profit, the Cost and the Selling Price, or the Cost and the Profit. As we learned in Art. 139, mark-up is calculated on the selling price. So that to find the rate per cent of a mark-up it is necessary to have only two figures: the amount of the profit and the amount of the selling price. When we know the cost and the selling price, the amount of the profit can be ascertained by deducting one from the other; and when we know the cost and the profit, we need but add one to the other to determine the selling price.

If an article costs $75.00 and sells for $100.00, we should know instantly that the profit of $25.00 represents a mark-up of 25 per cent. Reason? The rate per cent of the mark-up is equal to the ratio of the profit to the selling price, and $25.00 is to $100.00 as 25 is to 100. Similarly, if an article costs $40.00 and sells for $60.00, the per cent of the mark-up would be $33\frac{1}{3}$ per cent, for the profit of $20.00 is to the selling price of $60.00 as 1 is to 3, and we know from our study of aliquot parts that 1 is to 3 as $33\frac{1}{3}$ is to 100.

Example 1: If the profit on an article selling for $112.00 is $35.84, what is the rate per cent of the mark-up?

Solution: $35.84 is to $112.00 as x is to 100.
Since the product of the means equals the product of the extremes, $112x$ equals 3584.
If $112x$ equals 3584, $1x$ equals 3584 divided by 112, or 32.

Ans. The mark-up is 32%.

Example 2: Estimate the rate per cent of the mark-up on an article costing $54.72 and selling for $76.00.

Solution: $21.28 (the profit) is to $76.00 as x is to 100. $76x$ equals 2128.
Therefore $1x$ equals 2128 divided by 76, or 28.

Ans. The mark-up is 28%.

Example 3: The sale of an article costing $149.50 brings a profit of $34.50. How much per cent does the mark-up represent?

Solution: $34.50 is to $184.00 (the selling price) as x is to 100.
184x equals 3450.
Therefore 1x equals 3450 divided by 184, or 18.75.

Ans. The mark-up is 18.75%.

PROBLEMS

Find the rate per cent of the mark-up in each of the following problems, computing the answers to the nearest hundredth of a per cent.

1. Selling price $58.40; profit $17.52.   *Ans.* 30%.
2. Selling price $120.00; profit $18.00.   *Ans.* 15%.
3. Selling price $234.00; profit $34.00.   *Ans.* 14.53%.
4. Cost $111.00; selling price $148.00.   *Ans.* 25%.
5. Cost $52.60; selling price $78.90.   *Ans.* 33⅓%.
6. Cost $124.47; selling price $169.00.   *Ans.* 26.35%.
7. Cost $43.36; profit $10.84.   *Ans.* 20%.
8. Cost $140.92; profit $75.88.   *Ans.* 35%.
9. Cost $136.27; profit $43.73.   *Ans.* 24.29%.

CHAPTER XX

PARTIAL PAYMENTS AND INTEREST ON UNPAID BALANCES

It is a common practice in business for a debt to be liquidated by equal periodical installments. Under some arrangements a payment covering the interest due on the unpaid balance is made along with the installment. Under others, the unpaid balance is simply increased by the amount of the interest due.

In this chapter we will study, among other things, the preparation of schedules for the liquidation of debts by these different methods.

142. How to Prepare a Schedule for the Liquidation of an Indebtedness by a Specified Number of Equal Periodical Payments, Each of Which Is to Be Accompanied by a Payment of the Interest Due on the Unpaid Balance. Let us consider a debt of $4000.00 to be liquidated by quarterly installments of $500.00 with interest on the unpaid balance at 4 per cent per annum. At the end of the first quarterly period a payment will be due amounting to $500.00 plus interest (4 per cent per annum is equivalent to 1 per cent per 3-month period) on $4000.00. One per cent of $4000.00 equals $40.00 which, added to the installment payment of $500.00 equals $540.00. This payment will leave an unpaid balance of $3500.00. At the end of the second quarter the interest will be 1 per cent of $3500.00, or $35.00 which, together with the periodical installment payment of $500.00, will call for a total payment of $535.00, leaving an unpaid balance of $3000.00. And so on.

Assuming that the agreement was made on January 1, 1947, the schedule for the liquidation of this indebtedness would be prepared as shown in the illustration.

Note that as the unpaid balance decreases the amount of the interest decreases, so that while the interest at the end of the first quarter amounted to $40.00, the interest for the final quarter was only $5.00. Note also that the totals of the columns provide a

PRINCIPAL OF DEBT ON JANUARY 1, 1947, OF $4000.00, PAID IN QUARTERLY INSTALLMENTS OF $500.00 WITH INTEREST ON UNPAID BALANCE AT 4% PER ANNUM

Due Date of Quarterly Installment	Quarterly Unpaid Balance	Interest for Quarter Ended	Quarterly Installment	Quarterly Payment (Including Interest) (B plus C)
	A	B	C	D
Mar. 31, 1947	$4,000	$40	$500	$540
June 30, 1947	3,500	35	500	535
Sept. 30, 1947	3,000	30	500	530
Dec. 31, 1947	2,500	25	500	525
Mar. 31, 1948	2,000	20	500	520
June 30, 1948	1,500	15	500	515
Sept. 30, 1948	1,000	10	500	510
Dec. 31, 1948	500	5	500	505
	$18,000	$180	$4,000	$4,180

check on the accuracy of the computations. The total for column D, for instance, should equal the sum of the totals for columns B and C. The total amount of the interest charges, on the other hand, can be checked by multiplying the sum of the unpaid balances by the quarterly interest rate. Thus $18,000 (column A) at 1 per cent equals $180.00 (column B).

PROBLEMS

1. On March 31 Andrew White agrees to settle a debt of $2400.00 by quarterly installments of $600.00 plus interest on the unpaid balance at the rate of 5% per annum. The first payment is to be made on June 30. Prepare a schedule showing the liquidation of the debt. What will be Andrew White's total interest cost on the settlement?   *Ans.* $75.00.

2. On June 30 Richard Walters arranges to pay off his indebtedness of $5000.00 by semiannual installments of $1000.00 plus interest on the unpaid balance at the rate of 3% per annum. Payments are to begin on January 1. Prepare a schedule showing the payments, interest charges and unpaid balances. How much interest will Walters have paid in all to settle his account?   *Ans.* $225.00.

3. James Cullen owes Jack Roberts $3000.00, and agrees to make monthly payments of $500.00 until his indebtedness has been paid in full. An interest payment at the rate of 6% per annum on the unpaid balance is to be made with each installment payment, and payments are to begin on April 30. Prepare a schedule as in the preceding problems. What will the interest charges amount to on this settlement?

Ans. $52.50.

143. How to Prepare a Schedule for the Liquidation of an Indebtedness by Equal Periodical Payments, the Interest for Each Period to Be Added to the Unpaid Balance. Property is often purchased by a down payment, the balance to be paid in equal amounts at equal periods of time. A building, for example, priced at $18,500.00 may be sold on terms of a $3,000.00 down payment, the balance to be paid in monthly installments of $500.00, and the unpaid balance to earn interest at the rate of 3 per cent per annum —that is, the interest charge is not to be canceled by a separate payment (as in Art. 142) but is to be offset against the amount of the installment.

The method of preparing a schedule for the liquidation of an indebtedness of this nature is the same as that in the preceding article, except for the matter of interest. So instead of making up a schedule covering the aforementioned purchase of a building, let us prepare a schedule for the debt discussed in Art. 142, the settlement to be on the basis discussed here—namely, the interest for each period is to be added to the unpaid balance.

Note that the installment payment of Dec. 31, 1948, creates a credit of $493.18 which, when subtracted from $681.77, the balance at the beginning of the quarter, leaves an unpaid balance of $188.59. This balance, if not paid until the end of the following quarterly period, will, of course, accumulate an interest charge in the same way as all the other unpaid balances.

Here, too, as the unpaid balance decreases the amount of the interest decreases, so that while the interest at the end of the first quarter amounted to $40.00, the interest for the last full quarterly period was only $6.82. And similar to the schedule in

PRINCIPAL OF DEBT ON JANUARY 1, 1947, OF $4000, PAID IN QUARTERLY INSTALLMENTS OF $500.00 WITH INTEREST AT 4% PER ANNUM ADDED TO THE UNPAID BALANCE

Due Date of Quarterly Installment	Quarterly Unpaid Balance	Interest for Quarter Ended	Quarterly Installment	Net Amount Credited to Unpaid Balance (C minus B)
	A	B	C	D
Mar. 31, 1947	$4,000.00	$40.00	$500	$460.00
June 30, 1947	3,540.00	35.40	500	464.60
Sept. 30, 1947	3,075.40	30.75	500	469.25
Dec. 31, 1947	2,606.15	26.06	500	473.94
Mar. 31, 1948	2,132.21	21.32	500	478.68
June 30, 1948	1,653.53	16.54	500	483.46
Sept. 30, 1948	1,170.07	11.70	500	488.30
Dec. 31, 1948	681.77	6.82	500	493.18
	$18,859.13	$188.59	$4000	$3811.41

the preceding article, the columns provide a check on the accuracy of the computations. The total for column D equals the difference between the totals of columns C and B; and the total for column A at 1 per cent equals the total for column B.

It is interesting to observe the result, in so far as interest charges are concerned, between the one method of settlement and the other. Under the method of payment discussed in this article, the total amount of interest charged is $188.59, whereas when each interest charge was canceled by a payment made at the same time as the installment payment, the total amount of the interest is only $180.00. This is to be expected, for interest accumulates interest.

Or, looked at in another way, the net amount of each payment under the method discussed in this article was smaller than under the method discussed in Art. 142; and this resulted in larger unpaid balances, with correspondingly larger interest charges.

PROBLEMS

1. Leonard Stone makes a purchase amounting to $12,000.00 and pays $2000.00 cash. He agrees to pay the balance in quarterly installments of $2000.00 and to have interest at the rate of 4% per annum charged against him on unpaid balances. The first payment is to be made on March 31, 1947. Prepare a complete schedule for the liquidation of this indebtedness. Assume that the final payment of the small balance is made at the end of the quarterly period together with the interest charge it accumulated. How much will Stone have paid in all to settle the $10,000.00 debt?   *Ans.* $10,311.17.

2. Henry Wood agrees to settle a debt of $3000.00 by monthly payments of $750.00, an interest charge at the rate of 6% per annum to be charged against him on unpaid balances. He is to begin making payments on September 30, 1946. Prepare a schedule showing the month-to-month payments, interest charges and unpaid balances. What is the amount of the final unpaid balance?   *Ans.* $37.88.

3. Prepare a schedule for the liquidation of the indebtedness in Problem 2, using the interest rate of 3% instead of 6%. What will have been the interest cost on the liquidation of this account?   *Ans.* $18.89.

144. How to Determine Without the Use of a Schedule, the Total Amount of Interest to Be Paid on a Debt Settled by Equal Periodical Installments, Each of Which Is to Be Accompanied by a Payment of the Interest Due on the Unpaid Balance. Under the method of settlement discussed in Art. 142, the interest on each unpaid balance was computed separately. And we proved the correctness of the total of the interest payments (column B) by multiplying the total of the quarterly unpaid balances (column A) by the interest rate. But suppose we wished to determine instantly the total amount of interest that would be due on the debt, without the aid of a schedule. This total can be obtained very easily by a method known as arithmetical progression.

Arithmetical progression is a series of numbers or values which increase or decrease by a constant difference; thus in the series of numbers 3, 6, 9, 12, 15, the constant difference is 3. The series of values representing the quarterly unpaid balances in the schedule we are considering also constitutes an arithmetical progression, for each balance is $500.00 less than the preceding balance. This is understandable, since by the nature of the agreement the debt is to be liquidated by equal periodical payments of $500.00.

As our object here is to determine the total amount of the quarterly unpaid balances, let us consider how by arithmetical progression this total can be quickly obtained. The procedure is simple: Add the first and last terms, and multiply their sum by half of the number of terms in the series. The number of terms in the series is obtained by dividing the first term by the last term.

Example 1: Find the sum of the amounts in the series $4000, $3500, $3000, $2500, $2000, $1500, $1000, $500.

Solution: $4000 (the first term) plus $500 (the last term)   = $4500
Half of the number of terms in the series   = 4
4 times $4500 (the sum of the first and last terms)   = $18,000
This figure agrees exactly with the figure in the schedule in Art. 142

When the series of numbers is small, as in the foregoing example, one might, of course, readily obtain the total by simple addition. But see how useful this method of computation can be when the number of terms is large:

Example 2: Compute the total amount of interest to be paid on a debt amounting to $10,800 to be liquidated by monthly payments of $450 plus interest on the unpaid balance at 3% per annum.

Solution: $10,800 (the first term) plus $450 (the
last term) $= \$11,250$

The total number of terms in the series
equals 10,800 divided by 450, or 24.
Half of 24 $= 12$

12 times $11,250 (the sum of the first
and last terms) $= \$135,000$

6% per annum $= \frac{1}{2}$% per month

$135,000 at $\frac{1}{2}$% $= \$675.00$, which is the
total amount of interest to be paid on
the debt

Example 3: Compute the total amount of interest to be paid on
a debt amounting to $1500 to be liquidated by quarterly payments
of $125 plus interest on the unpaid balance at $2\frac{1}{2}$% per annum.

Solution: $1500 (the first term) plus $125 (the last
term) $= \$1625$

The total number of terms in the series
equals 1500 divided by 125, or 12. Half
of 12 $= 6$

6 times $1625 (the sum of the first and last
terms) $= \$9750$

$2\frac{1}{2}$% per annum $= \frac{5}{8}$% per quarter

$9750 at $\frac{5}{8}$% $= \$60.94$, which is the total
amount of interest to be paid on the debt

PROBLEMS

Compute by the method discussed in the text the total amount of
interest to be paid on the following debts settled by the periodical installments indicated plus interest on the unpaid balances.

1. $250 paid quarterly to liquidate a debt of $2000 with interest at
the rate of 5% per annum. *Ans.* $112.50.

2. $500 paid semiannually to settle a debt of $3000 with interest at
the rate of $4\frac{1}{2}$% per annum. *Ans.* $236.25.

3. A debt of $4800 settled by monthly payments of $300 with interest
at the rate of 6% per annum. *Ans.* $204.00.

**145. Two Different Legal Methods of Computing Interest on
Debts Settled by Partial Payments.** It is not generally known

that there are two different legal methods of computing interest on debts settled by partial payments: (1) the United States Rule, and (2) the Mercantile Rule, also known as the Merchant's Rule.

Under the United States Rule, when the first partial payment is made the face value of the note is reduced by the amount of the payment less the interest on the face value for the period between the date of the note and the date of the payment. And each time a partial payment is made thereafter, the unpaid balance is reduced in the same way—that is, it is reduced by the amount of the payment less the interest for the period that elapsed since the date of the preceding payment.

Under the Mercantile Rule, interest for the full period of the note is immediately charged to the borrower, and as each partial payment is made interest is credited for the unexpired period of the note.

The foregoing explanation will become clear after a study of the computation by each method of the interest due in the following transaction:

On July 1, 1946, Henry Jones borrowed $3000.00, which he agreed to pay back on July 1, 1948. He made partial payments as follows: Sept. 1, 1946, $300.00; Nov. 1, 1946, $200.00; Feb. 1, 1947, $500.00; June 1, 1947, $400.00; Mar. 1, 1948, $600.00. Compute the interest at the rate of 4 per cent per annum, and show the amount due at maturity.

Reference to the illustrations will show that there is a difference of $5.96 between the two methods, and that the United States Rule is in favor of the creditor or lender. It will also be seen that the larger the amounts involved and the longer the period of the note and the period for which the balance remains unpaid, the larger will be the difference.

For the benefit of the legally inclined reader it might be added that the question of which method applies arises in the absence of an agreement. While the United States Rule is generally accepted, some courts follow the Mercantile Rule, and the rule applied depends upon the state in which the action is brought. The United States Rule of computing interest was adopted by the United States Supreme Court on March 2, 1837, in the case of *Story* v. *Livingston*, 38 U. S. (13 Peters) 359.

Interest Computed by the United States Rule

Face amount of note............................		$3000.00
Payment on Sept. 1, 1946.................	$300.00	
Less interest on $3000.00 from July 1, 1946, to Sept. 1, 1946—2 months at 4%.......	20.00	280.00
Amount due on note Sept. 1, 1946.................		2720.00
Payment on Nov. 1, 1946.................	200.00	
Less interest on $2720.00 from Sept. 1, 1946, to Nov. 1, 1946—2 months at 4%........	18.14	181.86
Amount due on note Nov. 1, 1946.................		2538.14
Payment on Feb. 1, 1947.................	500.00	
Less interest on $2538.14 from Nov. 1, 1946, to Feb. 1, 1947—3 months at 4%........	25.38	474.62
Amount due on note Feb. 1, 1947.................		2063.52
Payment on June 1, 1947.................	400.00	
Less interest on $2063.52 from Feb. 1, 1947, to June 1, 1947—4 months at 4%........	27.51	372.49
Amount due on note June 1, 1947.................		1691.03
Payment on Mar. 1, 1948.................	600.00	
Less interest on $1691.03 from June 1, 1947, to Mar. 1, 1948—9 months at 4%........	50.73	549.27
Amount due on note Mar. 1, 1948.................		1141.76
Plus interest on $1141.76 from Mar. 1, 1948, to July 1, 1948 (date of maturity)—4 months at 4%..............................		15.22
Amount due at maturity.........................		$1156.98

Observe that in the computation by the Mercantile Rule, which follows, the interest for the full period of the note is immediately added to the principal.

Interest Computed by the Mercantile Rule

Face amount of note		$3000.00	
Interest for 2 years at 4% per annum		240.00	
		3240.00	

Payment on Sept. 1, 1946	$300.00		
Interest credit on $300.00 from Sept. 1, 1946, to July 1, 1948—1 yr. 10 mo. at 4%	22.00	$322.00	
Payment on Nov. 1, 1946	200.00		
Interest credit on $200.00 from Nov. 1, 1946, to July 1, 1948—1 yr. 8 mo. at 4%	13.32	213.32	
Payment on Feb. 1, 1947	500.00		
Interest credit on $500.00 from Feb. 1, 1947, to July 1, 1948—1 yr. 5 mo. at 4%	28.33	528.33	
Payment on June 1, 1947	400.00		
Interest credit on $400.00 from June 1, 1947, to July 1, 1948—1 yr. 1 mo. at 4%	17.33	417.33	
Payment on Mar. 1, 1948	600.00		
Interest credit on $600.00 from Mar. 1, 1948, to July 1, 1948—4 mo. at 4%	8.00	608.00	2088.98
Amount due at maturity			$1151.02

Problems

Estimate the amount due at maturity of the following notes (a) by the United States Rule, and (b) by the Mercantile Rule.

1. Richard Johnson borrowed $1000.00 on Jan. 1, 1947, which he agreed to pay back on Jan. 1, 1948. He made one partial payment of

$200.00 on April 1. Compute the interest at the rate of 6% per annum.
Ans. (a) $851.68; (b) $851.00.

2. Samuel Young borrowed $1500.00 on July 1, 1947, for a period of one year. He made a partial payment of $400.00 on Oct. 1, and a partial payment of $200.00 on Jan. 1. Compute the interest at $4\frac{1}{2}$% per annum. *Ans.* (a) $950.35; (b) $949.50.

3. Edward Milton borrowed $2500.00 on Oct. 1, 1947, for two years and made the following partial payments: $300.00 on Dec. 1, 1947, and $500.00 on Feb. 1, 1948. Compute the interest at the rate of 3% per annum. *Ans.* (a) $1809.74; (b) $1808.50.

4. On Jan. 1, 1946, Louis Knight purchased a farm for $28,000.00. He paid $3000.00 in cash and agreed to pay the balance on or before Jan. 1, 1950. How much will he owe on the date of maturity if he makes the following partial payments: $3000.00 on Jan. 1, 1947, $8000.00 on Jan. 1, 1948, and $10,000.00 on Jan. 1, 1949? Compute the interest at the rate of 8% per annum. *Ans.* (a) $10,101.89; (b) $9,200.00.

CHAPTER XXI

COMPOUND INTEREST AND ANNUITIES

The subject of annuities is another fascinating and intriguing phase of business mathematics. It is an important one, too, for in business or private life the question of annuities comes up sooner or later.

Many annuity problems which may seem difficult are really very simple, and it is hoped that the discussions in these pages will provide the reader with a rich and useful background that will enable him to solve such problems accurately and with great facility.

Since this book is not intended for students of advanced mathematics, we will be concerned only with average, every-day problems. While the conventional headings have been retained for the tables, the articles and article titles have been worded so they may be easily understood.

146. A Word About Annuities in General. Strange as it may seem, a surprisingly large number of business people do not know just what an annuity is. Perhaps the reason is that the word has several different meanings.

Rather than begin with a definition, let us take some typical examples. Suppose that each year, or every six months, for a stated number of years, you received $1000.00 from a trust fund. The *sum* of these payments is an annuity. Suppose, on the other hand, you had made the necessary payments to an insurance company to insure your receiving, beginning with some future date, a stipulated sum of money at equal intervals of time. The investment you had made to insure these payments by the insurance company may be described as an annuity, too, and, regardless of the conditions under which it is made, each payment—so long as it is always in the same amount and paid at equal intervals of time—also may be referred to as an annuity. Each payment, incidentally, is an annuity from the point of view of the one who receives it as well as from the one who pays it.

Many forms of business transactions may be looked upon as annuities. Periodic payments by life insurance companies, installment payments on debts or on purchases of merchandise or property, the regular payments to finance companies, rent paid on property, and payments into the endowment funds of a college, are just a few examples of annuities.

Generally speaking, it may be said that an annuity is a payment of an identical sum of money at equal intervals of time. The interval may be a year or less than a year.

There are different types of annuities. In the case of installment payments on a loan or purchase, the exact number of payments to be made is known in advance, and so we call this type of annuity an *annuity certain*. When the exact number of payments is not known, as for instance when a life insurance company has agreed to make periodical payments to an individual for as long as he lives, we have what is known as a *contingent annuity*. In our discussions we will be concerned only with annuities certain.

There are two methods of paying an annuity. When the payment is made at the *end* of the payment interval, it is known as an *ordinary annuity;* when it is made at the *beginning* of the payment interval, it is known as an *annuity due*. We will discuss here only ordinary annuities.

Summarizing the last two paragraphs, then, we are to confine ourselves to annuities of a definitely known duration, and to those annuities whose payments are made at the end of the payment interval.

The reader will do well to have in mind that the tables with the word *amount* in the headings, supply the *final value* of the annuity—that is, the value at the end of the term. (The term of an annuity is the time between the beginning of the first payment interval and the last payment.) The words *present value* in the headings mean *cash equivalent*—that is, the sum of money which, if invested at the beginning of the term at compound interest, will produce the annuity payments as they come due.

147. The Meaning of Compound Interest. For the reader who is not sure of himself on this subject the meaning of compound interest will become clear if he thinks of his savings—a thought, it is hoped, that will inspire a pleasant feeling. If he happens to be a depositor in two banks, and if for a period, say, of two years has confined his deposits to one of them, he will find, upon returning to the other bank, that despite his not having made a single deposit there in that time, the interest credited to his account for each period exceeds the amount of interest credited for the preceding period.

The reason is simply this: When interest is allowed to accumulate, the principal increases—it increases at the end of each interest period by the amount of interest earned for that period. Interest, therefore, is earned not only on the money actually deposited, but also on the interest earned by that money. This, in effect, is what compound interest really is—*interest earned on interest.*

Thus if on Jan. 1, 1946, a man had $5000.00 on deposit with a savings bank whose rate of interest is $1\frac{1}{2}\%$ per annum, computed and credited semiannually, the interest credited to his account on July 1, 1946 would be half of $1\frac{1}{2}$ per cent of $5000.00, or $37.50, bringing the amount of his deposit up to $5037.50. And the interest credited to his account on Jan. 1, 1947, assuming that no deposits had been made in the meanwhile, will be half of $1\frac{1}{2}$ per cent of $5037.00 (banks disregard fractions of a dollar in computing interest on deposits), or $37.78. And so on.

148. The Difference Between Simple Interest and Compound Interest. Compound interest is calculated in the same manner as simple interest—that is, it is found by multiplying the principal by the period by the interest rate. There is one difference however: Simple interest usually concerns itself with but one period, and this period is more often than not for less than a year or, when notes are involved, for 30, 60, 90 or 120 days. And if, in a simple interest transaction, more than one period is involved, the principal at the beginning of each period is the same. Compound interest, on the other hand, involves two or more periods, with an increased principal at the beginning of each succeeding period.

This difference might be best illustrated by considering two loans for identical amounts, periods and interest rates, the interest in one instance to be simple interest, and in the other instance compound interest.

Simple Interest Illustration. Let us suppose that Miller makes a loan to Smith of $2000.00 for two years at the interest rate of 4 per cent per annum, the interest to be paid quarterly. Under this arrangement Smith, at the end of each 3-month period, is to pay to Miller 1 per cent (4 per cent per annum is equivalent to 1 per cent per 3-month period) of $2000.00, or $20.00. The amount of the interest will not increase with each succeeding period, for since the interest is paid as it becomes due the principal at the beginning of each succeeding period is the same as it was at the beginning of the first period. Each interest computation is exactly the same as the preceding one. So it is easy to see that if the interest per quarterly period is $20.00, the total amount of interest paid in two years will be 8 times $20.00, or $160.00.

Compound Interest Illustration. Let us now suppose that Stone makes a loan to Frost of $2000.00 for two years, the interest at 4 per cent per annum to be computed quarterly as in the simple interest illustration, but *added to the principal*. That is to say, the principal plus all of the accumulated interest is to be paid in one sum upon the maturity date of the note. At the end of the two years, the effect of this arrangement would be as illustrated.

Principal at beginning of period........	$2000.00
Interest for 3 months—1% of $2000.00	20.00
Principal at end of *first* period..........	2020.00
Interest for 3 months—1% of $2020.00	20.20
Principal at end of *second* period........	2040.20
Interest for 3 months—1% of $2040.20	20.40
Principal at end of *third* period.........	2060.60
Interest for 3 months—1% of $2060.60	20.61
Principal at end of *fourth* period........	2081.21
Interest for 3 months—1% of $2081.21	20.81
Principal at end of *fifth* period..........	2102.02
Interest for 3 months—1% of $2102.02	21.02
Principal at end of *sixth* period.........	2123.04
Interest for 3 months—1% of $2123.04	21.23
Principal at end of *seventh* period.......	2144.27
Interest for 3 months—1% of $2144.27	21.44
Principal at end of *eighth* period........	$2165.71

Note that at the end of the loan period Frost owes Stone $2165.71, which includes a total interest charge of $165.71, or $5.71 more than Smith owed to Miller. This, of course, is explained by the fact that Smith had paid his interest by the *simple interest* method—that is, as the interest became due, whereas the interest on the loan to Frost was *compounded*—that is, it was allowed to accumulate, so that Frost was, in effect, paying interest on interest.

The illustration showing the constantly increasing amount of the interest, when it is added to the principal, is given here to provide a clear picture of the effect of such an arrangement. Actually, compound interest is never computed by this long, drawn-out process, as we will learn in the article that follows.

149. How to Quickly Determine, by the Use of a Table, What the Value Will Be, at the End of Any Period of Time, of a Sum of Money Subject to Compound Interest at a Specified Rate. Suppose you had just become the beneficiary to an estate of $10,000.00. It is your intention, let us say, to deposit this amount in a savings bank. Assuming that the bank compounds interest quarterly at the rate of $2\frac{1}{2}$ per cent per annum, to what amount would your original deposit have increased at the end of five years?

It is easy to see what a complicated and long drawn-out calculation this would be if the interest were computed quarter by quarter as in the illustration in the preceding article. First, our present problem involves not 8 but 20 quarterly periods, and second, while in the aforementioned illustration we were dealing with the easy-to-work-with interest rate of 1 per cent (4 per cent per annum equals 1 per cent per quarter), in the present problem the interest rate is $\frac{5}{8}$ per cent ($2\frac{1}{2}$ per cent per annum equals $\frac{5}{8}$ per cent per quarter), which would make the calculation so much more laborious and time-consuming.

Fortunately, a table has been devised which makes the calculation of compound interest at any interest rate and for any length of time, a very simple matter. It is Table XVII, "Compound Amount of 1." Let us turn to this table on p. 499 and reflect for a moment upon the formula in the heading—$(1 + i)^n$. The purpose of this formula is to show how the figures in the table are determined mathematically, so we need not concern ourselves with it very much, except to touch glancingly on its meaning. The 1 in the parentheses means one dollar (if we are concerned with United States currency) or any other unit of currency with which any problem may deal. The i stands for *interest rate* and signifies the equivalent interest rate per period; thus if the interest rate is 3 per cent per annum compounded annually, i equals 3 per cent; if the interest rate is 2 per cent per annum compounded semi-annually, i equals 1 per cent (because in this instance there are two interest periods in a year); and when the interest rate is 2 per cent per annum compounded quarterly, i equals $\frac{1}{2}$ per cent (because here there are four interest periods in a year).

The small superscript n outside of the parentheses refers to the number of interest periods.

Let us take a simple problem and see how, with the foregoing information as our guide, the answer to any problem of the type under consideration can be found in the table in a matter of seconds. How much will $1.00 amount to in one year at 2 per cent per annum, compounded semiannually? An interest rate of 2 per cent per annum compounded semiannually is equivalent to 1 per cent per interest period; in other words, i equals 1 per cent, and n equals 2 (because there are two interest periods in the time with which we are concerned). Now we go to work on the table itself. Since the equivalent interest rate per period is 1 per cent, we turn to the 1% column, and since the investment is for one year, or 2 interest periods, we look on line 2. The figure on this line is 1.0201, and our answer is $1.02.

Suppose, however, that the amount of the investment was $100.00 instead of $1.00. In that event, we would simply multiply $100.00 by 1.0201, and our answer would be $102.01.

Example 1: What will an investment of $100.00 amount to at the end of 3 years if it earned interest at 3% per annum, compounded semiannually?

Solution: An interest rate of 3% per annum, compounded semi-annually, is equivalent to $1\frac{1}{2}$% per semiannual period.

In 3 years there are 6 semiannual periods.

Referring to the $1\frac{1}{2}\%$ column in Table XVII, we run our eye along line 6 (6 being the number of interest periods), where we read 1.09344326. This is the value of $1.00 at the end of 3 years. Since the amount with which we are concerned is $100.00, we simply multiply $100.00 by 1.09344326, and we see at a glance that the answer is $109.34.

Example 2: What will $450.00 amount to at the end of 4 years if it earns interest at the rate of 3% per annum, compounded quarterly?

Solution: An interest rate of 3% per annum, compounded quarterly, is equivalent to $\frac{3}{4}\%$ per quarter.

In 4 years there are 16 quarterly periods.

Referring to Table XVII, column $\frac{3}{4}\%$, line 16 (16 being the number of interest periods), we read 1.12699211. This is the value of $1.00 at the end of 4 years. Since the amount of the investment with which we are concerned is $450.00, we simply multiply $450.00 by 1.12699211, which gives us $507.15.

Example 3: To what amount would a deposit of $10,000.00 have increased after 5 years at an interest rate of $2\frac{1}{2}\%$ per annum, compounded annually?

Solution: Our problem here is comparatively simple, for when the interest is compounded annually, the interest rate per period is the same as the interest rate per annum, and the number of periods is the same as the number of years.

Referring to the same table, column $2\frac{1}{2}\%$, line 5 (5 being the number of interest periods), we read 1.13140821, and we need but to multiply $10,000.00 by this figure to obtain the answer, $11,314.08.

It is important to remember that the per-cent rates at the top of the columns in the table are not the interest rates per annum, but the equivalent interest rates per period. Before referring to the table, therefore, care should be taken to convert the number of years in the problem to the number of interest periods, and the interest rate per annum to the equivalent interest rate per period.

1. How much will $1000.00 amount to in 10 years if it is invested at 6% per annum, compounded semiannually?   *Ans.* $1806.11.

2. How much will $700.00 have increased to in 6 years at $4\frac{1}{2}$% per annum, compounded semiannually?   *Ans.* $914.23.

3. At the interest rate of 4% per annum, compounded quarterly, what will an investment of $3000.00 be worth in 5 years? *Ans.* $3660.57.

4. At the interest rate of 7% per annum, compounded monthly, how much will an investment of $7500.00 amount to in 12 years? (Hint: 7% compounded monthly is equivalent to $\frac{7}{12}$% per month, and in 12 years there are 144 one-month interest periods.)   *Ans.* $17,330.40.

5. On Jan. 2, 1947, the sum of $3000.00 is invested at 2% per annum, compounded quarterly.   Three years later the investment is increased by $5000.00.   To what amount will these sums have grown on Jan. 2, 1957, assuming that the interest rate throughout the 10 years was 2% per annum, compounded quarterly? (Hint: There are really two problems here.)   *Ans.* $9411.74.

6. A manufacturer begins business with a capital of $20,000.00, and eight years later, having made no withdrawals, his net worth is $42,000.00. He could have invested the $20,000.00 in securities which paid at the rate of 6% per annum, compounded semiannually.   Which was the better investment, and why?

> *Ans.* The investment he made was better because the income from the business exceeded the income he would have had from the securities by nearly $10,000.00.

150. How to Find the Total Amount of Interest Earned on Any Sum for Any Period of Time at Any Compound Interest Rate. In the preceding article we learned how to find the *sum* of the principal and the interest after a specified number of years.   It is obvious, therefore, that if we wish to know the amount of the interest only, we need but to subtract the amount of the principal from the sum—that is, from the total of principal and interest.

Let us take, for instance, the last illustration in the preceding article, which showed that $10,000.00 invested at $2\frac{1}{2}$ per cent per annum, compounded annually, will have increased to $11,314.08 in 5 years. We need but to subtract $10,000.00 (the amount of the principal) from $11,314.08 (the sum of the principal and the interest) to know that the total amount of interest earned on the investment is $1,314.08.

Example: Estimate the total amount of interest earned on $25,000.00 in 8 years at 3% per annum, compounded quarterly.

Solution: 3% per annum, compounded quarterly, is equivalent to $\frac{3}{4}$% per quarter.

In 8 years there are 32 quarterly periods.

Referring to Table XVII, $\frac{3}{4}$% column, line 32, we read 1.27011122. This is the compound amount of 1—that is, the amount to which $1.00 would increase at 3% per annum, compounded quarterly, in 8 years. Since the amount of the investment with which we are concerned is $25,000.00, we simply multiply $25,000.00 by 1.27011122, which gives us $31,752.78.

$31,752.78 minus $25,000.00 equals $6,752.78.

The total amount of interest earned on the investment is, therefore, $6,752.78.

Problems

Estimate the total amount of interest earned on the following investments:

1. $2000.00 invested for 5 years at 4% per annum, compounded annually. *Ans.* $433.31.

2. $840.00 invested for 9 years at $3\frac{1}{2}$% per annum, compounded semiannually. *Ans.* $307.89. (*Art. 13*)

3. $2700.00 invested for 6 years at 5% per annum, compounded quarterly. *Ans.* $937.85. (*Art. 6*)

4. $1600.00 invested for 12 years at 7% per annum, compounded quarterly. *Ans.* $2079.36. (*Art. 5*)

5. $3800.00 invested for 10 years at 5% per annum, compounded monthly. *Ans.* $2458.64. (*Art. 12*)

151. How to Determine, by the Use of a Table, the Time in Which a Sum of Money, Subject to Compound Interest at a Specified Rate, Will Be Worth a Certain Amount. Here, as in the preceding articles, our answers will be found in Table XVII.

Let us suppose that it is desired to know how long it would take $1000.00 invested at 4 per cent per annum, compounded annually, to be worth approximately $1500.00.

As in Arts. 149 and 150, we must first determine the equivalent rate of interest per period. Since the interest in this problem is compounded annually, the rate is 4 per cent per period. The number of periods is unknown, but we do know that the ultimate worth of the investment is $1500.00. So here is how we proceed:

We state the relation of the amount of the investment ($1000.00) to the amount of the ultimate worth ($1500.00) in the form of a ratio in which the value of the investment equals 1. Thus $1000.00 is to $1500.00 as 1 is to x. The value of x is, of course, 1.5. Now we run our eye down the 4% column until we come to a figure which is as close as possible to 1.5. We find that at the end of the tenth period (line 10) the investment will be worth 1.48024428, and that at the end of the eleventh period (line 11) it will be worth 1.53945406. We may assume, therefore, that $1000.00 invested at 4 per cent per annum, compounded annually, will have reached the $1500.00 mark in value before the end of the eleventh year.

Example 1: How long would it take $2000.00 invested at 3% per annum, compounded semiannually, to be worth $4000.00?

Solution: 3% per annum, compounded semiannually, is equivalent to $1\frac{1}{2}$% per 6-month period.

$2000 : $4000 = 1 : 2

Running our eye down the $1\frac{1}{2}$% column in Table XVII, we find that an investment of 1 at the specified rate of interest will be worth 2 (or 2.01327910 to be exact) at the end of the forty-seventh interest period. We may assume, therefore, that $2000.00 invested at the specified rate of interest will be worth $4000.00 before the end of 47 interest periods, or $23\frac{1}{2}$ years.

Proof: $2000.00 multiplied by 2.0132791 equals $4026.56.

Example 2: In what period of time will $8000.00 invested at 5% per annum, compounded quarterly, be worth $12,000.00?

Solution: 5% per annum, compounded quarterly, is equivalent to $1\frac{1}{4}$% per 3-month period.

$8000:$12000 = 1:x$

$x = \frac{12000}{8000} = \frac{3}{2}$ or 1.5

Running our eye down the $1\frac{1}{4}$% column in Table XVII until we come to a figure in the neighborhood of 1.5, we find that an investment of 1 equals 1.50673214 at the end of the thirty-third interest period. An investment of $8000.00 will, therefore, have reached the value of $12,000.00 at the specified rate of interest after 33 interest periods—that is, at the end of 33 quarters, or $8\frac{1}{4}$ years.

Proof: $8000.00 multiplied by 1.50673214 equals $12,053.86.

Example 3: How long would it take $750.00 to reach a value of $1000.00 if it is invested at $4\frac{1}{2}$% per annum, compounded quarterly?

Solution: $4\frac{1}{2}$% per annum, compounded quarterly, equals $1\frac{1}{8}$% per 3-month period.

$750:$1000 = 1:x.$

$x = \frac{1000}{750} = \frac{4}{3}$ or 1.33.

Running our eye down the $1\frac{1}{8}$% column in Table XVII until we come to a figure in the neighborhood of 1.33, we find that an investment of 1 equals 1.33758657 at the end of the twenty-sixth interest period. An investment of $750.00 will, therefore, have reached the value of $1000.00 at the specified rate of interest after 26 interest periods—that is, at the end of 26 quarters, or $6\frac{1}{2}$ years.

Proof: $750.00 multiplied by 1.33758657 equals $1003.19.

1. How long would it take money to double itself at $2\frac{1}{2}\%$ per annum, compounded semiannually?   *Ans.* 28 years.

2. How long would it take money to double itself at $4\frac{1}{2}\%$ per annum, compounded quarterly?   *Ans.* $15\frac{1}{2}$ years.

3. In how many years will $1000.00 invested at 3% per annum, compounded semiannually, be worth $1250.00?   *Ans.* $7\frac{1}{2}$ years.

4. In how many years will $15,000.00 invested at 4% per annum, compounded semiannually, be worth $20,000.00?   *Ans.* $7\frac{1}{2}$ years.

5. In how many years will $2500.00 invested at 5% per annum, compounded quarterly, reach a value of $4000.00?   *Ans.* $9\frac{1}{2}$ years.

152. How to Determine, by the Use of a Table, the Present Value of a Sum of Money Due at a Future Date, Taking into Consideration the Fact That Money Accumulates Interest and That Interest Earns Interest. In this article we will be concerned with a process of computation which is the direct opposite of that discussed in the preceding three articles.

Thus far we have dealt with problems in which the amount started with was known. Here the situation will be reversed—we will know the amount we shall end up with and the number of interest periods, and it will be required to find what amount invested at the prevailing rate of interest will equal the specified sum at the end of the specified time.

To secure this information we will use the next table in our collection—Table XVIII, "Present Value of 1." A glance at the formula will show that the mathematical process by which the figures here are obtained is quite involved, so without bothering ourselves about the formula let us proceed directly with finding the answers to specific problems.

Walter Arnold promises to liquidate a debt of $1000.00 at the end of two years. At the prevailing rate of 2 per cent per annum, compounded semiannually, what sum invested today will provide Arnold with $1000.00 at the end of two years? In other words, what is the present value of a sum which, invested at 2 per cent per annum, compounded semiannually, will be worth $1000.00 at the end of two years?

An interest rate of 2 per cent per annum, compounded semiannually, is equivalent to 1 per cent per 6-month period. And since the time involved here is 2 years, the total number of interest periods is 4. All we need to do now is refer to the 1% column, line 4, in Table XVIII, where we read 0.96098034. This is the value which, invested at 2 per cent, compounded semiannually, will be worth 1 at the end of two years. We are concerned with a value, not of 1, but of $1000.00, so we simply multiply $1000.00 by 0.96098034, which gives us $960.98. And this amount, invested at 2 per cent per annum, compounded semiannually, will be worth $1000.00 at the end of two years.

Example 1: What is the present worth of a contract under which $6000.00 is to be received 5 years hence? Assume money to be worth 4% per annum, compounded annually.

Solution: Since the interest is compounded annually, this problem is comparatively simple. The interest rate per period here is the same as the interest rate per annum, so the number of periods is the same as the number of years. Referring to Table XVIII, 4% column, line 5, we read 0.82192711, and $6000.00 multiplied by this figure gives us $4931.56, the present worth of the contract.

Example 2: On his seventeenth birthday, Jim Watson was promised by his father that he would receive a gift of $4000.00 on his twenty-first birthday. Taking the current bank interest rate of 2% per annum, compounded semiannually, what is the worth of the gift on Jim's seventeenth birthday?

Solution: The interest rate of 2% per annum, compounded semiannually, is equivalent to 1% per 6-month period. And since there are two interest periods per year in this problem, the total number of interest periods is 8.

Line 8 in the 1% column in Table XVIII reads 0.92348322, and $4000.00 multiplied by this figure equals $3693.93, which is the present worth of the money Jim Watson will receive on his twenty-first birthday.

Example 3: Paul Gladwood is the holder of a note which is a promise to pay 4 years hence $10,000.00 with interest at 3 per cent per annum, compounded annually. What is the present worth of the note, assuming that money is worth 4%, compounded semiannually?

Solution: A little extra care needs to be taken here, for before we can proceed to find the present worth, we must determine the exact value of the note at maturity—that is, at the end of 4 years. Here, then, we will need to use two different tables, as indicated.

Referring to Table XVII, "Compound Amount of 1," 3% column, line 4, we read 1.12550881, and $10,000.00 multiplied by this figure equals $11,255.09, the maturity value of the note.

Now we refer to Table XVIII, "Present Value of 1," and remembering that the annual interest rate of 4% is compounded semiannually, we look in the 2% column; and since there are 8 interest periods in 4 years, we look on line 8. The figure indicated here is 0.85349037, and $11,255.09 multiplied by this figure equals $9606.11, which is the present value of the note.

The reader is cautioned to have in mind constantly that the per-cent rates in these tables are not necessarily the rates per annum, but the equivalent rates *per interest period*, and that likewise, the consecutive numbers at the left of each table represent, not the number of years, but the number of *interest periods*.

PROBLEMS

1. Harold Waters is to receive 6 years hence $8000.00. If money is worth 3½% per annum, compounded semiannually, what is the present worth of this sum?   *Ans.* $6496.46.

2. If money is worth 4% per annum, compounded quarterly, what sum should be invested now so it will accumulate to $3500.00 in 5 years?   *Ans.* $2868.41.

3. If money is worth 3% per annum, compounded semiannually how much should a father set aside on his son's 10th birthday so it will accumulate to $3000.00 by the time the son is 21 years of age?

Ans. $2162.06.

4. Robert Ellis holds a note which is a promise to pay $4200.00 3 years hence with interest at 4% per annum, compounded annually. If money is worth 3% per annum, compounded semiannually, what is the present worth of the note? (Hint: First find the maturity value of the note by referring to Table XVII.) *Ans.* $4320.69.

5. Leo Parks is the holder of a note which is a promise to pay 2 years hence $2000.00 with interest at $3\frac{1}{2}$% per annum, compounded semiannually. If money is worth 3% per annum, compounded semiannually, what is the present worth of the note? (Hint: First find the maturity value of the note by referring to Table XVII.) *Ans.* $2019.78.

153. How to Compute, by the Use of a Table, the Value at the End of a Stipulated Time of a Series of Like Payments Made at Equal Intervals and Subject to Compound Interest at a Specified Rate. (By *value* is meant the sum of the payments plus accumulated compound interest.) As explained in Art. 146, an annuity is the receipt or payment of a like sum of money *at equal intervals of time.* The last few words are italicized to stress the difference between the problems considered in the preceding articles and the problems we are to discuss here. In the preceding articles we were concerned with problems in which only one amount was involved— an amount, that is, that was paid or deposited (Arts. 149, 150 and 151) or was to be paid or deposited (Art. 152), only once. Here we will be concerned with annuities.

It is sometimes necessary to know just what an annuity will amount to after a certain number of payments has been made. Thus the beneficiary to an estate, receiving a like sum of money each year as provided by the testator, may want to know the value of these payments at the end of ten years. An individual making regular bank deposits of, say, $1000.00 each year, may desire to know what his deposits plus accumulated interest will amount to at the end of twelve years. Or a creditor, receiving a specified sum at regular intervals, may want to know the value of the amounts he received at the end of three years.

These values can, of course, be computed by ordinary arithmetic. But since a separate computation must be made for each interest period, the computation by this method is unnecessarily long and laborious. For example, to find the value at the end of four years of an annuity of $1000.00 payable annually and invested at 2 per cent per annum, compounded annually, the computation by ordinary arithmetic would be as illustrated.

COMPUTATION BY ORDINARY ARITHMETIC OF THE VALUE AT THE END OF 4 YEARS OF AN ANNUITY OF $1000.00 PAYABLE ANNUALLY, AND INVESTED AT 2% PER ANNUM, COMPOUNDED ANNUALLY

Payment at end of *first* year................... $1000.00

Interest at end of second year (2% of
　$1000.00)............................ 20.00
Payment at end of second year.......... 1000.00
　　　　　　　　　　　　　　　　　　　　───────
Accumulation at end of *second* year......... $2020.00

Interest at end of third year (2% of $2020.00) 40.40
Payment at end of third year............ 1000.00 1040.40
　　　　　　　　　　　　　　　　　　　　─────── ───────
Accumulation at end of *third* year........... 3060.40

Interest at end of fourth year (2% of $3060.40) 61.21
Payment at end of fourth year........... 1000.00 1061.21
　　　　　　　　　　　　　　　　　　　　─────── ───────
Accumulation at end of *fourth* year................... $4121.61

Note that our problem here involves but three interest periods. It will readily be seen that when the time involves many interest periods, finding the value of an annuity would indeed be a time-consuming task. So the mathematicians have come to the rescue with a table known as "Amount of Annuity of 1 per Period." This is Table XIX on p. 519, and we will presently see how by the use of this table the figure $4121.61 arrived at in the solution to the foregoing problem the long way, can be obtained quickly and easily.

In the problem under consideration, the interest rate is 2 per cent per annum, compounded annually. The number of interest

periods, therefore, is the same as the number of years—namely, 4.
So we refer to Table XIX, 2% column, line 4, where we read
4.12160800. This is the value at the end of 4 years of an annuity
that is 1. In our problem the annuity is $1000.00, so we multiply
$1000.00 by 4.12160800, which gives us $4121.61, the value of the
annuity at the end of the fourth year. This checks perfectly with
the amount obtained by the long drawn-out method.

Example 1: Louis Brandt intends to deposit in his savings account $500.00 regularly, every six months, beginning June 30,
1946. The bank's interest rate is $2\frac{1}{2}\%$ per annum, compounded
semiannually. What would be the value of the annuity on Dec.
31, 1952, assuming that the interest rate and method of compounding remained the same throughout the stated time? In other
words, what would Brandt's savings amount to at the end of 7
years if his intention to make the deposits regularly were carried
out?

Solution: $2\frac{1}{2}\%$ per annum, compounded semiannually, is equivalent to $1\frac{1}{4}\%$ per 6-month period. In 7 years there
are 14 semiannual periods. Referring to Table XIX,
we look in the $1\frac{1}{4}\%$ column, on line 14, where we are
given the figure 15.19637988. This is the value at
the end of 7 years of an annuity of 1 per period.
Since the annuity with which we are concerned is
$500.00 per period, we multiply $500.00 by
15.19637988, which equals $7598.19, the total value
of Brandt's deposits, including accumulated interest,
at the end of 7 years.

It is interesting to observe the accuracy of these tables. Note,
for instance, that in the table used here, much as in an arithmetic
computation, no interest is shown at the end of the first period. In
other words, when Louis Brandt, the gentleman mentioned in the
preceding example, made his first deposit on June 30, 1946—a
deposit, that is, made at the *end* of the first period of the annuity—
he was not entitled to any interest; he is first credited with interest

at the end of the *second* period of the annuity. So that on that date (Dec. 31, 1946) principal plus interest ($500.00 plus $1\frac{1}{4}\%$ of $500.00) would amount to $506.25 which, together with his second deposit of $500.00, equals $1006.25. Referring to line 2 in the $1\frac{1}{4}\%$ column of Table XIX, we read 2.01250000 which, multiplied by $500.00, gives us exactly that amount—namely, $1006.25.

Example 2: Helen Banks is the beneficiary of an estate which provides for an annuity of $350.00 to be paid her every 3 months, the first payment to be made on Mar. 31, 1946. Assuming that each payment is promptly deposited in a savings account, that the bank's rate of interest is 3% per annum, compounded quarterly, how much will Miss Banks have accumulated on Jan. 2, 1952, including the deposit made on that date?

Solution: 3% per annum, compounded quarterly, is equivalent to $\frac{3}{4}\%$ per 3-month period.

On Jan. 2, 1952, the annuity payments will have been received for exactly 6 years, or 24 interest periods. We therefore turn to Table XIX, $\frac{3}{4}\%$ column, line 24. The figure shown there is 26.18847059, and $350.00 multiplied by this figure gives us $9165.97, the value of the annuity (that is, the total value of the annuity payments plus accumulated interest) on Jan. 2, 1952.

Problems

1. Find the value of an annuity of $1000.00 payable at the end of each year for 10 years, invested at 3% per annum, compounded annually.
Ans. $11,463.88.

2. At the end of each year, for 7 years, the sum of $325.00 is deposited into a fund which earns interest at the rate of $3\frac{1}{2}\%$ per annum, compounded annually. What will be the value of the accumulation at the end of the seventh year?
Ans. $2528.31.

3. Find the value of an annuity of $1500.00 invested at the end of every 6 months, for 8 years, at $3\frac{1}{2}\%$ per annum, compounded semi-annually.
Ans. $27,422.52.

4. If $500.00 is invested at the end of each semiannual period for 15 years at $2\frac{1}{2}\%$ per annum, compounded semiannually, what will the value of the accumulation be after the thirtieth payment has been made?

Ans. $18,064.53.

5. If $250.00 is deposited at the end of each quarter for 6 years at the interest rate of 3% per annum, compounded quarterly, and if no withdrawals are made, what will the accumulated value be at the end of that time?   *Ans.* $6547.12.

6. An annuity of $50.00 a quarter has been accumulated for 10 years at 5% per annum, compounded quarterly. Find the accumulated value.

Ans. $2574.48.

7. If a payment of $275.00 is invested at the end of each quarterly period for 12 years at 6 per cent per annum, compounded quarterly, what will the accumulation be worth after the 48th payment has been made?

Ans. $19,130.44.

8. At the end of each quarterly period for 20 years the sum of $360.00 is deposited in a savings account which earns interest at 2% per annum, compounded quarterly. What will be the value of the account after the last payment in the 20th year has been made?   *Ans.* $35,304.37.

9. How much will be accumulated in 8 years if $100.00 is deposited each month into a fund which earns interest at the rate of 5% per annum, compounded monthly?   *Ans.* $11,774.05.

10. If the interest at 6% per annum is compounded monthly, what will be the value in 10 years of an accumulation resulting from the deposit of $50.00 at the end of each month?   *Ans.* $8193.97.

154. How to Determine, by the Use of a Table, the Time in Which the Sum of a Series of Like Payments Made at Equal Intervals, Plus Compounded Interest, Will Be Worth a Certain Amount. In the preceding article we considered problems in which the exact time involved was known, and it was required to find the total value at the end of that time. Here the situation will be reversed—the total value will be known, and it will be required to determine the time, or number of periods, in which the payments are to be made in order that the accumulation will equal the specified total value.

Let us suppose that an individual deposits $1000.00 at the end of every six months to a fund which earns interest at 3 per cent per annum, compounded semiannually. How long will it take before his savings amount to $12,500.00?

An interest rate of 3 per cent per annum, compounded semi-annually, is equivalent to $1\frac{1}{2}\%$ per 6-month period. The number of periods is unknown, but we do know the ultimate value. The procedure, then, will be exactly as that described in Art. 151. The relation of each payment (in this instance, $1000.00) to the amount of the ultimate worth (in this instance, $12,500.00) is stated in the form of a ratio in which the amount of each payment is represented by 1. Thus $1000:12,500$ equals $1:x$.

Since the product of the means equals the product of the extremes (Art. 130), $1000x$ equals 12,500, and $1x$ equals 12.5.

And since our problem concerns itself with a series of like payments, the table to use is Table XIX, "Amount of Annuity of 1 per Period."

Running our eye down the $1\frac{1}{2}\%$ column in this table until we come to a figure which is as close as possible to 12.5, we find that at the end of the eleventh period (that is, at the end of $5\frac{1}{2}$ years) the accumulation will have amounted to 11.86326249, and that at the end of the twelfth period (that is, at the end of 6 years) it will have amounted to 13.04121143. We may assume, therefore, that $1000.00 deposited at the end of every 6 months at 3 per cent per annum, compounded semiannually, will have accumulated to $12,500.00 before the end of the sixth year.

Example 1: How long would it take an investment of $500.00 at the end of every 6 months, earning interest at $2\frac{1}{2}\%$ per annum, compounded semiannually, to be worth $5000.00?

Solution: $2\frac{1}{2}\%$ per annum, compounded semiannually, is equivalent to $1\frac{1}{4}\%$ per 6-month period.

$$\$500:\$5000 = 1:x$$
$$x = \tfrac{5000}{500} = 10.$$

Running our eye down the $1\frac{1}{4}\%$ column in Table XIX until we come to a figure in the neighborhood of 10, we find that an investment of 1 per period equals 10.58166637 at the end of the tenth interest period. We may assume, therefore, that a deposit of $500.00 every 6 months, at the stipulated rate of interest, will have accumulated to $5000.00 before the end of the tenth interest period—that is, before the end of 5 years.

Proof: $500.00 multiplied by 10.58166637 equals $5290.83.

Example 2: How many years would it take for an annual payment of $600.00, earning interest at $2\frac{3}{4}\%$ per annum, compounded annually, to accumulate to $5000.00?

Solution: $2\frac{3}{4}\%$ per annum, compounded annually, equals $2\frac{3}{4}\%$ per interest period.

$600:$5000 = 1:x

$x = \frac{5000}{600} = \frac{25}{3}$ or 8.33

Running our eye down the $2\frac{3}{4}\%$ column in Table XIX until we come to a figure in the neighborhood of 8.33, we find that a payment of 1 per period equals 8.81383825 at the end of the eighth interest period. The sum of a series of annual payments of $600.00 will, therefore, have reached the value of $5000.00 before the end of the eighth interest period—that is, before the end of the eighth year.

Proof: $600.00 multiplied by 8.81383825 equals $5288.30.

Example 3: At the end of each quarter, for the last 2 years, Stanley Summers deposited $800.00 in a savings account that earns interest at the rate of 2% per annum, compounded quarterly. How many additional quarterly deposits of the same amount will need to be made if Summers desires to accumulate $15,000.00?

Solution: (Note that the question reads, "how many *additional* quarterly deposits?"; we will therefore proceed in the prescribed manner and simply deduct from the total number of payments the number of deposits already made.)

2% per annum, compounded quarterly, is equivalent to $\frac{1}{2}\%$ per quarter.

$800:$15000 = 1:x

$x = \frac{15000}{800} = \frac{150}{8}$ or 18.75

Running our eye down the $\frac{1}{2}\%$ column in Table XIX, we find that a deposit of 1 per period will be worth 18.78578791 just after the end of the eighteenth interest period. In other words, 18 quarterly payments will be necessary to accumulate $15,000.00. Since 8 payments have already been made, 10 additional payments will be needed.

Proof: $800.00 multiplied by 18.78578791 equals $15,028.63.

Problems

1. How many years would elapse before an annual payment of $400.00, earning interest at $2\frac{1}{4}\%$ per annum, compounded annually, accumulated to a sum of at least $5000.00?   *Ans.* 12 years.

2. If $350.00 is deposited every quarter to a savings account which earns interest at 4% per annum, compounded quarterly, how long would it take before the savings accumulated to at least $10,000.00?

Ans. $6\frac{1}{2}$ years.

3. If money earns interest at the rate of $2\frac{1}{2}\%$ per annum, compounded semiannually, how many full payments of $500.00 will need to be made at the end of each 6 months to accumulate to the sum of $33,500.00?

Ans. 49 full payments.

4. After $200.00 has been deposited every 3 months for 4 years in a savings account earning interest at 2% per annum, compounded quarterly, how many additional like payments must be made in order to accumulate the sum of $10,000.00?   *Ans.* 29 additional payments.

5. After $750.00 has been deposited every 6 months for 2 years to a savings account earning interest at $2\frac{1}{2}\%$ per annum, compounded semiannually, how many additional payments must be made in order to accumulate a sum of $15,000.00?   *Ans.* 14 additional payments.

155. How to Compute, by the Use of a Table, the Present Value of a Series of Like Payments to Be Made at Equal Intervals During a Stipulated Time.   In Art. 153, Example 2, we considered an annuity payment to Helen Banks of $350.00 every three months, and determined the value of these payments at the *end* of six years. Let us suppose now that Miss Banks wishes to know the *present* value of the payments—in other words, the worth on Jan.

1, 1946, of the annuity payments she is to receive in the next six years.

Now to compute this by ordinary arithmetic would be equally, if not more, laborious than the computation illustrated in Art. 153. A much quicker way is to obtain the desired figure from a table which the mathematicians have given us. Shown as Table XX on p. 529, this table is known as "Present Value of Annuity of 1 per Period," and is used in exactly the same way as the other tables discussed in this chapter.

Let us take, by way of illustration, the aforementioned problem of Helen Banks. An interest rate of 3 per cent per annum, compounded quarterly, is equivalent to $\frac{3}{4}$ per cent per quarter. And in six years there are 24 quarterly periods. So we turn to Table XX, $\frac{3}{4}\%$ column, line 24, where we read 21.88914614. This is the present value at the end of twenty-four quarters, or six years, of an annuity of 1. Since the annuity with which we are concerned is $350.00, we multiply $350.00 by 21.88914614, which equals $7661.19. And this is the present value to Miss Banks of all the annuity payments she is to receive from Mar. 31, 1946 to Jan. 2, 1952, inclusive.

Example: A building is sold for $50,000.00 on terms of $5000.00 payable at the end of each year. Assuming money to be worth $4\frac{1}{2}\%$ per annum, compounded annually, find the cash equivalent of the sale.

Solution: Table XX, $4\frac{1}{2}\%$ column, line 10, tells us that the present value of an annuity of 1 per period is 7.91271818. Since the amount of each payment is $5000.00, we multiply $5000.00 by 7.91271818, which gives us $39,563.59, the cash equivalent of the sale.

PROBLEMS

1. Find the value on Jan. 1, 1947, of an annuity payment of $425.00 to be made at the end of every 6 months for 8 years, the first payment to be on June 30, 1947. Assume that each payment will be promptly deposited in an account earning interest at $2\frac{1}{2}\%$ per annum, compounded semiannually.   *Ans.* $6128.62.

2. If money is worth $2\frac{1}{4}\%$ per annum, compounded annually, what will the present value be of an annuity of $300.00 per year for 12 years?

Ans. $3124.43.

3. Find the present value of an annuity of $50.00 a month for 10 years, which is to be deposited promptly upon its receipt in a fund on which interest is paid at 5% per annum, compounded monthly.

Ans. $4714.07.

4. Upon the death of the founder of a society, his widow is granted an annuity of $5000.00 payable annually for 5 years. If each payment is deposited promptly upon its receipt in an account earning interest at $2\frac{3}{4}\%$ per annum, compounded annually, what is the present worth of the annuity?

Ans. $23,062.91.

5. The asking price of a house offered for sale is $70,000.00, on which $30,000.00 is to be paid in cash, the balance at the rate of $10,000.00 each year, the first installment to be paid 12 months after the signing of the contract. If money is worth $3\frac{1}{2}\%$ per annum, compounded annually, what is the equivalent cash price of the house? (Hint: Be sure to add the $30,000.00 cash payment to the product of 10,000 times the figure indicated in the table.)

Ans. $66,730.79.

6. A manufacturer agrees to buy a machine for $1500.00 cash and $250.00 a month for 3 years. Assuming that money is worth 5% per annum, compounded monthly, what is the equivalent cash price of the machine? (Hint: Be sure to add the $1500.00 cash payment to the product of 250 times the figure indicated in the table.)

Ans. $9841.43.

156. How to Compute, by the Use of a Table, the Uniform Amount of a Periodical Payment Which, Made at the End of Equal Intervals of Time, Will Extinguish an Interest-Bearing Debt upon a Predetermined Date. The purchase of land, buildings or equipment, or the settlement of a debt, is frequently arranged on a plan known as *amortization*, by which a uniform sum is paid at equal intervals of time.

Let us say that a tract of land, purchased for $4000.00, is to be paid for in five equal annual installments, the payments to include interest at 4 per cent per annum.

If the terms did not call for *equal* annual payments, we might have assumed that the first payment would be for $800.00 (which is one fifth of $4000.00) plus 4 per cent on $800.00; that the second payment would be for $800.00 plus compound interest for two years on this sum, and so on. The payments, however, are to be *alike*, which would seem to complicate the problem—but not if we use Table XXI, "Periodical Payment of Annuity Whose Present Value Is 1."

The procedure here is the same as with the other tables discussed in this chapter. The interest rate of 4 per cent per annum, computed annually, is equivalent to 4 per cent per interest period, and since payments are to be made in five equal annual installments, the number of interest periods is 5. We therefore refer to Table XXI, 4% column, line 5, where we read 0.22462711, and $4000.00 (the purchase price) multiplied by this figure gives us $898.51, the amount of each annual payment.

It is interesting to note that in connection with transactions of this nature, an amortization schedule can be drawn up which shows the unpaid balance at the end of each period, the amount of each payment, the interest included in the payment, and the actual amount by which the debt is amortized. An amortization schedule for the aforementioned transaction, for instance, might be prepared somewhat as shown here.

	Annual Payment A	Interest on Unpaid Balance B		Amortization of Principal (A minus B) C	Balance of Principal Unpaid D
Principal					$4000.00
End of 1st year	$898.51	4% of $4000.00	$160.00	$738.51	3261.49
End of 2nd year	898.51	4% of 3261.49	130.46	768.05	2493.44
End of 3rd year	898.51	4% of 2493.44	99.74	798.77	1694.67
End of 4th year	898.51	4% of 1694.67	67.79	830.72	863.95
End of 5th year	898.51	4% of 863.95	34.56	863.95	
	$4492.55		$492.55	$4000.00	

Note that the sum of the annual payments (column A) includes total interest charges of $492.55, which checks perfectly with the total of column B, and that the fifth annual payment completes the amortization of the principal of $4000.00 (column C).

Example 1: A property owner decides to extend his holdings, and purchases a parcel of land costing $120,000.00. He pays $20,000.00 in cash and agrees to pay the balance with interest at $3\frac{1}{2}\%$ per annum, compounded annually, in 10 equal installments. What is the sum of each annual payment?

> *Solution:* $3\frac{1}{2}\%$ per annum, compounded annually, is equivalent to $3\frac{1}{2}\%$ per interest period. And since the payments are to be made annually, the number of interest periods is 10.
>
> Referring to Table XXI, $3\frac{1}{2}\%$ column, line 10, we are given the figure 0.12024137 which, multiplied by $100,000.00 (the balance due), equals $12,024.14, the amount of the annual payment.

It sometimes happens that after making several equal annual payments to settle an obligation, the debtor finds that he is able to liquidate the balance of the unpaid principal by a cash payment. Such an example follows.

Example 2: K. T. Archer arranges to settle a debt of $1800.00 by 6 equal annual payments with interest at $4\frac{1}{2}\%$ per annum, compounded annually. After making the third payment he decides to make a cash settlement. Compute (a) the annual payment, and (b) the sum that will liquidate the balance of the debt immediately after the third annual payment has been made.

> *Solution:* Since the interest rate is $4\frac{1}{2}\%$ per annum, compounded annually, and the number of payments is 6, we refer to line 6 in the $4\frac{1}{2}\%$ column of Table XXI, where we read 0.19387839, and $1800.00 (the debt) multiplied by this figure gives us $348.98, the sum of the annual payment.
>
> After making 3 payments there are still 3 to be made: one due 1 year hence, another due 2 years hence, and the third 3 years hence. It is obvious, therefore, that a cash settlement of these three sums will constitute their present worth. So we refer to Table XX, "Present Value of Annuity of 1 per Period,"

where on line 3 in the $4\frac{1}{2}\%$ column, we are given the figure 2.74896435. Multiplying this figure by $348.98 (the annual payment) we obtain $959.33, the sum that will liquidate the balance of the debt immediately after the third annual payment has been made.

Example 3: A construction company agrees to amortize a loan of $200,000.00 in 30 equal semiannual payments with interest at $4\frac{1}{2}\%$ per annum, compounded semiannually. What is the sum of each payment?

Solution: $4\frac{1}{2}\%$ per annum, compounded semiannually, is equivalent to $2\frac{1}{4}\%$ per 6-month period.

Referring to Table XXI, $2\frac{1}{4}\%$ column, line 30 (since there are to be 30 semiannual payments), we read 0.04619934, which figure, multiplied by $200,000.00, equals $9239.87, the sum of each payment.

Problems

1. The purchase price of a house is $23,500.00, of which amount $3500.00 is payable in cash, and the balance in 8 equal annual installments with interest at $4\frac{1}{2}\%$ per annum. What is the sum of the annual installment? *Ans.* $3032.19.

2. If a debt of $12,000.00 is to be settled in 10 equal annual payments with interest at $3\frac{1}{2}\%$ per annum, compounded annually, what sum will be represented by the annual payment? *Ans.* $1442.89.

3. Compute the sum of a semiannual payment to be made for 12 years with interest at 5% per annum, compounded semiannually, to liquidate a debt of $7500.00. *Ans.* $419.35.

4. An insurance company offers a beneficiary the choice between a cash settlement of $8000.00 and a monthly payment for the next 10 years. If money is worth 5% per annum, compounded monthly, what should be the sum of the monthly payment? *Ans.* $84.85.

5. A debt of $5500.00 is to be settled by equal monthly payments with interest over a period of 6 years. Assuming money to be worth 6% per annum, compounded monthly, what will the sum be of each monthly payment? *Ans.* $91.15.

157. The Difference Between Nominal and Effective Rates of Interest. In order not to confuse the reader, interest rates were specified thus far in this chapter as so much per annum, compounded so many times per year—for example, 4 per cent per annum, compounded annually; $3\frac{1}{2}$ per cent per annum, compounded semiannually; 3 per cent per annum, compounded quarterly; or 5 per cent per annum, compounded monthly. In actual practice, however, shorter descriptive terms are used.

Thus when interest is computed *more often than once a year*, the rate only need be stated, followed by the method of computation —e.g., 5 per cent per annum, compounded semiannually, would be stated as 5 per cent, convertible (or compounded) semiannually. An interest rate of 3 per cent per annum, compounded quarterly, could be stated simply as 3 per cent, compounded quarterly. And so on. Interest rates that are computed more often than once a year are known as *nominal*.

When interest is computed once a year, or when it is desired to state the annual equivalent of a rate computed more often than once a year, the rate is followed by the word *effective*. A rate of 4 per cent compounded semiannually, for example, may be expressed as 4.04 per cent effective.

Table XVII, "Compound Amount of 1," discussed in Art. 149, affords an interesting study of this subject. While this table shows the accumulation of an investment of 1, the amount of interest earned on the investment can be obtained simply by deducting 1 from the figure shown. And once we know the amount of interest earned in two semiannual periods, four quarterly periods, or twelve monthly periods, we have the equivalent effective rate. Thus to find the equivalent effective rate of 3 per cent, compounded semiannually, we refer to line 2 (because there are two semiannual periods in a year) in the $1\frac{1}{2}\%$ column (because 3 per cent per annum compounded semiannually is equivalent to $1\frac{1}{2}$ per cent per 6-month period), where we read 1.03022500. Subtracting from this figure 1 (1 representing the amount of the investment) we obtain 0.03022500. This means that the total amount of interest earned in one year on $1.00 at 3 per cent compounded semiannually is $0.030225, which may be expressed as 3.0225 per cent effective.

Example 1: A rate of 6% compounded semiannually is equivalent to what effective rate?

Solution: 6% compounded semiannually is equivalent to 3% per 6-month period.

To find the interest earned in one year (that is, in 2 periods) we refer to Table XVII, 3% column, line 2, where the figure given is 1.06090000. Subtracting 1 from this figure leaves 0.0609, which means that $1.00 invested for one year at the specified rate of interest will earn $0.0609, or 6.09%. The answer, therefore, is 6.09% effective.

Example 2: A rate of 5% compounded monthly is equivalent to what effective rate?

Solution: 5% compounded monthly is equivalent to $\frac{5}{12}$% per month. Since there are 12 months in a year, we look on line 12 in the $\frac{5}{12}$% column of Table XVII, where we read 1.05116190. Subtracting 1 from this figure, we find that $1.00 invested for one year at the specified interest rate will earn $0.0511619, or 5.11619%. The answer, therefore, is 5.11619% effective.

The reader is reminded that the figures in the table are given to the eighth decimal place in order to facilitate computation of large amounts. The importance of this arrangement will be appreciated when it is desired, for example, to compare the income under two different nominal rates, as illustrated by the following:

Example 3: What is the difference between the equivalent effective rates of $5\frac{1}{2}$%, computed semiannually, and 5%, computed quarterly?

Solution: $5\frac{1}{2}$% computed semiannually is equivalent to $2\frac{3}{4}$% per 6-month period. Referring to Table XVII, $2\frac{3}{4}$% column, line 2, we read 1.05575625, so that the equivalent effective rate is 5.575625%. 5% computed quarterly is equivalent to $1\frac{1}{4}$% per 3-month period. Referring to Table XVII, $1\frac{1}{4}$% column, line 4, we read 1.05094534, so that the equivalent effective rate here is 5.094534%. The effective equivalent of the $5\frac{1}{2}\%$ nominal rate therefore exceeds the effective equivalent of the 5% nominal rate by .481091%.

Attention is called to the fact that, although on an investment of a small amount like $10.00 an interest differential of .481091 per cent may be of little consequence, it may be important in the case of an investment amounting to $10,000.00, where the cash value of the difference would be $48.11.

It is interesting to note that the shorter the conversion period the greater the equivalent effective rate. Thus while 4 per cent compounded semiannually is equivalent to 4.04 per cent effective, 4 per cent compounded quarterly is equivalent to 4.060401 per cent—a difference of .0204 per cent.

PROBLEMS

1. What is the effective equivalent of $3\frac{1}{2}\%$ compounded semi-annually? *Ans.* 3.530625%.

2. What is the effective equivalent of $4\frac{1}{2}\%$ compounded quarterly? *Ans.* 4.576509%.

3. What is the effective equivalent of 6% compounded monthly? *Ans.* 6.167781%.

4. Compute the difference between the interest earned on $1000.00 at 4%, compounded quarterly, for 3 years, and the interest earned on the same amount invested for the same time at 4% effective. *Ans.* $1.97.

5. Compute the difference between the interest earned on $2500.00 at 3%, compounded semiannually, for 8 years, and the interest earned on the same amount invested for the same time at 3% effective.
Ans. $5.53.

6. Compute the difference between the interest earned on $4000.00 at 5%, compounded monthly, for 4 years, and the interest earned on the same amount invested for the same time at 5% effective. *Ans.* $21.56.

158. Brief Review of the Five Tables Discussed in This Chapter. Because of the infinite variety of problems that can be so easily solved by their use, it will be of value to make a collective study of these tables. A good mental conception of their relation to one another will help immensely in gaining the intimate acquaintance that will make it possible to quickly couple the right table with any problem.

If the reader has had any misgivings in his study of the subject of annuities, his worries in all likelihood will soon be found to have been needless. Let us begin by looking over the table headings.

Table XVII. Compound amount of 1
Table XVIII. Present value of 1
Table XIX. Amount of annuity of 1 per period
Table XX. Present value of annuity of 1 per period
Table XXI. Periodical payment of annuity
               whose present value is 1

A glance at the headings reveals some interesting facts: The tables can be separated into two groups—one which deals with a *single sum or payment* (Tables XVII and XVIII); the other which deals with a *series of sums paid or deposited* at equal intervals of time (Tables XIX, XX and XXI).

The Tables That Deal with a Single Sum. It will be recalled that Table XVII is concerned with a sum whose value at the beginning is known and whose *value at the end of a specified time is to be determined*, whereas Table XVIII deals with a sum whose value at the end of a specified time is known and whose *value at the beginning is to be determined*. So that to know which table to use in any problem dealing with one sum, it is but necessary to ask oneself whether the value to be determined is to be at the beginning or the end of the specified time.

The Tables That Deal with a Series of Sums Paid at Equal Intervals of Time. Having in mind the opposite relation of the two tables in the first group, a brief glance at the headings of the first two tables in the second group will reveal a similar oppositeness in their character. Table XIX deals with sums whose value at the time they are paid is known in advance, and whose *value at the end of a specified time is to be determined*, whereas Table XX is concerned with sums whose value at the end of a specified time is known, and whose *total value at the beginning of that time* (that is, when the series of payments is begun) *is to be determined*. And here, too, we need but ask ourselves whether the value of the series of payments is to be determined as of the beginning of the specified time or the end.

The words *present value* in the headings of Tables XVIII and XX simplify the problem of table selection, for present value means the value at the *beginning* of the specified time.

And since the headings of the first four tables specify "of 1" and "of 1 per period," it is easy to see that the one group deals with a single payment and the other group with several payments.

In the same way the separate functions of Table XVII ("Compound Amount of 1") and Table XIX ("Amount of Annuity of 1 per Period") will be readily seen. Table XVII shows the future value (that is, the sum of principal and interest) of a *single* sum, whereas Table XIX indicates the future value (principal and interest) of a *series of payments*.

Thus it will be seen that the tables whose headings do not include the words *present value* deal with future values, and that one of the two tables deals with a single sum and the other with a series of sums.

There now remains Table XXI. The first words in the heading help to separate this table from the others. "Periodical payments of annuity" tells us in unmistakable words that this table is concerned with payments to be made at equal intervals of time, and the words "whose present value is 1" indicate that the sum of the single amount which is to be broken up into equal payments, is known.

A rereading of this article will help to gain a desirable mental picture of the different functions of the five tables, and it is suggested that the reader look over the foregoing paragraphs once again before tackling the problems that follow.

Problems

Read each problem carefully. Then indicate which table you would use to find the answer. Do not work the problems themselves. Show only the table number.

1. Find the value at the end of 15 years of an annuity of $1250.00 invested each year at $2\frac{3}{4}\%$ effective.   *Ans.* Table XIX.

2. If I am to receive $5000.00 five years from now, what is the value of this sum to me today, if money is worth $3\frac{1}{2}\%$ effective?

Ans. Table XVIII.

3. A debtor agrees to settle an account of $8000.00 by 16 equal quarterly payments with interest at $4\frac{1}{2}\%$, compounded quarterly. What is the sum of each payment?   *Ans.* Table XXI.

4. At his son's fifth birthday a father decides to put away a sum of money so that it will have accumulated to $7500.00 when his son is 21 years of age. If money is worth 3%, compounded quarterly, how much should he put away?   *Ans.* Table XVIII.

5. A beneficiary to an estate is informed that he is to receive semi-annual payments of $500.00 for the next 10 years. If money is worth $3\frac{1}{2}\%$, compounded semiannually, what is the present worth of the annuity?

Ans. Table XX.

6. An annuity of $100.00 a month is deposited promptly upon its receipt to an account which earns interest at the rate of 5%, compounded monthly. What will the accumulation be worth at the end of 5 years?

Ans. Table XIX.

7. The asking price of a house is $20,000.00, of which $5000.00 is payable in cash, the balance in 5 equal annual installments with interest at 4%. Estimate the sum of the annual installment.   *Ans.* Table XXI.

8. An insurance company has a plan under which it agrees to make a payment of $200.00 every month for 20 years. What is the value of this annuity to the person who is to receive the payments on the day that the plan goes into effect, if money is worth 5%, compounded monthly?

Ans. Table XX.

9. A creditor is given a note for $2000.00 which is a promise to pay $250.00 every 3 months with interest at 4%, compounded quarterly. Assuming that payments will be made as due, what is the present worth of the note?   *Ans.* Table XX.

10. A savings account shows a balance on Jan. 1, 1947 of $7500.00. If the bank's interest rate of 2%, compounded quarterly, remains unchanged, and assuming that no deposits or withdrawals have been made in the meantime, what will the balance be on Jan. 1, 1952?

Ans. Table XVII.

11. The sum of $10,000.00 is deposited to a fund which earns interest at the rate of $4\frac{1}{2}\%$, compounded quarterly. To what amount will this deposit have increased at the end of 8 years?   *Ans.* Table XVII.

12. How much would have to be paid every 3 months to settle a debt of $6000.00 in 10 equal quarterly payments which included interest at 4%, compounded quarterly?   *Ans.* Table XXI.

13. If $400.00 is deposited at the end of every 6 months to a fund which earns interest at the rate of $3\frac{1}{2}\%$, compounded semiannually, what will the accumulation be worth at the end of 10 years? *Ans.* Table XIX.

14. On his daughter's second birthday a father decides to put away a sum of money each year so that he will have an accumulation of $10,000.00 to spend for her education when she is 17 years of age. If money is worth $3\frac{1}{2}\%$ effective, how much should he put away each year? (Hint: First find the present value of the $10,000.00, then use another table to find the periodical payments.) *Ans.* Tables XVIII and XXI.

CHAPTER XXII

STOCKS AND BONDS

Because the role played by securities in the financial and economic life of the nation is so vitally important, it may be to the considerable advantage of the reader to familiarize himself with some of the facts revealed by a study of the mathematics of stocks and bonds.

It is the purpose of this chapter to accomplish this for the reader with a minimum of discomfort to him. No pretense is made that the treatment is exhaustive, and it is not presumed to encompass here more than the lighter side of the subject. Indeed, the material can be expanded to book size.

Although our principal concern will be a discussion of some of the phases of the mathematics of securities, a few articles of a general nature have been included to help round out the reader's rudimentary knowledge of stocks and bonds. Many will doubtless read with particular interest the little-known facts about the advantages of listing and the listing requirements and costs as discussed in Arts. 170 and 171.

159. Some Important Differences Between Stocks and Bonds. The basic difference between a bond and a stock certificate is that the former represents a loan at a specified rate of interest, whereas the latter represents ownership in the corporation without any guarantee of income or return of the purchase price. The holder of a bond knows exactly what his investment will earn for him from one interest period to the next; the holder of a stock certificate does not know from one hour to the next whether the value of his investment will go up or down, or (except in the case of preferred stock) what dividend it will earn, if any, for the current period.

Bonds of well-established corporations involve comparatively little risk. The holder of a stock certificate—as the stock market crash of 1929 proved—may lose a sizable part of his investment or receive no dividends for an indefinite period; on the other hand, he may make a considerable fortune on his investment.

Another important difference is that bonds have a *maturity* date—that is, they specify a date on which a stated sum, known as the *redemption price*, is to be paid to the holder. Stocks do not have a maturity value and, consequently, have no maturity date.

A dividend check received by a shareholder represents the income derived from stock. Dividends are usually declared every three months, though some are declared semiannually, and a few monthly. The income derived from bonds is known as interest. Bond interest is always computed on the face value and at the rate specified in the security. As a rule, interest on bonds is paid by means of coupons that are cut from the bonds as they come due, and presented for payment. A bond-interest coupon can be deposited in a bank account just like a check or any other remittance.

Interest on bonds is usually paid semiannually, and the months of the interest periods are designated by initial letters as follows:

J–J	Interest payable on January 1 and July 1
F–A	Interest payable on February 1 and August 1
M–S	Interest payable on March 1 and September 1
A–O	Interest payable on April 1 and October 1
M–N	Interest payable on May 1 and November 1
J–D	Interest payable on June 1 and December 1

160. How Stocks and Bonds Are Quoted. Quotations on stocks are made in dollars and cents or in dollars and fractions of a dollar per share. Thus the price of a share quoted at $23.50 may also be expressed as $23\frac{1}{2}$. In the tables of transactions published in the financial sections of the newspapers, as we shall see later, the prices are always shown in the fractional form.

A share may have a par value of only $1.00 or less, and a stock price quotation is a quotation of the actual price; a stock price quotation of $6\frac{1}{2}$, for example, means $6.50 per share, and a stock price quotation of $227\frac{1}{8}$ means 227.12\frac{1}{2}$. Bonds, on the other hand, generally have a face value of $1000.00, and bond prices are usually quoted on a basis of 100, and—as in the case of stocks— to the nearest eighth of a dollar. A few typical examples of bond quotations are $102\frac{1}{2}$, $102\frac{3}{8}$, $98\frac{5}{8}$, $101\frac{1}{8}$, $101\frac{3}{4}$. A $1000.00 bond quoted at $102\frac{1}{2}$ would, therefore, cost $1025.00; quoted at $102\frac{3}{8}$, the cost would be $1037.50; at $98\frac{5}{8}$, $986.25; and so on. Similarly, a $500.00 bond quoted at the foregoing prices would cost, respectively, $512.50, $518.75, $493.13, and so on.

It was stated in the preceding paragraph that bonds are quoted to the nearest eighth of a dollar. The one exception to this rule is government bonds, which are listed to the nearest $\frac{1}{32}$. It is interesting to note the way in which the prices are quoted. The quotation of a government bond selling for $102\frac{7}{32}$ may be represented by the figure 102.7; the bond price of $103\frac{15}{32}$ may be quoted as 103.15; $104\frac{1}{2}$ as 104.16 (.16 because $\frac{1}{2}$ equals $\frac{16}{32}$). When reading quotations of government bonds care should, therefore, be taken to read the figures after the decimal point not as cents, but as so many thirty-seconds of a point.

The face value of a bond, as the face value of a stock, is known as *par*. So that a bond whose market value is above 100 is said to be selling at *above par*, or at a *premium*; a bond whose market value is below 100 is said to be selling *below par*, or at a *discount*.

161. Why a Bond May Sell at a Premium or Discount. If one were to choose between depositing $1000.00 in a savings bank which pays interest at the rate of 2 per cent per annum and purchasing a $1000.00 bond which bears interest at only $1\frac{1}{2}$ per cent per annum, it would not take very long to decide that the wiser plan would be to deposit the money in the savings bank. On the other hand, if the bank's interest rate were only $1\frac{1}{2}$ per cent, or if the rate of interest in the open market were no higher than $1\frac{1}{2}$ per cent, and the bond rate was 2 per cent, it would be more profitable to buy the bond.

It is clear, then, that when the interest rate in the open market is higher than the interest rate specified in the bond, something must be done about the bond to attract buyers. And what happens is this: the bond is offered at a *discount*—it is offered at a price below 100, and at as low a price as will insure for the purchaser a return comparable to the open market rate of interest. In other words, the price of the bond is so reduced that the lower-than-market-rate of interest specified in the bond, when paid on the investment of *less* than 100, will be equivalent to the return received on an investment of 100 at the market rate of interest. (It should be remembered that bond interest is paid on the face value of the bond, so that $1\frac{1}{2}$ per cent interest paid on a bond having a face value of $1000.00 *and purchased at a discount*, would exceed the income on an investment of $1000.00 at the same rate of interest.)

Bonds sell at a *premium* for exactly the opposite reason that they sell at a discount. When a bond bears interest at a rate higher than the interest rate in the open market, it is obvious that there would be many eager purchasers. In these circumstances, the price of the bond is increased. It is increased, so that the interest rate, while paid on the face value, actually represents a return on a larger investment.

In order that this may be clearly understood, think of an offer of a bond bearing interest at 6 per cent at a time when money is worth only 3 per cent. It is obvious that one would jump at the opportunity to purchase a bond whose interest rate is twice the rate in the open market. So something is done to reduce the investor's return. Since the interest rate specified in the bond cannot be changed, and since interest is always paid on the face value, the purchaser is expected to pay a higher price—that is, he is expected to pay a premium.

Regardless of whether a bond is purchased at a premium, at a discount, or at par, the interest specified in the bond is paid on the par value. Thus if the purchase price of a $1000.00, 6 per cent bond is $1100.00, the investor receives 6 per cent on only $1000.00, not on $1100.00, so that his return is *less* than 6 per cent on the actual amount of the investment. Similarly, if the purchase price of a $1000.00, 6 per cent bond is $920.00, the investor receives 6 per cent on $1000.00, not on $920.00, so that his return is *greater* than 6 per cent on the actual amount of the investment.

Since a comparison was made in the opening paragraph of this article between the relative advantages of an investment in the purchase of a bond and the deposit of a similar sum in a savings bank, it may be said, parenthetically, that it is customary for some savings banks to credit interest only on the amount on deposit at the beginning of the interest period. The result is that if funds are withdrawn before the last day of the period for which interest is computed, the accrued interest on such funds is forfeited; whereas the bondholder receives interest on his investment from the day of purchase to the day of sale.

In the articles that follow the rate of interest specified in the bond will be referred to as the *bond rate*, and the rate of interest representing the true income produced by the bond will be expressed as the *yield rate*.

162. How to Find the Purchase Price of a Bond When the Bond Rate and the Yield Rate Are Computed for the Same Intervals. The purchase price of a bond is determined by two considerations: (1) the present value of the redemption price, and (2) the present value of the interest payments.

The redemption price, as has been said, is the sum paid to the bondholder upon the maturity date of the bond. To find the present value of the redemption price we refer to Table XVIII, "Present Value of 1," on p. 509. The figure given in the per cent column which corresponds to the equivalent yield rate per interest period on the line whose number represents the number of interest periods is then multiplied by the redemption price, and the product thus obtained equals the present value of the redemption price.

The present value of the interest payments is determined in similar fashion. Having found the number of interest periods and the equivalent yield rate per period, we refer to Table XX, "Present Value of Annuity of 1 per Period," on p. 529. The figure obtained here is then multiplied by the amount of the interest payment.

It is important to remember that we are concerned in this article with calculations in which the bond rate and the yield rate are computed for the same intervals—that is, if the bond interest is payable semiannually, the yield rate too is based on a semiannual period.

Let us begin with a simple illustration.

Example 1: Find the purchase price of a $1000.00, 5% bond redeemable at par in 10 years, with interest, payable semiannually, to yield 3 per cent.

> *Solution:* We first summarize the figures in the problem as follows:
>
> The redemption price is $1000.00.
>
> 3% payable semiannually is equivalent to $1\frac{1}{2}$% per 6-month period.
>
> In 10 years there are 20 semiannual periods.
>
> The semiannual interest payment is $2\frac{1}{2}$% of $1000.00, or $25.00.

Step 1: To find the present value of the redemption price we refer to Table XVIII ("Present Value of 1"), $1\frac{1}{2}$% column (because that is the yield rate equivalent per 6-month period), line 20 (the number of interest payments), where we read 0.74247042. Since the redemption price is $1000.00, we simply multiply $1000.00 by this figure, which equals $742.47.

Step 2: To find the present value of the 20 interest payments we refer to Table XX ("Present Value of Annuity of 1 per Period"), $1\frac{1}{2}$% column, line 20, where we are given 17.16863879. Now $25.00 (the amount of each interest payment) multiplied by this figure equals $429.22.

Step 3: Present value of the redemption price   = $ 742.47
Present value of the interest payments   =   429.22
_____

Present value, or purchase price, of the bond   = $1171.69

Let us suppose that the bond in the foregoing illustration matured in 15 instead of in 10 years.

Example 2: Find the purchase price of a $1000.00, 5% bond redeemable at par in 15 years, with interest, payable semiannually, to yield 3 per cent.

Solution: The redemption price is $1000.00.

3% payable semiannually is equivalent to $1\frac{1}{2}$% per 6-month period.

In 15 years there are 30 semiannual periods.

The semiannual interest payment is $2\frac{1}{2}$% of $1000.00, or $25.00.

Step 1: Referring to Table XVIII, $1\frac{1}{2}$% column, line 30, we read 0.63976243, and $1000.00 (the redemption price) multiplied by this figure equals $639.76, the present value of the redemption price.

Step 2: Table XX, $1\frac{1}{2}$% column, line 30, gives us 24.01583801, and $25.00 (the amount of each interest payment) multiplied by this figure equals $600.40, the present value of the 30 interest payments.

Step 3:
Present value of the redemption price	=	$ 639.76
Present value of the interest payments	=	600.40

Present value, or purchase price, of the
bond   = $1240.16

Note the interesting contrasts between the present values of the bond which matured in 10 years (Example 1) and the bond which matured in 15 years (Example 2). The present value of the redemption price of the first bond is *greater* than that of the second, which is understandable, for the sooner the bond is to be redeemed the more it is worth. On the other hand, the present value of the interest payments is *less* when the bond matures in 10 years, for the shorter the life of the bond the fewer the number of interest payments. Note that as the net result the present value of the bond maturing in 15 years is $68.47 greater than that of the 10-year bond.

Let us now see what the difference would be if the bond maturing in 10 years yielded 4 per cent payable semiannually, instead of 3 per cent payable semiannually.

Example 3: Find the purchase price of a $1000.00, 5% bond redeemable at par in 10 years, with interest payable semiannually to yield 4%.

Solution: The redemption price is $1000.00.

                4% payable semiannually is equivalent to 2% per 6-month period.

                In 10 years there are 20 semiannual periods.

                The semiannual interest payment is $2\frac{1}{2}\%$ of $1000.00, or $25.00.

Step 1: Referring to Table XVIII, 2% column, line 20, we read 0.67297133, and $1000.00 (the redemption price) multiplied by this figure equals $672.97, the present value of the redemption price.

Step 2: Table XX, 2% column, line 20, gives us 16.35143334, and $25.00 (the amount of each interest payment) multiplied by this figure equals $408.79, the present value of the 20 interest payments.

Step 3: Present value of the redemption price   = $ 672.97
       Present value of the interest payments   =   408.79

       Present value, or purchase price, of the
       bond   = $1081.76

Note that the purchase price of the bond in the foregoing illustration, in which the yield rate is 4 per cent, is $89.93 less than the purchase price of the bond in Example 1, in which the yield rate is only 3 per cent, which is understandable, for the smaller the difference between the bond rate and the yield rate the smaller the amount of the premium.

In the three problems we have worked thus far the bond is redeemable at par. We will now take an example in which the redemption value is above par.

Example 4: Find the purchase price of a $1000.00, 4% bond redeemable at $1100.00 in 12 years, with interest, payable semi-annually, to yield 3%.

Solution: The redemption price is $1100.00.

> 3% payable semiannually is equivalent to $1\frac{1}{2}$% per 6-month period.
>
> In 12 years there are 24 semiannual periods.
>
> The semiannual interest payment is 2% of $1000.00, or $20.00.

Step 1: Referring to Table XVIII, $1\frac{1}{2}$% column, line 24, we read 0.69954392, and $1100.00 (the redemption price) multiplied by this figure equals $769.50, the present value of the redemption price.

Step 2: Table XX, $1\frac{1}{2}$% column, line 24, gives us 20.03040537, and $20.00 (the amount of each interest payment) multiplied by this figure equals $400.61, the present value of the 24 interest payments.

Step 3: Present value of the redemption price   = $ 769.50
Present value of the interest payments   =   400.61

Present value, or purchase price, of the
bond   = $1170.11

The relation of the bond rate to the yield rate does not affect the procedure in finding the purchase price. Thus, although in the foregoing example the yield rate was lower than the bond rate, the yield rate in the example that follows is greater than the bond rate.

Example 5: Find the purchase price of a $1000.00, 2% bond redeemable at $1030.00 in 8 years, with interest, payable semi-annually, to yield 3%.

Solution: The redemption price is $1030.00.

> 3% payable semiannually is equivalent to $1\frac{1}{2}$% per 6-month period.
>
> In 8 years there are 16 semiannual periods.

The semiannual interest payment is 1% of $1000.00, or $10.00.

Step 1: Referring to Table XVIII, $1\frac{1}{2}$% column, line 16, we read 0.78803104, and $1030.00 (the redemption price) multiplied by this figure equals $811.67, the present value of the redemption price.

Step 2: Table XX, $1\frac{1}{2}$% column, line 16, gives us 14.13126405, and $10.00 (the amount of each interest payment) multiplied by this figure equals $141.31.

Step 3: Present value of the redemption price   = $811.67
Present value of the interest payments   =   141.31

Present value, or purchase price, of the bond = $952.98

To guard against possible confusion with respect to the two interest rates (the bond rate and the yield rate), it should be remembered that when referring to the tables we are concerned with the equivalent *yield* rate. We are interested in the bond rate only to determine the amount of the interest payment, which amount is multiplied by the figure obtained in Table XX to find the present value of the sum of the interest payments.

PROBLEMS

Find the purchase price of each of the following bonds. Assume in each case that the interest is payable semiannually, and that the yield rate is likewise computed on a semiannual basis.

1. A $1000.00, 5% bond redeemable in 15 years at par, with interest to yield 4% per annum.   *Ans.* $1111.98.

2. A $1000.00, 3% bond redeemable in 20 years at par, with interest to yield $2\frac{1}{2}$% per annum.   *Ans.* $1078.32.

3. A $10,000.00, $4\frac{1}{2}$% bond redeemable in 8 years at par, to yield $3\frac{1}{2}$%per annum.   *Ans.* $10,692.53.

4. A $500.00 bond paying $3\frac{1}{2}$% F–A, and redeemable at 106 in 10 years, to yield 3% per annum. (Hint: F–A simply means that interest is payable on Feb. 1 and Aug. 1., as explained in Art. 159.)   *Ans.* $543.73.

5. A $1000.00, 3% bond redeemable in 11 years at par, to yield 4% per annum. *Ans.* $911.71.

6. A $1000.00, 2½% bond redeemable in 18 years at $1200.00, to yield 3% per annum. *Ans.* $1047.87.

7. A $1000.00, 2½% bond redeemable in 14 years at $1150.00, to yield 4% per annum. *Ans.* $926.55.

8. A $5000.00, 3½% bond redeemable in 16 years at $5600.00, to yield 5% per annum. *Ans.* $4452.92.

9. A $1000.00 bond bearing semiannual coupons of $25.00 each, redeemable in 15 years at 112, with interest to yield 3½% per annum. (Hint: A $1000.00 bond bearing $25.00 semiannual interest coupons is obviously a 5% bond, for the annual equivalent of a semiannual payment of $25.00 is $50.00, and $50.00 is to $1000.00 as 5 is to 100. Also, a $1000.00 bond redeemable at 112 has a redemption value at maturity of 10 times 112, or $1120.00.) *Ans.* $1245.20.

10. A $5000.00 bond bearing semiannual coupons of $75.00 each, redeemable in 10 years at 108, with interest to yield 2½% per annum. (Hint: A $5000.00 bond bearing $75.00 semiannual interest coupons is obviously a 3% bond, for the annual equivalent of a semiannual payment of $75.00 is $150.00, and $150.00 is to $5000.00 as 3 is to 100. Also, a $5000.00 bond redeemable at 108 has a redemption value at maturity of 50 times 108, or $5400.00.) *Ans.* $5532.00.

163. An Alternative Method of Finding the Purchase Price of a Bond When the Bond Rate and the Yield Rate Are Computed for the Same Intervals. As was seen in the preceding article, the purchase price of a bond is *above* par when the bond rate of interest is greater than the yield rate, and *below* par when the bond rate of interest is less than the yield rate.

When the bond rate of interest is greater than the yield rate, the amount by which the actual interest payment exceeds the amount earned by the yield rate is really an annuity. And it will be readily seen that the present worth of this annuity constitutes the amount which the purchaser should pay in excess of the redemption value. In other words, the purchase price of the bond will exceed the redemption value by the present worth of the aforementioned annuity. A few examples will make this clear, and we will take for our first illustration the figures in Example 1 in the preceding article.

Example 1: Find the purchase price of a $1000.00, 5% bond redeemable at par in 10 years, with interest, payable semiannually, to yield 3%.

Solution: The redemption price is $1000.00.

3% payable semiannually is equivalent to $1\frac{1}{2}\%$ per 6-month period.

In 10 years there are 20 semiannual periods.

The semiannual interest payment is $2\frac{1}{2}\%$ of $1000.00, or $25.00.

Step 1: Amount of semiannual interest payment   = $25.00
Yield—$1\frac{1}{2}\%$ on $1000.00 (redemption value) =   15.00

Excess of interest payment over amount
earned by yield rate   = $10.00

Step 2: $10.00—the amount by which the interest payment exceeds the interest earned by the yield rate—is the amount of the annuity. So we refer to Table XX, ("Present Value of Annuity of 1 per Period"), $1\frac{1}{2}\%$ column (because that is the yield rate equivalent per 6-month period), line 20 (the number of interest payments), where we read 17.16863879, and multiplying $10.00 (the difference between the two interest computations) by this figure gives us $171.69. This is the amount which the purchaser is expected to pay for the privilege of receiving interest payments at a rate which is higher than the yield rate. The amount of $171.69 is therefore added to the redemption value (which in this case is $1000.00), giving us a purchase price of $1171.69, which agrees with the figure arrived at in the preceding article.

Note the interesting fact that this method of computation calls for the use of only one annuity table (Table XX), whereas under the method considered in the preceding article it is necessary to use two tables (Tables XVIII and XX) and therefore to make two separate computations.

Let us now take a problem in which the redemption value is greater than par, using for this illustration the figures in Example 4 in the preceding article.

Example 2: Find the purchase price of a $1000.00, 4% bond redeemable at $1100.00 in 12 years, with interest, payable semiannually, to yield 3%.

Solution: The redemption price is $1100.00.

3% payable semiannually is equivalent to $1\frac{1}{2}$% per 6-month period.

In 12 years there are 24 semiannual periods.

The semiannual interest payment is 2% of $1000.00, or $20.00.

Step 1: Amount of semiannual interest payment   = $20.00
Yield—$1\frac{1}{2}$% on $1100.00 (redemption value) =   16.50

Excess of interest payment over amount earned by yield rate   = $ 3.50

Step 2: Referring to Table XX, $1\frac{1}{2}$% column, line 24, we read 20.03040537, and $3.50 multiplied by this figure equals $70.11. And this is the amount which the purchaser will be expected to pay for the privilege of receiving an interest payment which exceeds the amount earned by the yield rate by $3.50.

The amount of $70.11 is therefore added to the redemption value of $1100.00, so that the purchase price, or present value of the bond, is $1170.11, which is the figure obtained in the solution to Example 4 in the preceding article.

In dealing with bonds purchased at a discount, the procedure is the same, except that the present value of the annuity, instead of being added to the redemption value, is deducted. For an illustration we will take the figures in Example 5 in the preceding article.

Example 3: Find the purchase price of a $1000.00, 2% bond redeemable at $1030.00 in 8 years, with interest, payable semi-annually, to yield 3%.

Solution: The redemption price is $1030.00.

3% payable semiannually is equivalent to $1\frac{1}{2}$% per 6-month period.

In 8 years there are 16 semiannual periods.

The semiannual interest payment is 1% of $1000.00, or $10.00.

Step 1: Yield—$1\frac{1}{2}$% on $1030.00 (redemption value) = $15.45

Amount of semiannual interest payment   =   10.00

Excess of amount earned by yield rate over the interest payment   = $ 5.45

Step 2: Referring to Table XX, $1\frac{1}{2}$% column, line 16, we read 14.13126405, and $5.45 multiplied by this figure equals $77.02. Here, however, the amount of interest earned by the yield rate *exceeds* the amount of the interest payment, so $77.02 is the amount by which the purchaser will expect to be reimbursed.

From the redemption value of $1030.00 we will therefore *subtract* $77.02, giving us $952.98 as the purchase price of the bond. And this, too, is exactly the figure obtained in the solution to Example 5 in the preceding article.

Readers who have frequent occasion to compute present values on bonds will find it to their considerable advantage to familiarize themselves with both techniques—that is, the method discussed in the preceding article as well as the one discussed here—for the computation by one method will serve as an excellent check on the computation by the other.

Work each of the problems given in Art. 162, by the method considered in this article, and see if you obtain the same answers.

164. An Important Fact to Remember About Premiums and Discounts. It has been explained that a bond is sold at a premium when the bond rate of interest *exceeds* the yield rate, and that it is sold at a discount when the bond rate of interest is *less* than the yield rate. And, as the illustrations in the preceding article showed, the amount of the premium represents the present value—that is, the value at the time of purchase—of the difference between the actual amount of interest paid to the bondholder and the amount of interest he would have received at the yield rate; and that likewise, the amount of the discount represents the present value of the difference between the amount of interest the bondholder would have received at the yield rate and the actual amount of interest paid.

It is the purpose of this article to stress that, for our purposes, the premium on a bond is the difference between the purchase price and the redemption value, and that the discount on a bond is the difference between the redemption value and the purchase price. The premium or discount, in other words, is the difference between the amount paid for the bond and the amount that is to be returned to the purchaser on the date of maturity.

Thus it will be clear that on a bond having a redemption value of $1000.00 and costing $1140.00, the premium is $140.00; that when the redemption value is $1100.00 and the cost $1250.00, the premium is $150.00. Likewise, when the redemption value is $1000.00 and the cost $950.00, the discount is $50.00; and if the redemption value is $1020.00 and the cost $900.00, the discount is $120.00.

It should be further emphasized that a bond premium does not really constitute a loss, since part of the premium is returned to the investor in each interest payment, and by the time the last interest payment has been made the entire premium has been returned to him. Similarly, a discount does not constitute a gain, since part of the discount is, in effect, deducted each time an in-

terest payment is made, and by the time the last interest payment
has been made the entire discount has been accounted for.

This will be clarified still further in the article that follows,
which shows in schedule form the period-to-period effect of premiums and discounts on bonds.

**165. How to Prepare a Schedule for the Amortization of the
Premium and a Schedule for the Accumulation of the Discount.**
When we speak of the yield on an investment we refer to the yield
on the value of the investment at the beginning of the interest
period. Since the value of a bond purchased at a premium is reduced from one period to the next (so that upon the maturity
date the bond value equals the redemption value), and since the
interest earned at the yield rate is based on the actual value of
the investment, it is clear that the amount of interest earned at
the yield rate decreases with each successive period. On the other
hand, the amount of interest paid to the bondholder is the same
throughout the life of the bond, so that the difference between the
bond interest and the yield interest varies at each interest period—
the difference is progressively greater at the end of each period.

As we have seen, it is possible by means of tables to compute
quickly the sum total of these differences. However, since books
of account are required to show the value of an investment at the
end of the fiscal period, it is usual to have a schedule which shows
just how the premium—that is, the sum of the aforementioned
differences—is amortized, or written off, from one interest period
to the next.

Let us prepare such a schedule for a $1000.00, 4 per cent bond
purchased on Jan. 1, 1946, redeemable at par in three years, the
interest to be payable semiannually to yield 3 per cent, compounded semiannually. The purchase price of the bond, computed
by the methods discussed in preceding articles, is $1028.49, or
$1028.486 calculated to the third decimal point. And since the
redemption value is $1000.00, the amount of the premium is
$28.486.

Notice that with each successive interest payment the book value
is reduced to the figure shown in column D, which figure represents
the difference between the actual amount of interest paid and the

amount of interest earned at the yield rate. This difference, as has been explained, represents part of the premium paid by the purchaser for the privilege of receiving interest payments at a

Date	Book Value	Interest at $1\frac{1}{2}\%$ (Yield Rate) on Book Value	Interest at 2% (Bond Rate) on $1000.00	Amortization of Premium (C Minus B)
	A	B	C	D
Jan. 1, 1946	$1028.486	$15.427	$20.00	$4.573
July 1, 1946	1023.913	15.359	20.00	4.641
Jan. 1, 1947	1019.272	15.289	20.00	4.711
July 1, 1947	1014.561	15.218	20.00	4.782
Jan. 1, 1948	1009.779	15.147	20.00	4.853
July 1, 1948	1004.926	15.074	20.00	4.926
Jan. 1, 1949	1000.000			

$28.486

higher-than-the-yield rate. Notice, also, that on Jan. 1, 1949, the maturity date of the bond, the entire amount of the premium, $28.486, has been amortized, and only the redemption value of the bond—namely, $1000.00, is payable to the bondholder.

When a bond is purchased at a discount—that is, when the purchase price is less than the redemption price—the difference between the bond interest and the interest earned at the yield rate is *added* to the book value at the end of the interest period, instead of subtracted. Since in this case the book value increases with each "accumulation of discount," the amount of the discount increases too, because, as has been pointed out, interest at the yield rate is based on the actual value of the investment. And just as the amortization of a premium *reduces* the book value (so that upon the maturity date it equals the redemption value), so the accumulation of discount *increases* the book value (so that upon the maturity date it equals the redemption value).

Let us prepare a schedule for the accumulation of discount on a $1000.00, 2 per cent bond purchased on July 1, 1945, redeemable at 110 in $2\frac{1}{2}$ years, the interest to be payable semiannually to yield $2\frac{1}{2}$ per cent, compounded semiannually. The purchase price, computed by the methods discussed in preceding articles, is \$1081.933. And, since the redemption value is \$1100.00, the amount of the discount is \$18.067.

Date	Book Value	Interest at $1\frac{1}{4}\%$ (Yield Rate) on Book Value	Interest at 1% (Bond Rate) on \$1000.00	Accumulation of Discount (B Minus C)
	A	B	C	D
July 1, 1945	\$1081.933	\$13.524	\$10.00	\$ 3.524
Jan. 1, 1946	1085.457	13.568	10.00	3.568
July 1, 1946	1089.025	13.613	10.00	3.613
Jan. 1, 1947	1092.638	13.658	10.00	3.658
July 1, 1947	1096.296	13.704	10.00	3.704
Jan. 1, 1948	1100.000			

$$\$18.067$$

PROBLEMS

Compute by the method discussed in Art. 163, the purchase price of each of the following bonds. Then construct a schedule for the amortization of the premium or the accumulation of the discount, as the case may be, and see if the total amount of the premium or discount as per column D in the schedule, agrees with your original computation. Assume that the bond rates and yield rates are computed for semiannual periods.

1. A \$1000.00 4% bond redeemable at 110 in 3 years, to yield interest at 3%. *Ans.* \$1119.94.

2. A \$500.00 $3\frac{1}{2}$% bond redeemable at 104 in 4 years, to yield interest at $2\frac{1}{2}$%. *Ans.* \$537.03.

3. A \$5000.00 $3\frac{1}{2}$% bond redeemable at par in 5 years, to yield interest at 3%. *Ans.* \$5115.27.

4. A \$1000.00 $2\frac{1}{2}$% bond redeemable at 102 in $3\frac{1}{2}$ years, to yield interest at 4%. *Ans.* \$968.87.

5. A \$500.00 $3\frac{1}{2}$% bond redeemable at par in 4 years, to yield interest at $4\frac{1}{2}$%. *Ans.* \$481.88.

6. A \$5000.00 4% bond redeemable at par in 3 years, to yield interest at 5%. *Ans.* \$4862.30.

166. The Difference Between the "Current Yield" and "Approximate Net Yield" on a Bond, and How to Compute Their Values. The *current yield* on a bond is the annual income rate, regardless of the maturity date. It is obtained by dividing the annual income by the purchase price. Thus the current yield on a $1000.00, 3 per cent bond purchased at the quotation price of 120, equals $\frac{3}{120}$, or $2\frac{1}{2}$ per cent; and the current yield on a $1000.00, 4 per cent bond costing $1100.00 equals $\frac{4}{110}$, or 3.64 per cent.

The *approximate net yield* on a bond is obtained by a slightly more involved process which consists of three steps: (1) finding the annual income, (2) finding the average cost, and (3) dividing the figure obtained in the first step by the figure obtained in the second.

The annual income is found by subtracting from the sum of the interest payments for the year the average annual amortization of the premium (if the bond is purchased at a premium), or adding to the sum of the interest payments for the year the average accumulation of discount (if the bond is purchased at a discount).

The average cost is found by adding the redemption value to the purchase price, and dividing their sum by 2.

The process, which is clarified in the following illustrations, is really very simple.

Example 1: Find the approximate net yield on a $1000.00, $2\frac{1}{2}\%$ bond redeemable at par in 10 years, and purchased at 108—that is, for $1080.00.

Solution:

Step 1: Sum of the interest payments for one year:
$2\frac{1}{2}\%$ of $1000.00 = $25.00
Less average annual amortization:
$1080.00 (cost) minus $1000.00 (redemption value), divided by 10 (number of years) = 8.00

Annual income = $17.00

Step 2: Average cost: $\frac{1}{2}$ of the sum of $1080.00
(cost) plus $1000.00 (redemption value) = $1040.00

Step 3: Annual income divided by average cost:
$17.00 divided by $1040.00 = 1.63%

Ans. Approximate net yield is 1.63%.

Example 2: Find the approximate net yield on a $1000.00, 4% bond redeemable at $1100.00 in 12 years, and purchased for $1170.11.

Solution:

Step 1: Sum of the interest payments for one year:
4% of $1000.00 = $40.00
Less average annual amortization:
$1170.11 (cost) minus $1100.00 (redemption value), divided by 12 (number of years) = 5.84

___

Annual income = $34.16

Step 2: Average cost: $\frac{1}{2}$ of the sum of $1170.11
(cost) plus $1100.00 (redemption value) = $1135.05

Step 3: Annual income divided by average cost:
$34.16 divided by $1135.05 = 3%.

Ans. Approximate net yield is 3%.

It is interesting to note that the "approximate" net yield obtained in this computation agrees exactly with the yield rate given in Example 4 in Art. 162, whose values were used in this illustration.

Let us consider some problems in which the bond is purchased at a discount.

Example 3: Find the approximate net yield on a $1000.00, $1\frac{1}{2}$% bond redeemable at par in 12 years, and purchased at 94—that is, for $940.00.

Solution:

Step 1: Sum of the interest payments for one
      year: $1\frac{1}{2}\%$ of $1000.00   = \$ 15.00
      Plus average annual accumulation of dis-
      count: \$1000.00 (redemption value)
      minus \$940.00 (cost), divided by 12
      (number of years)   =   5.00

Annual income   = \$ 20.00

Step 2: Average cost: $\frac{1}{2}$ of the sum of \$940.00
      (cost) plus \$1000.00 (redemption value) = \$970.00

Step 3: Annual income divided by average cost:
      \$20.00 divided by \$970.00   = 2.06\%.

Ans. Approximate net yield is 2.06%.

Example 4: Find the approximate net yield on a \$1000.00, 2%
bond redeemable at \$1030.00 in 8 years with interest payable
semiannually, and costing \$952.98.

Solution:

Step 1: Sum of the interest payments for one year:
      2% of \$1000.00   = \$ 20.00
      Plus average annual accumulation of dis-
      count: \$1030.00 (redemption value)
      minus \$952.98 (cost), divided by 8
      (number of years)   =   9.63

Annual income   = \$ 29.63

Step 2: Average cost: $\frac{1}{2}$ of the sum of \$952.98
      (cost) plus \$1030.00 (redemption value) = \$991.49

Step 3: Annual income divided by average cost:
      \$29.63 divided by \$991.49   =   3%

Ans. Approximate net yield is 3%.

The figures in the last illustration were borrowed from Example 5 in Art. 162 where, it will be noted, the yield rate was given as 3 per cent, which agrees perfectly with the figure obtained here as the "approximate" net yield.

It should be emphasized that the technique we have considered here is recommended only when it is desired to find the *approximate* net yield on a bond. It is not recommended for finding the yield rate to the nearest hundredth or thousandth of a per cent. It might be mentioned that exact yield rates, the computation of which requires a knowledge of advanced mathematical principles, can be obtained from tables published especially for this purpose.

PROBLEMS

Compute the answers to the following problems to the nearest hundredth of a per cent.

1. Estimate the current yield on a $1000.00, 5% bond purchased for $1060.00.   *Ans.* 4.72%.

2. Estimate the current yield on a $500.00, 4% bond purchased for $520.00.   *Ans.* 3.85%.

3. Find the approximate net yield on a $1000.00, 3% bond redeemable at par in 9 years, and purchased for $1030.00.   *Ans.* 2.63%.

4. What is the approximate net yield on a $5000.00, $3\frac{1}{2}$% bond redeemable at par in 10 years, and purchased for $5300.00?   *Ans.* 2.82%.

5. What is the approximate net yield on a $1000.00, $2\frac{1}{2}$% bond redeemable at par in 6 years, and purchased for $950.00?   *Ans.* 3.42%.

167. A Simple Way of Calculating Stock Yields. Just as the yield on a bond is calculated on the amount paid for the bond, so the yield on a stock is calculated on the amount paid per share of the stock. The stock yield is equivalent to the current yield, and the current yield is simply the per-cent rate of the return on the purchase price. So that the stock yield is obtained by dividing the sum of the dividends earned on a share in one year by its purchase price.

Example 1: The quarterly dividends on a share of stock are 58 cents, 65 cents, 90 cents, and 87 cents. If the share cost $125.00, what is the stock yield?

Solution: Sum of the quarterly dividends = $3.00

$3.00 divided by $125.00 = 2.4%

Ans. The stock yield is 2.4%.

It is important to note that in calculating stock yields, it is the sum of the dividends earned in the current year, not the per-cent rate, that is divided by the purchase price. Thus when a dividend is declared in the form of a per cent (which means that the amount of the dividend is based on the par value of stock), care should be taken to divide the purchase price into the dollars-and-cents value of the dividends.

Example 2: A share, having a par value of $50.00 and costing $80.00, earns an annual dividend of $4\frac{1}{2}\%$. What is the yield?

Solution: $4\frac{1}{2}\%$ of $50.00 = $2.25

$2.25 divided by $80.00 (the purchase price) = 2.81%

Ans. The stock yield is 2.81%.

Example 3: Find the yield on a stock which maintains an annual dividend of $3\frac{1}{4}\%$, has a par value of $100.00, and was purchased for $186.00.

Solution: $3\frac{1}{4}\%$ of $100.00 = $3.25

$3.25 divided by $186.00 (the purchase price) = 1.75%

Ans. The stock yield is 1.75%.

PROBLEMS

Find the answers to the following problems to the nearest hundredth of a per cent.

1. A stock earned in one year the following dividends: 88 cents, 75 cents, 65 cents and 72 cents. If it was purchased at 124, what was its yield for the year? *Ans.* 2.42%.

2. What is the yield on a 4% preferred stock, whose par value is $100.00, purchased at 95? *Ans.* 4.21%.

3. A stock pays a quarterly dividend of $1.25. If it was purchased at $104\frac{3}{8}$, what is the yield? (Hint: Be sure to obtain the sum of the quarterly dividends.) *Ans.* 4.79%.

4. A stockholder receives a check for $36.00 representing a quarterly dividend on 30 shares of stock which he purchased at 140. What is the yield? (Hint: A quarterly dividend of $36.00 on 30 shares is equivalent to a quarterly dividend of $1.20 on one share, and a quarterly dividend of $1.20 per share is equivalent to an annual dividend of $4.80.)

Ans. 3.43%.

5. Which of the following shares yields the larger dividend: A stock quoted at 164 and paying an annual dividend of $6.25, or a stock quoted at 92 and paying an annual dividend of $4.50?

Ans. The stock quoted at 92 yields 4.89 per cent, which is 1.08% better than the other stock.

168. How to Find the Exact Cost of a Bond Purchased Between Interest Payment Dates. Thus far we have discussed bonds purchased on the first day of the interest period. In actual practice, however, a bond, more likely than not, is purchased *between* interest payment dates.

Let us consider a $1000.00, 6 per cent bond purchased on June 1 on which the interest is payable January 1 and July 1. Note that the purchase date is just one month away from the interest payment date; in other words, one month after the purchase date the bondholder will receive an interest payment of $30.00. This payment will cover a period of six months, and since the bondholder made the purchase only a month before, he obviously has not earned the full amount of the payment. As pointed out in the first article in this chapter, a bond represents a loan, and the interest on a bond should be regarded as the interest on a loan. Thus on the first interest payment date the bondholder is entitled to interest only for the period of the date of purchase to the date of the interest payment.

However, since bond interest is generally paid by coupons, each of which covers a full interest period—that is, six months if interest is payable semiannually, twelve months if interest is payable annually, etc.—and since the coupon for an unexpired interest period is considered as part of the security, the purchase of a bond between interest payment dates obligates the purchaser to reimburse the seller with a sum equivalent to the unearned amount that will be included in the first interest payment to be received by the purchaser. So that when a bond is quoted "and interest," as it usually is, it is understood that the amount of unearned interest, or accrual interest as it is also called, will be added to the quoted price. The total amount paid—that is, the quoted price plus the accrued interest—is usually referred to as the *flat price*.

Let us take a practical example:

Example 1: Find the exact cost of a $1000.00, 3% bond, interest payable on Jan. 1 and July 1, redeemable at 108 on Jan. 1, 1956, and purchased for delivery on April 11, 1946, to yield $2\frac{1}{2}\%$.

Solution: Proceeding by the method outlined in Art. 163, we find that the present value—that is, the purchase price on Jan. 1, 1946—of the bond is $1106.399, or $1106.40. The bond, however, was purchased, not for delivery on Jan. 1, 1946, but for delivery on April 11, 1946; and since interest has accrued since Jan. 1, 1946, the purchaser should reimburse the seller with the amount of the accrual. Accrual interest on bonds is calculated on the 360-days-to-the-year basis, so the amount of the accrual is found as follows:

Jan. 1 to Apr. 10 (day prior to delivery of bond) = 100 days

$\frac{100}{360}$ of $30.00 (amount of interest received in a year) = $8.333

$1106.399 (the quoted price as of Jan. 1) plus $8.333 = $1114.732

Ans. The exact cost of the bond at the time of purchase is $1114.73.

Example 2: Find the amount of interest accrual to be added to the quotation price of a $1000.00, 2% bond, interest payable Mar. 1 and Sept. 1, and purchased for delivery on April 15.

Solution: Mar. 1 to Apr. 14 (day prior to delivery of
        bond)   = 44 days
      $\frac{44}{360}$ of \$20.00 (amount of interest received
        in a year)   = \$2.44

    Ans. The amount of the interest accrual to be added to
the quoted price of the bond is \$2.44.

Example 3: Estimate the amount of the interest accrual to be
paid to the seller of a \$1000.00, $2\frac{1}{2}\%$ bond, interest payable Apr.
1 and Oct. 1, and purchased for delivery on July 26.

Solution: Apr. 1 to July 25 (day prior to delivery of
        bond)   = 115 days
      $\frac{115}{360}$ of \$25.00 (amount of interest received
        in a year)   = \$7.99

    Ans. The amount of interest accrual to be paid to the
seller is \$7.99.

Problems

Find the amount of interest accrual to be added to the quoted price
of each of the following bonds.

1. A \$1000.00, $3\frac{1}{2}\%$ bond, interest payable on May 1 and November
1, and purchased for delivery on June 16.   *Ans.* \$4.38.

2. A \$1000.00, 4% bond, interest payable June 1 and December 1,
and purchased for delivery on August 4.   *Ans.* \$7.00.

3. A \$500.00, $4\frac{1}{2}\%$ bond, interest payable January 1 and July 1,
and purchased for delivery on April 19.   *Ans.* \$6.75.

4. A \$500.00, 5% bond, interest payable March 1 and September 1,
and purchased for delivery on May 29.   *Ans.* \$6.11.

5. A \$5000.00, 2% bond, interest payable February 1 and August 1,
and purchased for delivery on June 25.   *Ans.* \$40.00.

6. A \$5000.00, $2\frac{1}{2}\%$ bond, interest payable April 1 and October 1,
and purchased for delivery on July 7.   *Ans.* \$33.33.

**169. How the Purchase of a Bond Between Interest Payment
Dates Affects the Amortization of the Premium or the Accumulation of the Discount.** Supplementing the discussion in Art. 165
on how to prepare a schedule for the amortization of the premium

or the accumulation of the discount, it will be interesting to observe what happens when a bond is purchased between interest payment dates.

The procedure is the same, except for the computations covering the unexpired part of the first interest period. The net amount of the first interest payment is easy to compute, for it consists simply of the difference between the actual amount of the interest payment and the amount of the accrual paid to the seller. The amount of the interest earned is computed on the "and interest" price—that is, the quoted price—and for the number of days that elapsed from the date of the purchase to the date of the interest payment.

We will take as an illustration the bond mentioned in Example 1 in the preceding article—a \$1000.00, 3 per cent bond, interest payable on January 1 and July 1, redeemable at 108 on January 1, 1956, and purchased for delivery on April 11, 1946, to yield $2\frac{1}{2}$ per cent.

We found that the value of the bond as of January 1, 1946 was \$1106.399, and that the amount of the interest accrual at the time of purchase was \$8.33, bringing the total cost on the date of purchase to \$1114.732. Let us compute, then, as of July 1, (1) the interest earned, (2) the net equivalent of the interest payment, (3) the amount of the amortization, and (4) the book value of the bond.

1. The bond was purchased for delivery on April 11, so it earned interest for the period April 11 to July 1, a total of 80 days. The yield rate is $2\frac{1}{2}\%$; therefore, the interest earned equals $\frac{80}{360}$ of $2\frac{1}{2}\%$ of \$1106.399, or \$6.147.

2. The amount of the semiannual interest payment is $\frac{1}{2}$ of 3% of \$1000.00, or \$15.00. Since the accrued interest was found to equal \$8.333, the net equivalent of the interest payment—that is, the amount of interest to which the bondholder was actually entitled—constitutes the difference between these figures, which is \$6.667.

3. The net equivalent of the interest payment being \$6.667, and the interest yield \$6.147, the amount to be amortized equals the difference between these figures, which is \$0.520.

4. The book value of the bond as of July 1 is therefore obtained by subtracting $0.520 (the amount to be amortized) from $1106.399 (the "and interest" price of the bond), which equals $1105.879.

The foregoing computations, as has been said, have to do with the unexpired part of the first interest period. All future calculations will, of course, be made as outlined in Art. 165, the interest yields and interest payments being computed for the full 6-month period in each instance.

When a bond quoted at a discount is purchased between interest payment dates, the accumulation of the discount for the unexpired part of the first period is based on exactly the same method of procedure. The only difference, as will be seen upon reference to the illustration in Art. 165, is that instead of subtracting the yield from the interest payment the interest payment is subtracted from the yield; the resulting figure (the accumulation of the discount) is added to the "and interest" price.

Problems

Calculate for each of these bonds, as of the first interest payment date, the following values: (a) the interest earned; (b) the net equivalent of the interest payment—that is, the difference between the amount of the interest payment and the amount of the accrual; (c) the amount of the amortization of the premium or accumulation of the discount; (d) the book value of the bond. Compute the answers to the third decimal place.

1. The "and interest" price of a $1000.00, 5% bond redeemable in 15 years at par, with interest to yield 4%, is $1111.980. The interest is payable Jan. 1 and July 1, and the bond is purchased for delivery on Mar. 11.   *Ans.* (a) $13.591; (b) $15.278; (c) $1.687; (d) $1110.293.

2. The "and interest" price of a $10,000.00, $4\frac{1}{2}$% bond redeemable in 8 years at par, with interest to yield $3\frac{1}{2}$%, is $10,692.525. The interest is payable Feb. 1 and Aug. 1, and the bond is purchased for delivery on May 19.   *Ans.* (a) $74.848; (b) $90.00; (c) $15.152; (d) $10,677.373.

3. The "and interest" price of a $500.00, $3\frac{1}{2}$% bond redeemable at 106 in 10 years, with interest to yield 3%, is $543.732. The interest is payable Mar. 1 and Sept. 1, and the bond is purchased for delivery on Apr. 21.   *Ans.* (a) $5.890; (b) $6.319; (c) $0.429; (d) $543.303.

4. The "and interest" price of a $1000.00, 3% bond redeemable at par in 11 years, with interest to yield 4%, is $911.710. The interest is payable Apr. 1 and Oct. 1, and the bond is purchased for delivery on May 25.   *Ans.* (a) $12.764; (b) $10.50; (c) $2.264; (d) $913.974.

5. The "and interest" price of a $1000.00, $2\frac{1}{2}$% bond redeemable in 18 years for $1200.00, with interest to yield 3%, is $1047.866. The interest is payable May 1 and Nov. 1, and the bond is purchased for delivery on July 16.   *Ans.* (a) $9.169; (b) $7.292; (c) $1.877; (d) $1049.743.

6. The "and interest" price of a $1000.00, $2\frac{1}{2}$% bond redeemable in 14 years for $1150.00, with interest to yield 4%, is $926.547. The interest is payable June 1 and Dec. 1, and the bond is purchased for delivery on Oct. 26.   *Ans.* (a) $3.603; (b) $2.431; (c) $1.172; (d) $927.719.

170. Listed, Unlisted, and "Over-the-Counter" Securities.

Generally speaking, the securities traded in on the exchanges are of two types: listed and unlisted. The securities traded in on some exchanges—notably the New York Stock Exchange and the Chicago, Cincinnati, Cleveland, St. Louis, San Francisco and Washington stock exchanges—must be listed. Other exchanges, such as the New York Curb Exchange, in addition to admitting issues to listed status, admit some securities to unlisted trading privileges.

Issues which are neither listed nor admitted to unlisted trading privileges are known as "over-the-counter" securities. It has been said that in the number of issues traded, the "over-the-counter" securities market is larger than all the United States stock exchanges combined, and that in volume of trading it equals or exceeds all organized exchanges. Compared with about 3000 issues listed on all United States stock exchanges, approximately 50,000 securities are traded "over-the-counter."

The "over-the-counter" market is the principal market for government issues, and the sole market for the obligations issued by the states, cities, counties, municipalities, etc. Numerous issues of bonds and stocks of the railroads, public utilities and industrial companies, of shares of banks, trust companies and insurance companies, and of foreign as well as American securities, are traded "over-the-counter."

Although in a broad sense the "over-the-counter" market is a seasoning ground for practically all securities, many listed securities are bought and sold "over-the-counter" as well as on the floors of the exchanges on which they are listed.

A lucid explanation published by the New York Curb Exchange, and quoted here by courtesy of the Exchange, provides an excellent first-hand account of some of the factors which make listing advantageous from the corporation's viewpoint and from the viewpoint of stockholders and investors.

From the corporation's viewpoint:

Listing has a distinct advertising value, particularly in cases where the products of the issuing corporation are distributed to the general public. Listing generally enlarges the stockholders' list, both numerically and geographically, thus creating new potential customers and boosters of the corporation's products. Furthermore, each day the tickers, the newspapers, the statistical services, etc. bring the names of listed corporations (and the names of their products if they coincide with the corporate name) to the attention of a vast number of people who are consumers as well as investors.

Listing aids corporate financing by facilitating the distribution of securities. Many prospective investors will not consider purchasing a security unless assured of an exchange market for public appraisal of prices, and for subsequent resale as necessity or inclination dictate. That is why many prospectuses state that application will be made to list on a specified national securities exchange. Underwriters realize that this represents a potent and valid selling point to prospective investors.

Listing facilitates future financing. The fact that a security has been listed on an exchange for a period of time aids in determining the price at which an additional issue may be sold, and additional capital obtained for expansion or other purposes. The publicity value and added marketability which have resulted from such prior listing facilitate the sale of the additional issue. Such prior listing also has a definite dollars-and-cents value, since it can effect substantial savings in the amount of time and work, and legal, accounting and other expenses involved in additional financing. As an example, most states which have laws requiring the registration of securities in advance of sale to their residents (so-called "Blue Sky" laws) exempt from such registration securities which are listed on recognized stock exchanges, although in many cases the exemption may not apply to unissued securities which have been authorized for listing but not yet distributed.

Listing provides a definite element of good will on the part of the management of a corporation—an evidence of willingness to disclose information essential to an evaluation of its securities and to provide stockholders with proper facilities for dealing therein.

From the viewpoint of stockholders and investors:

The competitive public auction market—the ideal medium for dealing in securities—is made available to the investing public by listing. The evolution and development of stock exchanges have been predicated upon the basic principle that the concentration of bids and offerings of all potential purchasers and sellers of a security at a single focal point (the floor of a stock exchange), in public competition under auction rules, assures buyers and sellers alike of paying and receiving the best prices prevailing at the time.

The public's transactions are made on an agency basis—through broker-members of the exchange who are agents working for, and with definite responsibilities to, their public customers. As an agent the broker must do his best for his customer. For his services the broker charges a commission at rates fixed by the exchange and known to the customer in advance.

Transactions are in the open. The customer knows, in advance of this transaction, the actual conditions prevailing. The previous range of prices and the latest sale price of every exchange security are available to him. He may obtain bid and asked quotations which are actual at the time given, not nominal or subject to negotiation. His own, as well as preceding and subsequent transactions, appear on the ticker tape. Moreover, each move in the trade from origin to completion is definitely recorded and timed and all circumstances may be accurately checked.

Stockholders are kept abreast of price changes. Listing, with the publicity given throughout the country to transactions on an exchange, enables a stockholder each day to know actual prices paid for his stock. He can see the price going up or going down, the number of shares dealt in, and he may thereby determine more intelligently than if in ignorance of these factors whether to sell or to increase his holdings. Ignorance of market prices may well lull the stockholder into a false sense of security.

Distant stockholders are protected. The importance of an exchange market is obvious in the case of any security with a substantial public distribution, but particularly so when the distribution is widespread geographically. When an issue is listed, every stockholder and potential investor, regardless of his location, is on a parity. Though the buyer and seller in any transaction may be separated by the entire continent, each knows what the other paid or received, as each transaction is immediately made public by being reported over the tickers throughout the nation.

Large stockholders are benefited, since listing provides an established market place and public and continuous appraisals of value over a period of time, which are of benefit in the liquidation of estate and large family holdings, and the settlement of tax problems.

The investing public is given the maximum of protection. Exchange rules are drawn with this purpose in view. Transactions are strictly supervised by exchange committees, and any complaints are carefully investigated. Transactions are also under constant observation by the Securities and Exchange Commission. Additional safeguards are constantly sought. Exchanges realize that a public convinced of fair dealings is essential to their continued prosperity.

Added collateral value is another important advantage which listing provides to security holders. Banks, in making loans, usually favor securities with an exchange market. Moreover, because of the credit restrictions imposed by the Securities Exchange Act, exchange securities are the only securities, except government and municipal securities, which exchange members and most brokers and dealers may accept as collateral in security loans.

It might be added that the listing of bonds is not quite as advantageous as the listing of stocks. This is particularly true of the high-grade investment type of bonds which, by their very nature, are not as readily adaptable to the auction type of market as conducted on exchanges. Bonds such as those of the United States government, municipalities, etc., have a wide over-the-counter market, where trading is conducted on a negotiation, as differentiated from the public auction, basis.

As will be seen in the article that follows, listing entails quite an expense, which is one of the reasons why many good securities are not listed. The importance and reliability of many unlisted securities will be gleaned from the fact that in this classification are found many state, municipal, public utility, bank and trust company, and insurance stocks and bonds.

171. The New York Stock Exchange and the New York Curb Exchange: A Word About Their Listing Requirements and the Costs. Here is an interesting comparison of the listing requirements of the New York Stock Exchange, the largest stock exchange

in America, and the New York Curb Exchange, the second largest.
In the case of the New York Stock Exchange:

The applicant must be a going concern, or be the successor to a going
concern, and must have substantial assets or demonstrated earning power,
or both. While the amount of assets and earnings are a consideration,
greater emphasis is placed on such questions as the degree of national
interest in the company, its standing in its particular field, the character
of the market for its products, its relative stability and position in its
industry, and whether or not it is engaged in an expanding industry with
prospects of maintaining its position.

The particular securities for which listing is sought should have a
sufficiently wide distribution to offer reasonable assurance that an ade-
quate auction market in the securities would exist.

The New York Curb Exchange, on the other hand,

has no rigid policy as to size of applicant corporations from the viewpoint
of either assets or earning power. Each case is considered on its own
merits. In certain cases, issues of corporations still in the development
stage, and without demonstrated earning power, have been listed. In
such cases the management of the company, the adequacy of its financing
and its future prospects in its particular line are important factors.

Likewise, there is no formal rule or policy of the New York Curb Exchange which specifies the minimum number of shares of stock which
must be publicly distributed or the minimum number of public stockholders among whom such shares must be distributed in order to qualify
a stock issue for listing.

Following is a comparison of the listing fees of stocks in effect
at the time that this book goes to press.

LISTING FEES OF THE NEW YORK STOCK EXCHANGE

Basic Initial Fee:

$\frac{1}{2}$ cent per share for first 2,000,000 shares listed; $\frac{1}{4}$ cent per
share for shares in excess of 2,000,000.

The fee is payable at the time of listing, as follows: $50.00 per
10,000 shares or fraction thereof for first 2,000,000; $25.00 per
10,000 shares or fraction thereof for shares in excess of 2,000,000.

The minimum initial fee for listing stock issues of corporations
having no securities listed is $2,000.00.

Continuing Annual Fee:

$\frac{3}{4}$ of $\frac{1}{10}$ of a cent per share for first 2,000,000 shares; $\frac{1}{20}$ of a cent per share for shares in excess of 2,000,000.

The continuing fee is payable annually for 15 years, but no longer than the stock remains listed.

The continuing fee will be calculated on the number of shares outstanding and listed on the anniversary date of the admission of the issue to dealing on the Exchange, at the rate of $75.00 per 100,000 shares or fraction thereof for the first 2,000,000 shares, and $50.00 per 100,000 shares or fraction thereof for shares in excess of 2,000,000.

The minimum continuing fee is $200 per stock issue per annum.

LISTING FEES OF THE NEW YORK CURB EXCHANGE

Initial Fee:

The original listing fee is $1,000 which covers the *total number of out-standing* shares of all classes of stock applied for in the original listing application. In addition, a service charge of $100 is made by the Exchange for its examination and certification of the applicant's registration application under the Securities Exchange Act of 1934. The applicant also pays the cost of printing the listing application which varies according to the size of the application and generally ranges between $200 and $300. Thus the total direct costs involved in an original listing generally approximate $1,300 to $1,400, unless the application also covers unissued shares which are reserved for future issuance for some specific purpose, such as conversion of senior securities, options, etc., which shares are listed subject to furnishing the Exchange with future "notice of issuance" for such purposes. In such cases an additional listing fee is charged at the rate of 1¢ for each additional share applied for, with a maximum charge of $1,000 on each block of stock issuable for a different purpose (i.e. if the additional amount applied for exceeds 100,000 shares issuable for one purpose, the fee is $1,000 regardless of the amount of shares).

Annual Fee:

No annual or other periodic fees are payable to the New York Curb Exchange, and the original listing fee of $1,000 is the only fee payable to the Exchange so long as the stock remains listed, unless subsequent to original listing the corporation desires to issue additional shares in excess of the amount listed at the time of original listing. In that event the corporation must file a listing application covering the additional amount of shares to be issued and the same additional listing fee referred to above is applicable (1¢ for each additional share up to a maximum charge of $1,000 for each block of stock issuable for a different purpose).

Thus it will be seen that the listing fees of the New York Curb Exchange are substantially smaller than those of the New York Stock Exchange. Also, while the New York Stock Exchange requires that an applicant have some degree of national prominence, substantial assets or demonstrated earning power, and reasonable widespread public distribution of its securities, the listing standards of the New York Curb Exchange are not so stringent in regard to these matters. The securities of smaller enterprises and companies in the formative stage are eligible for listing on the New York Curb Exchange.

It should not be assumed from this that the list of securities dealt in on the New York Curb Exchange is confined to newer and smaller companies; it includes the securities of many nationally prominent corporations. As a publication of this Exchange points out, "there are 266 common stock issues on this Exchange on which dividends have been paid continuously in each year for the past ten years or more, ranging up to more than eighty years for some issues. In the year 1945 dividends were paid on 76 per cent of all the stock issues (preferred and common) dealt in on the New York Curb Exchange."

172. How to Understand the Tables of Transactions on the Exchanges and Other Tables Published in the Financial Pages of the Daily Newspapers. To the uninitiated the financial pages of a newspaper may seem somewhat confusing. It will not be amiss, therefore, to discuss some of the tables in these pages. We will take for our study the financial section of *The New York Times*, which is one of the richest sources of information on the previous day's happenings in the securities world.

THE NEW YORK STOCK EXCHANGE

Let us consider first the significance of the figures in the table of transactions on the New York Stock Exchange, as published in *The New York Times* for Dec. 28, 1946, covering the business done on the previous day.

TRANSACTIONS ON THE NEW YORK STOCK EXCHANGE

FRIDAY, DEC. 27, 1946

Day's Sales.	Thursday.	Year Ago.	Year to Date 1946.	Year to Date 1945.
1,290,000	1,150,000	1,090,000	359,924,440	374,893,308

Range 1946 High.	Range 1946 Low.	Stock and Div'd In Dollars.	Sls. 100s.	First.	High.	Low.	Last.	Net Chge.
91	61½	Abbott Lab 2a.....	4	87½	87½	87	87	−1
41¾	24⅝	Address-Mul 1.10e..	2	32	32	32	32	..
103	90½	Aldens Inc. pf 4¼..	†20	91	91	91	91	−1¼
8¼	5⅜	Allegheny Corp.....	33	4	4	3⅞	3⅞	− ⅛
69¼	29¾	Allegheny pf........	8	36¼	37	36⅛	37	− ¼
106½	79	Am Can 3..........	10	89	89¾	89	89¾	+ ⅝
133⅝	97¼	Am P&L $6 pf 6k...	2	121	121	120	120	−2
15	6½	Childs Co...........	*10	6¾	6⅞	6½	6½	− ⅛
76⅞	60	Curtis Pub pr pf 3a.	1	67	67	67	67	−1
58¾	25	Duplan Corp. 60b..	2	29	29	29	29	−1¾
58¾	21½	Eversharp 1.20a xd.	10	23⅛	23⅜	23⅛	23⅜	− ¼
15¼	6⅜	Leh V Coal 2 pf ½.	8	7¾	8	7¾	8	..
57¼	43⅛	Mead Corp 2 pf 2...	2	47⅞	47⅞	47⅞	47⅞	− ⅜
39¾	23½	No Am Co 1.77f....	28	31½	31⅝	30⅞	31⅛	− ½

We will analyze the columns one by one, taking for our illustration the common stock issue of the ABBOTT LABORATORIES, which is the first in the table.

Range 1946. "High 91" means that the highest price at which this stock sold between Jan. 1, 1946 and Dec. 27, 1946 was $91.00 per share. "Low $61\frac{1}{2}$" means that the lowest price at which the stock sold between these dates was $61.50 per share.

Stock and Dividend in Dollars. Under this heading appears the name of the issuing corporation, and a description of the stock when it is other than common. The "dividend in dollars" is represented by the "2". A footnote to the table in the published report explains that the "rates of dividends are annual disbursements based on last quarterly or semiannual declaration." So that the 2 in this column means that the annual dividend, based on the last declaration, is $2.00.

Sales 100s. The 4 in this column means that 400 shares of this stock were sold during the day.

First $87\frac{1}{2}$. The first sale was made at $87.50 per share.

High $87\frac{1}{2}$. The highest price received or paid during the day was $87.50 per share.

Low 87. The lowest price received or paid during the day was $87.00 per share.

Last 87. The last sale for the day was at $87.00 per share.

Net Change. Here we are informed that the price received on the last sale—namely, $87.00, was " −1," which means that this was $1.00 per share less than the price received on the last sale for the previous day.

Let us now consider the different symbols and abbreviations in the column headed "Stock and Div'd In Dollars." Incidentally, the few stock issues shown in the table were selected for the purpose of our study; actually, more than a thousand issues were traded in on the New York Stock Exchange on the day under consideration. The symbols, it should be noted, are those used by *The New York Times.* Different publishers use different symbols.

To begin with ABBOTT LABORATORIES, note that an "a" appears after the dividend. This means that there was an extra dividend (or dividends) declared in addition to the usual dividend.

The "e" applying to ADDRESSOGRAPH-MULTIGRAPH CORP. indicates that $1.10 is the dividend, or the sum of the dividends, declared or paid so far this year. It is interesting to note that the "first," "high," "low," and "last" prices were the same for the entire day, and that there was no change between the last price for the day and the last price for the previous day.

ALDENS, INC.—"pf $4\frac{1}{4}$" means that the $4\frac{1}{4}$ per cent dividend specified in this preferred stock was paid. The symbol (†) indicates that in this instance the shares sold during the day were not in units of 100, but in units of 10, the 20 representing the entire number of shares sold. It is interesting to note that on the New York Stock Exchange the large majority of stocks are purchasable in 100-units only. However, there are a group of stocks which, due to limited activity or otherwise, may be purchased in 10-share lots.

In the case of the common stock of ALLEGHENY CORP., no dividends were paid in the past year.

The foregoing observation will be understandable when it is seen that ALLEGHENY pf (preferred stock) did not earn any dividends, either, for the past year.

AMERICAN CAN CO.—The figure shown after the name of the issuing corporation indicates the sum of the annual dividend earnings based on the last dividend declaration. The annual dividend of this stock may be considered as $3.00. It will be seen that unless the final dividend for the year has been declared, the figures shown in this column are not strictly accurate.

AMERICAN POWER & LIGHT CO.—"$6 pf 6" tells us that the full amount of the dividend specified in the stock was paid. The *k* means that accumulated dividends were paid or declared this year.

The (*) applying to the issue of CHILDS CO. signifies, as explained in the footnote, "In bankruptcy or receivership or being reorganized under Bankruptcy Act or securities assumed by such company."

CURTIS PUBLISHING CO.—The abbreviation "pr pf" stands for "prior preferred," which means that a dividend must be paid on this issue before any dividend can be declared on the "preferred" stock.

The "b" after the dividend figure applied to the DUPLAN CORP. issue tells us that in addition to the cash payment of 60 cents, a stock dividend was also paid.

EVERSHARP, INC.—The abbreviation "xd" signifies that the shares were sold "ex dividend"—that is, without the latest dividend. In other words, the stock now sold does not include the dividend declared and about to be paid to stockholders on record.

LEHIGH VALLEY COAL CORP.—Here is an example of a preferred stock on which the declared dividend (50 cents) is less than the amount specified in the share ($2.00). It should be noted that there is no guarantee that the dividend specified in a preferred stock will be paid promptly, or paid at all. The payment of the dividend specified in preferred stock is contingent upon there being a profit, or upon the profit being large enough to warrant a dividend declaration.

MEAD CORP.—Here, on the other hand, the dividend declared is exactly equal to the dividend specified in the share—namely, $2.00.

NORTH AMERICAN CO.—The "f" indicates that the dividend declared by this corporation is payable in stock.

Net Change. It is interesting to observe that the price at which the first sale for the day is made is sometimes a little higher than the closing price on the preceding day. This is usually due to favorable overnight developments. It so happens that among the stocks discussed in this article, only one opened on the day under discussion at a higher price than that on which it closed the preceding day: CHILDS CO. common, which opened on Dec. 27 at $6\frac{3}{4}$, having closed on Dec. 26 at $6\frac{5}{8}$.

On the other hand, quite a number of the shares we discussed opened at lower rather than higher prices. Thus ABBOTT LABORATORIES, which opened on Dec. 27 at $87\frac{1}{2}$, had closed on Dec. 26 at 88; ALDENS, INC., which opened at 91 had closed at $92\frac{1}{4}$; the EVERSHARP issue, which opened at $23\frac{1}{8}$ had closed at $24\frac{1}{4}$; and there were several others.

THE NEW YORK CURB EXCHANGE

The table of the stocks traded in on this Exchange is made up in the same manner as the table covering the transactions on the New York Stock Exchange, except that it includes those securities which are admitted by the Curb Exchange to unlisted trading privileges. So we will confine ourselves to the consideration of only a few of the stocks traded in on the Curb Exchange. Notice that here the tabulation covers bonds as well as stocks; this is because comparatively few bonds are traded in on the Curb Exchange, and the figures for these securities follow the figures for the stocks in the same table.

TRANSACTIONS ON THE NEW YORK CURB EXCHANGE

FRIDAY, DEC. 27, 1946

	Stocks.	Domestic Bonds.	Foreign Bonds.	Total Bonds.
Day's sales	420,000	$150,000	$130,000	$280,000
Thursday	400,000	260,000	80,000	340,000
Year to date	135,870,000	66,922,000	12,168,000	79,090,000

Range High.	1946. Low.	Stock and Div'd In Dollars.	Sls. 100s.	First.	High.	Low.	Last.	Net Chge.
31	25½	Brit Col Pw A h1.60.	2	27	27	27	27	..
23	10½	Pyle-Nat 1..........	z25	13	13	13	13	−½
15	7¾	Wilson Bros. ½e....	†2	8	8	7¾	7¾	−¼

As in the table of transactions on the New York Stock Exchange, the figures in the dividend column reflect the annual dividend based on the quarterly or semiannual declarations.

The "h," applying to the stock issue of BRITISH COLUMBIA POWER CORP. LTD., signifies that the dividend is payable in Canadian funds. The "A" before the "h" refers to the issue on which the dividend was declared.

The "z" before the number of shares sold of the PYLE-NATIONAL CO. stock means that this represents actual sales; in other words, the total number of shares sold is 25, not 2500.

And the symbol (†) preceding the number of shares sold of the WILSON BROS. stock tells us that this issue is fully listed, as distinguished from other issues which are not listed but are admitted on the New York Curb Exchange to unlisted trading privileges.

"*Over-the-Counter*" *Securities*. This table does not give as much information as the tables of transactions. It is impossible to show the figures for the actual sales consummated because, as mentioned in Art. 170, the "over-the-counter" security market is larger than all the United States stock exchanges combined, and it is as impossible to know the exact sales of these securities on the previous day as it is to know how many men's suits were sold in all the clothing stores in the United States on the previous day. It is for this reason that the only figures given in this table are the bid and asked prices.

"*Stock Exchange Bid and Asked Quotations.*" This table shows the bid and asked quotations on stocks which were not sold during the day. Here, for example, are the bid and asked quotations of the first few issues in the table published in *The New York Times* for Dec. 28, 1946, covering the previous day's business on the New York Stock Exchange.

	Bid	Asked
Abraham & Straus.	100	110
Adams-Mills......	$52\frac{1}{2}$	56
Ala & Vicks.......	106	110
Allegheny pr pf....	$58\frac{1}{2}$	60
Alleg & West......	96	100
Allen Industries ...	19	20

The foregoing, as has been said, are issues which were not traded in on the Stock Exchange on the day under discussion. Thus if we refer to the reports of the previous day we will find that the name Ala & Vicks does *not* appear in the table "Stock Exchange

Bid and Asked Quotations," but *does* appear in the table "Transactions on the New York Stock Exchange."

It is interesting to note that in every instance, in this table, the asked price is higher than the bid price. However, the significance of these bid and asked prices should not be confused with the meaning of the bid and asked prices in the "Over-the-Counter" Securities table.

173. How to Understand Bond Price Quotations on Completed Transactions, as Published in the Daily Newspapers. There are listed and unlisted bonds just as there are listed and unlisted stocks. Quotations on completed transactions in listed bonds are published in the same form as quotations on completed transactions in listed stocks. *The New York Times* publishes the quotations on bonds under three classifications: United States Government Bonds, Domestic Bonds, and Foreign Bonds—all under the heading, "Bond Trading on the New York Stock Exchange."

The report of the transactions in United States Government Bonds merely shows the bid and asked prices. Thus on Dec. 27, 1946, the bid price on Treasury 2s 1950–1948 was 102.6 and the asked price 102.8, which means that on Treasury Bonds bearing a 2 per cent interest rate, payable in 1950 and redeemable by the Government in the month of December of any year between 1948 and 1950, the bid price was $102\frac{6}{32}$ and the asked price $102\frac{8}{32}$.

The transactions in Domestic and Foreign Bonds are published in greater detail, and shown on p. 458 are a few typical quotations taken from each of these classifications in the table headed "Bond Trading on the New York Stock Exchange," covering the business done on Dec. 27, 1946. It should be noted that there are virtually hundreds of different kinds of bonds.

The securities in the Domestic Bonds tabulation are only a few of the large number of bond issues traded in on the New York Stock Exchange on the date under consideration and shown in the original published table. They were selected because of their distinct characteristics, which are explained as follows:

Item 1—This issue calls for little comment. The bond bears an interest rate of 3 per cent and is redeemable in 1956. The number 20 under the heading "Sales in $1,000," signifies that bonds of this issue having a total face value of $20,000 were sold on this date.

Item 2—The symbol (*) indicates bankruptcy or receivership, etc. The symbol (†) means that the bond, having matured in 1934, is selling flat on default, and that is why the quotation is so low. The symbol (§) is an additional indication that the bond has matured.

BOND TRADING ON THE NEW YORK STOCK EXCHANGE

TRANSACTIONS FRIDAY, DEC. 27, 1946

	U.S. Gov't Bonds.	Other Domestic Bonds.	Foreign Bonds.	Total All Bonds.
Day's sales	$5,000	$4,620,000	$310,000	$4,935,000
Thursday	50,000	4,490,000	330,000	4,870,000
Year to date	19,042,650	1,250,642,000	79,888,000	1,349,572,650
1945	7,952,550	2,136,132,800	104,749,460	2,248,834,810

DOMESTIC BONDS

Item No.	Range 1946. High.	Low.		Sales in $1,000	High.	Low.	Last.	Net Chge.
1	159⅛	118½	Am T & T 3s 56.........	20	127½	126⅝	127½	+ ½
2	58	30¼	Bur CR & No 5s 34*†§...	5	37	37	37	−2½
3	121	103½	Can Pac 4s perp........	5	105⅛	105	105	..
4	61⅜	26	Cen RR NJ 5s 87 reg*†..	27	30¾	30¼	30¼	..
5	107¼	105	C&O 3½s 96D..........	1	106¼	106¼	106¼	− ¼
6	107⅜	104¾	C&O 3½s 96E..........	4	105⅛	105	105⅛	+ ⅛
7	107½	74¾	CMSP&P inc 4½s 2019..	72	83½	83½	83½	..
8	94	75½	Hudson Coal 5s 62A.....	6	83½	83½	83½	− ¼
9	83	38½	NYNH&H cv 6s 48*†...	69	44⅜	43¼	44	..
10	15¾	4	NY O & W gen 4s 55*†...	19	4⅝	4⅝	4⅝	− ¼

NOTE: The item numbers at the left were inserted by the author to facilitate reference to the issues.

Item 3—"perp" means perpetual. A perpetual bond represents a permanent obligation on the part of the issuing company.

Item 4—Each bond in this issue is registered in the name of the owner. This means that ownership has been recorded on the books of the corporation. Bonds of this nature are payable only to the registered owner, and interest payments are made by check, payable to and mailed direct to the owner.

Items 5 and 6—The D in item 5 and the E in item 6 indicate that these issues are the fourth and fifth, respectively, in the series.

Item 7—The "inc" means that this is an income bond, a type of security on which the issuing corporation is not obligated to pay interest unless the net income warrants it.

Item 8—The "A" signifies that this is the first issue (A being the first letter in the alphabet) in a series of bonds put out by this corporation.

Item 9—The characters "cv" mean convertible. A convertible bond is one which gives the owner the right to convert it into stock.

Item 10—The abbreviation "gen" indicates that the position of this security is that of a general mortgage. These are usually known as "junior bonds," and securities of this nature have a secondary claim upon the property of the corporation.

In each instance the quotation is read much like a stock quotation. Taking the NEW YORK, NEW HAVEN AND HARTFORD RAILROAD issue (Item 9), *High 44⅜* means that the highest price for the day was 44⅜, or $443.75 on a $1000.00 bond; *Low 43¼*, that the lowest price for the day was 43¼, or $432.50; *Last 44*, that the final price for the day was 44, or $440.00.

Let us now consider a few of the foreign bonds traded in on the New York Stock Exchange on Dec. 27, 1946.

FOREIGN BONDS

Item No.	Range High.	1946. Low.		Sales in $1,000.	High.	Low.	Last.	Net Chge.
1	82½	62	Brazil 8s 41†§.......	11	62	62	62	..
2	30¾	21	Chile 6s 61 Feb asd†.	6	21¾	21½	21½	− ¼
3	90¾	81½	Colomb 6s 61 Jan†...	5	86	86	86	+1
4	91½	81½	Colomb 6s 61 Oct†...	1	86	86	86	..
5	103	100	Dom 5½s 69 ext.....	1	101¼	101¼	101¼	..

NOTE: The item numbers at the left were inserted by the author to facilitate reference to the issues.

Item 1—This issue was not redeemed at maturity. The symbol (†) indicates that it is selling "flat" on account of default. Note that the quotation on that day was the lowest for the year. The symbol (§) is an additional indication that these are matured bonds.

Item 2—Here is a bond which, due to default, is quoted at a very low figure. The abbreviation "asd" tells the reader that the bondholders have assented to a reorganization plan.

Items 3 and 4—When a corporation places on the market two or more issues of bonds which mature in the same year, it is usual to mention the date of maturity of the issues.

Item 5—"Ext" means that the maturity date has been extended to the year indicated—namely, 1969. Obviously, the issue was originally to have matured at an earlier date.

174. How to Understand Reports of Dividend Announcements as Published in the Daily Newspapers. Since there are tens of thousands of listed and unlisted securities on the market, dividends are announced on virtually every business day. The table published in *The New York Times* for Dec. 28, 1946, and reproduced here in its entirety is typical.

It will be noticed that the dividends in this tabulation are shown under various headings. *Year end,* for instance, refers to declarations so designated by the respective corporations. A "year end" dividend may be one in addition to a regular or irregular dividend, or it may be the dividend declared for the entire year.

Extra. These are dividends declared in addition to regular dividends.

Accumulated. Here are listed those dividends which are intended to make up for dividends not paid for previous periods. Poor business conditions may make it impossible for a corporation to declare a dividend for the usual period, but a business pick-up in the months that follow may make possible the declaration of an "accumulated" dividend.

Increased dividends are so called because they are at a higher rate than the previously declared dividends.

Initial. This applies to first dividend payments on new stock issues.

Stock. Here are listed those dividends which are paid in shares rather than in cash.

Regular dividends are those declared for the usual period and for the usual amount.

Irregular dividends are those declared for irregular periods or amounts.

It will be noticed that the majority of the dividends are for quarterly ("Q") periods. Most dividends are paid quarterly, and some semiannually. In some instances they are payable monthly. The two dots (..) in the *Period* column signify that the announce-

DIVIDENDS ANNOUNCED

Year End

Company.	Rate.	Pe-riod.	Pay-able.	Hldrs of Record.
Alabama Mills	40c	..	2-15	1-28
Beneficial In·ust Ln	30c	..	1-17	1- 7
Berland Shoe Stores	30c	..	2- 2	1-21
Blair & Co	10c	..	2-15	1- 3
Brooklyn Borough Gas	$1	..	12-27	12-23
Durham Enders pt pf	25c	..	12-31	12-24
East Mass St R pf "B"	$6.50	..	2- 1	1-15
East Mass St R pf "B"	$6.50	..	5- 1	4-15
Gorham Mfg	$2	..	1-15	1- 2
Ludlow Typograph	$3	..	1- 2	12-17
Nat Shirt Shops (Del)	20c	..	1- 3	12-27
Waterbury Farrell F & M.	.50c	..	12-27	12-16

Extra

Company.	Rate.	Pe-riod.	Pay-able.	Hldrs of Record.
Commer Tr (Jersey City)	25c	..	1- 2	12-28
F R Publish Corp	$2.25	..	12-27	12-20
Hecht & Co	25c	..	1-31	1- 8
Manhattan Bond Fund	4c	..	1-15	1- 4
Reading Trust (Pa)	10c	..	1- 1	12-16
Security Storage	$1	..	1-10	1- 6

Accumulated

Company.	Rate.	Pe-riod.	Pay-able.	Hldrs of Record.
Bohack (H C) C pf	$5	.	1-14	1- 4
E Mass St R 6% pf "B"	$6.50	..	2- 1	1-15
E Mass St R 6% pf "B"	$6.50	..	5- 1	4-15

Increased

Company.	Rate.	Pe-riod.	Pay-able.	Hldrs of Record.
Indust Tr Co (Phila)	.15c	S	1-10	12-31

Initial

Company.	Rate.	Pe-riod.	Pay-able.	Hldrs of Record.
Haloid Co 4% pf	$1	Q	1- 2	12-27
Roberts & Mander	.10c	..	1-15	12-30

Stock

Company.	Rate.	Pe-riod.	Pay-able.	Hldrs of Record.
U S Nat Bk (Portland)	25%	..	3- 1	2-15

Regular

Company.	Rate.	Pe-riod.	Pay-able.	Hldrs of Record.
Alabama Mills Inc	20c	..	1-15	12-14
All Penn Oil & Gas	2½c	.Q	1-15	1-10
Appalachian El P pf $1.12½		Q	2- 1	1- 6
Bartgis Bros	5c	Q	1-15	12-31
Beneficial Inds Loan	30c	Q	12-28	12-16
Beneficial Inds Loan pf 81¼c		Q	12-28	12-16
Blum (Ph) & Co	20c	..	2- 1	1-15
Boston Edison	60c	Q	2- 1	1-10
Centr Tr (Harrisburg)	$1.50	S	12-30	12-26
Chase N Bk (NY)	40c	Q	2- 1	1- 3
Cit Fld B & T (Louisv.)	$3.75	Q	1- 2	12-24
Comm Tr C (Jersey City)	50c	Q	1- 2	12-28
E Mass S R pf "A"	$1.50	..	3-15	3- 1
E Mass S R pf "A"	$1.50	..	6-16	6- 2
E Mass S R pf "A"	$1.50	..	9-15	9- 2
E Mass S R pf "A"	$1.50	..	12-15	12- 1
F R Publishing	50c	Q	12-27	12-20
Fulton Nat Bk (Lancaster)	$1	S	1- 2	12-24
Halle Bros Co pf	60c	Q	1-15	1- 8
Hecht & Co	40c	..	1-31	1- 8
Hecht & Co 3¾% pf	93¾c	Q	1-31	1- 8
Industrial Tr (Phila)	15c	S	1-10	12-31
Johnson Service	25c	Q	12-31	12-19
Ludlow Typograph	$1	..	1- 2	...
Manhattan Bond Fund, Inc.	8c	..	1-15	1- 4
Mass Util Assoc pf	62½c	Q	1-15	12-31
Montana Power pf	$1.50	Q	2- 1	1-13
Municipal R Est Tr	$1	S	12-31	12-27
N Y Telephone	$2	..	12-31	12-31
North Penn Gas pf	$1.75	Q	1-15	1- 2
Parke, Davis & Co	40c	..	1-31	1-14
Penn Traffic Co	15c	..	1-25	1-10
Phila & Reading C & I	.50c	..	1-20	1- 8
Piper Aircraft pf	11¼c	..	1-15	12-31
Pitts, Cinn, Chic&St L RR.	$2.50	S	2- 1	1-10
Reading Trust Co (Pa)	40c	S	1- 1	12-16
Rhinelander Paper	50c	Q	1- 1	12-20
Rhode Isl P S "A"	$1	Q	2- 1	1-15
Rhode Isl P S pf	50c	Q	2- 1	1-15
Rickel Paper	5c	Q	1-10	1- 2
Rio Grande Val Gas,	5c	..	2- 1	1-10
Royal Typewriter pf	$1.75	Q	1-15	1- 4
Schuster(Ed)&Co, Inc pf	$1.06½	Q	1- 2	12-20
Second Nat Bk (Boston)	$1	Q	1- 2	12-26
Security Storage	$1.25	Q	1-10	1- 6
Simplicity Pattern pf	13¾c	Q	1-15	12-31
Spotless Co, Inc	40c	..	1-14	1-14
Springfield Natl Bank	40c	S	1-10	12-31
Thermoid Co pf	62½c	Q	2- 1	1-25
ThirdNatBk&Tr(Dayton,O)	.50c	..	12-31	12-27
U S Trust Co of Paterson	$2	..	2- 1	1-25
Waterloo Tr & Savings	$2.50	S	1- 2	12-20
Woburn Natl Bank (Mass)	$1.50	S	12-27	12-23

461

ment did not specify the period for which the dividend was declared.

Attention is called to the fact that the amount in the *Rate* column is the amount of the individual dividend. Thus the quarterly dividend of $1.12½ declared on the Appalachian Electric Power preferred stock checks perfectly with the figure of $4.50 shown in the table of transactions on the New York Curb Exchange—$4.50 representing the annual dividend "based on the last quarterly declaration."

Holders of Record. This column shows the latest date on which a stockholder must have stock in his name in order that he may be entitled to the dividend. Thus a holder of Alabama Mills, Inc., common stock on January 28 would be entitled to the dividend payable on February 15.

It will be noted that in some instances there is quite an interval between the record date and the date that the dividend is payable. This is usually planned to allow time for the checks to be prepared and mailed—a formidable task for some corporations, involving, as in the case of American Telephone and Telegraph Co., hundreds of thousands of checks.

It is also interesting to note that whereas bonds are quoted "and interest," dividends accumulated on stocks between one dividend declaration and the next are automatically included in the quoted price, so that calculations of dividend accruals are not necessary.

175. *The New York Times, The Wall Street Journal,* the *Journal of Commerce* (New York), and the *Chicago Journal of Commerce:* **Some Interesting Observations.** Our study of stock and bond tables has been confined to those published in *The New York Times* primarily because of the richness and extensiveness of the material contained in the financial section of this nationally prominent daily newspaper. However, there are several daily business papers which cover, among other things and more or less exhaustively, the news of the financial world.

Each has its distinctive way of presenting this news and, as might be expected, each is known for its special features. Thus *The Wall Street Journal,* a national newspaper which stresses economic news, publishes financial reports of many corporations which have securities listed on the New York Stock Exchange and the New York Curb Exchange. This newspaper, which also publishes a West Coast edition, carries the closing bid and asked prices of stocks traded in on the New York Curb Exchange as well as those traded in on the New York Stock Exchange.

In contrast with *The Wall Street Journal* and with *The New York Times* whose "Over-the-Counter" Securities list is confined to a few hundred issues, the *Journal of Commerce* (New York) publishes more than 1500 quotations of these securities each day, along with the usual tables of transactions on the New York Stock Exchange and the New York Curb Exchange, and the financial reports of listed and unlisted securities. It might be mentioned, parenthetically, that this newspaper is known especially for its hundreds of price quotations on foods and groceries, chemicals, petroleum, building supplies, textiles, etc.

The *Chicago Journal of Commerce*, which concentrates on happenings in the central western area, prints quotations on a larger number of exchanges than do the other newspapers. Each Monday it publishes a table covering the transactions for the preceding week in stocks on the New York Stock Exchange and the New York Curb Exchange, showing the highs and lows and the bid and asked prices for the week, and similar weekly tables for Chicago stocks and New York bonds. On the first Monday of each month it publishes the highs and lows for the entire month. Another of its Monday listings is the "Current Market on New Bond Issues," which covers the previous twelve months.

Headings of Table Columns. The headings of the columns in the various stock and bond tables published in the different newspapers vary in a minor degree. Thus while *The New York Times* uses the captions "First," "High," "Low" and "Last," *The Wall Street Journal* and *Journal of Commerce* (New York) captions read "Open," "High," "Low" and "Close," and the *Chicago Journal of Commerce* shows only three of these columns: the "High," "Low" and "Close."

The reader will, of course, understand that some of the aforementioned features, headings, etc. are not necessarily permanent, and that, as time goes on and space permits, revisions will be made in the nature of the material published.

CHAPTER XXIII

DECIMALS AND FRACTIONS

Because it was planned as a supplement to the main text this chapter has been placed at the end of the volume rather than at the beginning.

Its purpose is to provide a necessary background for two types of readers: those not skilled in the use of decimals and fractions, and those who have had so little occasion to use this knowledge in the past as to have forgotten much of what they possessed of it.

It is hoped, however, that most readers will gain something from the pages that follow. For a knowledge of decimals and fractions will do more than pave the way to a more thorough understanding of many of the short-cuts discussed in this book; it is essential to anyone who has anything at all to do with business mathematics of one kind or another.

176. The Function of the Decmial Point. A quick mental picture of the function of the decimal point can be obtained by considering the origin of the word "decimal." It originated from two Latin words: *decimus*, tenth, and *decem*, ten.

Strictly speaking, the decimal point has many functions. By moving it to the left or right, a number can be multiplied or divided, respectively, by 10, 100, 1000, etc., according to the number of spaces it is moved. Thus to *multiply* 24.38 by 10 the decimal point is moved one place to the right, giving us 243.8; to multiply 24.38 by 100 the point is moved two places to the right, making the result 2438. To *divide* 24.38 by 10 the decimal point is moved one place to the left, changing the number to 2.438; and to divide 24.38 by 100 the point is moved two places to the left, when the number becomes .2438.

The decimal point may be said to separate the figures at the left of a number, which represent the number of *whole* units, from the figures at the right, which represent a *part* of a unit. Thus the figure in the first place *after* a decimal point represents tenths (.3 means three tenths); the figure in the second place after the decimal point, hundredths (.04 means four hundredths); the figure in the third place, thousandths (.007 means seven thousandths), etc.

The figure in the first place *before* a decimal point gives the number of units; the figure in the second place, tens; third place, hundreds, etc.

Here, then, is an important fact to remember: For each place the decimal point is moved to the right, the value of a number is *multiplied* by 10; for each place it is moved to the left, the value is *divided* by 10.

Problems

⋆ **1.**	Multiply 176 by 10.	*Ans.* 1760.
⋆ **2.**	Multiply 3925 by 100.	*Ans.* 392500.
⋆ **3.**	Multiply 16.4 by 10.	*Ans.* 164.
⋆ **4.**	Multiply 3.86 by 100.	*Ans.* 386.
⋆ **5.**	Multiply .1257 by 100.	*Ans.* 12.57.
⋆ **6.**	Divide 49 by 10.	*Ans.* 4.9.
⋆ **7.**	Divide 23863 by 100.	*Ans.* 238.63.
⋆ **8.**	Divide 2.475 by 10.	*Ans.* .2475.
⋆ **9.**	Divide .1462 by 100.	*Ans.* .001462.
⋆ **10.**	Divide 3.875 by 1000.	*Ans.* .003875.

177. How to Read Numbers Containing Decimal Points. There is no limit to the number of places the decimal point may be moved. The following illustration presents a picture of the values of places in decimal numbers and how they are read:

Millions
Hundred Thousands
Ten Thousands
Thousands
Hundreds
Tens
Units
DECIMAL POINT
Tenths
Hundredths
Thousandths
Ten Thousandths
Hundred Thousandths
Millionths
etc.

0000000 . 000000

14.1 would be read 14 and one tenth.

118.23 would be read 118 and 23 hundredths or, if the dollar sign preceded it, 118 dollars and 23 cents.

.192 would be read 192 thousandths.

33.0468 would be read 33 and 468 ten thousandths.

146.46328 would be read 146 and 46328 hundred thousandths.

3.762413 would be read 3 and 762413 millionths.

PROBLEMS

Show how you would read the decimal numbers mentioned in the following cases:

★ **1.** Music wire is available in a variety of thicknesses. One of them is .059 inch in diameter.   *Ans.* 59 thousandths of an inch.

★ **2.** One of the over-all diameters of a brand of cable cord having an insulation thickness of $\frac{3}{64}$ of an inch is .605 inch.

Ans. 605 thousandths of an inch.

★ **3.** The maximum thickness of a brand of asbestos paper is described as .020 inch. (Hint: When a zero after a decimal point is not followed by a digit, it may be disregarded.)   *Ans.* 2 hundredths of an inch.

★ **4.** A fingerprint remover that cleans steel and retards corrosion leaves a film of about 0.0002 inch thick. (Hint: When no other figure than a zero precedes a decimal point, the zero may be disregarded.)

Ans. 2 ten thousandths of an inch.

★ **5.** Sheets of natural cork, 0.0025 inch thick, are sliced from cork blocks and are used extensively on the tips of cigarettes.

Ans. 25 ten thousandths of an inch.

★ **6.** The disadvantages of a disagreeable odor and acrid taste of fish glue can be avoided if the glue is boiled with a little water with 1% of sodium phosphate and 0.025% of saccharine added.

Ans. 25 thousandths of 1 per cent.

★ **7.** An electronic stop-watch clocks one millionth of a second. Write one millionth in decimal form.   *Ans.* .000001.

Write each of the following numbers in decimal form:

★ **8.** $4\frac{7}{10}$.   *Ans.* 4.7.

★ **9.** $200\frac{8}{1000}$.   *Ans.* 200.008.

★ **10.** $12\frac{18}{100}$.   *Ans.* 12.18.

★ **11.** $19\frac{23}{1000}$.   *Ans.* 19.023.

178. Avoiding Confusion in Moving the Decimal Point. Confusion will be avoided if it is remembered that the insertion of the decimal point designates the figures after the point as a *part* of a unit, whereas the absence of a decimal point signifies whole units. Thus .36 indicates 36 hundredths of a unit; and $2.40, two dollars and forty cents. On the other hand, if, in working a problem, we showed 54 cents merely as 54, without a decimal point, we would have to remember to consider the figures in the answer as cents; it is usually better, however, to include the decimal point whenever possible, so the answer may be read in dollars and parts of a dollar, that is, in dollars and cents.

Another important fact which should be observed is this: When the moving of a decimal point places it before or after a blank space, that is, a space without a figure in it, a zero is inserted. Thus .3 multiplied by 100 equals 30, and .7 multiplied by 1000 equals 700. Similarly, .4 divided by 10 equals .04, and .8 divided by 100 equals .008.

Having in mind the principle discussed in Art. 176, let us study the following simple multiplication problems and the explanations which accompany each solution:

Example 1: Compute the value of 10 units costing .17 each.

Solution: We are to multiply .17 by 10, and so the decimal point is moved one place to the right, giving us 1.7 dollars. Since there is no figure in the second place after the decimal point, a zero is inserted, and our answer is $1.70.

Example 2: Find the cost of 100 articles at $1.02 each.

Solution: Here we are to multiply $1.02 by 100, and the decimal point is therefore moved *two* places to the right, making the result $102.00. Two zeros have been inserted after the decimal point to indicate that there are no cents in the answer.

Example 3: Estimate the value of 1000 units costing .04 each.

Solution: One thousand times .04 equals 40, and since we are dealing with dollars and cents, the answer is $40.00.

Example 4: Multiply 34 cents by 10,000.

Solution: Moving the decimal point in .34 four places to the right gives us 3400 or $3400.00.

Let us take a few problems in division:

Example 5: Find the cost of 10 units at .80 per 100.

Solution: Notice that the price is "per 100." The quantity with which we are concerned is one tenth of 100, so we divide .80 by 10. This, to use a very simple illustration, is effected by moving the decimal point one place to the left, which supplies the answer, .08 or 8 cents.

Example 6: Find the cost of 100 units at $24.00 per 1000.

Solution: Here the price is "per 1000." Since 100 is one tenth of 1000, we divide $24.00 by 10, which gives us $2.400. Since zeros after a decimal point, when they are not followed by a digit, have no value, we drop the last zero and simply show the answer as $2.40.

Example 7: Compute the value of 10 units priced at $862.00 per 1000.

Solution: Ten is one hundredth of 1000, so we move the decimal point in the price two places to the left, giving us $8.6200. Dropping the two unnecessary zeros supplies the answer, $8.62.

When working with per-cent rates remember that "per cent" means per hundred. So that 4 per cent means 4 per hundred, or 4 hundredths, or .04. Similarly, 28 per cent equals 28 hundredths, or .28. Conversely, .32 may also be written as 32 per cent; and .475 may be written as 47.5 per cent, or $47\frac{1}{2}$ per cent.

Example 8: Find 26% of $128.00.

Solution: 25% of $128.00 ($\frac{25}{100}$ or $\frac{1}{4}$ of $128.00) = $32.00

1% of $128.00 ($\frac{1}{100}$ of $128.00) = 1.28

_____

26% of $128.00 = $33.28

Example 9: Find .19 of $20.00.

Solution: .19 means 19 hundredths.

$\frac{1}{100}$ of $20.00 = $0.20

_____

$\frac{19}{100}$ of $20.00 (19 times $0.20) = $3.80

PROBLEMS

★ **1.** If 100 yards of sheeting costs $13.80, what is the cost per yard?
Ans. $0.138.

★ **2.** A printer quotes $142.50 per 1000 booklets. How much is that per booklet? *Ans.* $14\frac{1}{4}$ cents.

★ **3.** Write the following per cents as decimals: (a) 7%; (b) $8\frac{1}{2}$%; (c) 86%; (d) $91\frac{1}{4}$%. *Ans.* (a) .07; (b) .085; (c) .86; (d) .9125.

★ **4.** An instrument for the analysis of metals, coal, coke, etc., is said to be accurate to $\frac{1}{5}$ of 1%. Write this per cent as a decimal. *Ans.* .2%.

★ **5.** It costs the government about seven tenths of a cent to make each piece of paper money. Express $\frac{7}{10}$ of a cent (a) as the decimal part of a dollar and (b) as the decimal part of a cent.
Ans. (a) $0.007; (b) .7 cents.

★ **6.** If 300 clasp envelopes cost $15.78, what is the cost per unit? Show your answer to the nearest tenth of a cent. *Ans.* $0.053.

★ **7.** Copper sash cord, $\frac{7}{32}$ inch in diameter, weighs .083 pound per foot. How much will 200 feet of this cord weigh? *Ans.* 16.6 pounds.

★ **8.** Iron sash cord, $\frac{1}{8}$ inch in diameter, weighs .023 pound per foot. How much will 300 feet of this cord weigh? *Ans.* 6.9 pounds.

★ **9.** A building having an approximate area of 10,000 square feet is offered for sale at 65 cents per square foot. At this rate what would the total cost be? *Ans.* $6500.00.

★ **10.** If a newspaper sheet is .0025 inch thick, what is the approximate depth of a pile of 2000 of these sheets?　　　　*Ans.* 5 inches.

★ **11.** A thousand porcelain insulators $1\frac{7}{8}$ inches in height and $1\frac{3}{8}$ inches in diameter weigh 230 pounds. On this basis how much should 100 of these insulators weigh?　　　　*Ans.* 23 pounds.

★ **12.** The approximate weight of 1-inch, electrical metallic tubing is 711 pounds per 1000 feet. What weight would be represented by 10 feet of this tubing?　　　　*Ans.* 7.11 pounds.

179. The Distinction Between Decimal Fractions and Common Fractions. In Art. 176 it was demonstrated that a number may be divided by 10 by moving the decimal point one place to the left, so that 7 divided by 10 equals .7. However, .7 may also be written as $\frac{7}{10}$. Similarly, the result of 2.3 divided by 10 may be written as .23 or as $\frac{23}{100}$.

Both numbers—.23 and $\frac{23}{100}$—are known as fractions; .23 is a *decimal* fraction because its relation to a whole unit is indicated by a decimal point, and $\frac{23}{100}$ is a *common* fraction because it is shown with a denominator instead of with a decimal point.

From the foregoing it will be seen that many common fractions can be quickly converted into decimal fractions simply by changing the form of the fraction so that the denominator is a power of 10. Thus the common fraction $\frac{3}{5}$, which is equivalent to $\frac{6}{10}$, may be written as .6; $\frac{23}{25}$, which is equivalent to $\frac{92}{100}$, may be written as .92; and $\frac{7}{20}$, which is the same as $\frac{35}{100}$, may be expressed as .35; $\frac{419}{1000}$ has the same value as .419, and so on.

PROBLEMS

Express the following as common fractions:

★ **1.** .2.　　　　　　　　　　　　　　*Ans.* $\frac{2}{10}$.
★ **2.** .45.　　　　　　　　　　　　　*Ans.* $\frac{45}{100}$.
★ **3.** .375.　　　　　　　　　　　　*Ans.* $\frac{375}{1000}$.
★ **4.** .025.　　　　　　　　　　　　*Ans.* $\frac{25}{1000}$.
★ **5.** .0069.　　　　　　　　　　　*Ans.* $\frac{69}{10000}$.
★ **6.** .00073.　　　　　　　　　　*Ans.* $\frac{73}{100000}$.

Express the following as decimal fractions. Remember that when the denominator of a fraction is multiplied by a number, the numerator should be multiplied by the same number in order that the value of the original fraction may be retained.

★ 7. $\frac{3}{10}$.   Ans. .3.
★ 8. $\frac{8}{100}$.   Ans. .08.
★ 9. $\frac{29}{100}$.   Ans. .29.
★ 10. $\frac{17}{50}$.   Ans. .34.
★ 11. $\frac{5}{25}$.   Ans. .2.
★ 12. $\frac{19}{250}$.   Ans. .076.

180. How to Write Decimal Fractions as Common Fractions, and Common Fractions Whose Denominators Are a Power of 10 as Decimal Fractions. It was seen in Art. 179 that the decimal fraction .7 may also be written as a common fraction—namely, $\frac{7}{10}$; that .23 may be written as $\frac{23}{100}$, and so on. Now here is an interesting observation: notice that the denominators of these common fractions contain the same number of zeros as there are figures after the decimal point in the corresponding decimal fractions. This observation will be helpful in converting decimal fractions to common fractions, and vice versa.

Thus to write .13086 as a common fraction, it is unnecessary to first determine the value (tenths, hundredths, thousandths, etc.) of the figures after the decimal point. We simply write 13086 as the numerator, and in the denominator we write 1 followed by five zeros, obtaining $\frac{13086}{100000}$. We know, without giving the matter a second thought, that the number of zeros is five, since there are that many figures after the decimal point in .13086.

Similarly, 4.0032, converted into a common fraction, would read $4\frac{32}{10000}$; 1.749 would read $1\frac{749}{1000}$; and 2.87 would be $2\frac{87}{100}$.

To write a fraction having a denominator of 10 or a power of 10, in decimal form, we operate on the same principle in reverse. Take the fraction $\frac{6233}{10000}$, for example. Since the denominator is a power of 10 and the 1 is followed by four zeros, we know that in the decimal form there must be four figures after the decimal point. So we write 6233 and, moving the decimal point four places to the left (one place for each zero in the denominator), obtain the decimal form, .6233. If the fraction had been $\frac{233}{10000}$, the decimal form would read .0233; and if it had been $\frac{23}{10000}$, the decimal form would read .0023. And if each of the foregoing fractions were part of a mixed number, having, let us say, 29 as the whole number, the decimal forms would be written as 29.6233, 29.0233 and 29.0023, respectively.

PROBLEMS

Without pausing for more than a moment in each problem, write the decimal fractions as common fractions, and the common fractions as decimal fractions.

★ **1.** .25763.   *Ans.* $\frac{25763}{100000}$.

★ **2.** 4.3697.   *Ans.* $4\frac{3697}{10000}$.

★ **3.** 17.25439.   *Ans.* $17\frac{25439}{100000}$.

★ **4.** 10.1001.   *Ans.* $10\frac{1001}{10000}$.

★ **5.** 29.4360.   *Ans.* $29\frac{436}{1000}$.

★ **6.** $\frac{49}{100}$.   *Ans.* .49.

★ **7.** $\frac{724}{1000}$.   *Ans.* .724.

★ **8.** $\frac{6}{100}$.   *Ans.* .06.

★ **9.** $\frac{34}{1000}$.   *Ans.* .034.

★ **10.** $\frac{8}{100000}$.   *Ans.* .00008.

181. How to Convert Fractions Whose Denominators Are Not a Power of 10 into Decimal Fractions. All of us know that the common fraction $\frac{1}{2}$ is equivalent to the decimal fraction .5; that $\frac{1}{4}$ is the same as .25; that $\frac{1}{8}$ equals .125. However, in converting most other common fractions into decimal fractions, even the best of us must "figure it out," and the most practical way to do this is by *simple division.*

Assume we wanted to convert the common fraction $\frac{1}{7}$ into a decimal fraction. Knowing that $\frac{1}{7}$ means 1 divided by 7, we perform a simple operation in division, using exactly the same method as in proving that the common fraction $\frac{1}{2}$ is equivalent to the decimal fraction .5. Let us, then, study the procedure in dividing 1 by 2, showing the answer in decimal form:

$$\begin{array}{r} .5 \\ \hline 2)\overline{1.0} \end{array}$$

The method in arriving at .5 is as follows: 2 into 1 won't go. So we place a zero after the 1, taking care to also insert a decimal point after the 1, so that the zero does not change the value of the dividend.

Two into 10 (the number to be divided is read as 10, even though there is a decimal point after the 1) goes 5 times. So we place a 5 directly above the last figure of the dividend. Our answer is now complete, except for one thing: a decimal point must be inserted in the quotient, directly above the decimal point in the dividend. The answer, therefore, is .5.

The process will be more clearly understood after studying the following illustrations of conversion from a common fraction to a decimal fraction:

$$[\tfrac{1}{12}] \quad 12\overline{)1.00}^{\;.083} \qquad\qquad [\tfrac{1}{3}] \quad 3\overline{)1.0}^{\;.333}$$

	.083			.333
$[\tfrac{1}{12}]$	12)1.00		$[\tfrac{1}{3}]$	3)1.0
	96			9
	40			10
	36			9

	.166			.143
$[\tfrac{1}{6}]$	6)1.0		$[\tfrac{1}{7}]$	7)1.0
	6			7
	40			30
	36			28
	4			2

	.346			.2727
$[\tfrac{9}{26}]$	26)9.0		$[\tfrac{3}{11}]$	11)3.0
	78			22
	120			80
	104			77
	160			30
	156			22
	4			8

Note that in some instances the divisor goes into the dividend an exact number of times, while in others it does not. For instance, 4 goes into 1 exactly .25 times, whereas in each of the foregoing illustrations something is left over. For all practical purposes, and particularly when the figures after the decimal point represent cents, it is not necessary to work the problem beyond the third decimal place. The purpose of the third figure after the decimal point in the quotient is to determine the exact value of the preceding figure—that is, whether it is to be increased by 1. The general rule is that if the figure in the third decimal place is 5 or more, the preceding figure is increased by 1; if the third figure is less than 5, the preceding figure remains unchanged. Thus \$1.426 is read as \$1.43, and \$1.312 as \$1.31.

In many instances it would be useless to compute the answer beyond the first, second or third decimal place. Thus in dividing 1 by 3, each figure in the quotient is 3; in the quotient produced by dividing 1 by 6, the 6 repeats itself; and when 3 is divided by 11, 2 and 7 alternate indefinitely.

When the answer is to be expressed to the nearest whole number, it is unnecessary to work the problem beyond the first decimal place. Thus 14.3 gallons expressed to the nearest gallon, is 14 gallons; 2.7 ounces expressed to the nearest ounce, is 3 ounces; and 8.5 pounds would be considered as 9 pounds.

PROBLEMS

Compute to the nearest thousandth of a unit, the decimal equivalents of the following numbers.

1. $\frac{5}{9}$.	*Ans.* .556.
2. $\frac{2}{13}$.	*Ans.* .154.
3. $\frac{3}{7}$.	*Ans.* .429.
4. $\frac{7}{15}$.	*Ans.* .467.
5. $\frac{19}{22}$.	*Ans.* .864.
6. $2\frac{2}{3}$.	*Ans.* 2.667.
7. $15\frac{5}{6}$.	*Ans.* 15.833.
8. $124\frac{4}{7}$.	*Ans.* 124.571.
9. $71\frac{7}{12}$.	*Ans.* 71.583.
10. $100\frac{3}{8}$.	*Ans.* 100.375.

11. The fractional relation of 7 inches to one yard. (Hint: There are 36 inches to the yard.) *Ans.* .194.

12. The fractional relation of 6 ounces to one pound. (Hint: There are 16 ounces to the pound.) *Ans.* .375.

13. The fractional relation of 5 pints to one gallon. (Hint: There are 8 pints to the gallon.) *Ans.* .625.

14. The fractional relation of 16 square inches to one square foot. (Hint: There are 144 square inches to the square foot.) *Ans.* .111.

15. The fractional relation of 160 acres to one square mile. (Hint: There are 640 acres to the square mile.) *Ans.* .25.

182. Addition and Subtraction of Decimal Numbers. In setting down decimal numbers to be added, care should be taken to write all the tenths under each other, all the hundredths under each other, and so on. Thus to add .6, .18, .298, and .0456, we would write these numbers as follows:

$$.6$$
$$.18$$
$$.298$$
$$.0456$$
$$\overline{}$$
$$1.1236$$

Proceeding with the addition: There is only one digit in the column at the extreme right (the ten thousandths column)—namely, the digit 6—so we write 6 in that column. There are two digits in the thousandths column—5 and 8; their sum is 13, so we write 3 in that column and carry 1. In the hundredths column we have 4, 9 and 8; their sum is 21 which added to 1 we carried equals 22, so we write down 2 and carry 2. The sum of the digits in the tenths column equals 9 which added to the 2 we carried equals 11, so we write down 1 in the tenths column; and since there are no figures to be added at the left of this column, we write down the rest of the number, which is 1.

The subtraction of decimal numbers is performed in exactly the same way as the subtraction of whole numbers. However, when there are a larger number of figures after the decimal point in the minuend (the number to be subtracted) than there are after the decimal point in the subtrahend (the number from which we are to subtract), it is necessary to insert, or to imagine the insertion of, the necessary number of zeros in the subtrahend. Likewise, if there are more figures after the decimal point in the subtrahend, it is necessary to insert, or imagine the insertion of, the necessary number of zeros in the minuend.

Thus to subtract .34724 from .68, we would write three zeros after the 8 in the minuend, as follows:

$$.68000$$
$$.34724$$
$$\overline{}$$
$$.33276$$

Let us now subtract 1.4593 from 2.7 without taking the trouble to annex the zeros.

$$2.7$$
$$1.4593$$
$$\overline{}$$
$$1.2407$$

When there are more figures after the decimal point in the minuend than there are after the decimal point in the subtrahend, it is equally unnecessary to annex zeros. Simply imagine the zeros to be there and subtract them from the figures in the minuend. Thus to subtract 3.82 from 15.94763, we would write the numbers as follows:

$$15.94763$$
$$3.82$$
$$\overline{}$$
$$12.12763$$

It is really very simple: 0 from 3 equals 3; 0 from 6 equals 6; 0 from 7 equals 7; 2 from 4 equals 2; 8 from 9 equals 1; and 3 from 15 equals 12.

PROBLEMS

1. Add .47, .035, .6.   *Ans.* 1.105.
2. Add 13.2, 1.48, .967, 103.5682.   *Ans.* 119.2152.
3. Add 147.67, 1.4, 2.78, 39.002.   *Ans.* 190.852.
4. Add 4.0904, 6.703, 90.2, 11.38901.   *Ans.* 112.38241.
5. Add 10.045, 134.1, 4.9607, .32.   *Ans.* 149.4257.

6. Subtract .246 from .869.   *Ans.* .623.
7. Subtract .147 from .8064.   *Ans.* .6594.
8. Subtract .16 from .40372.   *Ans.* .24372.
9. Subtract 4.056 from 92.6274.   *Ans.* 88.5714.
10. Subtract 33.1004 from 106.27965.   *Ans.* 73.17925.

183. How to Multiply a Decimal Number by a Whole Number, or a Decimal Number by a Decimal Number. A very practical method of multiplying numbers, one or both of which include a decimal point, is to multiply the numbers without regard to the decimal points, and then point off, from right to left, as many decimal places in the product as there are decimal places in the multiplicand and multiplier together.

Example 1: Find the product of 236.78 times 43.

Solution:

$$236.78$$
$$43$$
$$\overline{}$$
$$71034$$
$$94712$$
$$\overline{}$$
$$1018154$$

There are 2 decimal places in the multiplicand and none in the multiplier, so we point off 2 decimal places in the product, which gives us 10181.54 as our answer.

Example 2: Find the product of 71426 times .153.

Solution:

$$71426$$
$$.153$$
$$\overline{}$$
$$214278$$
$$357130$$
$$71426$$
$$\overline{}$$
$$10928178$$

There are 3 decimal places in the multiplier and none in the multiplicand, so we point off 3 decimal places in the product, giving us as our answer 10928.178.

Example 3: Find the product of 14.834 times 6.27.

Solution: 14.834
                                  6.27
                                  ―――――
                                  103838
                                  29668
                                  89004
                                  ―――――
                                  9300918

Here we have 5 decimal places altogether—3 in the multiplicand and 2 in the multiplier, so we point off 5 decimal places in the product, which gives us 93.00918 as our answer.

PROBLEMS

Find the products of the following numbers:

1. 3.7 times 54.   *Ans.* 199.8.
2. 26 times 63.7.   *Ans.* 1656.2.
3. 1.093 times 43.   *Ans.* 46.999.
4. 24.8631 times 5.7.   *Ans.* 141.71967.
5. 1.24563 times 7.43.   *Ans.* 9.2550309.
6. 2167.2 times .3154.   *Ans.* 683.53488.

7. If a gallon of kerosene weighs 6.7 pounds, what will 23 gallons of kerosene weigh?   *Ans.* 154.1 pounds.

8. Estimate the amount due a workman for 37 hours at $1.34 an hour.   *Ans.* $49.58.

9. If one foot of round steel bar, $\frac{11}{32}$ inch in diameter, weighs 0.316 pound, how much will 73 feet of these bars weigh?   *Ans.* 23.068 pounds.

10. The Owners, Landlords & Tenants' Liability insurance rate on general bakery stores in which beverages and food are served on the premises, in an eastern city, is $1.54 per 100 square feet of area. Estimate the amount of a one-year premium for insurance of this character to cover an area of 1800 square feet.   *Ans.* $27.72.

11. A cotton driving rope $1\frac{3}{4}$ inches in diameter transmits, at a speed of 3600 feet per minute, 43.3 horsepower. Estimate the equivalent of this power in watts. One horsepower equals 746 watts.

Ans. 32,301.8 watts.

12. A ton of granite occupies 2.3 cubic yards. Estimate the space that would be occupied by 34.4 tons of this material.

Ans. 79.12 cubic yards.

13. If 100 square feet of 6-inch glass blocks laid with ¼-inch visible mortar joints requires the use of 4.3 cubic feet of mortar, how much mortar would be needed for placing 350 square feet of these blocks in the specified manner? *Ans.* 15.05 cubic feet.

14. The pic is an Egyptian unit of measurement which is equal to 22.835 inches. Estimate the equivalent in inches of 2.64 pics.

Ans. 60.2844 inches.

15. In the Philippine Islands in a recent year the average yield of unshelled peanuts was 586 kilograms per hectare. If a kilogram equals 2.2 pounds, and a hectare 2.47 acres, how many pounds of unshelled peanuts would represent the yield of 494 acres? (Hint: 494 acres is exactly 200 hectares.) *Ans.* 257,840 pounds.

184. How to Divide a Decimal Number by a Whole Number. In dividing a decimal number by a whole number the decimal point is handled in exactly the same way as in dividing a whole number by a whole number. It was seen in Art. 181, for instance, that in converting the common fraction $\frac{9}{26}$ to a decimal fraction, it was necessary to insert a decimal point after the 9 and to insert, or imagine the insertion of, zeros after the decimal point. The illustration as it appears in that article is as follows:

$$
\begin{array}{r}
.346 \\
26\overline{)9.0} \\
78 \\
\hline
120 \\
104 \\
\hline
160 \\
156 \\
\hline
4
\end{array}
$$

It will be noted that the insertion of a zero after the decimal point in the dividend does not alter the value of the dividend. The zero simply facilitates the process of division. Thus 26 is not divisible into 9, but it is divisible into 90.

If the dividend had been 9.2352 we would, of course, have divided 26 into 92, taking care to insert the decimal point in the quotient directly above the decimal point in the dividend, as will be seen in the following illustration.

Example 1: Divide 9.2352 by 26.

Solution:

```
          .3552
     26)9.2352
        78
        ──
        143
        130
        ──
        135
        130
        ──
         52
```

Ans. .3552.

Observe that in every problem in division, the figure in the quotient is inserted directly above the last figure of the part of the dividend being divided. Thus when 26 is divided into 92, the 3 in the quotient is inserted directly above the 2 in 92.

Example 2: Divide .049296 by 13.

Solution:

```
           .003792
     13).049296
        39
        ──
        102
         91
        ──
        119
        117
        ──
         26
```

Ans. .003792.

Example 3: Divide $364.47 by 7.

Solution:

```
        52.066
    7)364.47
      35
      --
      14
      14
      --
      047
      42
      --
      50
```

Ans. $52.07.

The last illustration provides an interesting example of the procedure followed when the deduction of a partial product leaves no remainder, as when 14 deducted from 14 does not complete the solution of the problem. A zero is therefore written down as the difference, and the next figure in the dividend is brought down in the usual way. Seven into 4 won't go, so a zero is inserted in the next space in the quotient, and another figure is brought down from the dividend. Seven into 47 goes six times, so 6 is inserted in the next space in the quotient, and the computation is continued in the usual manner.

PROBLEMS

Find the exact answer to each of the following problems:

★ 1. Divide 21.872 by 8.   *Ans.* 2.734.

2. Divide 2.31914 by 17.   *Ans.* 2.31914.

3. Divide 330.76159 by 43.   *Ans.* 7.69213.

4. Divide .4394 by 52.   *Ans.* .00845.

★ 5. Divide .04404 by 12.   *Ans.* .00367.

6. If it costs $1024.60 to produce 73 suits of clothes, what is the cost per suit?   *Ans.* $14.04.

★ 7. It takes 18.5 hours to assemble 5 electrical units. How much time does that average per unit?   *Ans.* 3.7 hours.

8. If it requires 308.25 pounds of whole milk to make 137 pounds of condensed or evaporated milk, how many pounds of whole milk would be required to make one pound of condensed milk?   *Ans.* 2.25 pounds.

9. If 137 yards of a Navy balloon cloth weigh 280.85 ounces, what is the weight per yard?   *Ans.* 2.05 ounces.

10. If 37 cubic inches of wrought iron weigh 10.2786 pounds, what is the weight per cubic inch?   *Ans.* .2778 pounds.

11. If 43 gallons of water weigh 359.695 pounds, what is the weight of one gallon of water?   *Ans.* 8.365 pounds.

12. A stack of 3480 sheets of aluminum occupies a space 1.74 inches deep. What is the thickness per sheet?   *Ans.* .0005 inches.

185. How to Divide a Whole Number by a Decimal Number, or a Decimal Number by a Decimal Number. To divide by a decimal number, the most practical procedure is to change the divisor to a whole number. Thus divisor 2.7 would be changed to 27; 8.41 to 841; and so on. The object of making the change is to facilitate computation.

We must remember, however, that when the divisor is multiplied by any number, the dividend, too, must be multiplied by the same number, for it is obvious that unless this is done the quotient will be affected. And this holds true whether the divisor is multiplied by 10, by a power of 10, or by any other number. The following illustrations will serve to make this clear:

Example 1: Divide 28 by 1.4.

Solution: 28 divided by 1.4 is equivalent to 280 divided by 14.

$$\frac{20}{14)\overline{280}}$$
$$\frac{28}{-}$$

Ans. 20.

Example 2: Divide 465 by 24.7, and state the answer to the nearest hundredth.

Solution: 465 divided by 24.7 is equivalent to 4650 divided by 247.

$$
\begin{array}{r}
18.825 \\
247)\overline{4650} \\
247 \\
\hline
2180 \\
1976 \\
\hline
2040 \\
1976 \\
\hline
640 \\
494 \\
\hline
1460 \\
1235 \\
\end{array}
$$

Ans. 18.83.

Example 3: Divide 945 by 3.15.

Solution: 945 divided by 3.15 is equivalent to 94500 divided by 315.

$$
\begin{array}{r}
300 \\
315)\overline{94500} \\
945 \\
\hline
\end{array}
$$

Ans. 300.

Note that when the divisor is exactly divisible into a part of the dividend which is followed only by zeros, the quotient is completed by the annexation of zeros over the zeros in the dividend. Thus in the foregoing problem, the insertion of 3 in the quotient over the 5 in the dividend is followed by the annexation of two zeros in the quotient over the two zeros in the dividend.

Example 4: Divide 105 by 3.5.

Solution: 105 divided by 3.5 is equivalent to 1050 divided by 35.

$$\begin{array}{r} 30 \\ \hline 35)\overline{1050} \\ 105 \\ \hline \end{array}$$

Ans. 30.

The reader may find it worth while at this point to refer to Chapter XV, "The 'Double-and-Halve' Method of Division," where some interesting techniques are discussed for dividing by mixed numbers. He will find, for instance, that by changing a divisor to a single-digit number (by the simple process of multiplying it by 2, 3, or 4, etc.) and multiplying the dividend by the same number, a problem can be considerably simplified. Thus 3.5 multiplied by 2 becomes the single-digit number 7; 105 multiplied by 2 equals 210; and quick as a flash it is seen that 210 divided by 7 equals 30.

When the dividend as well as the divisor contains a decimal point, the procedure in changing the divisor to a whole number is exactly the same as when the dividend is already a whole number. There is only this difference: Whereas when the dividend is already a whole number zeros are annexed to it, when the dividend is a decimal number the digits after the decimal point take the place of the zeros. Thus the problem 4.82 divided by .4 would be changed to 48.2 divided by 4; 131.62 divided by .73 would become 13162 divided by 73; 19.1 divided by .645 would be restated to read 19100 divided by 645; and so on.

PROBLEMS

Compute the answers to the following problems to the nearest hundredth.

1. Divide 574 by 1.3.   *Ans.* 441.54.
2. Divide 3689 by 21.4.   *Ans.* 172.38.
3. Divide 74 by 5.23.   *Ans.* 14.15.
4. Divide 36 by 1.5.   *Ans.* 24.
5. Divide 82.464 by 81.2.   *Ans.* 1.02.

6. Divide 7.3845 by 3.4.   *Ans.* 2.17.

★ **7.** Divide .00562 by .002.   *Ans.* 2.81.

8. Divide 68.625 by 15.25.   *Ans.* 4.5.

9. Compute the number of feet to a pound of wire of which 120 feet weigh 22.8 pounds. State the answer to the nearest hundredth of a foot.
                                                 Ans. 5.26 feet.

10. If 425 dozen units can be produced in 6.25 hours, what is the production capacity per hour?   *Ans.* 68 dozen.

11. If 6.4 pounds of a pharmaceutical preparation can be made with 32 ounces of a certain ingredient, how many ounces of the ingredient will make one pound?   *Ans.* 5 ounces.

12. Convert 688.975 inches to meters. (There are 39.37 inches to the meter.)   *Ans.* $17\frac{1}{2}$ meters.

13. Convert 19.1646 kilograms to pounds. (There are .4536 kilograms to the pound.)   *Ans.* 42.25 pounds.

14. If 1000 conductor terminals weigh 28 pounds, how many should be contained in a package whose net weight is 18 pounds 2 ounces? (Hint: Divide the net weight of the package by the weight of one conductor terminal.)   *Ans.* 647.

15. The protein contents of wheat and tapioca are 12.35% and .87%, respectively. How many times greater is the protein content of one than the other?   *Ans.* 14.2 times.

16. A molding powder weighs .86 ounces per cubic inch. Compute the number of cubic inches that would be occupied by 29.24 ounces of the powder.   *Ans.* 34 cubic inches.

186. A Word About Common Fractions, Proper Fractions, Improper Fractions, and Mixed Numbers. Frequent reference will be made to these terms in the articles that follow, and the reader will do well to familiarize himself with their meaning.

A *common fraction*, as we have already seen, is distinct from a decimal fraction in that it is written with a numerator and a denominator. Thus $\frac{1}{2}$, $\frac{3}{4}$, $\frac{4}{5}$, $\frac{13}{11}$, are all common fractions.

A *proper fraction* is one in which the numerator is smaller than the denominator. Thus only the first three fractions in the preceding paragraph are proper fractions.

An *improper fraction* is one in which the numerator is greater than or equals the denominator. Thus $\frac{9}{8}$ and $\frac{3}{3}$ are improper fractions.

A *mixed number* is one which consists of a whole number and a fraction. Thus $7\frac{1}{4}$ and $42\frac{8}{9}$ are mixed numbers.

187. How to Reduce Common Fractions to Their Lowest Terms, and How to Increase the Terms of Common Fractions Without Changing Their Value. Imagine yourself at the grocer's, making some purchases. You order half a pound of cheese, and when the clerk is about to remove the cheese from the scale you see the indicator pointing to 8. You know that since there are 16 ounces to the pound, the 8 represents half a pound. In other words, $\frac{8}{16}$ is reduced to $\frac{1}{2}$. In this simple illustration lies the explanation of what is meant by reducing a common fraction to its lowest terms.

It is clear, therefore, that in dealing with fractions, it is frequently advisable to reduce them to their lowest terms. However, if a fraction is to be so reduced, the numerator and the denominator must be divisible by the same number, which number is known as a *common factor*. Thus in the fraction $\frac{8}{16}$ the common factor is 8. Of course, 2 and 4 are also common factors of 8 and 16, but 8 is the largest common factor in this instance.

The following illustrations of fractions reduced to their lowest terms will help to fix in mind this process:

$$\frac{3}{6} = \frac{1}{2} \qquad \frac{12}{21} = \frac{4}{7} \qquad \frac{5}{15} = \frac{1}{3}$$

$$\frac{3}{27} = \frac{1}{9} \qquad \frac{24}{96} = \frac{1}{4} \qquad \frac{14}{26} = \frac{7}{13}$$

$$\frac{17}{85} = \frac{1}{5} \qquad \frac{20}{46} = \frac{10}{23} \qquad \frac{28}{32} = \frac{7}{8}$$

When we speak of increasing the terms of a fraction we usually have in mind changing the denominator to a specific higher number. For instance, it may be desired to change the fraction $\frac{4}{5}$ so that the denominator is 10 instead of 5. As we have already seen, if we multiply both terms of a fraction by the same number the value of the fraction is unchanged. Thus $\frac{4}{5}$ equals $\frac{8}{10}$. Likewise, if it is desired to increase the terms of the fraction $\frac{2}{3}$ so that the denominator is 9 instead of 3, we simply multiply each of the numbers in the fraction by 3, which gives us $\frac{6}{9}$. All we need do, then, in increasing the terms of a common fraction, is to determine the number of times that the original denominator is contained in the desired denominator, and multiply numerator and denominator by that number.

Reduce the following fractions to their lowest terms:

★ **1.** $\frac{2}{4}$.   *Ans.* $\frac{1}{2}$.

★ **2.** $\frac{5}{20}$.   *Ans.* $\frac{1}{4}$.

★ **3.** $\frac{3}{9}$.   *Ans.* $\frac{1}{3}$.

★ **4.** $\frac{12}{18}$.   *Ans.* $\frac{2}{3}$.

★ **5.** $\frac{13}{39}$.   *Ans.* $\frac{1}{3}$.

★ **6.** $\frac{25}{100}$.   *Ans.* $\frac{1}{4}$.

★ **7.** $\frac{4}{24}$.   *Ans.* $\frac{1}{6}$.

★ **8.** $\frac{14}{16}$.   *Ans.* $\frac{7}{8}$.

Increase the terms of the fraction $\frac{1}{4}$ so that the denominator is represented by the number indicated:

★ **9.** 12.   *Ans.* $\frac{3}{12}$.

★ **10.** 16.   *Ans.* $\frac{4}{16}$.

★ **11.** 28.   *Ans.* $\frac{7}{28}$.

★ **12.** 36.   *Ans.* $\frac{9}{36}$.

★ **13.** 44.   *Ans.* $\frac{11}{44}$.

★ **14.** 8.   *Ans.* $\frac{2}{8}$.

★ **15.** 72.   *Ans.* $\frac{18}{72}$.

★ **16.** 56.   *Ans.* $\frac{14}{56}$.

188. How to Add or Subtract Common Fractions with Unlike Denominators. How would you add $\frac{1}{2}$ plus $\frac{1}{3}$? The two denominators are unlike, and obviously it is just as impossible to add these fractions in their present form as it would be to add oranges to apples and obtain one total.

Before we can add fractions with unlike denominators, it is necessary to find a common denominator—that is, a number into which each of the original denominators is divisible. This is accomplished by multiplying one denominator by the other.

The denominators in the fractions $\frac{1}{2}$ and $\frac{1}{3}$ are 2 and 3; so their common denominator is 6. And since the value of a fraction is not changed when its numerator and denominator are multiplied (or divided) by the same number, it is a very simple matter to convert the two fractions in our problem so that the denominator in each instance is 6: $\frac{1}{2}$ becomes $\frac{3}{6}$, and $\frac{1}{3}$ becomes $\frac{2}{6}$; and the sum of $\frac{3}{6}$ plus $\frac{2}{6}$ equals $\frac{5}{6}$.

This method of finding a common denominator may be applied regardless of the number of different denominators in a problem. Thus to add $\frac{1}{2}$ plus $\frac{1}{3}$ plus $\frac{2}{5}$, we should find a common denominator by multiplying 2 by 3 by 5, which equals 30. Our problem now becomes $\frac{15}{30}$ plus $\frac{10}{30}$ plus $\frac{12}{30}$, which equals $\frac{37}{30}$, or $1\frac{7}{30}$.

In the preceding problem the common denominator happens to be the product of all the denominators in the original fractions. However, to add $\frac{1}{3}$ plus $\frac{1}{2}$ plus $\frac{1}{4}$, it would not be necessary to multiply 3 by 2 by 4 to find a common denominator. Since denominator 4 is divisible by denominator 2, it is only necessary to multiply 3 by 4, arriving at 12 as the common denominator.

A practical way of writing down converted fractions to be added is demonstrated in the following illustrations:

Example 1: Add $\frac{3}{4}$ plus $\frac{2}{3}$ plus $\frac{1}{6}$ plus $\frac{5}{12}$.

Solution: The highest denominator is 12, and each of the other denominators is exactly divisible into it, so we will change the other denominators to 12.

$$\frac{9 + 8 + 2 + 5}{12} = \frac{24}{12} = 2.$$

Ans. 2.

Example 2: Add $2\frac{1}{9}$ plus $8\frac{2}{3}$ plus $\frac{5}{6}$ plus $13\frac{1}{6}$.

Solution: The sum of the whole numbers (2, 8 and 13) = 23. The lowest common denominator is 18, and converting each of the fractions to eighteenths, we obtain

$$\frac{2 + 12 + 15 + 3}{18} = \frac{32}{18} \text{ or } \frac{16}{9} \text{ or } 1\frac{7}{9}.$$

23 (the sum of the whole numbers) plus $1\frac{7}{9}$ (the sum of the fractions) = $24\frac{7}{9}$.

Ans. $24\frac{7}{9}$.

The subtraction of common fractions with unlike denominators calls for exactly the same procedure in converting the denominators as when adding. Thus to subtract $\frac{1}{4}$ from $\frac{1}{2}$ we would simply change the second fraction to $\frac{2}{4}$, and it is seen immediately that $\frac{1}{4}$ subtracted from $\frac{2}{4}$ equals $\frac{1}{4}$. Likewise, the problem $\frac{1}{3}$ subtracted from $\frac{8}{9}$ would be revised to read $\frac{3}{9}$ subtracted from $\frac{8}{9}$, and so on.

To subtract one mixed number from another, subtract one fraction from the other fraction, and one whole number from the other whole number. Thus:

Example 3: Subtract $7\frac{3}{8}$ from $9\frac{1}{2}$.

Solution: $9\frac{1}{2} = 9\frac{4}{8}$.

$$\frac{3}{8} \text{ subtracted from } \frac{4}{8} \quad = \frac{1}{8}$$
$$7 \text{ subtracted from } 9 \quad = 2$$

$$7\frac{3}{8} \text{ subtracted from } 9\frac{1}{2} = 2\frac{1}{8}$$

In actual practice, of course, $7\frac{3}{8}$ would be written under $9\frac{1}{2}$, the same as when subtracting whole numbers, as follows:

$$9\frac{1}{2}$$
$$7\frac{3}{8}$$
$$\overline{}$$
$$2\frac{1}{8}$$

When the value of the fraction in the subtrahend exceeds the value of the fraction in the minuend, simply borrow 1 from the whole number in the minuend. Thus:

Example 4: Subtract $3\frac{1}{2}$ from $10\frac{1}{4}$.

Solution: $10\frac{1}{4}$ is equivalent to the improper fraction $9\frac{5}{4}$.

$3\frac{1}{2}$ is equivalent to $3\frac{2}{4}$.
$3\frac{2}{4}$ subtracted from $9\frac{5}{4} = 6\frac{3}{4}$.

Ans. $6\frac{3}{4}$.

Problems

Find the sums of the following fractions:

★ 1. $\frac{1}{2}$ plus $\frac{1}{3}$.   Ans. $\frac{5}{6}$.

★ 2. $\frac{1}{4}$ plus $\frac{2}{5}$.   Ans. $\frac{13}{20}$.

★ 3. $4\frac{3}{8}$ plus $\frac{3}{4}$.   Ans. $5\frac{1}{8}$.

★ 4. $\frac{2}{3}$ plus $2\frac{4}{9}$.   Ans. $3\frac{1}{9}$.

★ 5. Subtract $\frac{1}{6}$ from $\frac{2}{3}$.   Ans. $\frac{1}{2}$.

★ 6. Subtract $\frac{1}{2}$ from $\frac{9}{10}$.   Ans. $\frac{2}{5}$.

↑ 7. Subtract $\frac{2}{5}$ from $6\frac{13}{20}$.   Ans. $6\frac{1}{4}$.

8. Subtract $1\frac{15}{16}$ from $4\frac{5}{8}$.   Ans. $2\frac{11}{16}$.

9. A dealer sold 4 lengths of cloth: $3\frac{1}{2}$ yards, $4\frac{1}{4}$ yards, $7\frac{1}{3}$ yards and $5\frac{1}{6}$ yards. How many yards did he sell in all?   Ans. $20\frac{1}{4}$ yards.

10. The treatment of a building exterior required the use of $3\frac{1}{4}$ gallons, $4\frac{1}{2}$ gallons and $5\frac{3}{8}$ gallons of paint. What was the total amount of paint used?   Ans. $13\frac{1}{8}$ gallons.

11. Find the total weight of the following upholsterers' shears: a $10\frac{1}{2}$-inch weighing $1\frac{3}{8}$ pounds, an $11\frac{1}{4}$-inch weighing $1\frac{1}{2}$ pounds, a 12-inch weighing $1\frac{5}{8}$ pounds, and a $12\frac{1}{2}$-inch weighing $1\frac{3}{4}$ pounds.

Ans. $6\frac{1}{4}$ pounds.

12. One girl can produce 2 gross units in 6 days, and a second girl, 2 gross units in 4 days. What fraction of a gross would be produced in one day by both girls working together?   Ans. $\frac{5}{6}$ gross.

13. From a sheet of metal $4\frac{1}{2}$ feet long 2 lengths are cut: $1\frac{1}{3}$ feet and $2\frac{1}{4}$ feet. Disregarding the amount of waste in cutting, what part of the sheet remained?   Ans. $\frac{11}{12}$ of a foot.

14. By how many yards does $\frac{5}{8}$ of a mile exceed $\frac{1}{2}$ a mile? (There are 1760 yards to the mile.)   Ans. 220 yards.

15. How much larger is $8\frac{1}{3}\%$ than $6\frac{1}{4}\%$?   Ans. $2\frac{1}{12}\%$.

★ 16. The first and last sales of a stock issue on a certain day were at $36\frac{3}{4}$ and $36\frac{1}{8}$, respectively. By what fraction of a dollar per share had the price dropped at the close of the day's business?   Ans. $\frac{5}{8}$ of a dollar.

189. How to Multiply or Divide a Fraction by a Whole Number, or a Fraction by a Fraction. In problems such as 3 divided by 5, or 1 divided by 4, both the dividend and the divisor are whole numbers, and so the process of division is quite simple. The answer to the first problem is simply $\frac{3}{5}$, and the answer to the second is $\frac{1}{4}$. But how do we go about multiplying or dividing a fraction by a whole number, or a fraction by a fraction? It is really very simple, as the following rules show:

1. To multiply a fraction by a whole number, multiply the *numerator* of the fraction by the whole number. Thus $\frac{1}{3}$ multiplied by 2 equals $\frac{1 \times 2}{3} = \frac{2}{3}$.

2. To divide a fraction by a whole number, multiply the *denominator* of the fraction by the whole number. Thus $\frac{1}{3}$ divided by 2 equals $\frac{1}{3 \times 2} = \frac{1}{6}$.

3. To multiply one fraction by another fraction, multiply the numerator of one fraction by the numerator of the other fraction, and multiply the denominator of one fraction by the denominator of the other fraction. Thus $\frac{2}{7}$ multiplied by $\frac{5}{9}$ equals $\frac{2 \times 5}{7 \times 9} = \frac{10}{63}$.

4. To divide one fraction by another fraction, reverse the position of the numerator and denominator in the divisor, and proceed to multiply one fraction by the other fraction. Thus $\frac{2}{7}$ divided by $\frac{5}{9}$ equals $\frac{2}{7}$ multiplied by $\frac{9}{5} = \frac{2 \times 9}{7 \times 5}$ or $\frac{18}{35}$.

It should be remembered that in any mathematical problem, the word "of" means "multiplied by." Thus one-half of 8 means $\frac{1}{2}$ multiplied by 8.

PROBLEMS

The final answers to Problems 1 to 8 are not required; show only how you would write the multiplicand and multiplier or the dividend and divisor, as the case may be, in each of these 8 problems, with a single dividing line.

★ **1.** Multiply $\frac{4}{11}$ by 32.   *Ans.* $\frac{4 \times 32}{11}$.

★ **2.** Multiply $\frac{13}{15}$ by 90.   *Ans.* $\frac{13 \times 90}{15}$.

★ **3.** Divide $\frac{6}{7}$ by 12.   *Ans.* $\frac{6}{7 \times 12}$.

★ **4.** Divide $\frac{3}{4}$ by 8.   *Ans.* $\frac{3}{4 \times 8}$.

★ 5. Multiply $\frac{5}{8}$ by $\frac{3}{8}$.   *Ans.* $\dfrac{5 \times 3}{8 \times 8}$.

★ 6. Multiply $\frac{7}{12}$ by $\frac{1}{3}$.   *Ans.* $\dfrac{7 \times 1}{12 \times 3}$.

★ 7. Divide $\frac{8}{13}$ by $\frac{5}{7}$.   *Ans.* $\dfrac{8 \times 7}{13 \times 5}$.

★ 8. Divide $\frac{2}{3}$ by $\frac{3}{4}$.   *Ans.* $\dfrac{2 \times 4}{3 \times 3}$.

★ 9. What is the height in inches of a stack of 240 sheets of Plexiglas, each $\frac{3}{16}$ inch thick?   *Ans.* 45 inches.

★ 10. If it takes 8 hours to complete $\frac{2}{7}$ of a job, what part of the job is completed every hour?   *Ans.* $\frac{1}{28}$.

★ 11. What fraction of a gross is $\frac{1}{4}$ of $\frac{1}{3}$ of a gross?   *Ans.* $\frac{1}{12}$ of a gross.

★ 12. How many times is $\frac{1}{8}$ of an ounce contained in $\frac{3}{4}$ of an ounce?

Ans. 6 times.

190. Cancellation, and How It Simplifies the Process of Multiplying Fractions.   Problems in fractions are often solved quickly and easily by the simple process of cancellation, which is really a process of division.   Take, for instance, the problem of multiplying $\frac{3}{5}$ by $\frac{10}{9}$:

$$\frac{3}{5} \times \frac{10}{9} \text{ or } \frac{3 \times 10}{5 \times 9}$$

According to the rule, the product of the numerators (3 and 10 in this problem) divided by the product of the denominators (5 and 9) will supply the answer.   Often, however, it is unnecessary to multiply all the original numerators by each other and all the original denominators by each other.   When a numerator or one of its factors is divisible into a denominator, or vice versa, the process of division should be carried out.   Thus in the example $\frac{3}{5}$ multiplied by $\frac{10}{9}$, the denominator 5 can be canceled into the numerator 10, and the numerator 3 into the denominator 9.   When the process of division (or cancellation, as it is called) is completed, the problem will look as follows:

$$\frac{\overset{1}{\cancel{3}} \times \overset{2}{\cancel{10}}}{\underset{1}{\cancel{5}} \times \underset{3}{\cancel{9}}} = \frac{2}{3}$$

Note that it is not necessary to cancel a whole numerator or a whole denominator at one time: only a factor may be canceled, as shown in the following solution of the problem $\frac{14}{33}$ multiplied by $\frac{22}{35}$.

$$\frac{\overset{2}{\cancel{14}} \times \overset{2}{\cancel{22}}}{\underset{3}{\cancel{33}} \times \underset{5}{\cancel{35}}} = \frac{4}{15}$$

Canceling the factor 7 into 14 and 35, and the factor 11 into 22 and 33 reduced the problem to the equivalent of 4 divided by 15.

Let us take a more difficult problem:

$$\frac{\overset{\overset{1}{\cancel{2}}}{\cancel{32}} \times \overset{\overset{1}{\cancel{2}}}{\cancel{6}} \times \overset{1}{\cancel{7}} \times \overset{1}{\cancel{3}} \times \overset{1}{\cancel{15}}}{\underset{\underset{1}{\cancel{1}}}{\cancel{16}} \times \underset{1}{\cancel{15}} \times \underset{3}{\cancel{9}} \times \underset{\underset{1}{\cancel{2}}}{\cancel{14}} \times \underset{1}{\cancel{2}}}$$

The step-by-step procedure in working this problem is as follows: The numerator 32 contains the denominator 16 twice, so a line is drawn through each number, and 2 is substituted for 32.

There is a 15 in the numerator and another in the denominator, so these numbers are eliminated by cancellation.

The numerator 7 will go twice into the denominator 14, so a line is drawn through each of these numbers, and 2 is substituted for 14.

Numerator 3 goes into denominator 9 three times, so 3 is substituted for 9.

Now the 3 in the denominator will go twice into the 6 in the numerator, so 2 is substituted for 6.

And since the two 2's in the numerator will cancel the two 2's in the denominator, lines may be drawn through all four 2's, and a 1 substituted for each 2.

We now have nothing but 1's in the numerator and 1's in the denominator. The answer, therefore, is $\frac{1}{1}$, and since 1 divided by 1 equals 1, the answer may be stated simply as 1.

It is important to observe that the cancellation process may be used only when all the signs between the numerators and all the signs between the denominators are *multiplication* signs. If there is a plus or a minus sign between any two numerators or denominators, it is necessary to compute the net value of the figures above the line and the net value of the figures below the line. Thus in the example

$$\frac{6 + 4}{6 \times 5}$$

the plus sign in the numerator prevents the cancellation of one 6 into the other 6. The net value of the numerator is 10, and the net value of the denominator is 30. The answer, therefore, is $\frac{10}{30}$ or $\frac{1}{3}$.

PROBLEMS

The following problems are to be worked by the process of cancellation, as discussed in the text:

1. Multiply $\frac{7}{8}$ by $\frac{16}{25}$. *Ans.* $\frac{14}{25}$.
2. Multiply $\frac{3}{4}$ by $\frac{5}{6}$. *Ans.* $\frac{5}{8}$.
3. Multiply $\frac{1}{2}$ by $\frac{8}{9}$ by $\frac{3}{4}$. *Ans.* $\frac{1}{3}$.
4. Divide $\frac{24}{25}$ by $\frac{12}{13}$. *Ans.* $1\frac{1}{25}$.
5. Divide $\frac{8}{11}$ by $\frac{16}{33}$. *Ans.* $1\frac{1}{2}$.
6. Divide $\frac{19}{20}$ by $\frac{3}{10}$. *Ans.* $3\frac{1}{6}$.
★ 7. Divide the sum of 12 plus 3 by the product of 10 times 3. *Ans.* $\frac{1}{2}$.
★ 8. Divide the sum of 24 plus 1 by the product of 6 times 25. *Ans.* $\frac{1}{6}$.

9. A glass mattress weighs 40 pounds against 55 pounds for a conventional cotton innerspring mattress. If the net weight of a shipment of the cotton product is 693 pounds, what would the approximate weight be of a shipment of the same number of glass mattresses?

Ans. 504 pounds.

10. The circumference of a circle is approximately $3\frac{1}{7}$ times the diameter. If the diameter is 56 inches, what is the circumference?

Ans. 176 inches, or 14 feet 8 inches.

11. If one cubic foot holds approximately $\frac{4}{5}$ of a bushel of grain, how many bushels of grain could be placed in a bin whose capacity is 476 cubic feet? *Ans.* 595 bushels.

★ 12. How many sheets of wire glass $\frac{3}{8}$ inch thick can be stacked in a pile 24 inches high? *Ans.* 64.

191. How to Multiply a Common Fraction by a Mixed Number, or a Mixed Number by a Mixed Number. Having in mind the simple rules given in Art. 189, the multiplication of a common fraction by a mixed number or the multiplication of a mixed number by a mixed number will be found to be a relatively simple matter.

It should be remembered that a mixed number is really two numbers in one: a whole number and a fraction. So that to multiply a common fraction by a mixed number two partial products should be found—the product of the common fraction times the whole number, and the product of the common fraction times the common fraction.

Example: Multiply $\frac{3}{7}$ by $5\frac{4}{9}$.

Solution: $\frac{3}{7}$ times $5 = \dfrac{3 \times 5}{7} = \dfrac{15}{7} = 2\frac{1}{7}$.

$\frac{3}{7}$ times $\dfrac{4}{9} = \dfrac{3 \times 4}{7 \times 9} = \dfrac{4}{21}$.

Our problem now is to add the two partial products. The fractions $\frac{1}{7}$ and $\frac{4}{21}$, however, must have a common denominator before they can be added (see Art. 187). But this can be easily effected, for we see at a glance that the denominator 7 is divisible into the denominator 21 three times. Multiplying the numerator and denominator in the fraction $\frac{1}{7}$ by 3 gives us $\frac{3}{21}$, and $\frac{3}{21}$ plus $\frac{4}{21}$ equals $\frac{7}{21}$ or $\frac{1}{3}$. Adding the whole number 2 to the fraction $\frac{1}{3}$ supplies the answer, $2\frac{1}{3}$.

Another way to find the product of $\frac{3}{7}$ times $5\frac{4}{9}$ is to convert the mixed number into an improper fraction $(\frac{49}{9})$ and to multiply one fraction by the other, as explained in Art. 189, canceling the numerators and denominators into each other, as explained in Art. 190, thus:

$$\dfrac{\overset{1}{3} \times \overset{7}{49}}{\underset{1}{7} \times \underset{3}{9}}$$

See how beautifully the process of cancellation works out here: the 3 cancels into the 9, and the 7 cancels into 49. In an instant we have the fraction $\frac{7}{3}$, or $2\frac{1}{3}$, as the answer.

It will be seen from the foregoing that in multiplying a common fraction by a mixed number it is sometimes a good plan to convert the mixed number into an improper fraction to see if the numerators and denominators cancel into each other, before working the problem by any other method.

Still another method is to multiply the mixed number by the numerator of the common fraction, and then divide the result by the denominator of the common fraction, thus:

3 times $5\frac{4}{9}$:

$$3 \text{ times } 5 = 15$$
$$3 \text{ times } \tfrac{4}{9} = \tfrac{12}{9} = 1\tfrac{3}{9} = 1\tfrac{1}{3}$$

$$\overline{\qquad}$$
$$16\tfrac{1}{3}$$

$16\frac{1}{3}$ divided by 7: $\quad$ 16 divided by 7 $\quad = 2\frac{2}{7}$

$$\tfrac{1}{3} \text{ divided by } 7 = \frac{1}{3 \times 7} = \tfrac{1}{21}$$

$$\overline{\qquad}$$
$$2\tfrac{2}{7} \text{ plus } \tfrac{1}{21}$$

The fraction $\frac{2}{7}$ is equivalent to $\frac{6}{21}$; $2\frac{6}{21}$ plus $\frac{1}{21} = 2\frac{7}{21}$, or $2\frac{1}{3}$.

In multiplying a mixed number by a mixed number, the nature of the numbers is a very helpful guide in selecting the method of procedure. If both numbers are small—as, for example, in the problem $3\frac{5}{9}$ times $2\frac{1}{8}$—it would be a simple matter to convert both numbers to improper fractions and proceed from there.

On the other hand, if the numbers are large—as, for example, in the problem $348\frac{12}{19}$ times $91\frac{1}{3}$—it would obviously be better to multiply $348\frac{12}{19}$ by 91, $348\frac{12}{19}$ by $\frac{1}{3}$ (which is equivalent to dividing $348\frac{12}{19}$ by 3), and then add the results.

PROBLEMS

1. If a girl can sew $\frac{2}{3}$ of a gross of bags in one hour, how many can she be expected to produce in $8\frac{1}{4}$ hours? *Ans.* $5\frac{1}{2}$ gross.

2. A pharmaceutical manufacturer uses 7 ounces of a certain drug to each dozen bottles of a preparation. If he needed $16\frac{1}{2}$ dozen bottles altogether, how many pounds of the drug will be required? Use the apothecaries' weight of 12 ounces to the pound. *Ans.* $9\frac{5}{8}$ pounds.

3. If a salesman's commission is $37\frac{1}{2}\%$, how much will he have earned on a sale amounting to \$65.33? (Hint: $37\frac{1}{2}\%$ is equivalent to $\frac{3}{8}$, and consider \$0.33 as $\frac{1}{3}$ of a dollar.) *Ans.* \$24.50.

4. A surveyor reports the width of a field as $23\frac{1}{2}$ rods. Convert this figure to yards. (There are $5\frac{1}{2}$ yards to the rod.) *Ans.* $129\frac{1}{4}$ yards.

5. If 100 square feet of a 4-mesh copper wire cloth weigh $65\frac{7}{10}$ pounds, how much will 325 square feet weigh? Compute the answer to the nearest fortieth of a pound. (Hint: Multiply $65\frac{7}{10}$ by $3\frac{1}{4}$.) *Ans.* $213\frac{21}{40}$ pounds.

6. One ounce is equivalent to $28\frac{7}{20}$ grams. Estimate the number of grams in $4\frac{1}{2}$ ounces. *Ans.* $127\frac{23}{40}$ grams.

7. If the weight per dozen paint brushes is $4\frac{3}{8}$ pounds, what would the weight be of 32 of these brushes? (Hint: 32 equals $2\frac{2}{3}$ dozen.)
Ans. $11\frac{2}{3}$ pounds.

8. If a pound of fat supplies $2\frac{1}{4}$ times as much energy as a pound of digestible carbohydrates, how many pounds of digestible carbohydrates would be needed to supply the energy provided by $3\frac{1}{4}$ pounds of fat?
Ans. $7\frac{5}{16}$ pounds.

9. Compute in square feet the area of a floor of a boxcar 40 feet 4 inches long by 8 feet 4 inches wide. (Hint: 4 inches equals $\frac{1}{3}$ of a foot.)
Ans. $336\frac{1}{9}$ square feet.

10. A device for producing pure water has a flow rate of $13\frac{1}{2}$ gallons per hour. At this rate, how many gallons would be produced in $3\frac{1}{4}$ hours?
Ans. $43\frac{7}{8}$ gallons.

192. How to Divide by a Mixed Number. To divide by a mixed number it is only necessary to convert the mixed number to an improper fraction, invert the numerator and denominator and multiply. Thus to divide 36 by $2\frac{1}{4}$, change $2\frac{1}{4}$ to $\frac{9}{4}$ which, inverted, becomes $\frac{4}{9}$; then revise the problem to read 36 multiplied by $\frac{4}{9}$, which may be written as $\dfrac{36 \times 4}{9}$. If the problem had been to divide $\frac{23}{25}$ by $3\frac{3}{4}$, it would be restated as $\frac{23}{25}$ divided by $\frac{15}{4}$, which is equivalent to multiplying $\frac{23}{25}$ by $\frac{4}{15}$.

PROBLEMS

★ **1.** Divide 6 by $2\frac{1}{2}$. *Ans.* $2\frac{2}{5}$.

2. Divide 144 by $1\frac{1}{8}$. *Ans.* 128.

3. Divide $\frac{11}{12}$ by $1\frac{1}{2}$. *Ans.* $\frac{11}{18}$.

4. Divide $\frac{8}{15}$ by $6\frac{2}{3}$. *Ans.* $\frac{2}{25}$.

5. Divide $9\frac{1}{2}$ by $2\frac{1}{4}$. *Ans.* $4\frac{2}{9}$.

6. Divide $36\frac{2}{3}$ by $3\frac{1}{3}$.   *Ans.* 11.

7. If 210 units can be inspected in $8\frac{3}{4}$ hours, what is the average per hour?   *Ans.* 24 units.

8. Estimate the number of $1\frac{1}{3}$ yard lengths that can be cut from a bolt containing $49\frac{1}{3}$ yards of rayon cloth.   *Ans.* 37 lengths.

9. An oriental rug having an area of $172\frac{1}{2}$ square feet is priced at $850.00. How much does this average per square foot?   *Ans.* $4.93.

10. If $2\frac{1}{4}$ gallons of chaulmoogra oil can be obtained from 108 bushels of nuts, how many bushels of nuts will produce 1 pint of this oil? (Hint: Divide the number of bushels per gallon by 8.)   *Ans.* 6 bushels.

11. A paper box manufacturer finds that in $4\frac{1}{4}$ hours $5\frac{2}{3}$ gross rims were secured to the boxes. At this rate how many gross rims may be expected to be secured in one hour?   *Ans.* $1\frac{1}{3}$ gross.

12. How many lineal feet of a plastic screen cloth 28 inches wide would comprise an area of $116\frac{2}{3}$ square feet? (Hint: 28 inches is equivalent to $2\frac{1}{3}$ feet.)   *Ans.* 50 lineal feet.

13. If the average weight per foot of carbon-and-graphite pipe, having an inside diameter of 4 inches, is $7\frac{1}{5}$ pounds, how many feet would make up a total weight of $201\frac{3}{5}$ pounds?   *Ans.* 28 feet.

14. How many shovelfuls would it take to load $8\frac{5}{8}$ cubic yards of dirt onto a truck, using a $\frac{3}{8}$ cubic yard crawler shovel?   *Ans.* 23.

15. The total depth of a stack of cork tile $\frac{5}{16}$ of an inch thick is $32\frac{1}{2}$ inches. Estimate the number of tiles in the stack.   *Ans.* 104.

16. How many $\frac{3}{4}$-ounce packages can be made up from $97\frac{1}{2}$ ounces of a botanical drug?   *Ans.* 130.

TABLE XVII

Compound Amount of 1

$$(1 + i)^n$$

n	$\frac{5}{12}\%$	$\frac{1}{2}\%$	$\frac{7}{12}\%$	$\frac{3}{4}\%$	1%
1	1.0041 6667	1.0050 0000	1.0058 3333	1.0075 0000	1 0100 0000
2	1.0083 5069	1.0100 2500	1.0117 0069	1.0150 5625	1 0201 0000
3	1.0125 5216	1.0150 7513	1.0176 0228	1.0226 6917	1 0303 0100
4	1.0167 7112	1.0201 5050	1.0235 3830	1.0303 3919	1 0406 0401
5	1.0210 0767	1.0252 5125	1.0295 0894	1.0380 6673	1 0510 1005
6	1.0252 6187	1.0303 7751	1 0355 1440	1.0458 5224	1 0615 2015
7	1.0295 3379	1.0355 2940	1.0415 5490	1.0536 9613	1 0721 3535
8	1.0338 2352	1.0407 0704	1.0476 3064	1.0615 9885	1 0828 5671
9	1.0381 3111	1.0459 1058	1 0537 4182	1.0695 6084	1 0936 8527
10	1 0424 5666	1.0511 4013	1.0598 8865	1.0775 8255	1 1046 2213
11	1 0468 0023	1.0563 9583	1.0660 7133	1.0856 6441	1 1156 6835
12	1 0511 6190	1 0616 7781	1.0722 9008	1.0938 0690	1 1268 2503
13	1 0555 4174	1 0669 8620	1 0785 4511	1 1020 1045	1 1380 9328
14	1 0599 3983	1 0723 2113	1.0848 3662	1 1102 7553	1 1494 7421
15	1 0643 5625	1 0776 8274	1.0911 6483	1.1186 0259	1 1609 6896
16	1 0687 9106	1 0830 7115	1.0975 2996	1 1269 9211	1 1725 7864
17	1.0732 4436	1 0884 8651	1 1039 3222	1 1354 4455	1 1843 0443
18	1.0777 1621	1 0939 2894	1 1103 7182	1 1439 6039	1 1961 4748
19	1.0822 0670	1 0993 9858	1 1168 4899	1 1525 4009	1.2081 0895
20	1.0867 1589	1 1048 9558	1 1233 6395	1.1611 8414	1.2201 9004
21	1.0912 4387	1 1104 2006	1 1299 1690	1 1698 9302	1 2323 9194
22	1 0957 9072	1 1159 7216	1 1365 0808	1 1786 6722	1 2447 1586
23	1 1003 5652	1 1215 5202	1 1431 3771	1 1875 0723	1 2571 6302
24	1 1049 4134	1 1271 5978	1 1498 0602	1 1964 1353	1 2697 3465
25	1 1095 4526	1 1327 9558	1 1565 1322	1 2053 8663	1.2824 3200
26	1 1141 6836	1 1384 5955	1 1632 5955	1 2144 2703	1.2952 5631
27	1 1188 1073	1 1441 5185	1 1700 4523	1 2235 3523	1.3082 0888
28	1 1234 7244	1 1498 7261	1 1768 7049	1.2327 1175	1.3212 9097
29	1.1281 5358	1.1556 2197	1 1837 3557	1.2419 5709	1.3345 0388
30	1 1328 5422	1 1614 0008	1 1906 4069	1.2512 7176	1.3478 4892
31	1 1375 7444	1 1672 0708	1 1975 8610	1.2606 5630	1 3613 2740
32	1 1423 1434	1 1730 4312	1 2045 7202	1.2701 1122	1.3749 4068
33	1 1470 7398	1 1789 0833	1.2115 9869	1.2796 3706	1.3886 9009
34	1 1518 5346	1 1848 0288	1.2186 6634	1.2892 3434	1.4025 7699
35	1 1566 5284	1 1907 2689	1.2257 7523	1.2989 0359	1.4166 0276
36	1 1614 7223	1 1966 8052	1 2329 2559	1 3086 4537	1.4307 6878
37	1 1663 1170	1.2026 6393	1 2401 1765	1.3184 6021	1.4450 7647
38	1 1711 7133	1.2086 7725	1.2473 5167	1 3283 4866	1.4595 2724
39	1 1760 5121	1.2147 2063	1.2546 2789	1.3383 1128	1.4741 2251
40	1 1809 5142	1.2207 9424	1.2619 4655	1.3483 4861	1.4888 6373
41	1 1858 7206	1.2268 9821	1 2693 0791	1 3584 6123	1 5037 5237
42	1 1908 1319	1 2330 3270	1 2767 1220	1 3686 4969	1 5187 8989
43	1 1957 7491	1 2391 9786	1 2841 5969	1 3789 1456	1.5339 7779
44	1 2007 5731	1 2453 9385	1 2916 5062	1 3892 5642	1.5493 1757
45	1 2057 6046	1 2516 2082	1 2991 8525	1 3996 7584	1.5648 1075
46	1 2107 8446	1.2578 7892	1 3067 6383	1 4101 7341	1.5804 5885
47	1 2158 2940	1.2641 6832	1 3143 8662	1 4207 4971	1.5962 6344
48	1 2208 9536	1.2704 8916	1.3220 5388	1 4314 0533	1.6122 2608
49	1.2259 8242	1.2768 4161	1 3297 6586	1.4421 4087	1.6283 4834
50	1 2310 9068	1 2832 2581	1.3375 2283	1 4529 5693	1.6446 3182

TABLE XVII (Continued)

COMPOUND AMOUNT OF 1

$$(1 + i)^n$$

n	$\frac{5}{12}\%$	$\frac{1}{2}\%$	$\frac{7}{12}\%$	$\frac{3}{4}\%$	1%
51	1 2362 2002	1 2896 4194	1.3453 2504	1 4638 5411	1.6610 7814
52	1.2413 7114	1 2960 9015	1.3531 7277	1.4748 3301	1.6776 8892
53	1 2465 4352	1 3025 7060	1.3610 6628	1.4858 9426	1.6944 6581
54	1 2517 3745	1.3090 8346	1.3690 0583	1.4970 3847	1.7114 1047
55	1.2569 5302	1.3156 2887	1.3769 9170	1.5082 6626	1.7285 2457
56	1 2621 9033	1.3222 0702	1.3850 2415	1.5195 7825	1 7458 0982
57	1 2674 4946	1.3288 1805	1.3931 0346	1.5309 7509	1 7632 6792
58	1.2727 3050	1.3354 6214	1.4012 2990	1.5424 5740	1.7809 0060
59	1.2780 3354	1.3421 3946	1.4094 0374	1.5540 2583	1.7987 0960
60	1.2833 5868	1.3488 5015	1.4176 2526	1.5656 8103	1.8166 9670
61	1.2887 0601	1 3555 9440	1.4258 9474	1 5774 2363	1.8348 6367
62	1 2940 7561	1.3623·7238	1.4342 1246	1.5892 5431	1.8532 1230
63	1.2994 6760	1.3691 8424	1 4425 7870	1.6011 7372	1.8717 4443
64	1 3048 8204	1.3760 3016	1 4509 9374	1.6131 8252	1.8904 6187
65	1.3103 1905	1.3829 1031	1.4594 5787	1.6252 8139	1.9093 6649
66	1 3157 7872	1.3898 2486	1.4679 7138	1.6374 7100	1.9284 6015
67	1.3212 6113	1 3967 7399	1.4765 3454	1.6497 5203	1.9477 4475
68	1 3267 6638	1.4037 5785	1.4851 4766	1.6621 2517	1.9672 2220
69	1.3322 9458	1.4107 7664	1.4938 1102	1.6745 9111	1.9868 9442
70	1.3378 4580	1 4178 3053	1.5025 2492	1.6871 5055	2.0067 6337
71	1.3434 2016	1 4249 1968	1.5112 8965	1 6998 0418	2.0268 3100
72	1.3490 1774	1 4320 4428	1.5201 0550	1 7125 5271	2.0470 9931
73	1.3546 3865	1 4392 0450	1 5289 7279	1 7253 9685	2.0675 7031
74	1.3602 8298	1 4464 0052	1 5378 9179	1 7383 3733	2.0882 4601
75	1.3659 5082	1.4536 3252	1.5468 6283	1 7513 7486	2.1091 2847
76	1.3716 4229	1 4609 0069	1 5558 8620	1 7645 1017	2.1302 1975
77	1.3773 5746	1.4682 0519	1 5649 6220	1 7777 4400	2.1515 2195
78	1.3830 9645	1 4755 4622	1 5740 9115	1 7910 7708	2.1730 3717
79	1.3888 5935	1.4829 2395	1 5832 7334	1 8045 1015	2.1947 6754
80	1.3946 4627	1.4903 3857	1.5925 0910	1.8180 4398	2.2167 1522
81	1.4004 5729	1.4977 9026	1.6017 9874	1.8316 7931	2.2388 8237
82	1.4062 9253	1 5052 7921	1.6111 4257	1.8454 1691	2.2612 7119
83	1.4121 5209	1.5128 0561	1.6205 4090	1.8592 5753	2.2838 8390
84	1.4180 3605	1.5203 6964	1.6299 9405	1.8732 0196	2.3067 2274
85	1.4239 4454	1.5279 7148	1.6395 0235	1.8872 5098	2.3297 8997
86	1 4298 7764	1.5356 1134	1.6490 6612	1.9014 0536	2.3530 8787
87	1.4358 3546	1.5432 8940	1.6586 8567	1.9156 6590	2.3766 1875
88	1.4418 1811	1.5510 0585	1 6683 6134	1.9300 3339	2.4003 8494
89	1.4478 2568	1.5587 6087	1.6780'9344	1.9445 0865	2.4243 8879
90	1.4538 5829	1.5665 5468	1.6878 8232	1.9590 9246	2.4486 3267
91	1.4599 1603	1.5743 8745	1 6977 2830	1 9737 8565	2.4731 1900
92	1.4659 9902	1.5822 5939	1 7076 3172	1.9885 8905	2.4978 5019
93	1.4721 0735	1.5901 7069	1.7175 9290	2.0035 0346	2.5228 2869
94	1.4782 4113	1.5981 2154	1.7276 1219	2.0185 2974	2.5480 5698
95	1.4844 0047	1.6061 1215	1.7376 8993	2.0336 6871	2.5735 3755
96	1.4905 8547	1.6141 4271	1 7478 2646	2.0489 2123	2 5992 7293
97	1.4967 9624	1.6222 1342	1 7580 2211	2.0642 8814	2.6252 6565
98	1.5030 3289	1.6303 2449	1.7682 7724	2.0797 7030	2.6515 1831
99	1.5092 9553	1.6384 7611	1.7785 9219	2.0953 6858	2.6780 3349
100	1.5155 8426	1.6466 6849	1.7889 6731	2.1110 8384	2.7048 1383

TABLE XVII (*Continued*)

COMPOUND AMOUNT OF 1

$$(1 + i)^n$$

n	$\frac{5}{12}\%$	$\frac{1}{2}\%$	$\frac{7}{12}\%$	$\frac{3}{4}\%$	1%
101	1 5218 9919	1 6549 0183	1 7994 0295	2 1269 1697	2 7318 6197
102	1 5282 4044	1 6631 7634	1 8098 9947	2 1428 6885	2 7591 8050
103	1 5346 0811	1 6714 9223	1 8204 5722	2.1589 4036	2 7867 7239
104	1 5410 0231	1 6798 4969	1 8310 7655	2 1751 3242	2.8146 4012
105	1 5474 2315	1.6882 4894	1 8417 5783	2 1914 4591	2.8427 8652
106	1 5538 7075	1 6966 9018	1 8525 0142	2.2078 8175	2.8712 1438
107	1 5603 4521	1 7051 7363	1 8633 0768	2.2244 4087	2.8999 2653
108	1 5668 4665	1.7136 9950	1 8741 7697	2 2411 2417	2 9289 2579
109	1 5733 7518	1.7222 6800	1 8851 0967	2.2579 3260	2.9582 1505
110	1 5799 3091	1 7308 7934	1 8961 0614	2.2748 6710	2 9877 9720
111	1 5865 1395	1 7395 3373	1 9071 6676	2 2919 2860	3 0176 7517
112	1.5931 2443	1 7482 3140	1 9182 9190	2 3091 1807	3 0478 5192
113	1 5997 6245	1 7569 7256	1 9294 8194	2.3264 3645	3 0783 3044
114	1 6064 2812	1 7657 5742	1 9407 3725	2 3438 8472	3 1091 1375
115	1 6131 2157	1 7745 8621	1.9520 5832	2 3614 6386	3 1402 0489
116	1 6198 4291	1 7834 5914	1 9634 4522	2.3791 7484	3 1716 0693
117	1 6265 9226	1 7923 7644	1 9748 9865	2.3970 1865	3.2033 2300
118	1.6333 6973	1 8013 3832	1 9864 1890	2 4149 9629	3 2353 5623
119	1 6401 7543	1.8103 4501	1 9980 0634	2 4331 0876	3.2677 0980
120	1 6470 0950	1.8193 9673	2 0096 6138	2 4513 5708	3.3003 8689
121	1 6538 7204	1 8284 9372	2 0213 8440	2 4697 4226	3.3333 9076
122	1 6607 6317	1 8376 3619	2.0331 7581	2 4882 6532	3.3667 2467
123	1 6676 8302	1 8468 2437	2 0450 3600	2 5069 2731	3.4003 9192
124	1 6746 3170	1.8560 5849	2 0569 6538	2 5257 2927	3 4343 9584
125	1 6816 0933	1.8653 3878	2 0689 6434	2 5446 7224	3 4687 3980
126	1 6886 1603	1 8746 6548	2 0810 3330	2 5637 5728	3.5034 2719
127	1 6956 5193	1 8840 3880	2 0931 7266	2 5829 8546	3.5384 6147
128	1 7027 1715	1 8934 5900	2 1053 8284	2 6023 5785	3.5738 4608
129	1 7098 1181	1 9029 2629	2 1176 6424	2 6218 7553	3.6095 8454
130	1 7169 3602	1 9124 4092	2 1300 1728	2 6415 3960	3.6456 8039
131	1 7240 8992	1 9220 0313	2 1424 4238	2 6613 5115	3.6821 3719
132	1 7312 7363	1 9316 1314	2 1549 3996	2 6813 1128	3 7189 5856
133	1.7384 8727	1.9412 7121	2 1675 1044	2 7014 2112	3.7561 4815
134	1.7457 3097	1 9509 7757	2 1801 5425	2 7216 8177	3.7937 0963
135	1.7530 0485	1 9607 3245	2 1928 7182	2 7420 9439	3.8316 4673
136	1 7603 0903	1 9705 3612	2.2056 6357	2 7626 6009	3.8699 6319
137	1 7676 4365	1 9803 8880	2.2185 2994	2 7833 8005	3.9086 6282
138	1 7750 0884	1 9902 9074	2.2314 7137	2 8042 5540	3.9477 4945
139	1 7824 0471	2 0002 4219	2 2444 8828	2.8252 8731	3.9872 2695
140	1 7898 3139	2.0102 4340	2 2575 8113	2.8464 7697	4.0270 9922
141	1 7972 8902	2 0202 9462	2.2707 5036	2 8678 2554	4 0673 7021
142	1.8047 7773	2 0303 9609	2.2839 9640	2 8893 3424	4 1080 4391
143	1.8122 9763	2 0405 4808	2 2973 1971	2 9110 0424	4.1491 2435
144	1.8198 4887	2 0507 5082	2 3107 2074	2 9328 3677	4 1906 1559
145	1.8274 3158	2 0610 0457	2.3241 9995	2.9548 3305	4.2325 2175
146	1.8350 4588	2 0713 0959	2 3377 5778	2.9769 9430	4 2748 4697
147	1.8426 9190	2.0816 6614	2 3513 9470	2.9993 2175	4 3175 9544
148	1.8503 6978	2 0920 7447	2 3651 1117	3.0218 1667	4.3607 7139
149	1.8580 7966	2 1025 3484	2 3789 0765	3.0444 8029	4 4043 7910
150	1.8658 2166	2 1130 4752	2.3927 8461	3 0673 1389	4 4484 2290

TABLE XVII (Continued)

COMPOUND AMOUNT OF 1

$$(1 + i)^n$$

n	$1\frac{1}{8}\%$	$1\frac{1}{4}\%$	$1\frac{1}{2}\%$	$1\frac{3}{4}\%$	2%
1	1 0112 5000	1 0125 0000	1 0150 0000	1 0175 0000	1 0200 0000
2	1 0226 2656	1 0251 5625	1 0302 2500	1 0353 0625	1 0404 0000
3	1 0341 3111	1.0379 7070	1.0456 7838	1 0534 2411	1 0612 0800
4	1 0457 6509	1 0509 4534	1 0613 6355	1 0718 5903	1 0824 3216
5	1 0575 2994	1.0640 8215	1 0772 8400	1 0906 1656	1 1040 8080
6	1 0694 2716	1 0773 8318	1.0934 4326	1 1097 0235	1 1261 6242
7	1 0814 5821	1 0908 5047	1 1098 4491	1 1291 2215	1 1486 8567
8	1 0936 2462	1 1044 8610	1 1264 9259	1 1488 8178	1 1716 5938
9	1 1059 2789	1 1182 9218	1 1433 8998	1 1689 8721	1 1950 9257
10	1 1183 6958	1.1322 7083	1 1605 4083	1 1894 4449	1 2189 9442
11	1 1309 5124	1 1464 2422	1 1779 4894	1.2102 5977	1 2433 7431
12	1 1436 7444	1 1607 5452	1 1956 1817	1 2314 3931	1 2682 4179
13	1 1565 4078	1 1752 6395	1.2135 5244	1 2529 8950	1 2936 0663
14	1 1695 5186	1 1899 5475	1 2317 5573	1 2749 1682	1 3194 7876
15	1 1827 0932	1.2048 2918	1 2502 3207	1.2972 2786	1 3458 6834
16	1 1960 1480	1 2198 8955	1 2689 8555	1 3199 2935	1 3727 8571
17	1 2094 6997	1 2351 3817	1 2880 2033	1 3430 2811	1 4002 4142
18	1 2230 7650	1 2505 7739	1 3073 4064	1 3665 3111	1 4282 4625
19	1 2368 3611	1 2662 0961	1 3269 5075	1 3904 4540	1 4568 1117
20	1 2507 5052	1.2820 3723	1.3468 5501	1 4147 7820	1 4859 4740
21	1 2648 2146	1 2980 6270	1 3670 5783	1 4395 3681	1.5156 6634
22	1 2790 5071	1 3142 8848	1 3875 6370	1 4647 2871	1.5459 7967
23	1 2934 4003	1.3307 1709	1 4083 7715	1 4903 6146	1 5768 9926
24	1 3079 9123	1.3473 5105	1 4295 0281	1 5164 4279	1 6084 3725
25	1.3227 0613	1.3641 9294	1.4509 4535	1.5429 8054	1 6406 0599
26	1 3375 8657	1.3812 4535	1 4727 0953	1 5699 8269	1 6734 1811
27	1.3526 3442	1 3985 1092	1 4948 0018	1 5974 5739	1 7068 8648
28	1 3678 5156	1 4159 9230	1 5172 2218	1 6254 1290	1 7410 2421
29	1 3832 3989	1 4336 9221	1 5399 8051	1 6538 5762	1 7758 4469
30	1.3988 0134	1 4516 1336	1 5630 8022	1 6828 0013	1 8113 6158
31	1 4145 3785	1 4697 5853	1 5865 2642	1 7122 4913	1 8475 8882
32	1 4304 5140	1 4881 3051	1 6103 2432	1 7422 1349	1 8845 4059
33	1 4465 4398	1 5067 3214	1 6344 7918	1 7727 0223	1 9222 3140
34	1 4628 1760	1 5255 6629	1 6589 9637	1 8037 2452	1 9606 7603
35	1 4792 7430	1.5446 3587	1 6838 8132	1 8352 8970	1 9998 8955
36	1 4959 1613	1 5639 4382	1 7091 3954	1 8674 0727	2.0398 8734
37	1 5127 4519	1 5834 9312	1 7347 7663	1 9000 8689	2.0806 8509
38	1 5297 6357	1 6032 8678	1 7607 9828	1 9333 3841	2 1222 9879
39	1 5469 7341	1 6233 2787	1 7872 1025	1 9671 7184	2 1647 4477
40	1.5643 7687	1.6436 1946	1.8140 1841	2.0015 9734	2.2080 3966
41	1 5819 7611	1 6641 6471	1 8412 2868	2.0366 2530	2 2522 0046
42	1.5997 7334	1 6849 6677	1.8688 4712	2.0722 6624	2 2972 4447
43	1.6177 7079	1.7060 2885	1.8968 7982	2 1085 3090	2 3431 8936
44	1 6359 7071	1.7273 5421	1 9253 3302	2.1454 3019	2.3900 5314
45	1.6543 7538	1.7489 4614	1 9542 1301	2 1829 7522	2 4378 5421
46	1 6729 8710	1 7708 0797	1 9835 2621	2 2211 7728	2.4866 1129
47	1 6918 0821	1 7929 4306	2 0132 7910	2.2600 4789	2.5363 4351
48	1 7108 4105	1 8153 5485	2.0434 7829	2 2995 9872	2 5870 7039
49	1 7300 8801	1.8380 4679	2.0741 3046	2.3398 4170	2.6388 1179
50	1.7495 5150	1.8610 2237	2.1052 4242	2.3807 8893	2.6915 8803

TABLE XVII (*Continued*)

Compound Amount of 1

$$(1 + i)^n$$

n	$1\frac{1}{8}\%$	$1\frac{1}{4}\%$	$1\frac{1}{2}\%$	$1\frac{3}{4}\%$	2%
51	1.7692 3395	1.8842 8515	2.1368 2106	2.4224 5274	2.7454 1979
52	1.7891 3784	1.9078 3872	2.1688 7337	2.4648 4566	2.8003 2819
53	1.8092 6564	1.9316 8670	2.2014 0647	2.5079 8046	2.8563 3475
54	1.8296 1988	1.9558 3279	2.2344 2757	2.5518 7012	2.9134 6144
55	1.8502 0310	1.9802 8070	2.2679 4398	2.5965 2785	2.9717 3067
56	1.8710 1788	2.0050 3420	2.3019 6314	2.6419 6708	3.0311 6529
57	1.8920 6684	2.0300 9713	2.3364 9259	2.6882 0151	3.0917 8859
58	1.9133 5259	2.0554 7335	2.3715 3998	2.7352 4503	3.1536 2436
59	1.9348 7780	2.0811 6676	2.4071 1308	2.7831 1182	3.2166 9685
60	1.9566 4518	2.1071 8135	2.4432 1978	2.8318 1628	3.2810 3079
61	1.9786 5744	2.1335 2111	2.4798 6807	2.8813 7306	3.3466 5140
62	2.0009 1733	2.1601 9013	2.5170 6609	2.9317 9709	3.4135 8443
63	2.0234 2765	2.1871 9250	2.5548 2208	2.9831 0354	3.4818 5612
64	2.0461 9121	2.2145 3241	2.5931 4442	3.0343 0785	3.5514 9324
65	2.6092 1087	2.2422 1407	2.6320 4158	3.0884 2574	3.6225 2311
66	2.0924 8949	2.2702 4174	2.6715 2221	3.1424 7319	3.6949 7357
67	2.1160 2999	2.2986 1976	2.7115 9504	3.1974 6647	3.7688 7304
68	2.1398 3533	2.3273 5251	2.7522 6896	3.2534 2213	3.8442 5050
69	2.1639 0848	2.3564 4442	2.7935 5300	3.3103 5702	3.9211 3551
70	2.1882 5245	2.3858 9997	2.8354 5629	3.3682 8827	3.9995 5822
71	2.2128 7029	2.4157 2372	2.8779 8814	3.4272 3331	4.0795 4939
72	2.2377 6508	2.4459 2027	2.9211 5796	3.4872 0990	4.1611 4038
73	2.2629 3994	2.4764 9427	2.9649 7533	3.5482 3607	4.2443 6318
74	2.2833 9801	2.5074 5045	3.0094 4996	3.6103 3020	4.3292 5045
75	2.3141 4249	2.5387 9358	3.0545 9171	3.6735 1098	4.4158 3546
76	2.3401 7659	2.5705 2850	3.1004 1059	3.7377 9742	4.5041 5216
77	2.3665 0358	2.6026 6011	3.1469 1674	3.8032 0888	4.5942 3521
78	2.3931 2675	2.6351 9336	3.1941 2050	3.8697 6503	4.6861 1991
79	2.4200 4942	2.6681 3327	3.2420 3230	3.9374 8592	4.7798 4231
80	2.4472 7498	2.7014 8494	3.2906 6279	4.0063 9192	4.8754 3916
81	2.4748 0682	2.7352 5350	3.3400 2273	4.0765 0378	4.9729 4794
82	2.5026 4840	2.7694 4417	3.3901 2307	4.1478 4260	5.0724 0690
83	2.5308 0319	2.8040 6222	3.4409 7492	4.2204 2984	5.1738 5504
84	2.5592 7473	2.8391 1300	3.4925 8954	4.2942 8737	5.2773 3214
85	2.5880 6657	2.8746 0191	3.5449 7838	4.3694 3740	5.3828 7878
86	2.6171 8232	2.9105 3444	3.5981 5306	4.4459 0255	5.4905 3636
87	2.6466 2562	2.9469 1612	3.6521 2535	4.5237 0584	5.6003 4708
88	2.6764 0016	2.9837 5257	3.7069 0723	4.6028 7070	5.7123 5402
89	2.7065 0966	3.0210 4948	3.7625 1084	4.6834 2093	5.8266 0110
90	2.7369 5789	3.0588 1260	3.8189 4851	4.7653 8080	5.9431 3313
91	2.7677 4867	3.0970 4775	3.8762 3273	4.8487 7496	6.0619 9579
92	2.7988 8584	3.1357 6085	3.9343 7622	4.9336 2853	6.1832 3570
93	2.8303 7331	3.1749 5786	3.9933 9187	5.0199 6703	6.3069 0042
94	2.8622 1501	3.2146 4483	4.0532 9275	5.1078 1645	6.4330 3843
95	2.8944 1492	3.2548 2789	4.1140 9214	5.1972 0324	6.5616 9920
96	2.9269 7709	3.2955 1324	4.1758 0352	5.2881 5429	6.6929 3318
97	2.9599 0559	3.3367 0716	4.2384 4057	5.3806 9699	6.8267 9184
98	2.9932 0452	3.3784 1600	4.3020 1718	5.4748 5919	6.9633 2768
99	3.0268 7807	3.4206 4620	4.3665 4744	5.5706 6923	7.1025 9423
100	3.0609 3045	3.4634 0427	4.4320 4565	5.6681 5594	7.2446 4612

HIGH-SPEED MATHEMATICS

TABLE XVII (Continued)

Compound Amount of 1

$$(1 + i)^n$$

n	$2\frac{1}{4}\%$	$2\frac{1}{2}\%$	$2\frac{3}{4}\%$	3%	$3\frac{1}{2}\%$
1	1.0225 0000	1.0250 0000	1.0275 0000	1.0300 0000	1.0350 0000
2	1.0455 0625	1.0506 2500	1.0557 5625	1.0609 0000	1.0712 2500
3	1.0690 3014	1.0768 9063	1.0847 8955	1.0927 2700	1.1087 1788
4	1.0930 8332	1.1038 1289	1.1146 2126	1.1255 0881	1.1475 ·2300
5	1.1176 7769	1.1314 0821	1.1452 7334	1.1592 7407	1.1876 8631
6	1.1428 2544	1.1596 9342	1.1767 6836	1.1940 5230	1.2292 5533
7	1.1685 3901	1.1886 8575	1.2091 2949	1.2298 7387	1.2722 7926
8	1.1948 3114	1.2184 0290	1.2423 8055	1.2667 7008	1.3168 0904
9	1.2217 1484	1.2488 6297	1.2765 4602	1.3047 7318	1.3628 9735
10	1.2492 0343	1.2800 8454	1.3116 5103	1.3439 1638	1.4105 9876
11	1.2773 1050	1.3120 8666	1.3477 2144	1.3842 3387	1.4599 6972
12	1.3060 4999	1.3448 8882	1.3847 8378	1.4257 6089	1.5110 6866
13	1.3354 3611	1.3785 1104	1.4228 6533	1.4685 3371	1.5639 5606
14	1.3654 8343	1.4129 7382	1.4619 9413	1.5125 8972	1.6186 9452
15	1.3962 0680	1.4482 9817	1.5021 9896	1.5579 6742	1.6753 4883
16	1.4276 2146	1.4845 0562	1.5435 0944	1.6047 0644	1.7339 8604
17	1.4597 4294	1.5216 1826	1.5859 5595	1.6528 4763	1.7946 7555
18	1.4925 8716	1.5596 5872·	1.6295 6973	1.7024 3306	1.8574 8920
19	1.5261 7037	1.5986 5019	1.6743 8290	1.7535 0605	1.9225 0132
20	1.5605 0920	1.6386 1644	1.7204 2843	1.8061 1123	1.9897 8886
21	1.5956 2066	1.6795 8185	1.7677 4021	1.8602 9457	2.0594 3147
22	1.6315 2212	1.7215 7140	1.8163 5307	1.9161 0341	2.1315 1158
23	1.6682 3137	1.7646 1068	1.8663 0278	1.9735 8651	2.2061 1448
24	1.7057 6658	1.8087 2595	1.9176 2610	2.0327 9411	2.2833 2849
25	1.7441 4632	1.8539 4410	1.9703 6082	2.0937 7793	2.3632 4493
26	1.7833 8962	1.9002 9270	2.0245 4575·	2.1565 9127	2.4459 5856
27	1.8235 1588	1.9478 0002	2.0802 2075	2.2212 8901	2.5315 6711
28	1.8645 4499	1.9964 9502	2.1374 2682	2.2879 2768	2.6201 7196
29	1.9064 9725	2.0464 0739	2.1962 0606	2.3565 6551	2.7118 7798
30	1.9493 9344	2.0975 6758	2.2566 0173	2.4272 6247	2.8067 9370
31	1.9932 5479	2.1500 0677	2.3186 5828	2.5000 8035	2.9050 3148
32	2.0381 0303	2.2037 5694	2.3824 2138	2.5750 8276	3.0067 0759
33	2.0839 6034	2.2588 5086	2.4479 3797	2.6523 3524	3.1119 4235
34	2.1308. 4945	2.3153 2213	2.5152 5626	2.7319 0530	3.2208 6033
35	2.1787 9356	2.3732 0519	2.5844 2581	2.8138 6245	3.3335 9045
36	2.2278 1642	2.4325 3532	2.6554 9752	2.8982 7833	3.4502 6611
37	2.2779 4229	2.4933 4870	2.7285 2370	2.9852 2668	3.5710 2543
38	2.3291 9599	2.5556 8242	2.8035 5810	3.0747 8348	3.6960 ·1132
39	2.3816 0290	2.6195 7448	2.8806 5595	3.1670 2698	3.8253 7171
40	2.4351 8897	2.6850 6384	2.9598 7399	3.2620 3779	3.9592 5972
41	2.4899 8072	2.7521 9043	3.0412 7052	3.3598 9893	4.0978 3331
42	2.5460 0528	2.8209 9520	3.1249 0546	3.4606 9589	4.2412 5799
43	2.6032 9040	2.8915 2008	3.2108 4036	3.5645 1677	4.3897 0202
44	2.6618 6444	2.9638 0808	3.2991 3847	3.6714 5227	4.5433 4160
45	2.7217 5639	3.0379 0328	3.3898· 6478	3.7815 9584	4.7023 5855
46	2.7829 9590	3.1138 5086	3.4830 8606	3.8950 4372	4.8669 4110
47	2.8456 1331	3.1916 9713	3.5788 7093	4.0118 9503	5.0372 8404
48	2.9096 3961	3.2714 8956	3.6772 8988	4.1322 5188	5.2135 8898
49	2.9751 0650	3.3532 7680	3.7784 1535	4.2562 1944	5.3960 ·6459
50	3.0420 4640	3.4371 0872	3.8823 2177	4.3839 0602	5.5849 2686

TABLE XVII (*Continued*)

COMPOUND AMOUNT OF 1

$$(1 + i)^n$$

n	$2\frac{1}{4}\%$	$2\frac{1}{2}\%$	$2\frac{3}{4}\%$	3%	$3\frac{1}{2}\%$
51	3.1104 9244	3.5230 3644	3.9890 8562	4.5154 2320	5 7803 9930
52	3.1804 7852	3.6111 1235	4.0987 8547	4.6508 8590	5.9827 1327
53	3.2520 3929	3.7013 9016	4 2115 0208	4.7904 1247	6.1921 0824
54	3.3252 1017	3.7939 2491	4.3273 1838	4.9341 2485	6.4088 3202
55	3.4000 2740	3.8887 7303	4.4463 1964	5.0821 4859	6.6331 4114
56	3.4765 2802	3.9859 9236	4.5685 9343	5.2346 1305	6.8653 0108
57	3.5547 4990	4.0856 4217	4.6942 2975	5.3916 5144	7 1055 8662
58	3.6347 3177	4.1877 8322	4.8233 2107	5.5534 0098	7.3542 8215
59	3.7165 1324	4.2924 7780	4.9559 6239	5.7200 0301	7 6116 8203
60	3.8001 3479	4.3997 8975	5.0922 5136	5.8916 0310	7.8780 9090
61	3.8856 3782	4.5097 8449	5 2322 8827	6 0683 5120	8.1538 2408
62	3.9730 6467	4.6225 2910	5.3761 7620	6.2504 0173	8.4392 0793
63	4.0624 5862	4.7380 9233	5.5240 2105	6.4379 1379	8.7345 8020
64	4 1538 6394	4.8565 4464	5.6759 3162	6.6310 5120	9.0402 9051
65	4.2473 2588	4.9779 5826	5.8320 1974	6.8299 8273	9.3567 0068
66	4.3428 9071	5.1024 0721	5.9924 0029	7.0348 8222	9 6841 8520
67	4.4406 0576	5.2299 6739	6 1571 9130	7.2459 2868	10.0231 3168
68	4.5405 1939	5.3607 1658	6.3265 1406	7 4633 0654	10.3739 4129
69	4.6426 8107	5.4947 3449	6.5004 9319	7.6872 0574	10.7370 2924
70	4.7471 4140	5.6321 0286	6.6792 5676	7 9178 2191	11.1128 2526
71	4.8539 5208	5.7729 0543	6.8629 3632	8 1553 5657	11 5017 7414
72	4.9631 6600	5.9172 2806	7.0516 6706	8.4000 1727	11.9043 3624
73	5.0748 3723	6.0651 5876	7.2455 8791	8.6520 1778	12.3209 8801
74	5.1890 2107	6.2167 8773	7 4448 4158	8.9115 7832	12.7522 2259
75	5.3057 7405	6.3722 0743	7.6495 7472	9.1789 2567	13.1985 5038
76	5.4251 5396	6.5315 1261	7.8599 3802	9.4542 9344	13.6604 9964
77	5.5472 1993	6.6948 0043	8.0760 8632	9.7379 2224	14 1386 1713
78	5.6720 3237	6.8621 7044	8.2981 7869	10.0300 5991	14 6334 6873
79	5.7996 5310	7.0337 2470	8.5263 7861	10.3309 6171	15 1456 4013
80	5.9301 4530	7.2095 6782	8.7608 5402	10.6408 9056	15.6757 3754
81	6.0635 7357	7.3898 0701	9.0017 7751	10 9601 1727	16.2243 8835
82	6.2000 0397	7.5745 5219	9.2493 2639	11.2889 2079	16.7922 4195
83	6.3395 0406	7.7639 1599	9.5036 8286	11 6275 8842	17.3799 7041
84	6.4821 4290	7.9580 1389	9.7650 3414	11 9764 1607	17 9882 6938
85	6.6279 9112	8.1569 6424	10.0335 7258	12.3357 0855	18.6178 5881
86	6.7771 2092	8.3608 8834	10.3094 9583	12.7057 7981	19.2694 8387
87	6.9296 0614	8.5699 1055	10.5930 0696	13.0869 5320	19 9439 1580
88	7.0855 2228	8.7841 5832	10.8843 1465	13.4795 6180	20 6419 5285
89	7.2449 4653	9.0037 6228	11 1836 3331	13.8839 4865	21.3644 2120
90	7 4079 5782	9.2288 5633	11.4911 8322	14.3004 6711	22.1121 7595
91	7 5746 3688	9.4595 7774	11 8071 9076	14.7294 8112	22.8861 0210
92	7 7450 6621	9.6960 6718	12.1318 8851	15.1713 6556	23.6871 1568
93	7 9193 3020	9.9384 6886	12.4655 1544	15.6265 0652	24.5161 6473
94	8.0975 1512	10.1869 3058	12.8083 1711	16.0953 0172	25.3742 3049
95	8.2797 0921	10.4416 0385	13.1605 4584	16.5781 6077	26.2623 2856
96	8.4660 0267	10.7026 4395	13.5224 6085	17.0755 0559	27 1815 1006
97	8.6564 8773	10.9702 1004	13.8943 2852	17.5877 7076	28.1328 6291
98	8.8512 5871	11.2444 6530	14.2764 2255	18.1154 0388	29.1175 1311
99	9.0504 1203	11.5255 7693	14.6690 2417	18.6588 6600	30.1366 2607
100	9.2540 4630	11.8137 1635	15.0724 2234	19.2186 3198	31.1914 0798

TABLE XVII (Continued)

Compound Amount of 1

$$(1 + i)^n$$

n	4%	4½%	5%	5½%	6%
1	1.0400 0000	1.0450 0000	1.0500 0000	1.0550 0000	1.0600 0000
2	1.0816 0000	1.0920 2500	1.1025 0000	1.1130 2500	1.1236 0000
3	1.1248 6400	1.1411 6613	1.1576 2500	1.1742 4138	1.1910 1600
4	1.1698 5856	1.1925 1860	1.2155 0625	1.2388 2465	1.2624 7696
5	1.2166 5290	1.2461 8194	1.2762 8156	1.3069 6001	1.3382 2558
6	1.2653 1902	1.3022 6012	1.3400 9564	1.3788 4281	1.4185 1911
7	1.3159 3178	1.3608 6183	1.4071 0042	1.4546 7916	1.5036 3026
8	1.3685 6905	1.4221 0061	1.4774 5544	1.5346 8651	1.5938 4807
9	1.4233 1181	1.4860 9514	1.5513 2822	1.6190 9427	1.6894 7896
10	1.4802 4428	1.5529 6942	1.6288 9463	1.7081 4446	1.7908 4770
11	1.5394 5406	1.6228 5305	1.7103 3936	1.8020 9240	1.8982 9856
12	1.6010 3222	1.6958 8143	1.7958 5633	1.9012 0749	2.0121 9647
13	1.6650 7351	1.7721 9610	1.8856 4914	2.0057 7390	2.1329 2826
14	1.7316 7645	1.8519 4492	1.9799 3160	2.1160 9146	2.2609 0396
15	1.8009 4351	1.9352 8244	2.0789 2818	2.2324 7649	2.3965 5819
16	1.8729 8125	2.0223 7015	2.1828 7459	2.3552 6270	2.5403 5168
17	1.9479 0050	2.1133 7681	2.2920 1832	2.4848 0215	2.6927 7279
18	2.0258 1652	2.2084 7877	2.4066 1923	2.6214 6627	2.8543 3915
19	2.1068 4918	2.3078 6031	2.5269 5020	2.7656 4691	3.0255 9950
20	2.1911 2314	2.4117 1402	2.6532 9771	2.9177 5749	3.2071 3547
21	2.2787 6807	2.5202 4116	2.7859 6259	3.0782 3415	3.3995 6360
22	2.3699 1879	2.6336 5201	2.9252 6072	3.2475 3703	3.6035 3742
23	2.4647 1554	2.7521 6635	3.0715 2376	3.4261 5157	3.8197 4966
24	2.5633 0416	2.8760 1383	3.2250 9994	3.6145 8990	4.0489 3464
25	2.6658 3633	3.0054 3446	3.3863 5494	3.8133 9235	4.2918 7072
26	2.7724 6978	3.1406 7901	3.5556 7269	4.0231 2893	4.5493 8296
27	2.8833 6858	3.2820 0956	3.7334 5632	4.2444 0102	4.8223 4594
28	2.9987 0332	3.4296 9999	3.9201 2914	4.4778 4307	5.1116 8670
29	3.1186 5145	3.5840 3649	4.1161 3560	4.7241 2444	5.4183 8790
30	3.2433 9751	3.7453 1813	4.3219 4238	4.9839 5129	5.7434 9117
31	3.3731 3341	3.9138 5745	4.5380 3949	5.2580 6861	6.0881 0064
32	3.5080 5875	4.0899 8104	4.7649 4147	5.5472 6238	6.4533 8668
33	3.6483 8110	4.2740 3018	5.0031 8854	5.8523 6181	6.8405 8988
34	3.7943 1634	4.4663 6154	5.2533 4797	6.1742 4171	7.2510 2528
35	3.9460 8899	4.6673 4781	5.5160 1537	6.5138 2501	7.6860 8679
36	4.1039 3255	4.8773 7846	5.7918 1614	6.8720 8538	8.1472 5200
37	4.2680 8986	5.0968 6049	6.0814 0694	7.2500 5008	8.6360 8712
38	4.4388 1345	5.3262 1921	6.3854 7729	7.6488 0283	9.1542 5235
39	4.6163 6599	5.5658 9908	6.7047 5115	8.0694 8699	9.7035 0749
40	4.8010 2063	5.8163 6454	7.0399 8871	8.5133 0877	10.2857 1794
41	4.9930 6145	6.0781 0094	7.3919 8815	8.9815 4076	10.9028 6101
42	5.1927 8391	6.3516 1548	7.7615 8756	9.4755 2550	11.5570 3267
43	5.4004 9527	6.6374 3818	8.1496 6693	9.9966 7940	12.2504 5463
44	5.6165 1508	6.9361 2290	8.5571 5028	10.5464 9677	12.9854 8191
45	5.8411 7568	7.2482 4843	8.9850 0779	11.1265 5409	13.7646 1083
46	6.0748 2271	7.5744 1961	9.4342 5818	11.7385 1456	14.5904 8748
47	6.3178 1562	7.9152 6849	9.9059 7109	12.3841 3287	15.4659 1673
48	6.5705 2824	8.2714 5557	10.4012 6965	13.0652 6017	16.3938 7173
49	6.8333 4937	8.6436 7107	10.9213 3313	13.7838 4948	17.3775 0403
50	7.1066 8335	9.0326 3627	11.4673 9979	14.5419 6120	18.4201 5427

TABLE XVII (*Continued*)

COMPOUND AMOUNT OF 1

$$(1 + i)^n$$

n	4%	4½%	5%	5½%	6%
51	7.3909 5068	9.4391 0490	12.0407 6978	15.3417 6907	19.5253 6353
52	7.6865 8871	9.8638 6463	12.6428 0826	16.1855 6637	20.6968 8534
53	7.9940 5226	10.3077 3853	13.2749 4868	17.0757 7252	21.9386 9846
54	8.3138 1435	10.7715 8677	13.9386 9611	18.0149 4001	23.2550 2037
55	8.6463 6692	11.2563 0817	14.6356 3092	19.0057 6171	24 6503 2159
56	8.9922 2160	11.7628 4204	15.3674 1246	20.0510 7860	26.1293 4089
57	9.3519 1046	12.2921 6993	16.1357 8309	21.1538 8793	27.6971 0134
58	9.7259 8688	12.8453 1758	16.9425 7224	22.3173 5176	29.3589 2742
59	10.1150 2635	13.4233 5687	17.7897 0085	23.5448 0611	31.1204 6307
60	10.5196 2741	14.0274 0793	18.6791 8589	24.8397 7045	32.9876 9085
61	10.9404 1250	14.6586 4129	19.6131 4519	26.2059 5782	34.9669 5230
62	11.3780 2900	15.3182 8014	20.5938 0245	27.6472 8550	37.0649 6944
63	11.8331 5016	16.0076 0275	21.6234 9257	29.1678 8620	39.2888 6761
64	12.3064 7617	16.7279 4487	22.7046 6720	30.7721 1994	41.6461 9967
65	12.7987 3522	17.4807 0239	23.8399 0056	32.4645 8654	44.1449 7165
66	13.3106 8463	18.2673 3400	25.0318 9559	34.2501 3880	46.7936 6994
67	13.8431 1201	19.0893 6403	26.2834 9037	36.1338 9643	49.6012 9014
68	14.3968 3649	19.9483 8541	27.5976 6488	38 1212 6074	52.5773 6755
69	14.9727 0995	20.8460 6276	28.9775 4813	40.2179 3008	55.7320 0960
70	15.5716 1835	21.7841 3558	30.4264 2554	42.4299 1623	59.0759 3018
71	16.1944 8308	22.7644 2168	31 9477 4681	44.7635 6163	62.6204 8599
72	16.8422 6241	23.7888 2066	33 5451 3415	47 2255 5751	66.3777 1515
73	17.5159 5290	24.8593 1759	35.2223 9086	49.8229 6318	70.3603 7806
74	18.2165 9102	25.9779 8688	36.9835 1040	52.5632 2615	74.5820 0074
75	18.9452 5466	27.1469 9629	38.8326 8592	55.4542 0359	79.0569 2079
76	19.7030 6485	28.3686 1112	40.7743 2022	58.5041 8479	83.8003 3603
77	20.4911 8744	29.6451 9862	42.8130 3623	61.7219 1495	88.8283 5620
78	21.3108 3494	30 9792 3256	44.9536 8804	65.1166 2027	94.1580 5757
79	22.1632 6834	32.3732 9802	47.2013 7244	68.6980 3439	99.8075 4102
80	23.0497 9907	33.8300 9643	49.5614 4107	72.4764 2628	105.7959 9348
81	23.9717 9103	35.3524 5077	52.0395 1312	76.4626 2973	112.1437 5309
82	24.9306 6267	36.9433 1106	54.6414 8878	80.6680 7436	118.8723 7828
83	25.9278 8918	38.6057 6006	57.3735 6322	85.1048 1845	126.0047 2097
84	26.9650 0475	40.3430 1926	60.2422 4138	89.7855 8347	133.5650 0423
85	28.0436 0494	42.1584 5513	63.2543 5344	94.7237 9056	141.5789 0449
86	29.1653 4914	44.0555 8561	66.4170 7112	99.9335 9904	150.0736 3875
87	30.3319 6310	46.0380 8696	69.7379 2467	105.4299 4698	159.0780 5708
88	31.5452 4163	48.1098 0087	73.2248 2091	111.2285 9407	168.6227 4050
89	32.8070 5129	50.2747 4191	76.8860 6195	117.3461 6674	178.7401 0493
90	34.1193 3334	52.5371 0530	80.7303 6505	123.8002 0591	189.4645 1123
91	35.4841 0668	54.9012 7503	84.7668 8330	130.6092 1724	200.8323 8190
92	36.9034 7094	57.3718 3241	89.0052 2747	137 7927 2419	212.8823 2482
93	38.3796 0978	59.9535 6487	93.4554 8884	145.3713 2402	225.6552 6431
94	39.9147 9417	62.6514 7529	98.1282 6328	153.3667 4684	239.1945 8017
95	41.5113 8594	65.4707 9168	103.0346 7645	161.8019 1791	253.5462 5498
96	43.1718 4138	68.4169 7730	108.1864 1027	170.7010 2340	268.7590 3028
97	44.8987 1503	71.4957 4128	113.5957 3078	180.0895 7969	284.8845 7209
98	46.6946 6363	74.7130 4964	119.2755 1732	189.9945 0657	301.9776 4642
99	48.5624 5018	78.0751 3687	125.2392 9319	200.4442 0443	320.0963 0520
100	50.5049 4818	81.5885 1803	131.5012 5785	211.4686 3567	339.3020 8351

TABLE XVII (Continued)

Compound Amount of 1

$$(1 + i)^n$$

n	$6\frac{1}{2}\%$	7%	$7\frac{1}{2}\%$	8%	$8\frac{1}{2}\%$
1	1 0650 0000	1.0700 0000	1 0750 0000	1 0800 0000	1 0850 0000
2	1 1342 2500	1 1449 0000	1 1556 2500	1 1664 0000	1 1772 2500
3	1 2079 4963	1 2250 4300	1 2422 9688	1 2597 1200	1 2772 8913
4	1 2864 6635	1 3107 9601	1 3354 6914	1 3604 8896	1 3858 5870
5	1.3700 8666	1 4025 5173	1 4356 2933	1 4693 2808	1 5036 5669
6	1 4591 4230	1 5007 3035	1 5433 0153	1 5868 7432	1 6314 6751
7	1 5539 8655	1 6057 8148	1 6590 4914	1 7138 2427	1 7701 4225
8	1 6549 5567	1 7181 8618	1 7834 7783	1 8509 3021	1 9206 0434
9	1 7625 7039	1 8384 5921	1 9172 3866	1 9990 0463	2 0838 5571
10	1 8771 3747	1 9671 5136	2 0610 3156	2 1589 2500	2 2609 8344
11	1 9991 5140	2 1048 5195	2 2156 0893	2 3316 3900	2 4531 6703
12	2 1290 9624	2 2521 9159	2 3817 7960	2 5181 7012	2 6616 8623
13	2 2674 8750	2 4098 4500	2 5604 1307	2 7196 2373	2 8879 2956
14	2 4148 7418	2 5785 3415	2 7524 4405	2 9371 9362	3 1334 0357
15	2 5718 4101	2 7590 3154	2 9588 7735	3 1721 6911	3 3997 4288
16	2 7390 1067	2 9521 6375	3 1807 9315	3 4259 4264	3 6887 2102
17	2 9170 4637	3 1588 1521	3 4193 5264	3 7000 1805	4 0022 6231
18	3 1066 5438	3 3799 3228	3 6758 0409	3 9960 1950	4 3424 5461
19	3.3085 8691	3.6165 2754	3 9514 8940	4 3157 0106	4 7115 6325
20	3 5236 4506	3 8696 8446	4 2478 5110	4 6609 5714	5 1120 4612
21	3 7526 8199	4 1405 6237	4 5664 3993	5 0338 3372	5 5465 7005
22	3 9966 0632	4 4304 0174	4 9089 2293	5 4365 4041	6 0180 2850
23	4 2563 8573	4 7405 2986	5 2770 9215	5 8714 6365	6 5295 6092
24	4 5330 5081	5 0723 6695	5 6728 7406	6 3411 8074	7 0845 7360
25	4 8276 9911	5 4274 3264	6 0983 3961	6 8484 7520	7 6867 6236
26	5 1414 9955	5 8073 5292	6 5557 1508	7 3963 5321	8 3401 3716
27	5 4756 9702	6 2138 6763	7 0473 9371	7 9880 6147	9 0490 4881
28	5 8316 1733	6 6488 3836	7 5759 4824	8 6271 0639	9 8182 1790
29	6 2106 7245	7 1142 5705	8 1441 4436	9 3172 7490	10 6527 6649
30	6 6143 6616	7 6122 5504	8 7549 5519	10 0626 5689	11 5582 5164
31	7 0442 9996	8 1451 1290	9 4115 7683	10 8676 6944	12 5407 0303
32	7 5021 7946	8.7152 7080	10 1174 4509	11 7370 8300	13 6066 6279
33	7 9898 2113	9 3253 3975	10.8762 5347	12 6760 4964	14 7632 2913
34	8 5091 5950	9 9781 1354	11 6919 7248	13 6901 3361	16 0181 0360
35	9 0622 5487	10 6765 8148	12 5688 7042	14 7853 4429	17 3796 4241
36	9 6513 0143	11 4239 4219	13 5115 3570	15 9681 7184	18 8569 1201
37	10 2786 3603	12 2236 1814	14 5249 0088	17 2456 2558	20 4597 4953
38	10 9467 4737	13 0792 7141	15 6142 6844	18 6252 7563	22 1988 2824
39	11 6582 8595	13 9948 2041	16 7853 3858	20 1152 9768	24 0857 2865
40	12 4160 7453	14 9744 5784	18 0442 3897	21 7245 2150	26 1330 1558
41	13 2231 1938	16 0226 6989	19 3975 5689	23 4624 8322	28.3543 2190
42	14 0826 2214	17 1442 5678	20 8523 7366	25 3394 8187	30 7644 3927
43	14 9979 9258	18.3443 5475	22 4163 0168	27 3666 4042	33 3794 1660
44	15 9728 6209	19 6284 5959	24 0975 2431	29 5559 7166	36 2166 6702
45	17 0110 9813	21 0024 5176	25 9048 3863	31 9204 4939	39 2950 8371
46	18 1168 1951	22 4726 2338	27 8477 0153	34 4740 8534	42 6351 6583
47	19.2944 1278	24 0457 0702	29 9362 7915	37 2320 1217	46 2591 5492
48	20 5485 4961	25.7289 0651	32 1815 0008	40 2105 7314	50 1911 8309
49	21 8842 0533	27 5299 2997	34 5951 1259	43 4274 1899	54 4574 3365
50	23.3066 7868	29 4570 2506	37 1897 4603	46 9016 1251	59 0863 1551

TABLE XVIII

Present Value of 1

$$v^n = (1 + i)^{-n}$$

n	$\frac{5}{12}\%$	$\frac{1}{2}\%$	$\frac{7}{12}\%$	$\frac{3}{4}\%$	1%
1	0.9958 5062	0.9950 2488	0.9942 0050	0.9925 5583	0.9900 9901
2	0.9917 1846	0.9900 7450	0.9844 3463	0.9851 6708	0.9802 9605
3	0.9876 0345	0.9851 4876	0.9827 0220	0.9778 3333	0.9705 9015
4	0.9835 0551	0.9802 4752	0.9770 0302	0.9705 5417	0.9609 8034
5	0.9794 2457	0.9753 7067	0.9713 3688	0.9633 2920	0.9514 6569
6	0.9753 6057	0.9705 1808	0.9657 0361	0.9561 5802	0.9420 4524
7	0.9713 1343	0.9656 8963	0.9601 0301	0.9490 4022	0.9327 1805
8	0.9672 8308	0.9608 8520	0.9545 3489	0.9419 7540	0.9234 8322
9	0.9632 6946	0.9561 0468	0.9489 9907	0.9349 6318	0.9143 3982
10	0.9592 7249	0 9513 4794	0.9434 9534	0.9280 0315	0.9052 8695
11	0.9552 9211	0.9466 1489	0.9380 2354	0 9210 9494	0.8963 2372
12	0.9513 2824	0.9419 0534	0.9325 8347	0 9142 3815	0.8874 4923
13	0.9473 8082	0.9372 1924	0.9271 7495	0.9074 3241	0.8786 6260
14	0.9434 4978	0.9325 5646	0.9217 9780	0 9006 7733	0.8699 6297
15	0.9395 3505	0.9279 1688	0.9164 5183	0.8939 7254	0.8613 4947
16	0.9356 3656	0.9233 0037	0.9111 3686	0.8873 1766	0.8528 2126
17	0.9317 5425	0.9187 0684	0.9058 5272	0.8807 1231	0.8443 7749
18	0.9278 8805	0.9141 3616	0.9005 9923	0.8741 5614	0.8360 1731
19	0.9240 3789	0.9095 8822	0.8953 7620	0.8676 4878	0.8277 3992
20	0.9202 0371	0.9050 6290	0.8901 8346	0.8611 8985	0.8195 4447
21	0.9163 8544	0.9005 6010	0.8850 2084	0.8547 7901	0.8114 3017
22	0.9125 8301	0.8960 7971	0.8798 8816	0.8484 1589	0.8033 9621
23	0.9087 9636	0.8916 2160	0.8747 8525	0.8421 0014	0.7954 4179
24	0.9050 2542	0.8871 8567	0.8697 1193	0.8358 3140	0.7875 6613
25	0.9012 7012	0.8827 7181	0.8646 6803	0.8296 0933	0.7797 6844
26	0.8975 3041	0.8783 7991	0.8596 5339	0.8234 3358	0.7720 4796
27	0.8938 0622	0.8740 0986	0.8546 6782	0.8173 0380	0 7644 0392
28	0.8900 9748	0.8696 6155	0.8497 1118	0.8112 1966	0.7568 3557
29	0.8864 0413	0.8653 3488	0.8447 8327	0.8051 8080	0.7493 4215
30	0.8827 2610	0.8610 2973	0.8398 8395	0.7991 8690	0.7419 2292
31	0.8790 6334	0.8567 4600	0.8350 1304	0.7932 3762	0 7345 7715
32	0.8754 1577	0.8524 8358	0.8301 7038	0.7873 3262	0.7273 0411
33	0.8717 8334	0.8482 4237	0 8253 5581	0 7814 7158	0.7201 0307
34	0.8681 6599	0.8440 2226	0.8205 6915	0.7756 5418	0.7129 7334
35	0.8645 6364	0.8398 2314	0.8158 1026	0.7698 8008	0.7059 1420
36	0.8609 7624	0.8356 4492	0.8110 7897	0.7641 4896	0.6989 2495
37	0.8574 0372	0.8314 8748	0.8063 7511	0.7584 6051	0.6920 0490
38	0.8538 4603	0.8273 5073	0.8016 9854	0 7528 1440	0.6851 5337
39	0.8503 0310	0.8232 3455	0.7970 4908	0.7472 1032	0.6783 6967
40	0.8467 7487	0.8191 3886	0 7924 2660	0.7416 4796	0.6716 5314
41	0.8432 6128	0.8150 6354	0.7878 3092	0.7361 2701	0 6650 0311
42	0.8397 6227	0.8110 0850	0.7832 6189	0.7306 4716	0.6584 1892
43	0.8362 7778	0.8069 7363	0.7787 1936	0 7252 0809	0 6518 9992
44	0.8328 0775	0.8029 5884	0.7742 0317	0.7198 0952	0.6454 4546
45	0.8293 5211	0.7989 6402	0.7697 1318	0.7144 5114	0.6390 5492
46	0.8259 1082	0.7949 8907	0.7652 4923	0.7091 3264	0.6327 2764
47	0.8224 8380	0 7910 3390	0.7608 1116	0.7038 5374	0.6264 6301
48	0.8190 7100	0 7870 9841	0 7563 9884	0.6986 1414	0.6202 6041
49	0.8156 7237	0.7831 8250	0.7520 1210	0.6934 1353	0.6141 1921
50	0.8122 8784	0.7792 8607	0.7476 5080	0.6882 5165	0.6080 3882

HIGH-SPEED MATHEMATICS

TABLE XVIII (*Continued*)

PRESENT VALUE OF 1

$$v^n = (1 + i)^{-n}$$

n	$\frac{5}{12}\%$	$\frac{1}{2}\%$	$\frac{7}{12}\%$	$\frac{3}{4}\%$	1%
51	0.8089 1735	0.7754 0902	0.7433 1480	0.6831 2819	0.6020 1864
52	0.8055 6084	0.7715 5127	0.7390 0394	0.6780 4286	0.5960 5806
53	0.8022 1827	0.7677 1270	0.7347 1809	0.6729 9540	0.5901 5649
54	0.7988 8956	0.7638 9324	0.7304 5709	0.6679 8551	0.5843 1336
55	0.7955 7467	0.7600 9277	0.7262 2080	0.6630 1291	0.5785 2808
56	0.7922 7353	0.7563 1122	0.7220 0908	0.6580 7733	0.5728 0008
57	0.7889 8608	0.7525 4847	0.7178 2179	0.6531 7849	0.5671 2879
58	0.7857 1228	0.7488 0445	0.7136 5878	0.6483 1612	0.5615 1365
59	0.7824 5207	0.7450 7906	0.7095 1991	0.6434 8995	0.5559 5411
60	0.7792 0538	0.7413 7220	0.7054 0505	0.6386 9970	0.5504 4962
61	0.7759 7216	0.7376 8378	0.7013 1405	0.6339 4511	0.5449 9962
62	0.7727 5236	0.7340 1371	0.6972 4678	0.6292 2592	0.5396 0358
63	0.7695 4591	0.7303 6190	0.6932 0310	0.6245 4185	0.5342 6097
64	0.7663 5278	0.7267 2826	0.6891 8286	0.6198 9266	0.5289 7126
65	0.7631 7289	0.7231 1269	0.6851 8594	0.6152 7807	0.5237 3392
66	0.7600 0620	0.7195 1512	0.6812 1221	0.6106 9784	0.5185 4844
67	0.7568 5265	0.7159 3544	0.6772 6151	0.6061 5170	0.5134 1429
68	0.7537 1218	0.7123 7357	0.6733 3373	0.6016 3940	0.5083 3099
69	0.7505 8474	0.7088 2943	0.6694 2873	0.5971 6070	0.5032 9801
70	0.7474 7028	0.7053 0291	0.6655 4638	0.5927 1533	0.4983 1486
71	0.7443 6874	0.7017 9394	0.6616 8654	0.5883 0306	0.4933 8105
72	0.7412 8008	0.6983 0243	0.6578 4909	0.5839 2363	0.4884 9609
73	0.7382 0423	0.6948 2829	0.6540 3389	0.5795 7681	0.4836 5949
74	0.7351 4114	0.6913 7143	0.6502 4082	0.5752 6234	0.4788 7078
75	0.7320 9076	0.6879 3177	0.6464 6975	0.5709 7999	0.4741 2949
76	0.7290 5304	0.6845 0923	0.6427 2054	0.5667 2952	0.4694 3514
77	0.7260 2792	0.6811 0371	0.6389 9308	0.5625 1069	0.4647 8726
78	0.7230 1536	0.6777 1513	0.6352 8724	0.5583 2326	0.4601 8541
79	0.7200 1529	0.6743 4342	0.6316 0289	0.5541 6701	0.4556 2912
80	0.7170 2768	0.6709 8847	0.6279 3991	0.5500 4170	0.4511 1794
81	0.7140 5246	0.6676 5022	0.6242 9817	0.5459 4710	0.4466 5142
82	0.7110 8959	0.6643 2858	0.6206 7755	0.5418 8297	0.4422 2913
83	0.7081 3901	0.6610 2346	0.6170 7793	0.5378 4911	0.4378 5063
84	0.7052 0067	0.6577 3479	0.6134 9919	0.5338 4527	0.4335 1547
85	0.7022 7453	0.6544 6248	0.6099 4120	0.5298 7123	0.4292 2324
86	0.6993 6052	0.6512 0644	0.6064 0384	0.5259 2678	0.4249 7350
87	0.6964 5861	0.6479 6661	0.6028 8700	0.5220 1169	0.4207 6585
88	0.6935 6874	0.6447 4290	0.5993 9056	0.5181 2575	0.4165 9985
89	0.6906 9086	0.6415 3522	0.5959 1439	0.5142 6873	0.4124 7510
90	0.6878 2493	0.6383 4350	0.5924 5838	0.5104 4043	0.4083 9119
91	0.6849 7088	0.6351 6766	0.5890 2242	0.5066 4063	0.4043 4771
92	0.6821 2868	0.6320 0763	0.5856 0638	0.5028 6911	0.4003 4427
93	0.6792 9827	0.6288 6331	0.5822 1015	0.4991 2567	0.3963 8046
94	0.6764 7960	0.6257 3464	0.5788 3363	0.4954 1009	0.3924 5590
95	0.6736 7263	0.6226 2153	0.5754 7668	0.4917 2217	0.3885 7020
96	0.6708 7731	0.6195 2391	0.5721 3920	0.4880 6171	0.3847 2297
97	0.6680 9359	0.6164 4170	0.5688 2108	0.4844 2850	0.3809 1383
98	0.6653 2141	0.6133 7483	0.5655 2220	0.4808 2233	0.3771 4241
99	0.6625 6074	0.6103 2321	0.5622 4245	0.4772 4301	0.3734 0832
100	0.6598 1153	0.6072 8678	0.5589 8172	0.4736 9033	0.3697 1121

TABLE XVIII (Continued)

Present Value of 1

$$v^n = (1 + i)^{-n}$$

n	$\frac{5}{12}\%$	$\frac{1}{2}\%$	$\frac{7}{12}\%$	$\frac{3}{4}\%$	1%
101	0.6570 7372	0.6042 6545	0.5557 3991	0.4701 6410	0.3660 5071
102	0.6543 4727	0.6012 5015	0.5525 1689	0.4666 6412	0.3624 2644
103	0.6516 3214	0.5982 6781	0.5493 1257	0.4631 9019	0.3588 3806
104	0.6489 2827	0.5952 9136	0.5461 2683	0.4597 4213	0.3552 8521
105	0.6462 3562	0.5923 2971	0.5429 5957	0.4563 1973	0.3517 6753
106	0.6435 5415	0.5893 8279	0.5398 1067	0.4529 2281	0.3482 8469
107	0.6408 8380	0.5864 5054	0.5366 8004	0.4495 5117	0.3448 3632
108	0.6382 2453	0.5835 3288	0.5335 6756	0.4462 0464	0.3414 2210
109	0.6355 7630	0.5806 2973	0.5304 7313	0.4428 8302	0.3380 4168
110	0.6329 3905	0.5777 4102	0.5273 9665	0.4395 8612	0.3346 9474
111	0.6303 1275	0.5748 6669·	0.5243 3801	0.4363 1377	0.3213 8093
112	0.6276 9734	0.5720 0666	0.5212 9711	0.4330 6577	0.3280 9993
113	0.6250 9279	0.5691 6085	0.5182 7385	0.4298 4196	0.3248 5141
114	0.6224 9904	0.5663 2921	0.5152 6812	0.4266 4124	0.3216 3506
115	0.6199 1606	0.5635 1165	0.5122 7982	0.4234 6615	0.3184 5056
116	0.6173 4379	0.5607 0811	0.5093 0885	0.4203 1379	0.3152 9758
117	0.6147 8220	0.5579 1852	0.5063 5512	0.4171 8491	0.3121 7582
118	0.6122 3123	0.5551 4280	0.5034 1851	0.4140 7931	0.3090 8497
119	0.6096 9086	0.5523 8090	0.5004 9893	0.4109 9683	0.3060 2473
120	0.6071 6102	0.5496 3273	0.4975 9629	0.4079 3730	0.3029 9478
121	0.6046 4168	0.5468 9824	0.4947 1047	0.4049 0055	0.2999 9483
122	0.6021 3279	0.5441 7736	0.4918 4140	0.4018 8640	0.2970 2459
123	0.5996 3431	0.5414 7001	0.4889 8896	0.3988 9469	0.2940 8375
124	0.5971 4620	0.5387 7612	0.4861 5307	0.3959 2525	0.2911 7203
125	0.5946 6842	0.5360 9565	0.4833 3363	0.3929 7792	0.2882 8914
126	0.5922 0091	0.5334 2850	0.4805 3053	0.3900 5252	0.2854 3479
127	0.5897 4365	0.5307 7463	0.4777 4369	0.3871 4891	0.2826 0870
128	0.5872 9658	0.5281 3396	0.4749 7302	0.3842 6691	0.2798 1060
129	0.5848 5966	0.5255 0643	0.4722 1841	0.3814 0636	0.2770 4019
130	0.5824 3286	0.5228 9197	0.4694 7978	0.3785 6711	0.2742 9722
131	0.5800 1613	0.5202 9052	0.4667 5703	0.3757 4899	0.2715 8141
132	0.5776 0942	0.5177 0201	0.4640 5007	0.3729 5185	0.2688 9248
133	0.5752 1270	0.5151 2637	0.4613 5881	0.3701 7553	0.2662 3018
134	0.5728 2593	0.5125 6356	0.4586 8316	0.3674 1988	0.2635 9424
135	0.5704 4906	0.5100 1349	0.4560 2303	0.3646 8475	0.2609 8439
136	0.5680 8205	0.5074 7611	0.4533 7832	0.3619 6997	0.2584 0039
137	0.5657 2486	0.5049 5135	0.4507 4895	0.3592 7541	0.2558 4197
138	0.5633 7745	0.5024 3916	0.4481 3483	0.3566 0090	0.2533 0888
139	0.5610 3979	0.4999 3946	0.4455 3587	0.3539 4630	0.2508 0087
140	0.5587 1182	0.4974 5220	0.4429 5198	0.3513 1147	0.2483 1770
141	0.5563 9351	0.4949 7731	0.4403 8308	0.3486 9625	0.2458 5911
142	0.5540 8483	0.4925 1474	0.4378 2908	0.3461 0049	0.2434 2486
143	0.5517 8572	0.4900 6442	0.4352 8989	0.3435 2406	0.2410 1471
144	0.5494 9615	0.4876 2628	0.4327 6542	0.3409 6681	0.2386 2843
145	0.5472 1609	0.4852 0028	0.4302 5560	0.3384 2860	0.2362 6577
146	0.5449 4548	0.4827 8635	0.4277 6033	0.3359 0928	0.2339 2650
147	0.5426 8429	0.4803 8443	0.4252 7953	0.3334 0871	0.2316 1040
148	0.5404 3249	0.4779 9446	0.4228 1312	0.3309 2676	0.2293 1723
149	0.5381 9003	0.4756 1637	0.4203 6102	0.3284 6329	0.2270 4676
150	0.5359 5688	0.4732 5012	0.4179 2313	0.3260 1815	0.2247 9877

TABLE XVIII (*Continued*)

Present Value of 1

$$v^n = (1 + i)^{-n}$$

n	$1\frac{1}{8}\%$	$1\frac{1}{4}\%$	$1\frac{1}{2}\%$	$1\frac{3}{4}\%$	2%
1	0.9888 7515	0.9876 5432	0.9852 2167	0.9828 0098	0.9803 9216
2	0.9778 7407	0.9754 6106	0.9706 6175	0.9658 9777	0.9611 6878
3	0.9669 9537	0.9634 1833	0.9563 1699	0.9492 8528	0.9423 2233
4	0.9562 3770	0.9515 2428	0.9421 8423	0.9329 5851	0.9238 4543
5	0.9455 9970	0.9397 7706	0.9282 6033	0.9169 1254	0.9057 3081
6	0.9350 8005	0.9281 7488	0.9145 4219	0.9011 4254	0.8879 7138
7	0.9246 7743	0.9167 1593	0.9010 2679	0.8856 4378	0.8705 6018
8	0.9143 9054	0.9053 9845	0.8877 1112	0.8704 1157	0 8534 9037
9	0.9042 1808	0.8942 2069	0.8745 9224	0.8554 4135	0.8367 5527
10	0.8941 5881	0.8831 8093	0.8616 6723	0.8407 2860	0.8203 4830
11	0.8842 1142	0.8722 7746	0.8489 3323	0.8262 6889	0.8042 6304
12	0.8743 7470	0.8615 0860	0.8363 8742	0 8120 5788	0.7884 9318
13	0.8646 4742	0.8508 7269	0.8240 2702	0.7980 9128	0.7730 3253
14	0.8550 2835	0.8403 6809	0.8118 4928	0.7843 6490	0.7578 7502
15	0.8455 1629	0.8299 9318	0.7998 5150	0.7708 7459	0.7430 1473
16	0.8361 1005	0.8197 4635	0 7880 3104	0.7576 1631	0.7284 4581
17	0.8268 0846	0 8096 2602	0 7763 8526	0.7445 8605	0.7141 6256
18	0.8176 1034	0 7996 3064	0 7649 1159	0 7317 7990	0.7001 5937
19	0.8085 1455	0 7897 5866	0 7536 0747	0.7191 9401	0.6864 3076
20	0.7995 1995	0.7800 0855	0.7424 7042	0.7068 2458	0.6729 7133
21	0.7906 2542	0.7703 7881	0 7314 9795	0.6946 6789	0.6597 7582
22	0.7818 2983	0.7608 6796	0.7206 8763	0 6827 2028	0.6468 3904
23	0.7731 3210	0 7514 7453	0 7100 3708	0 6709 7817	0.6341 5592
24	0.7645 3112	0.7421 9707	0.6995 4392	0.6594 3800	0 6217 2149
25	0.7560 2583	0.7330 3414	0.6892 0583	0 6480 9632	0 6095 3087
26	0.7476 1516	0.7239 8434	0.6790 2052	0.6369 4970	0 5975 7928
27	0.7392 9806	0.7150 4626	0.6689 8574	0 6259 9479	0.5858 6204
28	0.7310 7348	0.7062 1853	0.6590 9925	0 6152 2829	0.5743 7455
29	0.7229 4040	0.6974 9978	0.6493 5887	0.6046 4697	0.5631 1231
30	0.7148 9780	0.6888 8867	0.6397 6243	0.5942 4764	0.5520 7089
31	0.7069 4467	0.6803 8387	0.6303 0781	0.5840 2716	0.5412 4597
32	0.6990 8002	0.6719 8407	0.6209 9292	0.5739 8247	0.5306 3330
33	0.6913 0287	0.6636 8797	0.6118 1568	0 5641 1053	0.5202 2873
34	0.6836 1223	0.6554 9429	0.6027 7407	0 5544 0839	0.5100 2817
35	0.6760 0715	0.6474 0177	0.5938 6608	0 5448 7311	0.5000 2761
36	0.6684 8667	0.6394 0916	0.5850 8974	0.5355 0183	0.4902 2315
37	0.6610 4986	0.6315 1522	0.5764 4309	0.5262 9172	0.4806 1093
38	0.6536 9578	0.6237 1873	0.5679 2423	0.5172 4002	0.4711 8719
39	0.6464 2352	0.6160 1850	0.5595 3126	0.5083 4400	0.4619 4822
40	0.6392 3216	0.6084 1334	0.5512 6232	0.4996 0098	0.4528 9042
41	0.6321 2080	0.6009 0206	0.5431 1559	0.4910 0834	0.4440 1021
42	0.6250 8855	0.5934 8352	0.5350 8925	0.4825 6348	0.4353 0413
43	0.6181 3454	0.5861 5656	0.5271 8153	0 4742 6386	0 4267 6875
44	0.6112 5789	0.5789 2006	0.5193 9067	0 4661 0699	0 4184 0074
45	0.6044 5774	0.5717 7290	0.5117 1494	0.4580 9040	0 4101 9680
46	0.5977 3324	0.5647 1397	0.5041 5265	0.4502 1170	0 4021 5373
47	0.5910 8355	0.5577 4219	0.4967 0212	0.4424 6850	0 3942 6836
48	0.5845 0784	0 5508 5649	0.4893 6170	0 4348 5848	0.3865 3761
49	0.5780 0528	0.5440 5579	0.4821 2975	0.4273 7934	0.3789 5844
50	0.5715 7506	0 5373 3905	0.4750 0468	0.4200 2883	0.3715 2788

TABLE XVIII (Continued)

Present Value of 1

$$v^n = (1 + i)^{-n}$$

n	$1\frac{1}{8}\%$	$1\frac{1}{4}\%$	$1\frac{1}{2}\%$	$1\frac{3}{4}\%$	2%
51	0.5652 1637	0.5307 0524	0.4679 8491	0.4128 0475	0.3642 4302
52	0.5589 2843	0.5241 5332	0.4610 6887	0.4057 0492	0.3571 0100
53	0.5527 1044	0.5176 8229	0.4542 5505	0.3987 2719	0.3500 9902
54	0.5465 6162	0.5112 9115	0.4475 4192	0.3918 6947	0.3432 3433
55	0.5404 8120	0.5049 7892	0.4409 2800	0.3851 2970	0.3365 0425
56	0.5344 6843	0.4987 4461	0.4344 1182	0.3785 0585	0.3299 0613
57	0.5285 2256	0.4925 8727	0.4279 9194	0.3719 9592	0.3234 3738
58	0.5226 4282	0.4865 0594	0.4216 6694	0.3655 9796	0.3170 9547
59	0.5168 2850	0.4804 9970	0.4154 3541	0.3593 1003	0.3108 7791
60	0.5110 7887	0.4745 6760	0.4092 9597	0.3531 3025	0.3047 8227
61	0.5053 9319	0.4687 0874	0.4032 4726	0.3470 5676	0.2988 0614
62	0.4997 7077	0.4629 2222	0.3972 8794	0.3410 8772	0.2929 4720
63	0.4942 1090	0.4572 0713	0.3914 1669	0.3352 2135	0.2872 0314
64	0.4887 1288	0.4515 6259	0.3856 3221	0.3294 5587	0.2815 7170
65	0.4832 7602	0.4459 8775	0.3799 3321	0.3237 8956	0.2760 5069
66	0.4778 9965	0.4404 8173	0.3743 1843	0.3182 2069	0.2706 3793
67	0.4725 8309	0.4350 4368	0.3687 8663	0.3127 4761	0.2653 3130
68	0.4673 2568	0.4296 7277	0.3633 3658	0.3073 6866	0.2601 2873
69	0.4621 2675	0.4243 6817	0.3579 6708	0.3020 8222	0.2550 2817
70	0.4569 8566	0.4191 2905	0.3526 7692	0.2968 8670	0.2500 2761
71	0.4519 0177	0.4139 5462	0.3474 6495	0.2917 8054	0.2451 2511
72	0.4468 7443	0.4088 4407	0.3423 3000	0.2867 6221	0.2403 1874
73	0.4419 0302	0.4037 9661	0.3372 7093	0.2818 3018	0.2356 0661
74	0.4369 8692	0.3988 1147	0.3322 8663	0.2769 8298	0.2309 8687
75	0.4321 2551	0.3938 8787	0.3273 7599	0.2722 1914	0.2264 5771
76	0.4273 1818	0.3890 2506	0.3225 3793	0.2675 3724	0.2220 1737
77	0.4225 6433	0.3842 2228	0.3177 7136	0.2629 3586	0.2176 6408
78	0.4178 6337	0.3794 7879	0.3130 7523	0.2584 1362	0.2133 9616
79	0.4132 1470	0.3747 9387	0.3084 4850	0.2539 6916	0.2092 1192
80	0.4086 1775	0.3701 6679	0.3038 9015	0.2496 0114	0.2051 0973
81	0.4040 7194	0.3655 9683	0.2993 9916	0.2453 0825	0.2010 8797
82	0.3995 7670	0.3610 8329	0.2949 7454	0.2410 8919	0.1971 4507
83	0.3951 3148	0.3566 2547	0.2906 1531	0.2369 4269	0.1932 7948
84	0.3907 3570	0.3522 2268	0.2863 2050	0.2328 6751	0.1894 8968
85	0.3863 8882	0.3478 7426	0.2820 8917	0.2288 6242	0.1857 7420
86	0.3820 9031	0.3435 7951	0.2779 2036	0.2249 2621	0.1821 3157
87	0.3778 3961	0.3393 3779	0.2738 1316	0.2210 5770	0.1785 6036
88	0.3736 3621	0.3351 4843	0.2697 6666	0.2172 5572	0.1750 5918
89	0.3694 7956	0.3310 1080	0.2657 7997	0.2135 1914	0.1716 2665
90	0.3653 6916	0.3269 2425	0.2618 5218	0.2098 4682	0.1682 6142
91	0.3613 0448	0.3228 8814	0.2579 8245	0.2062 3766	0.1649 6217
92	0.3572 8503	0.3189 0187	0.2541 6990	0.2026 9057	0.1617 2762
93	0.3533 1029	0.3149 6481	0.2504 1369	0.1992 0450	0.1585 5649
94	0.3493 7976	0.3110 7636	0.2467 1300	0.1957 7837	0.1554 4754
95	0.3454 9297	0.3072 3591	0.2430 6699	0.1924 1118	0.1523 9955
96	0.3416 4941	0.3034 4287	0.2394 7487	0.1891 0190	0.1494 1132
97	0.3378 4861	0.2996 9666	0.2359 3583	0.1858 4953	0.1464 8169
98	0.3340 9010	0.2959 9670	0.2324 4909	0.1826 5310	0.1436 0950
99	0.3303 7340	0.2923 4242	0.2290 1389	0.1795 1165	0.1407 9363
100	0.3266 9805	0.2887 3326	0.2256 2944	0.1764 2422	0.1380 3297

TABLE XVIII (*Continued*)

PRESENT VALUE OF 1

$$v^n = (1 + i)^{-n}$$

n	$2\frac{1}{4}\%$	$2\frac{1}{2}\%$	$2\frac{3}{4}\%$	3%	$3\frac{1}{2}\%$
1	0.9779 9511	0.9756 0976	0.9732 3601	0.9708 7379	0.9661 8357
2	0.9564 7444	0.9518 1440	0.9471 8833	0.9425 9591	0.9335 1070
3	0.9354 2732	0.9285 9941	0.9218 3779	0.9151 4166	0.9019 4271
4	0.9148 4335	0.9059 5064	0.8971 6573	0.8884 8705	0.8714 4223
5	0.8947 1232	0.8838 5429	0.8731 5400	0.8626 0878	0.8419 7317
6	0.8750 2427	0.8622 9687	0.8497 8491	0.8374 8426	0.8135 0064
7	0.8557 6946	0.8412 6524	0.8270 4128	0.8130 9151	0.7859 9096
8	0.8369 3835	0.8207 4657	0.8049 0635	0.7894 0923	0.7594 1156
9	0.8185 2161	0.8007 2836	0.7833 6385	0.7664 1673	0.7337 3097
10	0.8005 1013	0.7811 9840	0.7623 9791	0.7440 9391	0.7089 1881
11	0.7828 9499	0.7621 4478	0.7419 9310	0.7224 2128	0.6849 4571
12	0.7656 6748	0.7435 5589	0.7221 3440	0.7013 7988	0.6617 8330
13	0.7488 1905	0.7254 2038	0.7028 0720	0.6809 5134	0.6394 0415
14	0.7323 4137	0.7077 2720	0.6839 9728	0.6611 1781	0.6177 8179
15	0.7162 2628	0.6904 6556	0.6656 9078	0.6418 6195	0.5968 9062
16	0.7004 6580	0.6736 2493	0.6478 7424	0.6231 6694	0.5767 0591
17	0.6850 5212	0.6571 9506	0.6305 3454	0.6050 1645	0.5572 0378
18	0.6699 7763	0.6411 6591	0.6136 5892	0.5873 9461	0.5383 6114
19	0.6552 3484	0.6255 2772	0.5972 3496	0.5702 8603	0.5201 5569
20	0.6408 1647	0.6102 7094	0.5812 5057	0.5536 7575	0.5025 6588
21	0.6267 1538	0.5953 8629	0.5656 9398	0.5375 4928	0.4855 7090
22	0.6129 2457	0.5808 6467	0.5505 5375	0.5218 9250	0.4691 5063
23	0.5994 3724	0.5666 9724	0.5358 1874	0.5066 9175	0.4532 8563
24	0.5862 4668	0.5528 7535	0.5214 7809	0.4919 3374	0.4379 5713
25	0.5733 4639	0.5393 9059	0.5075 2126	0.4776 0557	0.4231 4699
26	0.5607 2997	0.5262 3472	0.4939 3796	0.4636 9473	0.4088 3767
27	0.5483 9117	0.5133 9973	0.4807 1821	0.4501 8906	0.3950 1224
28	0.5363 2388	0.5008 7778	0.4678 5227	0.4370 7675	0.3816 5434
29	0.5245 2213	0.4886 6125	0.4553 3068	0.4243 4636	0.3687 4815
30	0.5129 8008	0.4767 4269	0.4431 4421	0.4119 8676	0.3562 7841
31	0.5016 9201	0.4651 1481	0.4312 8301	0.3999 8715	0.3442 3035
32	0.4906 5233	0.4537 7055	0.4197 4103	0.3883 3703	0.3325 8971
33	0.4798 5558	0.4427 0298	0.4085 0708	0.3770 2625	0.3213 4271
34	0.4692 9641	0.4319 0534	0.3975 7380	0.3660 4490	0.3104 7605
35	0.4589 6960	0.4213 7107	0.3869 3314	0.3553 8340	0.2999 7686
36	0.4488 7002	0.4110 9372	0.3765 7727	0.3450 3243	0.2898 3272
37	0.4389 9268	0.4010 6705	0.3664 9856	0.3349 8294	0.2800 3161
38	0.4293 3270	0.3912 8492	0.3566 8959	0.3252 2615	0.2705 6194
39	0.4198 8528	0.3817 4139	0.3471 4316	0.3157 5355	0.2614 1250
40	0.4106 4575	0.3724 3062	0.3378 5222	0.3065 5684	0.2525 7247
41	0.4016 0954	0.3633 4695	0.3288 0995	0.2976 2800	0.2440 3137
42	0.3927 7216	0.3544 8483	0.3200 0968	0.2889 5922	0.2357 7910
43	0.3841 2925	0.3458 3886	0.3114 4495	0.2805 4294	0.2278 0590
44	0.3756 7653	0.3374 0376	0.3031 0944	0.2723 7178	0.2201 0231
45	0.3674 0981	0.3291 7440	0.2949 9702	0.2644 3862	0.2126 5924
46	0.3593 2500	0.3211 4576	0.2871 0172	0.2567 3653	0.2054 6787
47	0.3514 1809	0.3133 1294	0.2794 1773	0.2492 5876	0.1985 1968
48	0.3436 8518	0.3056 7116	0.2719 3940	0.2419 9880	0.1918 0645
49	0.3361 2242	0.2982 1576	0.2646 6122	0.2349 5029	0.1853 2024
50	0.3287 2608	0.2909 4221	0.2575 7783	0.2281 0708	0.1790 5337

TABLE XVIII (*Continued*)

Present Value of 1

$$v^n = (1 + i)^{-n}$$

n	$2\frac{1}{4}\%$	$2\frac{1}{2}\%$	$2\frac{3}{4}\%$	3%	$3\frac{1}{2}\%$
51	0.3214 9250	0.2838 4606	0.2506 8402	0.2214 6318	0.1729 9843
52	0.3144 1810	0.2769 2298	0.2439 7471	0.2150 1280	0.1671 4824
53	0.3074 9936	0.2701 6876	0.2374 4497	0.2087 5029	0.1614 9589
54	0.3007 3287	0.2635 7928	0.2310 9000	0.2026 7019	0.1560 3467
55	0.2941 1528	0.2571 5052	0.2249 0511	0.1967 6717	0.1507 5814
56	0.2876 4330	0.2508 7855	0.2188 8575	0.1910 3609	0.1456 6004
57	0.2813 1374	0.2447 5956	0.2130 2749	0.1854 7193	0.1407 3433
58	0.2751 2347	0.2387 8982	0.2073 2603	0.1800 6984	0.1359 7520
59	0.2690 6940	0.2329 6568	0.2017 7716	0.1748 2508	0.1313 7701
60	0.2631 4856	0.2272 8359	0.1963 7679	0.1697 3309	0.1269 3431
61	0.2573 5801	0.2217 4009	0.1911 2097	0.1647 8941	0.1226 4184
62	0.2516 9487	0.2163 3179	0.1860 0581	0.1599 8972	0.1184 9453
63	0.2461 5635	0.2110 5541	0.1810 2755	0.1553 2982	0.1144 8747
64	0.2407 3971	0.2059 0771	0.1761 8253	0.1508 0565	0.1106 1591
65	0.2354 4226	0.2008 8557	0.1714 6718	0.1464 1325	0.1068 7528
66	0.2302 6138	0.1959 8593	0 1668 7804	0.1421 4879	0.1032 6114
67	0.2251 9450	0.1912 0578	0.1624 1172	0.1380 0853	0.0997 6922
68	0.2202 3912	0.1865 4223	0.1580 6493	0.1339 8887	0.0963 9538
69	0.2153 9278	0.1819 9241	0.1538 3448	0.1300 8628	0.0931 3563
70	0.2106 5309	0.1775 5358	0.1497 1726	0.1262 9736	0.0899 8612
71	0.2060 1769	0.1732 2300	0.1457 1023	0.1226 1880	0.0869 4311
72	0.2014 8429	0.1689 9805	0.1418 1044	0.1190 4737	0.0840 0300
73	0.1970 5065	0.1648 7615	0.1380 1503	0.1155 7998	0.0811 6232
74	0.1927 1458	0.1608 5478	0.1343 2119	0.1122 1357	0.0784 1770
75	0.1884 7391	0.1569 3149	0.1307 2622	0.1089 4521	0.0757 6590
76	0.1843 2657	0.1531 0389	0.1272 2747	0.1057 7205	0.0732 0376
77	0.1802 7048	0.1493 6965	0.1238 2235	0.1026 9131	0.0707 2827
78	0.1763 0365	0.1457 2649	0.1205 0837	0.0997 0030	0.0683 3650
79	0.1724 2411	0.1421 7218	0.1172 8309	0.0967 9641	0.0660 2560
80	0.1686 2993	0.1387 0457	0.1141 4412	0.0939 7710	0.0637 9285
81	0.1649 1925	0.1353 2153	0.1110 8917	0.0912 3990	0.0616 3561
82	0.1612 9022	0.1320 2101	0.1081 1598	0.0885 8243	0.0595 5131
83	0.1577 4105	0.1288 0098	0.1052 2237	0.0860 0236	0.0575 3750
84	0.1542 6997	0.1256 5949	0.1024 0620	0.0834 9743	0.0555 9178
85	0.1508 7528	0.1225 9463	0.0996 6540	0.0810 6547	0.0537 1187
86	0.1475 5528	0 1196 0452	0.0969 9795	0.0787 0434	0.0518 9553
87	0.1443 0835	0 1166 8733	0.0944 0190	0.0764 1198	0.0501 4060
88	0.1411 3286	0.1138 4130	0.0918 7533	0.0741 8639	0.0484 4503
89	0.1380 2724	0.1110 6468	0.0894 1638	0.0720 2562	0.0468 0679
90	0.1349 8997	0.1083 5579	0.0870 2324	0.0699 2779	0.0452 2395
91	0.1320 1953	0.1057 1296	0.0846 9415	0.0678 9105	0.0436 9464
92	0.1291 1445	0.1031 3460	0.0824 2740	0.0659 1364	0.0422 1704
93	0.1262 7331	0.1006 1912	0.0802 2131	0.0639 9383	0.0407 8941
94	0.1234 9468	0.0981 6500	0.0780 7427	0.0621 2993	0.0394 1006
95	0.1207 7719	0.0957 7073	0.0759 8469	0.0603 2032	0.0380 7735
96	0.1181 1950	0.0934 3486	0.0739 5104	0.0585 6342	0.0367 8971
97	0.1155 2029	0.0911 1595	0.0719 7181	0.0568 5769	0.0355 4562
98	0.1129 7828	0.0889 3264	0.0700 4556	0.0552 0164	0.0343 4359
99	0.1104 9221	0.0867 6355	0.0681 7086	0.0535 9383	0.0331 8221
100	0.1080 6084	0.0846 4737	0.0663 4634	0.0520 3284	0.0320 6011

TABLE XVIII (*Continued*)

PRESENT VALUE OF 1

$$v^n = (1 + i)^{-n}$$

n	4%	4½%	5%	5½%	6%
1	0 9615 3846	0 9569 3780	0 9523 8095	0 9478 6730	0 9433 9623
2	0 9245 5621	0 9157 2995	0 9070 2948	0.8984 5242	0 8899 9644
3	0 8889 9636	0 8762 9660	0 8638 3760	0 8516 1366	0.8396 1928
4	0 8548 0419	0 8385 6134	0 8227 0247	0 8072 1674	0 7920 9366
5	0 8219 2711	0 8024 5105	0 7835 2617	0 7651 3435	0 7472 5817
6	0 7903 1453	0 7678 9574	0 7462 1540	0 7252 4583	0 7049 6054
7	0 7599 1781	0 7348 2846	0 7106 8133	0 6874 3681	0.6650 5711
8	0 7306 9021	0 7031 8513	0 6768 3936	0 6515 9887	0 6274 1237
9	0 7025 8674	0 6729 0443	0 6446 0892	0 6176 2926	0 5918 9846
10	0 6755 6417	0 6439 2768	0 6139 1325	0 5854 3058	0 5583 9478
11	0 6495 8093	0 6161 9874	0 5846 7929	0 5549 1050	0 5267 8753
12	0 6245 9705	0 5896 6386	0 5568 3742	0 5259 8152	0 4969 6936
13	0 6005 7409	0 5642 7164	0 5303 2135	0 4985 6068	0 4688 3902
14	0 5774 7508	0 5399 7286	0 5050 6795	0 4725 6937	0 4423 0096
15	0.5552 6450	0 5167 2044	0 4810 1710	0 4479 3305	0 4172 6506
16	0 5339 0818	0 4944 6932	0 4581 1152	0 4245 8109	0 3936 4628
17	0 5133 7325	0 4731 7639	0 4362 9669	0 4024 4653	0 3713 6442
18	0 4936 2812	0 4528 0037	0 4155 2065	0 3814 6590	0 3503 4379
19	0 4746 4242	0 4333 0179	0 3957 3396	0 3615 7906	0 3305 1301
20	0 4563 8695	0 4146 4286	0 3768 8948	0 3427 2896	0 3118 0473
21	0 4388 3360	0 3967 8743	0 3589 4236	0 3248 6158	0 2941 5540
22	0 4219 5539	0 3797 0089	0 3418 4987	0 3079 2567	0 2775 0510
23	0 4057 2633	0 3633 5013	0 3255 7131	0 2918 7267	0 2617 9726
24	0 3901 2147	0 3477 0347	0 3100 6791	0 2766 5656	0 2469 7855
25	0 3751 1680	0 3327 3060	0 2953 0277	0 2622 3370	0.2329 9863
26	0 3606 8923	0 3184 0248	0 2812 4073	0 2485 6275	0 2198 1003
27	0 3468 1657	0 3046 9137	0.2678 4832	0 2356 0450	0 2073 6795
28	0 3334 7747	0 2915 7069	0 2550 9364	0 2233 2181	0 1956 3014
29	0 3206 5141	0.2790 1502	0 2429 4632	0.2116 7944	0 1845 5674
30	0 3083 1867	0 2670 0002	0.2313 7745	0 2006 4402	0 1741 1013
31	0 2964 6026	0 2555 0241	0 2203 5947	0 1901 8390	0 1642 5484
32	0 2850 5794	0 2444 9991	0 2098 6617	0 1802 6910	0 1549 5740
33	0.2740 9417	0 2339 7121	0 1998 7254	0 1708 7119	0.1461 8622
34	0.2635 5209	0 2238 9589	0 1903 5480	0 1619 6321	0.1379 1153
35	0.2534 1547	0 2142 5444	0 1812 9029	0 1535 1963	0.1301 0522
36	0 2436 6872	0 2050 2817	0 1726 5741	0 1455 1624	0.1227 4077
37	0 2342 9685	0 1961 9921	0 1644 3563	0 1379 3008	0.1157 9318
38	0.2252 8543	0 1877 5044	0 1566 0536	0 1307 3941	0.1092 3885
39	0.2166 2061	0 1796 6549	0 1491 4797	0 1239 2362	0.1030 5552
40	0 2082 8904	0 1719 2870	0 1420 4568	0 1174 6314	0.0972 2219
41	0 2002 7793	0 1645 2507	0 1352 8160	0 1113 3947	0.0917 1905
42	0 1925 7493	0 1574 4026	0 1288 3962	0 1055 3504	0.0865 2740
43	0 1851 6820	0 1506 6054	0 1227 0440	0.1000 3322	0 0816 2962
44	0 1780 4635	0 1441 7276	0 1168 6133	0.0948 1822	0.0770 0908
45	0 1711 9841	0 1379 6437	0 1112 9651	0.0898 7509	0.0726 5007
46	0 1646 1386	0.1320 2332	0.1059 9668	0.0851 8965	0.0685 3781
47	0 1582 8256	0.1263 3810	0.1009 4921	0.0807 4849	0.0646 5831
48	0.1521 9476	0.1208 9771	0 0961 4211	0.0765 3885	0.0609 9840
49	0 1463 4112	0.1156 9158	0 0915 6391	0.0725 4867	0.0575 4566
50	0 1407 1262	0 1107 0965	0.0872 0373	0 0687 6652	0.0542 8836

TABLE XVIII (*Continued*)

Present Value of 1

$$v^n = (1 + i)^{-n}$$

n	4%	$4\frac{1}{2}\%$	5%	$5\frac{1}{2}\%$	6%
51	0.1353 0059	0.1059 4225	0.0830 5117	0.0651 8153	0.0512 1544
52	0.1300 9672	0.1013 8014	0.0790 9635	0.0617 8344	0.0483 1645
53	0.1250 9300	0.0970 1449	0.0753 2986	0.0585 6250	0.0455 8156
54	0.1202 8173	0.0928 3683	0.0717 4272	0.0555 0948	0.0430 0147
55	0.1156 5551	0.0888 3907	0.0683 2640	0.0526 1562	0.0405 6742
56	0.1112 0722	0.0850 1347	0.0650 7276	0.0498 7263	0.0382 7115
57	0.1069 3002	0.0813 5260	0.0619 7406	0.0472 7263	0.0361 0486
58	0.1028 1733	0.0778 4938	0.0590 2291	0.0448 0818	0.0340 6119
59	0.0988 6282	0.0744 9701	0.0562 1230	0.0424 7221	0.0321 3320
60	0.0950 6040	0.0712 8901	0.0535 3552	0.0402 5802	0.0303 1434
61	0.0914 0423	0.0682 1915	0.0509 8621	0.0381 5926	0.0285 9843
62	0.0878 8868	0.0652 8148	0.0485 5830	0.0361 6992	0.0269 7965
63	0.0845 0835	0.0624 7032	0.0462 4600	0.0342 8428	0.0254 5250
64	0.0812 5803	0.0597 8021	0.0440 4381	0.0324 9695	0.0240 1179
65	0.0781 3272	0.0572 0594	0.0419 4648	0.0308 0279	0.0226 5264
66	0.0751 2762	0.0547 4253	0.0399 4903	0.0291 9696	0.0213 7041
67	0.0722 3809	0.0523 8519	0.0380 4670	0.0276 7485	0.0201 6077
68	0.0694 5970	0.0501 2937	0.0362 3495	0.0262 3208	0.0190 1959
69	0.0667 8818	0.0479 7069	0.0345 0948	0.0248 6453	0.0179 4301
70	0.0642 1940	0.0459 0497	0.0328 6617	0.0235 6828	0.0169 2737
71	0.0617 4942	0.0439 2820	0.0313 0111	0.0223 3960	0.0159 6921
72	0.0593 7445	0.0420 3655	0.0298 1058	0.0211 7498	0.0150 6530
73	0.0570 9081	0.0402 2637	0.0283 9103	0.0200 7107	0.0142 1254
74	0.0548 9501	0.0384 9413	0.0270 3908	0.0190 2471	0.0134 0806
75	0.0527 8367	0.0368 3649	0.0257 5150	0.0180 3290	0.0126 4911
76	0.0507 5353	0.0352 5023	0.0245 2524	0.0170 9279	0.0119 3313
77	0.0488 0147	0.0337 3228	0.0233 5737	0.0162 0170	0.0112 5767
78	0.0469 2449	0.0322 7969	0.0222 4512	0.0153 5706	0.0106 2044
79	0.0451 1970	0.0308 8965	0.0211 8582	0.0145 5646	0.0100 1928
80	0.0433 8433	0.0295 5948	0.0201 7698	0.0137 9759	0.0094 5215
81	0.0417 1570	0.0282 8658	0.0192 1617	0.0130 7828	0.0089 1713
82	0.0401 1125	0.0270 6850	0.0183 0111	0.0123 9648	0.0084 1238
83	0.0385 6851	0.0259 0287	0.0174 2963	0.0117 5022	0.0079 3621
84	0.0370 8510	0.0247 8744	0.0165 9965	0.0111 3765	0.0074 8699
85	0.0356 5875	0.0237 2003	0.0158 0919	0.0105 5701	0.0070 6320
86	0.0342 8726	0.0226 9860	0.0150 5637	0.0100 0664	0.0066 6340
87	0.0329 6852	0.0217 2115	0.0143 3940	0.0094 8497	0.0062 8622
88	0.0317 0050	0.0207 8579	0.0136 5657	0.0089 9049	0.0059 3040
89	0.0304 8125	0.0198 9070	0.0130 0626	0.0085 2180	0.0055 9472
90	0.0293 0890	0.0190 3417	0.0123 8691	0.0080 7753	0.0052 7803
91	0.0281 8163	0.0182 1451	0.0117 9706	0.0076 5643	0.0049 7928
92	0.0270 9772	0.0174 3016	0.0112 3530	0.0072 5728	0.0046 9743
93	0.0260 5550	0.0166 7958	0.0107 0028	0.0068 7894	0.0044 3154
94	0.0250 5337	0.0159 6132	0.0101 9074	0.0065 2032	0.0041 8070
95	0.0240 8978	0.0152 7399	0.0097 0547	0.0061 8040	0.0039 4405
96	0.0231 6325	0.0146 1626	0.0092 4331	0.0058 5820	0.0037 2081
97	0.0222 7235	0.0139 8685	0.0088 0315	0.0055 5279	0.0035 1019
98	0.0214 1572	0.0133 8454	0.0083 8395	0.0052 6331	0.0033 1150
99	0.0205 9204	0.0128 0817	0.0079 8471	0.0049 8892	0.0031 2406
100	0.0198 0004	0.0122 5663	0.0076 0449	0.0047 2883	0.0029 4723

HIGH-SPEED MATHEMATICS

TABLE XVIII (*Continued*)

PRESENT VALUE OF 1

$$v^n = (1 + i)^{-n}$$

n	$6\frac{1}{2}\%$	7%	$7\frac{1}{2}\%$	8%	$8\frac{1}{2}\%$
1	0.9389 6714	0.9345 7944	0.9302 3256	0.9259 2593	0.9216 5899
2	0.8816 5928	0.8734 3873	0.8653 3261	0.8573 3882	0.8494 5529
3	0.8278 4909	0.8162 9788	0.8049 6057	0.7938 3224	0.7829 0810
4	0.7773 2309	0.7628 9521	0.7488 0053	0.7350 2985	0.7215 7428
5	0.7298 8084	0.7129 8618	0.6965 5863	0.6805 8320	0.6650 4542
6	0.6853 3412	0.6663 4222	0.6479 6152	0.6301 6963	0.6129 4509
7	0.6435 0621	0.6227 4974	0.6027 5490	0.5834 9040	0.5649 2635
8	0.6042 3119	0.5820 0910	0.5607 0223	0.5402 6888	0.5206 6945
9	0.5673 5323	0.5439 3374	0.5215 8347	0.5002 4897	0.4798 7968
10	0.5327 2604	0.5083 4929	0.4851 9393	0.4631 9349	0.4422 8542
11	0.5002 1224	0.4750 9280	0.4513 4319	0.4288 8286	0.4076 3633
12	0.4696 8285	0.4440 1196	0.4198 5413	0.3971 1376	0.3757 0163
13	0.4410 1676	0.4149 6445	0.3905 6198	0.3676 9792	0.3462 6883
14	0.4141 0025	0.3878 1724	0.3633 1347	0.3404 6104	0.3191 4178
15	0.3888 2652	0.3624 4602	0.3379 6602	0.3152 4170	0.2941 3989
16	0.3650 9533	0.3387 3460	0.3143 8699	0.2918 9047	0.2710 9667
17	0.3428 1251	0.3165 7439	0.2924 5302	0.2702 6895	0.2498 5869
18	0.3218 8969	0.2958 6392	0.2720 4932	0.2502 4903	0.2302 8450
19	0.3022 4384	0.2765 0832	0.2530 6913	0.2317-1206	0.2122 4378
20	0.2837 9703	0.2584 1900	0.2354 1315	0.2145 4821	0.1956 1639
21	0.2664 7608	0.2415 1309	0.2189 8897	0.1986 5575	0.1802 9160
22	0.2502 1228	0.2257 1317	0.2037 1067	0.1839 4051	0.1661 6738
23	0.2349 4111	0.2109 4688	0.1894 9830	0.1703 1528	0.1531 4965
24	0.2206 0198	0.1971 4662	0.1762 7749	0.1576 9934	0.1411 5176
25	0.2071 3801	0.1842 4918	0.1639 7906	0.1460 1790	0.1300 9378
26	0.1944 9579	0.1721 954́9	0.1525 3866	0.1352 0176	0.1199 0210
27	0.1826 2515	0.1609 3037	0.1418 9643	0.1251 8682	0.1105 0885
28	0.1714 7902	0.1504 0221	0.1319 9668	0.1159 1372	0.1018 5148
29	0.1610 1316	0.1405 6282	0.1227 8761	0.1073 2752	0.0938 7233
30	0.1511 8607	0.1313 6712	0.1142 2103	0.0993 7733	0.0865 1828
31	0.1419 5875	0.1227 7301	0.1062 5212	0.0920 1605	0.0797 4035
32	0.1332 9460	0.1147 4113	0.0988 3918	0.0852 0005	0.0734 9341
33	0.1251 5925	0.1072 3470	0.0919 4343	0.0788 8893	0.0677 3586
34	0.1175 2042	0.1002 1934	0.0855 2877	0.0730 4531	0.0624 2936
35	0.1103 4781	0.0936 6294	0.0795 6164	0.0676 3454	0.0575 3858
36	0.1036 1297	0.0875 3546	0.0740 1083	0 0626 2458	0.0530 3095
37	0.0972 8917	0.0818 0884	0.0688 4729	0.0579 8572	0.0488 7645
38	0.0913 5134	0.0764 5686	0.0640 4399	0 0536 9048	0.0450 4742
39	0.0857 7590	0.0714 5501	0.0595 7580	0.0497 1341	0.0415 1836
40	0.0805 4075	0.0667 8038	0.0554 1935	0.0460 3093	0.0382 6577
41	0.0756 2512	0.0624 1157	0.0515 5288	0.0426 2123	0.0352 6799
42	0.0710 0950	0.0583 2857	0.0479 5617	0.0394 6411	0.0325 0506
43	0.0666 7559	0.0545 1268	0.0446 1039	0.0365 4084	0.0299 5858
44	0.0626 0619	0.0509 4643	0.0414 9804	0.0338 3411	0.0276 1160
45	0.0587 8515	0.0476 1349	0.0386 0283	0.0313 2788	0.0254 4848
46	0.0551 9733	0.0444 9859	0.0359 0961	0.0290 0730	0.0234 5482
47	0.0518 2848	0.0415 8747	0.0334 0428	0.0268 5861	0.0216 1734
48	0.0486 6524	0.0388 6679	0.0310 7375	0.0248 6908	0.0199 2382
49	0.0456 9506	0.0363 2410	0.0289 0582	0.0230 2693	0.0183 6297
50	0.0429 0616	0.0339 4776	0.0268 8913	0.0213 2123	0.0169 2439

TABLE XIX

AMOUNT OF ANNUITY OF 1 PER PERIOD

$$s_{\overline{n}|} = \frac{(1 + i)^n - 1}{i}$$

n	$\frac{5}{12}\%$	$\frac{1}{2}\%$	$\frac{7}{12}\%$	$\frac{3}{4}\%$	1%
1	1.0000 0000	1.0000 0000	1.0000 0000	1.0000 0000	1.0000 0000
2	2.0041 6667	2.0050 0000	2.0058 3333	2.0075 0000	2.0100 0000
3	3.0125 1736	3.0150 2500	3.0175 3403	3.0225 5625	3.0301 0000
4	4.0250 6952	4.0301 0013	4.0351 3631	4.0452 2542	4.0604 0100
5	5.0418 4064	5.0502 5063	5.0586 7460	5.0755 6461	5.1010 0501
6	6.0628 4831	6.0755 0188	6.0881 8354	6.1136 3135	6.1520 1506
7	7.0881 1018	7.1058 7939	7.1236 9794	7.1594 8358	7.2135 3521
8	8.1176 4397	8.1414 0879	8.1652 5284	8.2131 7971	8.2856 7056
9	9.1514 6749	9.1821 1583	9.2128 8349	9.2747 7856	9.3685 2727
10	10.1895 9860	10.2280 2641	10.2666 2531	10.3443 3940	10.4622 1254
11	11.2320 5526	11.2791 6654	11.3265 1396	11.4219 2194	11.5668 3467
12	12.2788 5549	12.3355 6237	12.3925 8529	12.5075 8636	12.6825 0301
13	13.3300 1739	13.3972 4018	13.4648 7537	13.6013 9325	13.8093 2804
14	14.3855 5913	14.4642 2639	14.5434 2048	14.7034 0370	14.9474 2132
15	15.4454 9896	15.5365 4752	15.6282 5710	15.8136 7923	16.0968 9554
16	16.5098 5520	16.6142 3026	16.7194 2193	16.9322 8183	17.2578 6449
17	17.5786 4627	17.6973 0141	17.8169 5189	18.0592 7394	18.4304 4314
18	18.6518 9063	18.7857 8791	18.9208 8411	19.1947 1849	19.6147 4757
19	19.7296 0684	19.8797 1685	20.0312 5593	20.3386 7888	20.8108 9504
20	20.8118 1353	20.9791 1544	21.1481 0493	21.4012 1897	22.0190 0399
21	21.8985 2942	22.0840 1101	22.2714 6887	22.6524 0312	23.2391 9403
22	22.9897 7330	23.1944 3107	23.4013 8577	23.8222 9614	24.4715 8598
23	24.0855 6402	24.3104 0322	24.5378 9386	25.0009 6336	25.7163 0183
24	25.1859 2054	25.4319 5524	25.6810 3157	26.1884 7059	26.9734 6485
25	26.2908 6187	26.5591 1502	26.8308 3759	27.3848 8412	28.2431 9950
26	27.4004 0713	27.6919 1059	27.9873 5081	28.5902 7075	29.5256 3150
27	28.5145 7549	28.8303 7015	29.1506 1035	29.8046 9778	30.8208 8781
28	29.6333 8622	29.9745 2200	30.3206 5558	31.0282 3301	32.1290 9669
29	30.7568 5867	31.1243 9461	31.4975 2607	32.2609 4476	33.4503 8766
30	31.8850 1224	32.2800 1658	32.6812 6164	33.5020 0154	34.7848 9153
31	33.0178 6646	33.4414 1666	33.8719 0233	34.7541 7361	36.1327 4045
32	34.1554 4090	34.0086 2375	35.0694 8843	36.0148 2991	37.4940 6785
33	35.2977 5524	35.7816 6686	36.2740 6045	37.2849 4113	38.8690 0853
34	36.4448 2922	36.9605 7520	37.4856 5913	38.5645 7819	40.2576 9862
35	37.5966 8268	38.1453 7807	38.7043 2548	39.8538 1253	41.6602 7560
36	38.7533 3552	39.3361 0496	39.9301 0071	41.1527 1612	43.0768 7836
37	39.9148 0775	40.5327 8549	41.1630 2630	42.4613 6149	44.5076 4714
38	41.0811 1945	41.7354 4942	42.4031 4395	43.7798 2170	45.9527 2361
39	42.2522 9078	42.9441 2666	43.6504 9562	45.1081 7037	47.4122 5085
40	43.4283 4199	44.1588 4730	44.9051 2352	46.4464 8164	48.8863 7336
41	44.6092 9342	45.3796 4153	46.1670 7007	47.7948 3026	50.3752 3709
42	45.7951 6548	46.6065 3974	47.4363 7798	49.1532 9148	51.8789 8946
43	46.9859 7866	47.8395 7244	48.7130 9018	50.5219 4117	53.3977 7936
44	48.1817 5358	49.0787 7030	49.9972 4988	51.9008 5573	54.9317 5715
45	49.3825 1088	50.3241 6415	51.2889 0050	53.2901 1215	56.4810 7472
46	50.5882 7134	51.5757 8497	52.5880 8575	54.6897 8799	58.0458 8547
47	51.7990 5581	52.8336 6390	53.8948 4959	56.0999 6140	59.6263 4432
48	53.0148 8521	54.0978 3222	55.2092 3621	57.5207 1111	61.2226 0777
49	54.2357 8056	55.3683 2138	56.5312 9009	58.9521 1644	62.8348 3385
50	55.4617 6298	56.6451 6299	57.8610 5595	60.3942 5732	64.4631 8218

HIGH-SPEED MATHEMATICS

TABLE XIX (*Continued*)

Amount of Annuity of 1 per Period

$$s_{\overline{n}|} = \frac{(1+i)^n - 1}{i}$$

n	$\frac{5}{12}\%$	$\frac{1}{2}\%$	$\frac{7}{12}\%$	$\frac{3}{4}\%$	1%
51	56.6928 5366	57.9283 8880	59.1985 7877	61.8472 1424	66.1078 1401
52	57.9290 7388	59.2180 3075	60.5439 0381	63.3110 6835	67.7688 9215
53	59.1704 4503	60.5141 2090	61.8970 7659	64.7859 0136	69.4465 8107
54	60.4169 8855	61.8166 9150	63.2581 4287	66.2717 9562	71.1410 4688
55	61.6687 2600	63.1257 7496	64.6271 4870	67.7688 3409	72.8524 5735
56	62.9256 7902	64.4414 0384	66.0041 4040	69.2771 0035	74.5809 8192
57	64.1878 6935	65.7636 1086	67.3891 6455	70.7966 7860	76.3267 9174
58	65.4553 1881	67.0924 2891	68.7822 6801	72.3276 5369	78.0900 5966
59	66.7280 4930	68.4278 9105	70.1834 9791	73.8701 1109	79.8709 6025
60	68.0060 8284	69.7700 3051	71.5929 0165	75.4241 3693	81.6696 6986
61	69.2894 4152	71.1188 8066	73.0105 2691	76.9898 1795	83.4863 6655
62	70.5781 4753	72.4744 7507	74.4364 2165	78.5672 4159	85.3212 3022
63	71.8722 2314	73.8368 4744	75.8706 3411	80.1564 9590	87.1744 4252
64	73.1716 9074	75.2060 3168	77.3132 1281	81.7576 6962	89.0461 8695
65	74.4765 7278	76.5820 6184	78.7642 0655	83.3708 5214	90.9366 4882
66	75.7868 9184	77.9649 7215	80.2236 6442	84.9961 3353	92.8460 1531
67	77.1026 7055	79.3547 9701	81.6916 3579	86.6336 0453	94.7744 7546
68	78.4239 3168	80.7515 7099	83.1681 7034	88.2833 5657	96.7222 2021
69	79.7506 9806	82.1553 2885	84.6533 1800	89.9454 8174	98.6894 4242
70	81.0829 9264	83.5661 0549	86.1471 2902	91.6200 7285	100.6763 3684
71	82.4208 3844	84.9839 3602	87.6496 5394	93.3072 2340	102.6831 0021
72	83.7642 5560	86.4088 5570	89.1609 4359	95.0070 2758	104.7099 3121
73	85.1132 7634	87.8408 9998	90.6810 4909	96.7195 8028	106.7570 3052
74	86.4679 1500	89.2801 0448	92.2100 2188	98.4449 7714	108.8246 0083
75	87.8281 9797	90.7265 0500	93.7479 1367	100.1833 1446	110.9128 4684
76	89.1941 4880	92.1801 3752	95.2947 7650	101.9346 8932	113.0219 7530
77	90.5657 9109	93.6410 3821	96.8506 6270	103.6991 9949	115.1521 9506
78	91.9431 4855	95.1092 4340	98.4156 2490	105.4769 4349	117.3037 1701
79	93.3262 4500	96.5847 8962	99.9897 1604	107.2680 2056	119.4767 5418
80	94.7151 0436	98.0677 1357	101.5729 8938	109.0725 3072	121.6715 2172
81	96.1097 5062	99.5580 5214	103.1654 9849	110.8905 7470	123.8882 3694
82	97.5102 0792	101.0558 4240	104.7672 9723	112.7222 5401	126.1271 1931
83	98.9165 0045	102.5611 2161	106.3784 3980	114.5676 7091	128.3883 9050
84	100.3286 5254	104.0739 2722	107.9989 8070	116.4269 2845	130.6722 7440
85	101.7466 8859	105.5942 9685	109.6289 7475	118.3001 3041	132.9789 9715
86	103.1706 3312	107.1222 6834	111.2684 7710	120.1873 8139	135.3087 8712
87	104.6005 1076	108.6578 7968	112.9175 4322	122.0887 8675	137.6618 7499
88	106.0363 4622	110.2011 6908	114.5762 2889	124.0044 5265	140.0384 9374
89	107.4781 6433	111.7521 7492	116.2445 9022	125.9344 8604	142.4388 7868
90	108.9259 9002	113.3109 3580	117.9226 8367	127.8789 9469	144.8632 6746
91	110.3798 4831	114.8774 9048	119.6105 6599	129.8380 8715	147.3119 0014
92	111.8397 6434	116.4518 7793	121.3082 9429	131.8118 7280	149.7850 1914
93	113.3057 6336	118.0341 3732	123.0159 2601	133.8004 6185	152.2828 6933
94	114.7778 7071	119.6243 0800	124.7335 1891	135.8039 6531	154.8056 9803
95	116.2561 1184	121.2224 2954	126.4611 3110	137.8224 9505	157.3537 5501
96	117.7405 1230	122.8285 4169	128.1988 2103	139.8561 6377	159.9272 9256
97	119.2310 9777	124.4426 8440	129.9466 4749	141.9050 8499	162.5265 6548
98	120.7278 9401	126.0648 9782	131.7046 6960	143.9693 7313	165.1518 3114
99	122.2309 2690	127.6952 2231	133.4729 4684	146.0491 4343	167.8033 4945
100	123.7402 2243	129.3336 9842	135.2515 3903	148.1445 1201	170.4813 8294

TABLE XIX (Continued)

Amount of Annuity of 1 per Period

$$s_{\overline{n}|} = \frac{(1+i)^n - 1}{i}$$

n	$\frac{5}{12}\%$	$\frac{1}{2}\%$	$\frac{7}{12}\%$	$\frac{3}{4}\%$	1%
101	125.2558 0669	130.9803 6692	137.0405 0634	150.2555 9585	173.1861 9677
102	126.7777 0589	132.6352 6875	138.8399 0929	152.3825 1281	175.9180 5874
103	128.3059 4633	134.2984 4509	140.6498 0876	154.5253 8166	178.6772 3933
104	129.8405 5444	135.9699 3732	142.4702 6598	156.6843 2202	181.4640 1172
105	131.3815 5675	137.6497 8701	144.3013 4253	158.8594 5444	184.2786 5184
106	132.9289 7990	139.3380 3594	146.1431 0036	161.0509 0035	187.1214 3836
107	134.4828 5065	141.0347 2612	147.9956 0178	163.2587 8210	189.9926 5274
108	136.0431 9586	142.7398 9975	149.8589 0946	165.4832 2296	192.8925 7927
109	137.6100 4251	144.4535 9925	151.7330 8643	167.7243 4714	195.8215 0506
110	139.1834 1769	146.1758 6725	153.6181 9610	169.9822 7974	198.7797 2011
111	140.7633 4860	147.9067 4658	155.5143 0225	172.2571 4684	201.7675 1731
112	142.3498 6255	149.6462 8032	157.4214 6901	174.5490 7544	204.7851 9248
113	143.9429 8698	151.3945 1172	159.3397 6091	176.8581 9351	207.8330 4441
114	145.5427 4942	153.1514 8428	161.2692 4285	179.1846 2996	210.9113 7485
115	147.1491 7754	154.9172 4170	163.2099 8010	181.5285 1468	214.0204 8860
116	148.7622 9912	156.6918 2791	165.1620 3832	183.8899 7854	217.1606 9349
117	150.3821 4203	158.4752 8704	167.1254 8354	186.2691 5338	220.3323 0042
118	152.0087 3429	160.2676 6348	169.1003 8219	188.6661 7203	223.5356 2343
119	153.6421 0401	162.0690 0180	171.0868 0109	191.0811 6832	226.7709 7966
120	155.2822 7945	163.8793 4681	173.0848 0743	193.5142 7708	230.0386 8946
121	156.9292 8895	165.6987 4354	175.0944 6881	195.9656 3416	233.3390 7635
122	158.5831 6098	167.5272 3726	177.1158 5321	198.4353 7642	236.6724 6712
123	160.2439 2415	169.3648 7344	179.1490 2902	200.9236 4714	240.0391 9179
124	161.9116 0717	171.2116 9781	181.1940 6502	203.4305 6905	243.4395 8370
125	163.5862 3887	173.0677 5630	183.2510 3040	205.9562 9832	246.8739 7954
126	165.2678 4819	174.9330 9508	185.3199 9474	208.5009 7056	250.3427 1934
127	166.9564 6423	176.8077 6056	187.4010 2805	211.0647 2784	253.8461 4653
128	168.6521 1616	178.6917 9936	189.4942 0071	213.6477 1330	257.3846 0800
129	170.3548 3331	180.5852 5836	191.5995 8355	216.2500 7115	260.9584 5408
130	172.0646 4512	182.4881 8465	193.7172 4778	218.8719 4668	264.5680 3862
131	173.7815 8114	184.4006 2557	195.8472 6506	221.5134 8628	268.2137 1900
132	175.5056 7106	186.3226 2870	197.9897 0744	224.1748 3743	271.8958 5619
133	177.2369 4469	188.2542 4184	200.1446 4740	226.8561 4871	275.6148 1475
134	178.9754 3196	190.1955 1305	202.3121 5785	229.5575 6982	279.3709 6290
135	180.7211 6293	192.1464 9062	204.4923 1210	232.2792 5160	283.1646 7253
136	182.4741 6777	194.1072 2307	206.6851 8392	235.0213 4598	286.9963 1926
137	184.2344 7681	196.0777 5919	208.8908 4749	237.7840 0608	290.8662 8245
138	186.0021 2046	198.0581 4798	211.1093 7744	240.5673 8612	294.7749 4527
139	187.7771 2929	200.0484 3872	213.3408 4881	243.3716 4152	298.7226 9473
140	189.5595 3400	202.0486 8092	215.5853 3709	246.1969 2883	302.7099 2167
141	191.3493 6539	204.0589 2432	217.8429 1822	249.0434 0580	306.7370 2089
142	193.1466 5441	206.0792 1894	220.1136 6858	251.9112 3134	310.8043 9110
143	194.9514 3214	208.1096 1504	222.3976 6498	254.8005 6558	314.9124 3501
144	196.7637 2977	210.1501 6311	224.6949 8469	257.7115 6982	319.0615 5936
145	198.5835 7865	212.2009 1393	227.0057 0544	260.6444 0659	323.2521 7495
146	200.4110 1023	214.2619 1850	229.3299 0538	263.5992 3964	327.4846 9670
147	202.2460 5610	216.3332 2809	231.6676 6317	266.5762 3394	331.7595 4367
148	204.0887 4800	218.4148 9423	234.0190 5787	269.5755 5569	336.0771 3911
149	205.9391 1779	220.5069 6870	236.3841 6904	272.5973 7236	340.4379 1050
150	207.7971 9744	222.6095 0354	238.7630 7669	275.6418 5265	344.8422 8960

HIGH-SPEED MATHEMATICS

TABLE XIX (Continued)

AMOUNT OF ANNUITY OF 1 PER PERIOD

$$s_{\overline{n}|} = \frac{(1 + i)^n - 1}{i}$$

n	$1\frac{1}{8}\%$	$1\frac{1}{4}\%$	$1\frac{1}{2}\%$	$1\frac{3}{4}\%$	2%
1	1.0000 0000	1.0000 0000	1.0000 0000	1.0000 0000	1.0000 0000
2	2.0112 5000	2.0125 0000	2.0150 0000	2.0175 0000	2.0200 0000
3	3.0338 7656	3.0376 5625	3.0452 2500	3.0528 0625	3.0604 0000
4	4.0680 0767	4.0756 2695	4.0909 0338	4.1062 3036	4.1216 0800
5	5.1137 7276	5.1265 7229	5.1522 6693	5.1780 8938	5.2040 4016
6	6.1713 0270	6.1906 5444	6.2295 5093	6 2687 0596	6.3081 2096
7	7.2407 2986	7.2680 3762	7.3229 9419	7 3784 0831	7.4342 8338
8	8.3221 8807	·8.3588 8809	8.4328 3911	8.5075 3045	8.5829 6905
9	9.4158 1269	9.4633 7420	9.5593 3169	9.6564 1224	9.7546 2843
10	10.5217 4058	10.5816 6637	10.7027 2167	10.8253 9945	10.9497 2100
11	11.6401 1016	11.7139 3720	11.8632 6249	12.0148 4394	12.1687 1542
12	12.7710 6140	12.8603 6142	13.0412 1143	13.2251 0371	13.4120 8973
13	13.9147 3584	14.0211 1594	14.2368 2960	14.4565 4303	14.6803 3152
14	15.0712 7662	15.1963 7988	15.4503 8205	15.7095 3253	15.9739 3815
15	16.2408 2848	16.3863 3463	16.6821 3778	16.9844 4935	17.2934 1692
16	17.4235 3780	17.5911 6382	17.9323 6984	18.2816 7721	18.6392 8525
17	18.6195 5260	18.8110 5336	19.2013 5539	19.6016 0656	20.0120 7096
18	19.8290 2257	20.0461 9153	20.4893 7572	20.9446 3468	21.4123 1238
19	21.0520 9907	21.2967 6893	21.7967 1636	22.3111 6578	22.8405 5863
20	22.2889 3519	22.5629 7854	23.1236 6710	23.7016 1119	24.2973 6980
21	23.5396 8571	23.8450 1577	24.4705 2211	25.1163 8938	25.7833 1719
22	24.8045 0717	25.1430 7847	25.8375 7994	26.5559 2620	27.2989 8354
23	26.0835 5788	26.4573 6695	27.2251 4364	28.0206 5490	28.8449 6321
24	27.3769 9790	27.7880 8403	28.6335 2080	29.5110 1637	30.4218 6247
25	28.6849 8913	29.1354 3508	30.0630 2361	31.0274 5915	32.0302 9972
26	30.0076 9526	30.4996 2802	31.5139 6896	32.5704 3969	33.6709 0572
27	31.3452 8183	31.8808 7337	32.9866 7850	34.1404 2238	35.3443 2383
28	32.6979 1625	33.2793 8429	34.4814 7867	35.7378 7977	37.0512 1031
29	34.0657 6781	34.6953 7059	35.9987 0085	37.3632 9267	38.7922 3451
30	35.4490 0769	36.1290 6880	37.5386 8137	39.0171 5029	40.5680 7921
31	36.8478 0903	37.5806 8216	39.1017 6159	40.6999 5042	42.3794 4079
32	38.2623 4688	39.0504 4069	40.6882 8801	42.4121 9955	44.2270 2961
33	39.6927 9829	40.5385 7120	42.2986 1233	44.1544 1305	46.1115 7020
34	41.1393 4227	42.0453 0334	43.9330 9152	45.9271 1527	48.0338 0160
35	42.6021 5987	43.5708 6963	45.5920 8789	47.7308 3979	49.9944 7763
36	44.0814 3417	45.1155 0550	47.2759 6921	49.5661 2949	51.9943 6719
37	45.5773 5030	46.6794 4932	48.9851 0874	51.4335 3675	54.0342 5453
38	47.0900 9549	48.2926 4243	50.7198 8538	53.3336 2365	56.1149 3962
39	48.6198 5906	49.8862 2921	52.4806 8366	55.2669 6206	58.2372 3841
40	50.1668 3248	51.4895 5708	54.2678 9391	57.2341 3390	60.4019 8318
41	51.7312 0934	53.1331 7654	56.0819 1232	59.2357 3124	62.6100 2284
42	53.3131 8545	54.7973 4125	57.9231 4100	61.2723 5654	64.8622 2330
43	54.9129 5879	56.4823 0801	59.7919 8812	63.3446 2278	67.1594 6777
44	56.5307 2957	58.1883 3687	61.6888 6794	65.4531 5367	69.5026 5712
45	58.1667 0028	59.9156 9108	63.6142 0096	67.5985 8386	71.8927 1027
46	59.8210 7566	61.6646 1398	65.5684 1398	69.7815 5908	74.3305 6447
47	61.4940 6276	63.4354 4518	67.5519 4018	72.0027 3637	76.8171 7576
48	63.1858 7097	65.2283 8824	69.5652 1929	74.2627 8425	79.3535 1927
49	64.8967 1201	67.0437 4310	71.6086 9758	76.5623 8298	81.9405 8966
50	66.6268 0002	68.8817 8989	73.6828 2804	78.9022 2468	84.5794 0145

TABLE XIX (Continued)

AMOUNT OF ANNUITY OF 1 PER PERIOD

$$s_{\overline{n}|} = \frac{(1 + i)^n - 1}{i}$$

n	$1\frac{1}{8}\%$	$1\frac{1}{4}\%$	$1\frac{1}{2}\%$	$1\frac{3}{4}\%$	2%
51	68.3763 5152	70.7428 1226	75.7880 7046	81.2830 1361	87.2709 8948
52	70.1455 8548	72.6270 9741	77.9248 9152	83.7054 6635	90.0164 0927
53	71.9347 2332	74.5349 3613	80.0937 6489	86.1703 1201	92.8167 3746
54	73.7439 8895	76.4666 2283	82.2951 7136	88.6782 9247	95.6730 7221
55	75.5736 0883	78.4224 5562	84.5295 9893	91.2301 6259	98.5865 3365
56	77.4238 1193	80.4027 3631	86.7975 4292	93.8266 9043	101.5582 6432
57	79.2948 2981	82.4077 7052	89.0995 0606	96.4686 5752	104.5894 2961
58	81.1868 9665	84.4378 6765	91.4359 9865	99.1568 5902	107.6812 1820
59	83.1002 4923	86.4933 4099	93.8075 3863	101.8921 0405	110.8348 4257
60	85.0351 2704	88.5745 0776	96.2146 5171	104.6752 1588	114.0515 3942
61	86.9917 7222	90.6816 8910	98.6578 7149	107.5070 3215	117.3325 7021
62	88.9704 2966	92.8152 1022	101.1377 3956	110.3884 0522	120.6792 2161
63	90.9713 4699	94.9754 0034	103.6548 0565	113.3202 0231	124.0928 0604
64	91.9947 7464	97.1625 9285	106.2096 2774	116.3033 0585	127.5746 6216
65	95.0409 6586	99.3771 2526	108.8027 7215	119.3386 1370	131.1261 5541
66	97.1101 7672	101.6193 3933	111.4348 1374	122.4270 3944	134.7486 7852
67	99.2026 6621	103.8895 8107	114.1063 3594	125.5695 1263	138.4436 5209
68	101.3186 9621	106.1882 0083	116.8179 3098	128.7669 7910	142.2125 2513
69	103.4585 3154	108.5155 5334	119.5701 9995	132.0204 0124	146.0567 7563
70	105.6224 4002	110.8719 9776	122.3637 5295	135.3307 5826	149.9779 1114
71	107.8106 9247	113.2578 9773	125.1992 0924	138.6990 4653	153.9774 6937
72	110.0235 6276	115.6736 2145	128.0771 9738	142.1262 7984	158.0570 1875
73	112.2613 2784	118.1195 4172	130.9983 5534	145.6134 8974	162.2181 5913
74	114.5242 6778	120.5960 3599	133.9633 3067	149.1617 2581	166.4625 2231
75	116.8126 6579	123.1034 8644	136.9727 8063	152.7720 5601	170.7917 7276
76	119.1268 0828	125.6422 8002	140.0273 7234	156.4455 6699	175.2076 0821
77	121.4669 8487	128.2128 0852	143.1277 8292	160.1833 6441	179.7117 6038
78	123.8334 8845	130.8154 6863	146.2746 9967	163.9865 7329	184.3059 9558
79	126.2266 1520	133.4506 6199	149.4688 2016	167.8563 3832	188.9921 1549
80	128.6466 6462	136.1187 9526	152.7108 5247	171.7938 2424	193.7719 5780
81	131.0939 3960	138.8202 8020	156.0015 1525	175.8002 1617	198.6473 9696
82	133.5687 4642	141.5555 3370	159.3415 3798	179.8767 1995	203.6203 4490
83	136.0713 9481	144.3249 7787	162.7316 6105	184.0245 6255	208.6927 5180
84	138.6021 9801	147.1290 4010	166.1726 3597	188.2449 9239	213.8666 0683
85	141.1614 7273	149.9681 5310	169.6652 2551	192.5392 7976	219.1439 3897
86	143.7495 3930	152.8427 5501	173.2102 0389	196.9087 1716	224.5268 1775
87	146.3667 2162	155.7532 8945	176.8083 5695	201.3546 1971	230.0173 5411
88	149.0133 4724	158.7002 0557	180.4604 8230	205.8783 2555	235.6177 0119
89	151.6897 4739	161.6839 5814	184.1673 8954	210.4811 9625	241.3300 5521
90	154.3962 5705	164.7050 0762	187.9299 0038	215.1646 1718	247.1566 5632
91	157.1332 1494	167.7638 2021	191.7488 4889	219.9299 9798	253.0997 8944
92	159.9009 6361	170.8608 6796	195.6250 8162	224.7787 7295	259.1617 8523
93	162.6998 4945	173.9966 2881	199.5594 5784	229.7124 0148	265.3450 2094
94	165.5302 2276	177.1715 8667	203.5528 4971	234.7323 6850	271.6519 2135
95	168.3924 3776	180.3862 3151	207.6061 4246	239.8401 8495	278.0849 5978
96	171.2868 5269	183.6410 5940	211.7202 3459	245.0373 8819	284.6466 5898
97	174.2138 2978	186.9365 7264	215.8960 3811	250.3255 4248	291.3395 9216
98	177.1737 3537	190.2732 7980	220.1344 7868	255.7062 3947	298.1663 8400
99	180.1669 3989	193.6516 9580	224.4364 9586	261.1810 9866	305.1297 1168
100	183.1938 1796	197.0723 4200	228.8030 4330	266.7517 6789	312.2323 0591

TABLE XIX (*Continued*)

AMOUNT OF ANNUITY OF 1 PER PERIOD

$$s_{\overline{n}|} = \frac{(1+i)^n - 1}{i}$$

n	$2\frac{1}{4}\%$	$2\frac{1}{2}\%$	$2\frac{3}{4}\%$	3%	$3\frac{1}{2}\%$
1	1.0000 0000	1.0000 0000	1.0000 0000	1.0000 0000	1.0000 0000
2	2.0225 0000	2.0250 0000	2.0275 0000	2.0300 0000	2.0350 0000
3	3.0680 0625	3.0756 2500	3.0832 5625	3.0909 0000	3.1062 2500
4	4.1370 3639	4.1525 1563	4.1680 4580	4.1836 2700	4.2149 4288
5	5.2301 1971	5.2563 2852	5.2826 6706	5.3091 3581	5.3624 6588
6	6.3477 9740	6.3877 3673	6.4279 4040	6.4684 0088	6.5501 5218
7	7.4906 2284	7.5474 3015	7.6047 0876	7.6624 6218	7.7794 0751
8	8.6591 6186	8.7361 1590	8.8138 3825	8.8923 3605	9.0516 8677
9	9.8539 9300	9.9545 1880	10.0562 1880	10.1591 0613	10.3684 9581
10	11.0757 0784	11.2033 8177	11.3327 6482	11.4638 7931	11.7313 9316
11	12.3249 1127	12.4834 6631	12.6444 1585	12.8077 9569	13.1419 9192
12	13.6022 2177	13.7955 5297	13.9921 3729	14.1920 2956	14.6019 6164
13	14.9082 7176	15.1404 4179	15.3769 2107	15.6177 9045	16.1130 3030
14	16.2437 0788	16.5189 5284	16.7997 8639	17.0863 2416	17.6769 8636
15	17.6091 9130	17.9319 2666	18.2617 8052	18.5989 1389	19.2956 8088
16	19.0053 9811	19.3802 2483	19.7639 7948	20.1568 8130	20.9710 2971
17	20.4330 1957	20.8647 3045	21.3074 8892	21.7615 8774	22.7050 1575
18	21.8927 6251	22.3863 4871	22.8934 4487	23.4144 3537	24.4996 9130
19	23.3853 4066	23.9460 0743	24.5230 1460	25.1168 6844	26.3571 8050
20	24.9115 2003	25.5446 5761	26.1973 9750	26.8703 7449	28.2796 8181
21	26.4720 2923	27.1832 7405	27.9178 2593	28.6764 8572	30.2694 7068
22	28.0676 4989	28.8628 5590	29.6855 6615	30.5367 8030	32.3289 0215
23	29.6991 7201	30.5844 2730	31.5019 1921	32.4528 8370	34.4604 1373
24	31.3674 0338	32.3490 3798	33.3682 2199	34.4264 7022	36.6665 2821
25	33.0731 6996	34.1577 6393	35.2858 4810	36.4592 6432	38.9498 5669
26	34.8173 1628	36.0117 0803	37.2562 0892	38.5530 4225	41.3131 0168
27	36.6007 0590	37.9120 0073	39.2807 5467	40.7096 3352	43.7590 6024
28	38.4242 2178	39.8598 0075	41.3609 7542	42.9309 2252	46.2906 2734
29	40.2887 6677	41.8562 9577	43.4984 0224	45.2188 5020	48.9107 9930
30	42.1952 6402	43.9027 0316	45.6946 0830	47.5754 1571	51.6226 7728
31	44.1446 5746	46.0002 7074	47.9512 1003	50.0026 7818	54.4294 7098
32	46.1379 1226	48.1502 7751	50.2698 6831	52.5027 5852	57.3345 0247
33	48.1760 1528	50.3540 3445	52.6522 8969	55.0778 4128	60.3412 1005
34	50.2599 7563	52.6128 8531	55.1002 2765	57.7301 7652	63.4531 5240
35	52.3908 2508	54.9282 0744	57.6154 8391	60.4620 8181	66.6740 1274
36	54.5696 1864	57.3014 1263	60.1999 0972	63.2759 4427	70.0076 0318
37	56.7974 3506	59.7339 4794	62.8554 0724	66.1742 2259	73.4578 6930
38	59.0753 7735	62.2272 9664	65.5839 3094	69.1594 4927	77.0288 9472
39	61.4045 7334	64.7829 7906	68.3874 8904	72.2342 3275	80.7249 0604
40	63.7861 7624	67.4025 5354	71.2681 4499	75.4012 5973	84.5502 7775
41	66.2213 6521	70.0876 1737	74.2280 1898	78.6632 9753	88.5095 3747
42	68.7113 4592	72.8398 0781	77.2692 8950	82.0231 9645	92.6073 7128
43	71.2573 5121	75.6608 0300	80.3941 9496	85.4838 9234	96.8486 2928
44	73.8606 4161	78.5523 2308	83.6050 3532	89.0484 0911	101.2383 3130
45	76.5225 0605	81.5161 3116	86.9041 7379	92.7198 6139	105.7816 7290
46	79.2442 6243	84.5540 3443	90.2940 3857	96.5014 5723	110.4840 3145
47	82.0272 5834	87.6678 8530	93.7771 2463	100.3965 0095	115.3509 7255
48	84.8728 7165	90.8595 8243	97.3559 9556	104.4083 9598	120.3882 5659
49	87.7825 1126	94.1310 7199	101.0332 8544	108.5406 4785	125.6018 4557
50	90.7576 1776	97.4843 4879	104.8117 0079	112.7968 6729	130.9979 1016

TABLE XIX (*Continued*)

AMOUNT OF ANNUITY OF 1 PER PERIOD

$$s_{\overline{n}|} = \frac{(1 + i)^n - 1}{i}$$

n	$2\frac{1}{4}\%$	$2\frac{1}{2}\%$	$2\frac{3}{4}\%$	3%	$3\frac{1}{2}\%$
51	93.7996 6416	100.9214 5751	108.6940 2256	117.1807 7331	136.5828 3702
52	96.9101 5661	104.4444 9395	112.6831 0818	121.6961 9651	142.3632 3631
53	100.0906 3513	108.0556 0629	116.7818 9365	126.3470 8240	148.3459 4958
54	103.3426 7442	111.7569 9645	120.9933 9573	131.1374 9488	154.5380 5782
55	106.6678 8460	115.5509 2136	125.3207 1411	136.0716 1972	160.9468 8984
56	110.0679 1200	119.4396 9440	129.7670 3375	141.1537 6831	167.5800 3099
57	113.5444 4002	123.4256 8676	134.3356 2718	146.3883 8136	174.4453 3207
58	117.0991 8992	127.5113 2893	139.0298 5692	151.7800 3280	181.5509 1869
59	120.7339 2169	131.6991 1215	143.8531 7799	157.3334 3379	188.9052 0085
60	124.4504 3493	135.9915 8995	148.8091 4038	163.0534 3680	196.5168 8288
61	128.2505 6972	140.3913 7970	153.9013 9174	168.9450 3991	204.3949 7378
62	132.1362 0754	144.9011 6419	159.1336 8002	175.0133 9110	212.5487 9786
63	136.1092 7221	149.5236 9330	164.5098 5622	181.2637 9284	220.9880 0579
64	140.1717 3083	154.2617 8563	170.0338 7726	187.7017 0662	229.7225 8599
65	144.3255 9477	159.1183 3027	175.7098 0889	194.3327 5782	238.7628 7650
66	148.5729 2066	164.0962 8853	181.5418 2863	201.1627 4055	248.1195 7718
67	152.9158 1137	169.1986 9574	187.5342 2892	208.1976 2277	257.8037 6238
68	157.3564 1713	174.4286 6314	193.6914 2021	215.4435 5145	267.8268 9406
69	161.8969 3651	179.7893 7971	200.0179 3427	222.9068 5800	278.2008 3535
70	166.5396 1758	185.2841 1421	206.5184 2746	230.5940 6374	288.9378 6459
71	171.2867 5898	190.9162 1706	213.1976 8422	238.5118 8565	300.0506 8985
72	176.1407 1106	196.6891 2249	220.0606 2054	246.6672 4222	311.5524 6400
73	181.1038 7705	202.6063 5055	227.1122 8760	255.0672 5949	323.4568 0024
74	186.1787 1429	208.6715 0931	234.3578 7551	263.7192 7727	335.7777 8824
75	191.3677 3536	214.8882 9705	241.8027 1709	272.6308 5559	348.5300 1083
76	196.6735 0941	221.2605 0447	249.4522 9181	281.8097 8126	361.7285 6121
77	202.0986 6337	227.7920 1709	257.3122 2983	291.2640 7469	375.3890 6085
78	207.6458 8329	234.4868 1751	265.3883 1615	301.0019 9693	389.5276 7798
79	213.3179 1567	241.3489 8795	273.6864 9485	311.0320 5684	404.1611 4671
80	219.1175 6877	248.3827 1265	282.2128 7345	321.3630 1855	419.3067 8685
81	225.0477 1407	255.5922 8047	290.9737 2747	332.0039 0910	434.9825 2439
82	231.1112 8763	262.9820 8748	299.9755 0498	342.9640 2638	451.2069 1274
83	237.3112 9160	270.5566 3966	309.2248 3137	354.2529 4717	467.9991 5469
84	243.6507 9567	278.3205 5566	318.7285 1423	365.8805 3558	485.3791 2510
85	250.1329 3857	286.2785 6955	328.4935 4837	377.8569 5165	503.3673 9448
86	256.7609 2969	294.4355 3379	338.5271 2095	390.1926 6020	521.9852 5329
87	263.5380 5060	302.7964 2213	348.8366 1678	402.8984 4001	541.2547 3715
88	270.4676 5674	311.3663 3268	359.4296 2374	415.9863 9321	561.1986 5295
89	277.5531 7902	320.1504 9100	370.3139 3839	429.4649 5500	581.8406 0581
90	284.7981 2555	329.1542 5328	381.4975 7170	443.3489 0365	603.2050 2701
91	292.2060 8337	338.3831 0961	392.9887 5492	457.6493 7076	625.3172 0295
92	299.7807 2025	347.8426 8735	404.7959 4568	472.3788 5189	648.2033 0506
93	307.5257 8645	357.5387 5453	416.9278 3418	487.5502 1744	671.8904 2073
94	315.4451 1665	367.4772 2339	429.3933 4962	503.1767 2397	696.4065 8546
95	323.5426 3177	377.6641 5398	442.2016 6674	519.2720 2569	721.7803 1595
96	331.8223 4099	388.1057 5783	455.3622 1257	535.8501 8645	748.0431 4451
97	340.2883 4366	398.8084 0177	468.8846 7342	552.9256 9205	775.2246 5457
98	348.9448 3139	409.7786 1182	482.7790 0194	570.5134 6281	803.3575 1748
99	357.7960 9010	421.0230 7711	497.0554 2449	588.6288 6669	832.4750 3059
100	366.8465 0213	432.5486 5404	511.7244 4867	607.2877 3270	862.6116 5666

TABLE XIX (*Continued*)

Amount of Annuity of 1 per Period

$$s_{\overline{n}|} = \frac{(1 + i)^n - 1}{i}$$

n	4%	$4\frac{1}{2}\%$	5%	$5\frac{1}{2}\%$	6%
1	1.0000 0000	1.0000 0000	1.0000 0000	1.0000 0000	1.0000 0000
2	2.0400 0000	2.0450 0000	2.0500 0000	2.0550 0000	2.0600 0000
3	3.1216 0000	3.1370 2500	3.1525 0000	3.1680 2500	3.1836 0000
4	4.2464 6400	4.2781 9113	4.3101 2500	4.3422 6638	4.3746 1600
5	5.4163 2256	5.4707 0973	5.5256 3125	5.5810 9103	5.6370 9296
6	6.6329 7546	6.7168 9166	6.8019 1281	6.8880 5103	6.9753 1854
7	7.8982 9448	8.0191 5179	8.1420 0845	8.2668 9384	8.3938 3765
8	9.2142 2626	9.3800 1362	9.5491 0888	9.7215 7300	9.8974 6791
9	10.5827 9531	10.8021 1423	11.0265 6432	11.2562 5951	11.4913 1598
10	12.0061 0712	12.2882 0937	12.5778 9254	12.8753 5379	13.1807 9494
11	13.4863 5141	13.8411 7879	14.2067 8716	14.5834 9825	14.9716 4264
12	15.0258 0546	15.4650 3184	15.9171 2652	16.3855 9065	16.8699 4120
13	16.6268 3768	17.1599 1327	17.7129 8285	18.2867 9814	18.8821 3767
14	18.2919 1119	18.9321 0937	19.5986 3199	20.2925 7203	21.0150 6593
15	20.0235 8764	20.7840 5429	21.5785 6359	22.4086 6350	23.2759 6988
16	21.8245 3114	22.7193 3673	23.6574 9177	24.6411 3999	25.6725 2808
17	23.6975 1239	24.7417 0689	25.8403 6636	26.9964 0269	28.2128 7076
18	25.6454 1288	26.8550 8370	28.1323 8467	29.4812 0483	30.9056 5255
19	27.6712 2940	29.0635 6246	30.5390 0391	32.1026 7110	33.7599 9170
20	29.7780 7858	31.3714 2277	33.0659 5410	34.8683 1801	36.7855 9120
21	31.9692 0172	33.7831 3680	35.7192 5181	37.7860 7550	39.9927 2668
22	34.2479 6979	36.3033 7795	38.5052 1440	40.8643 0965	43.3922 9028
23	36.6178 8858	38.9370 2996	41.4304 7512	44.1118 4669	46.9958 2769
24	39.0826 0412	41.6891 9631	44.5019 9887	47.5379 9825	50.8155 7735
25	41.6459 0829	44.5652 1015	47.7270 9882	51.1525 8816	54.8645 1200
26	44.3117 4462	47.5706 4460	51.1134 5376	54.9659 8051	59.1563 8272
27	47.0842 1440	50.7113 2361	54.6691 2645	58.9891 0943	63.7057 6568
28	49.9675 8298	53.9933 3317	58.4025 8277	63.2335 1045	68.5281 1162
29	52.9662 8630	57.4230 3316	62.3227 1191	67.7113 5353	73.6397 9832
30	56.0849 3775	61.0070 6966	66.4388 4750	72.4354 7797	79.0581 8622
31	59.3283 3526	64.7523 8779	70.7607 8988	77.4194 2926	84.8016 7739
32	62.7014 6867	68.6662 4524	75.2988 2937	82.6774 9787	90.8897 7803
33	66.2095 2742	72.7562 2628	80.0637 7084	88.2247 6025	97.3431 6471
34	69.8579 0851	77.0302 5646	85.0669 5938	94.0771 2207	104.1837 5460
35	73.6522 2486	81.4966 1800	90.3203 0735	100.2513 6378	111.4347 7987
36	77.5983 1385	86.1639 6581	95.8363 2272	106.7651 8879	119.1208 6666
37	81.7022 4640	91.0413 4427	101.6281 3886	113.6372 7417	127.2681 1866
38	85.9703 3626	96.1382 0476	107.7095 4580	120.8873 2425	135.9042 0578
39	90.4091 4971	101.4644 2398	114.0950 2309	128.5361 2708	145.0584 5813
40	95.0255 1570	107.0303 2306	120.7997 7424	136.6056 1407	154.7619 6562
41	99.8265 3633	112.8466 8760	127.8397 6295	145.1189 2285	165.0476 8356
42	104.8195 9778	118.9247 8854	135.2317 5110	154.1004 6360	175.9505 4457
43	110.0123 8169	125.2764 0402	142.9933 3866	163.5759 8910	187.5075 7724
44	115.4128 7696	131.9138 4221	151.1430 0559	173.5726 6850	199.7580 3188
45	121.0293 9204	138.8499 6510	159.7001 5587	184.1191 6527	212.7435 1379
46	126.8705 6772	146.0982 1353	168.6851 6366	195.2457 1936	226.5081 2462
47	132.9453 9043	153.6726 3314	178.1194 2185	206.9842 3392	241.0986 1210
48	139.2632 0604	161.5879 0163	188.0253 9294	219.3683 6579	256.5645 2882
49	145.8337 3429	169.8593 5720	198.4266 6259	232.4336 2696	272.9584 0055
50	152.6670 8366	178.5030 2828	209.3479 9572	246.2174 7645	290.3359 0458

TABLE XIX (Continued)

Amount of Annuity of 1 per Period

$$s_{\overline{n}|} = \frac{(1 + i)^n - 1}{i}$$

n	4%	4½%	5%	5½%	6%
51	159.7737 6700	187.5356 6455	220.8153 9550	260.7594 3765	308.7560 5886
52	167.1647 1768	196.9747 6946	232.8561 6528	276 1012 0672	328.2814 2239
53	174.8513 0639	206.8386 3408	245.4989 7354	292.2867 7309	348.9783 0773
54	182.8453 5865	217.1463 7262	258.7739 2222	309.3625 4561	370.9170 0620
55	191 1591 7299	227.9179 5938	272.7126 1833	327.3774 8562	394.1720 2657
56	199.8055 3991	239.1742 6756	287.3482 4924	346.3832 4733	418.8223 4816
57	208.7977 6151	250.9371 0960	302.7156 6171	366 4343 2593	444.9516 8905
58	218.1496 7197	263.2292 7953	318.8514 4479	387 5882 1386	472.6487 9040
59	227.8756 5885	276.0745 9711	335.7940 1703	409.9055 6562	502.0077 1782
60	237.9906 8520	289.4979 5398	353.5837 1788	433.4503 7173	533.1281 8089
61	248.5103 1261	303.5253 6190	372.2629 0378	458.2901 4217	566.1158 7174
62	259.4507 2511	318.1840 0319	391.8760 4897	484 4960 9999	601.0828 2405
63	270.8287 5412	333.5022 8333	412 4698 5141	512 1433 8549	638.1477 9349
64	282.6619 0428	349.5008 8608	434.0933 4398	541.3112 7170	677.4366 6110
65	294.9683 8045	366.2378 3096	456.7980 1118	572.0833 9164	719.0828 6076
66	307.7671 1567	383.7185 3335	480.6379 1174	604.5479 7818	763.2278 3241
67	321.0778 0030	401.9858 6735	505.6698 0733	638.7981 1698	810.0215 0236
68	334.9209 1231	421.0752 3138	531.9532 9770	674.9320 1341	859.6227 9250
69	349.3177 4880	441.0236 1679	559.5509 6258	713.0532 7415	912.2001 6005
70	364.2904 5876	461.8696 7955	588.5285 1071	753.2712 0423	967.9321 6965
71	379.8620 7711	483.6538 1513	618 9549 3625	795.7011 2046	1027 0080 9983
72	396.0565 6019	506.4182 3681	650.9026 8306	840.4646 8209	1089 6285 8582
73	412.8988 2260	530 2070 5747	684.4478 1721	887 6902 3960	1156.0063 0097
74	430.4147 7550	555.0663 7505	719.6702 0807	937 5132 0278	1226 3666 7903
75	448.6313 6652	581.0443 6193	756.6537 1848	990.0764 2893	1300.9486 7977
76	467.5766 2118	608.1913 5822	795.4864 0440	1045.5306 3252	1380.0056 0055
77	487.2796 8603	636.5599 6934	836.2607 2462	1104.0348 1731	1463.8059 3659
78	507.7708 7347	666.2051 6796	879.0737 6085	1165.7567 3226	1552.6342 9278
79	529.0817 0841	697.1844 0052	924.0274 4889	1230.8733 5254	1646.7923 5035
80	551.2449 7675	729.5576 9854	971.2288 2134	1299.5713 8693	1746.5998 9137
81	574.2947 7582	763.3877 9497	1020.7902 6240	1372.0478 1321	1852 3958 8485
82	598.2665 6685	798.7402 4575	1072.8297 7552	1448.5104 4294	1964.5396 3794
83	623.1972 2952	835.6835 5680	1127.4712 6430	1529.1785 1730	2083.4120 1622
84	649.1251 1870	874.2893 1686	1184.8448 2752	1614 2833 3575	2209.4167 3719
85	676.0901 2345	914.6323 3612	1245.0870 6889	1704.0689 1921	2342.9817 4142
86	704.1337 2839	956.7907 9125	1308.3414 2234	1798.7927 0977	2484.5606 4591
87	733.2990 7753	1000.8463 7685	1374 7584 9345	1898.7263 0881	2634.6342 8466
88	763.6310 4063	1046.8844 6351	1444 4964 1812	2004 1562 5579	2793.7123 4174
89	795.1762 8225	1094.9942 6468	1517.7212 3903	2115 3848 4986	2962.3350 8225
90	827.9833 3354	1145.2690 0659	1594.6073 0098	2232.7310 1660	3141.0751 8718
91	862.1026 6688	1197.8061 1189	1675.3376 6603	2356.5312 2252	3330.5396 9841
92	897.5867 7356	1252.7073 8692	1760 1045 4933	2487 1404 3976	3531.3720 8032
93	934 4902 4450	1310.0792 1933	1849 1097 7680	2624 9331 6394	3744 2544 0514
94	972.8698 5428	1370.0327 8420	1942 5652 6564	2770.3044 8796	3969.9096 6944
95	1012.7846 4845	1432.6842 5949	2040.6935 2892	2923.6712 3480	4209.1042 4961
96	1054.2960 3439	1498.1550 5117	2143.7282 0537	3085.4731 5271	4462.6505 0459
97	1097.4678 7577	1566.5720 2847	2251.9146 1564	3256.1741 7611	4731.4095 3486
98	1142.3665 9080	1638.0677 6976	2365.5103 4642	3436 2637 5580	5016.2941 0696
99	1189.0612 5443	1712.7808 1939	2484.7858 6374	3626.2582 6237	5318.2717 5337
100	1237.6237 0461	1790.8559 5627	2610.0251 5693	3826.7024 6680	5638.3680 5857

HIGH-SPEED MATHEMATICS

TABLE XIX (*Continued*)

Amount of Annuity of 1 per Period

$$s_{\overline{n}|} = \frac{(1 + i)^n - 1}{i}$$

n	$6\frac{1}{2}\%$	7%	$7\frac{1}{2}\%$	8%	$8\frac{1}{2}\%$
1	1.0000 0000	1.0000 0000	1.0000 0000	1.0000 0000	1.0000 0000
2	2.0650 0000	2.0700 0000	2.0750 0000	2.0800 0000	2.0850 0000
3	3.1992 2500	3.2149 0000	3.2306 2500	3.2464 0000	3.2622 2500
4	4.4071 7463	4.4399 4300	4.4729 2188	4.5061 1200	4.5395 1413
5	5.6936 4098	5.7507 3901	5.8083 9102	5.8666 0096	5.9253 7283
6	7.0637 2764	7.1532 9074	7.2440 2034	7.3359 2904	7.4290 2952
7	8.5228 6994	8.6540 2109	8.7873 2187	8.9228 0336	9.0604 9702
8	10.0768 5648	10.2598 0257	10.4463 7101	10.6366 2763	10.8306 3927
9	11.7318 5215	11.9779 8875	12.2298 4883	12.4875 5784	12.7512 4361
10	13.4944 2254	13.8164 4796	14.1470 8750	14.4865 6247	14.8350 9932
11	15.3715 6001	15.7835 9932	16.2081 1906	16.6454 8746	17.0960 8276
12	17.3707 1141	17.8884 5127	18.4237 2799	18.9771 2646	19.5492 4979
13	19.4998 0765	20.1406 4286	20.8055 0759	21.4952 9658	22.2109 3603
14	21.7672 9515	22.5504 8786	23.3659 2066	24.2149 2030	25.0988 6559
15	24.1821 6933	25.1290 2201	26.1183 6470	27.1521 1393	28.2322 6916
16	26.7540 1034	27.8880 5355	29.0772 4206	30.3242 8304	31.6320 1204
17	29.4930 2101	30.8402 1730	32.2580 3521	33.7502 2569	35.3207 3306
18	32.4100 6738	33.9990 3251	35.6773 8785	37.4502 4374	39.3229 9538
19	35.5167 2176	37.3789 6479	39.3531 9194	41.4462 6324	43.6654 4998
20	38.8253 0867	40.9954 9232	43.3046 8134	45.7619 6430	48.3770 1323
21	42.3489 5373	44.8651 7678	47.5525 3244	50.4229 2144	53.4890 5936
22	46.1016 3573	49.0057 3916	52.1189 7237	55.4567 5516	59.0356 2940
23	50.0982 4205	53.4361 4090	57.0278 9530	60.8932 9557	65.0536 5790
24	54.3546 2778	58.1766 7076	62.3049 8744	66.7647 5922	71.5832 1882
25	58.8876 7859	63.2490 3772	67.9778 6150	73.1059 3995	78.6677 9242
26	63.7153 7769	68.6764 7036	74.0762 0112	79.9544 1515	86.3545 5478
27	68.8568 7725	74.4838 2328	80.6319 1620	87.3507 6836	94.6946 9193
28	74.3325 7427	80.6976 9091	87.6793 0991	95.3388 2983	103.7437 4075
29	80.1641 9159	87.3465 2927	95.2552 5816	103.9659 3622	113.5619 5871
30	86.3748 6405	94.4607 8632	103.3994 0252	113.2832 1111	124.2147 2520
31	92.9892 3021	102.0730 4137	112.1543 5771	123.3458 6800	135.7729 7684
32	100.0335 3017	110.2181 5426	121.5659 3454	134.2135 3744	148.3136 7987
33	107.5357 0963	118.9334 2506	131.6833 7963	145.9506 2044	161.9203 4266
34	115.5255 3076	128.2587 6481	142.5596 3310	158.6266 7007	176.6835 7179
35	124.0346 9026	138.2368 7835	154.2516 0558	172.3168 0368	192.7016 7539
36	133.0969 4513	148.9134 5984	166.8204 7600	187.1021 4797	210.0813 1780
37	142.7482 4656	160.3374 0202	180.3320 1170	203.0703 1981	228.9382 2981
38	153.0268 8259	172.5610 2017	194.8569 1258	220.3159 4540	249.3979 7935
39	163.9736 2995	185.6402 9158	210.4711 8102	238.9412 2103	271.5968 0759
40	175.6319 1590	199.6351 1199	227.2565 1960	259.0565 1871	295.6825 3624
41	188.0479 9044	214.6095 6983	245.3007 5857	280.7810 4021	321.8155 5182
42	201.2711 0981	230.6322 3972	264.6983 1546	304.2435 2342	350.1698 7372
43	215.3537 3195	247.7764 9650	285.5506 8912	329.5830 0530	380.9343 1299
44	230.3517 2453	266.1208 5125	307.9669 9080	356.9496 4572	414.3137 2959
45	246.3245 8662	285.7493 1084	332.0645 1511	386.5056 1738	450.5303 9661
46	263.3356 8475	306.7517 6260	357.9693 5375	418.4260 6677	489.8254 8032
47	281.4525 0426	329.2243 8598	385.8170 5528	452.9001 5211	532.4606 4615
48	300.7469 1704	353.2700 9300	415.7533 3442	490.1321 6428	578.7198 0107
49	321.2954 6665	378.9989 9951	447.9348 3451	530.3427 3742	628.9109 8416
50	343.1796 7198	406.5289 2947	482.5299 4709	573.7701 5642	683.3684 1782

TABLE XX

Present Value of Annuity of 1 per Period

$$a_{\overline{n}|} = \frac{1 - (1 + i)^{-n}}{i}$$

n	$\frac{5}{12}\%$	$\frac{1}{2}\%$	$\frac{7}{12}\%$	$\frac{3}{4}\%$	1%
1	0.9958 5062	0.9950 2488	0.9942 0050	0.9925 5583	0.9900 9901
2	1.9875 6908	1.9850 9938	1.9826 3513	1.9777 2291	1.9703 9506
3	2.9751 7253	2.9702 4814	2.9653 3733	2.9555 5624	2.9409 8521
4	3.9586 7804	3.9504 9566	3.9423 4034	3.9261 1041	3.9019 6555
5	4.9381 0261	4.9258 6633	4.9136 7723	4.8894 3961	4.8534 3124
6	5.9134 6318	5.8963 8441	5.8793 8084	5.8455 9763	5.7954 7647
7	6.8847 7661	6.8620 7404	6.8394 8385	6.7946 3785	6.7281 9453
8	7.8520 5969	7.8229 5924	7.7940 1875	7.7366 1325	7.6516 7775
9	8.8153 2915	8.7790 6392	8.7430 1781	8.6715 7642	8.5660 1758
10	9.7746 0164	9.7304 1186	9.6865 1315	9.5995 7958	9.4713 0453
11	10.7298 9374	10.6770 2673	10.6245 3669	10.5206 7452	10.3676 2825
12	11.6812 2198	11.6189 3207	11.5571 2016	11.4349 1267	11.2550 7747
13	12.6286 0280	12.5561 5131	12.4842 9511	12.3423 4508	12.1337 4007
14	13.5720 5257	13.4887 0777	13.4060 9291	13.2430 2242	13.0037 0304
15	14.5115 8762	14.4166 2465	14.3225 4473	14.1369 9495	13.8650 5252
16	15.4472 2418	15.3399 2502	15.2336 8160	15.0243 1261	14.7178 7378
17	16.3789 7843	16.2586 3186	16.1395 3432	15.9050 2492	15.5622 5127
18	17.3068 6648	17.1727 6802	17.0401 3354	16.7791 8107	16.3982 6858
19	18.2309 0438	18.0823 5624	17.9355 0074	17.6468 2984	17.2260 0850
20	19.1511 0809	18.9874 1915	18.8256 9320	18.5080 1969	18.0455 5297
21	20.0674 9352	19.8879 7925	19.7107 1404	19.3627 9870	18.8569 8313
22	20.9800 7653	20.7840 5896	20.5906 0220	20.2112 1459	19.6603 7934
23	21.8888 7289	21.6756 8055	21.4653 8745	21.0533 1473	20.4558 2113
24	22.7938 9831	22.5628 6622	22.3350 9938	21.8891 4614	21.2433 8726
25	23.6951 6843	23.4456 3803	23.1997 6741	22.7187 5547	22.0231 5570
26	24.5926 9884	24.3240 1794	24.0594 2079	23.5421 8905	22.7952 0366
27	25.4865 0506	25.1980 2780	24.9140 8862	24.3594 9286	23.5596 0759
28	26.3766 0254	26.0676 8936	25.7637 9979	25.1707 1251	24.3164 4316
29	27.2630 0668	26.9330 2423	26.6085 8307	25.9758 3031	25.0657 8530
30	28.1457 3278	27.7940 5397	27.4484 6702	26.7750 8021	25.8077 0822
31	29.0247 9612	28.6507 9997	28.2834 8006	27.5683 1783	26.5422 8537
32	29.9002 1189	29.5032 8355	29.1136 5044	28.3556 5045	27.2695 8947
33	30.7719 9524	30.3515 2592	29.9390 0625	29.1371 2203	27.9896 9255
34	31.6401 6122	31.1955 4818	30.7595 7540	29.9127 7621	28.7026 6589
35	32.5047 2486	32.0353 7132	31.5753 8566	30.6826 5629	29.4085 8009
36	33.3657 0109	32.8710 1624	32.3864 6463	31.4468 0525	30.1075 0504
37	34.2231 0481	33.7025 0372	33.1928 3974	32.2052 6576	30.7995 0994
38	35.0769 5084	34.5298 5445	33.9945 3828	32.9580 8016	31.4846 6330
39	35.9272 5394	35.3530 8900	34.7915 8736	33.7052 9048	32.1630 3298
40	36.7740 2881	36.1722 2786	35.5840 1396	34.4469 3844	32.8346 8611
41	37.6172 9009	36.9872 9141	36.3718 4487	35.1830 6545	33.4996 8922
42	38.4570 5236	37.7982 9991	37.1551 0676	35.9137 1260	34.1581 0814
43	39.2933 3013	38.6052 7354	37.9338 2612	36.6389 2070	34.8100 0806
44	40.1261 3788	39.4082 3238	38.7080 2929	37.3587 3022	35.4554 5352
45	40.9554 8999	40.2071 9640	39.4777 4248	38.0731 8136	36.0945 0844
46	41.7814 0081	41.0021 8547	40.2429 9170	38.7823 1401	36.7272 3608
47	42.6038 8461	41.7932 1937	41.0038 0287	39.4861 6774	37.3536 9909
48	43.4229 5562	42.5803 1778	41.7602 0170	40.1847 8189	37.9739 5949
49	44.2386 2799	43.3635 0028	42.5122 1380	40.8781 9542	38.5880 7871
50	45.0509 1582	44.1427 8635	43.2598 6460	41.5664 4707	39.1961 1753

TABLE XX (Continued)

Present Value of Annuity of 1 per Period

$$a_{\overline{n}|} = \frac{1 - (1 + i)^{-n}}{i}$$

n	$\frac{5}{12}\%$	$\frac{1}{2}\%$	$\frac{7}{12}\%$	$\frac{3}{4}\%$	1%
51	45.8598 3317	44.9181 9537	44.0031 7940	42.2495 7525	39.7981 3617
52	46.6653 9401	45.6897 4664	44.7421 8335	42.9276 1812	40.3941 9423
53	47.4676 1228	46.4574 5934	45.4769 0144	43.6006 1351	40.9843 5072
54	48.2665 0184	47.2213 5258	46.2073 5853	44.2685 9902	41.5686 6408
55	49.0620 7651	47.9814 4535	46.9335 7933	44.9316 1193	42.1471 9216
56	49.8543 5003	48.7377 5657	47.6555 8841	45.5896 8926	42.7199 9224
57	50.6433 3612	49.4903 0505	48.3734 1020	46.2428 6776	43.2871 2102
58	51.4290 4840	50.2391 0950	49.0870 6898	46.8911 8388	43.8486 3468
59	52.2115 0046	50.9841 8855	49.7965 8889	47.5346 7382	44.4045 8879
60	52.9907 0584	51.7255 6075	50.5019 9394	48.1733 7352	44.9550 3841
61	53.7666 7800	52.4632 4453	51.2033 0800	48.8073 1863	45.5000 3803
62	54.5394 3035	53.1972 5324	51.9005 5478	49.4365 4455	46.0396 4161
63	55.3089 7627	53.9276 2014	52.5937 5787	50.0610 8640	46.5739 0258
64	56.0753 2905	54.6543 4839	53.2829 4073	50.6809 7906	47.1028 7385
65	56.8385 0194	55.3774 6109	53.9681 2668	51.2962 5713	47.6266 0777
66	57.5985 0814	56.0969 7621	54.6493 3888	51.9069 5497	48.1451 5621
67	58.3553 6078	56.8129 1165	55.3206 0040	52.5131 0667	48.6585 7050
68	59.1090 7296	57.5252 8522	55.9999 3413	53.1147 4607	49.1669 0149
69	59.8596 5770	58.2341 1465	56.6693 6287	53.7119 0677	49.6701 9949
70	60.6071 2798	58.9394 1756	57.3349 0925	54.3046 2210	50.1685 1435
71	61.3514 9672	59.6412 1151	57.9965 9579	54.8929 2516	50.6618 9539
72	62.0927 7680	60.3395 1394	58.6544 4488	55.4768 4880	51.1503 9148
73	62.8309 8103	61.0343 4222	59.3084 7877	56.0564 2561	51.6340 5097
74	63.5661 2216	61.7257 1366	59.9587 1959	56.6316 8795	52.1129 2175
75	64.2982 1292	62.4136 4543	60.6051 8934	57.2026 6794	52.5870 5124
76	65.0272 6596	63.0981 5466	61.2479 0988	57.7693 9746	53.0564 8637
77	65.7532 9388	63.7792 5836	61.8869 0297	58.3319 0815	53.5212 7364
78	66.4763 0924	64.4569 7350	62.5221 9021	58.8902 3141	53.9814 5905
79	67.1963 2453	65.1313 1691	63.1537 9310	59.4443 9842	54.4370 8817
80	67.9133 5221	65.8023 0538	63.7817 3301	59.9944 4012	54.8882 0611
81	68.6274 0467	66.4699 5561	64.4060 3118	60.5403 8722	55.3348 5753
82	69.3384 9426	67.1342 8419	65.0267 0874	61.0822 7019	55.7770 8666
83	70.0466 3326	67.7953 0765	65.6437 8667	61.6201 1930	56.2149 3729
84	70.7518 3393	68.4530 4244	66.2572 8585	62.1539 6456	56.6484 5270
85	71.4541 0846	69.1075 0491	66.8672 2705	62.6838 3579	57.0776 7600
86	72.1534 6898	69.7587 1135	67.4736 3089	63.2097•6257	57.5026 4951
87	72.8499 2759	70.4066 7796	68.0765 1789	63.7317 7427	57.9234 1535
88	73.5434 9633	71.0514 2086	68.6759 0845	64.2499 0002	58.3400 1520
89	74.2341 8720	71.6929 5608	69.2718 2283	64.7641 6875	58.7524 9030
90	74.9220 1212	72.3312 9958	69.8642 8121	65.2746 0918	59.1608 8148
91	75.6069 8300	72.9664 6725	70.4533 0363	65.7812 4981	59.5652 2919
92	76.2891 1168	73.5984 7487	71.0389 1001	66.2841 1892	59.9655 7346
93	76.9684 0995	74.2273 3818	71.6211 2017	66.7832 4458	60.3619 5392
94	77.6448 8955	74.8530 7282	72.1999 5379	67.2786 5467	60.7544 0982
95	78.3185 6218	75.4756 9434	72.7754 3047	67.7703 7685	61.1429 8002
96	78.9894 3950	76.0952 1825	73.3475 6967	68.2584 3856	61.5277 0299
97	79.6575 3308	76.7116 5995	73.9163 9075	68.7428 6705	61.9086 1682
98	80.3228 5450	77.3250 3478	74.4819 1294	69.2236 8938	62.2857 5923
99	80.9854 1524	77.9353 5799	75.0441 5539	69.7009 3239	62.6591 6755
100	81.6452 2677	78.5426 4477	75.6031 3712	70.1746 2272	63.0288 7877

TABLE XX (*Continued*)

PRESENT VALUE OF ANNUITY OF 1 PER PERIOD

$$a_{\overline{n}|} = \frac{1 - (1 + i)^{-n}}{i}$$

n	$\frac{5}{12}\%$	$\frac{1}{2}\%$	$\frac{7}{12}\%$	$\frac{3}{4}\%$	1%
101	82.3023 0049	79.1469 1021	76.1588 7702	70.6447 8682	63.3949 2947
102	82.9566 4777	79.7481 6937	76.7113 9392	71.1114 5094	63.7573 5591
103	83.6082 7991	80.3464 3718	77.2607 0648	71.5746 4113	64.1161 9397
104	84.2572 0818	80.9417 2854	77.8068 3331	72.0343 8325	64.4714 7918
105	84.9034 4381	81.5340 5825	78.3497 9288	72.4907 0298	64.8232 4671
106	85.5469 9795	82.1234 4104	78.8896 0355	72.9436 2579	65.1715 3140
107	86.1878 8175	82.7098 9158	79.4262 8359	73.3931 7696	65.5163 6772
108	86.8261 0628	83.2934 2446	79.9598 5115	73.8393 8160	65.8577 8983
109	87.4616 8258	83.8740 5419	80.4903 2428	74.2822 6461	66.1958 3151
110	88.0946 2163	84.4517 9522	81.0177 2093	74.7218 5073	66.5305 2625
111	88.7249 3437	85.0266 6191	81.5420 5895	75.1581 6450	66.8619 0718
112	89.3526 3171	85.5986 6856	82.0633 5606	75.5912 3027	67.1900 0710
113	89.9777 2450	86.1678 2942	82.5816 2991	76.0210 7223	67.5148 5852
114	90.6002 2354	86.7341 5862	83.0968 9803	76.4477 1437	67.8364 9358
115	91.2201 3959	87.2976 7027	83.6091 7785	76.8711 8052	68.1549 4414
116	91.8374 8338	87.8583 7838	84.1184 8671	77.2914 9431	68.4702 4172
117	92.4522 6558	88.4162 9690	84.6248 4182	77.7086 7922	68.7824 1755
118	93.0644 9681	88.9714 3970	85.1282 6033	78.1227 5853	69.0915 0252
119	93.6741 8767	89.5238 2059	85.6287 5926	78.5337 5536	69.3975 2725
120	94.2813 4869	90.0734 5333	86.1263 5554	78.9416 9267	69.7005 2203
121	94.8859 9036	90.6203 5157	86.6210 6602	79.3465 9322	70.0005 1686
122	95.4881 2315	91.1645 2892	87.1129 0742	79.7484 7962	70.2975 4145
123	96.0877 5747	91.7059 9893	87.6018 9638	80.1473 7432	70.5916 2520
124	96.6849 0367	92.2447 7505	88.0880 4946	80.5432 9957	70.8827 9722
125	97.2795 7209	92.7808 7070	88.5713 8308	80.9362 7749	71.1710 8636
126	97.8717 7301	93.3142 9920	89.0519 1361	81.3263 3001	71.4565 2115
127	98.4615 1666	93.8450 7384	89.5296 5731	81.7134 7892	71.7391 2985
128	99.0488 1324	94.3732 0780	90.0046 3032	82.0977 4583	72.0189 4045
129	99.6336 7290	94.8987 1422	90.4768 4873	82.4791 5219	72.2959 8064
130	100.2161 0576	95.4216 0619	90.9463 2851	82.8577 1929	72.5702 7786
131	100.7961 2189	95.9418 9671	91.4130 8554	83.2334 6828	72.8418 5927
132	101.3737 3131	96.4595 9872	91.8771 3561	83.6064 2013	73.1107 5175
133	101.9489 4401	96.9747 2509	92.3384 9442	83.9765 9566	73.3769 8193
134	102.5217 6994	97.4872 8865	92.7971 7758	84.3440 1554	73.6405 7617
135	103.0922 1899	97.9973 0214	93.2532 0060	84.7087 0029	73.9015 6056
136	103.6603 0104	98.5047 7825	93.7065 7892	85.0706 7026	74.1599 6095
137	104.2260 2590	99.0097 2960	94.1573 2787	85.4299 4567	74.4158 0293
138	104.7894 0335	99.5121 6875	94.6054 6270	85.7865 4657	74.6691 1181
139	105.3504 4314	100.0121 0821	95.0509 9857	86.1404 9288	74.9199 1268
140	105.9091 5496	100.5095 6041	95.4939 5056	86.4918 0434	75.1682 3038
141	106.4655 4847	101.0045 3772	95.9343 3364	86.8405 0059	75.4140 8948
142	107.0196 3330	101.4970 5246	96.3721 6272	87.1866 0108	75.6575 1434
143	107.5714 1902	101.9871 1688	96.8074 5261	87.5301 2514	75.8985 2905
144	108.1209 1517	102.4747 4316	97.2402 1804	87.8710 9195	76.1371 5747
145	108.6681 3126	102.9599 4344	97.6704 7364	88.2095 2055	76.3734 2324
146	109.2130 7674	103.4427 2979	98.0982 3397	88.5454 2982	76.6073 4974
147	109.7557 6103	103.9231 1422	98.5235 1350	88.8788 3854	76.8389 6014
148	110.2961 9353	104.4011 0868	98.9463 2663	89.2097 6530	77.0682 7737
149	110.8343 8356	104.8767 2505	99.3666 8765	89.5382 2858	77.2953 2413
150	111.3703 4044	105.3499 7518	99.7846 1078	89.8642 4673	77.5201 2290

HIGH-SPEED MATHEMATICS

TABLE XX (*Continued*)

PRESENT VALUE OF ANNUITY OF 1 PER PERIOD

$$a_{\overline{n}|} = \frac{1 - (1 + i)^{-n}}{i}$$

n	$1\frac{1}{8}\%$	$1\frac{1}{4}\%$	$1\frac{1}{2}\%$	$1\frac{3}{4}\%$	2%
1	0.9888 7515	0.9876 5432	0.9852 2167	0.9828 0098	0.9803 9216
2	1.9667 4923	1.9631 1538	1.9558 8342	1.9486 9875	1.9415 6094
3	2.9337 4460	2.9265 3371	2.9122 0042	2.8979. 8403	2.8838 8327
4	3.8899 8230	3.8780 5798	3.8543 8465	3.8309 4254	3.8077 2870
5	4.8355 8200	4.8178 3504	4.7826 4497	4.7478 5508	4.7134 5951
6	5.7706 6205	5.7460 0992	5.6971 8717	5.6489 9762	5.6014 3089
7	6.6953 3948	6.6627 2585	6.5982 1396	6.5346 4139	6.4719 9107
8	7.6097 3002	7.5681 2429	7.4859 2508	7.4050 5297	7.3254 8144
9	8.5139 4810	8.4623 4498	8.3605 1732	8.2604 9432	8.1622 3671
10	9.4081 0690	9.3455 2591	9.2221 8455	9.1012 2291	8.9825 8501
11	10.2923 1832	10.2178 0337	10.0711 1779	9.9274 9181	9.7868 4805
12	11.1666 9302	11.0793 1197	10.9075 0521	10.7395 4969	10.5753 4122
13	12.0313 4044	11.9301 8466	11.7315 3222	11.5376 4097	11.3483 7375
14	12.8863 6880	12.7705 5275	12.5433 8150	12.3220 0587	12.1062 4877
15	13.7318 8509	13.6005 4592	13.3432 3301	13.0928 8046	12.8492 6350
16	14.5679 9514	14.4202 9227	14.1312 6405	13.8504 9677	13.5777 0931
17	15.3948 0360	15.2299 1829	14.9076 4931	14.5950 8282	14.2918 7188
18	16.2124 1395	16.0295 4893	15.6725 6089	15.3268 6272	14.9920 3125
19	17.0209 2850	16.8193 0759	16.4261 6837	16.0460 5673	15.6784 6201
20	17.8204 4845	17.5993 1613	17.1686 3879	16.7528 8130	16.3514 3334
21	18.6110 7387	18.3696 9495	17.9001 3673	17.4475 4919	17.0112 0916
22	19.3929 0371	19.1305 6291	18.6208 2437	18.1302 6948	17.6580 4820
23	20.1660 3580	19.8820 3744	19.3308 6145	18.8012 4764	18.2922 0412
24	20.9305 6693	20.6242 3451	20.0304 0537	19.4606 8565	18.9139 2560
25	21.6865 9276	21.3572 6865	20.7196 1120	20.1087 8196	19.5234 5647
26	22.4342 0792	22.0812 5299	21.3986 3172	20.7457 3166	20.1210 3576
27	23.1735 0598	22.7962 9925	22.0676 1746	21.3717 2644	20.7068 9780
28	23.9045 7946	23.5025 1778	22.7267 1671	21.9869 5474	21.2812 7236
29	24.6275 1986	24.2000 1756	23.3760 7558	22.5916 0171	21.8443 8466
30	25.3424 1766	24.8889 0623	24.0158 3801	23.1858 4934	22.3964 5555
31	26.0.93 6233	25.5692 9010	24.6461 4582	23.7698 7650	22.9377 0152
32	26.7484 4236	26.2412 7418	25.2671 3874	24.3438 5897	23.4683 3482
33	27.4397 4522	26.9049 6215	25.8789 5442	24.9079 6951	23.9885 6355
34	28.1233 5745	27.5604 5644	26.4817 2849	25.4623 7789	24.4985 9172
35	28.7993 6460	28.2078 5822	27.0755 9458	26.0072 5100	24.9986 1933
36	29.4678 5127	28.8472 6737	27.6606 8431	26.5427 5283	25.4888 4248
37	30.1289 0114	29.4787 8259	28.2371 2740	27.0690 4455	25.9694 5341
38	30.7825 9692	30.1025 0133	28.8050 5163	27.5862 8457	26.4406 4060
39	31.4290 2044	30.7185 1983	29.3645 8288	28.0946 2857	26.9025 8883
40	32.0682 5260	31.3269 3316	29.9158 4520	28.5942 2955	27.3554 7924
41	32.7903 7340	31.9278 3522	30.4589 6079	29.0852 3789	27.7994 8945
42	33.3254 6195	32.5213 1874	30.9940 5004	29.5678 0135	28.2347 9358
43	33.9435 9649	33.1074 7530	31.5212 3157	30.0420 6522	28.6615 6233
44	34.5548 5438	33.6863 9536	32.0406 2223	30.5081 7221	29.0799 6307
45	35.1593 1212	34.2581 6825	32.5523 3718	30.9662 6261	29.4901 5987
46	35.7570 4536	34.8228 8222	33.0564 8983	31.4164 7431	29.8923 1360
47	36.3481 2891	35.3806 2442	33.5531 9195	31.8589 4281	30.2865 8196
48	36.9326 3674	35.9314 8091	34.0425 5365	32.2938 0129	30.6731 1957
49	37.5106 4202	36.4755 3670	34.5246 8339	32.7211 8063	31.0520 7801
50	38.0822 1708	37.0128 7574	34.9996 8807	33.1412 0946	31.4236 0589

TABLE XX (Continued)

Present Value of Annuity of 1 per Period

$$a_{\overline{n}|} = \frac{1 - (1 + i)^{-n}}{i}$$

n	$1\frac{1}{8}\%$	$1\frac{1}{4}\%$	$1\frac{1}{2}\%$	$1\frac{3}{4}\%$	2%
51	38.6474 3345	37.5435 8099	35.4676 7298	33.5540 1421	31.7878 4892
52	39.2063 6188	38.0677 3431	35.9287 4185	33.9597 1913	32.1449 4992
53	39.7590 7232	38.5854 1660	36.3829 9690	34.3584 4633	32.4950 4894
54	40.3056 3394	39.0967 0776	36.8305 3882	34.7503 1579	32.8382 8327
55	40.8461 1514	39.6016 8667	37.2714 6681	35.1354 4550	33.1747 8752
56	41.3805 8358	40.1004 3128	37.7058 7863	35.5139 5135	33.5046 9365
57	41.9091 0613	40.5930 1855	38.1338 7058	35.8859 4727	33.8281 3103
58	42.4317 4896	41.0795 2449	38.5555 3751	36.2515 4523	34.1452 2650
59	42.9485 7746	41.5600 2419	38.9709 7292	36.6108 5526	34.4561 0441
60	43.4596 5633	42.0345 9179	39.3802 6889	36.9639 8552	34.7608 8668
61	43.9650 4952	42.5033 0054	39.7835 1614	37.3110 4228	35.0596 9282
62	44.4648 2029	42.9662 2275	40.1808 0408	37.6521 3000	35.3526 4002
63	44.9590 3119	43.4234 2988	40.5722 2077	37.9873 5135	35.6398 4316
64	45.4477 4407	43.8749 9247	40.9578 5298	38.3168 0723	35.9214 1486
65	45.9310 2009	44.3209 8022	41.3377 8618	38.6405 9678	36.1974 6555
66	46.4089 1975	44.7614 6195	41.7121 0461	38.9588 1748	36.4681 0348
67	46.8815 0284	45.1965 0563	42.0808 9125	39.2715 6509	36.7334 3478
68	47.3488 2852	45.6261 7840	42.4442 2783	39.5789 3375	36.9935 6351
69	47.8109 5527	46.0505 4656	42.8021 9490	39.8810 1597	37.2485 9168
70	48.2679 4094	46.4696 7562	43.1548 7183	40.1779 0267	37.4986 1929
71	48.7198 4270	46.8836 3024	43.5023 3678	40.4696 8321	37.7437 4441
72	49.1667 1714	47.2924 7431	43.8446 6677	40.7564 4542	37.9840 6314
73	49.6086 2016	47.6962 7093	44.1819 3771	41.0382 7560	38.2196 6975
74	50.0456 0708	48.0950 8240	44.5142 2434	41.3152 5857	38.4506 5662
75	50.4777 3259	48.4889 7027	44.8416 0034	41.5874 7771	38.6771 1433
76	50.9050 5077	48.8779 9533	45.1641 3826	41.8550 1495	38.8991 3170
77	51.3276 1510	49.2622 1761	45.4819 0962	42.1179 5081	39.1167 9578
78	51.7454 7847	49.6416 9640	45.7949 8485	42.3763 6443	39.3301 9194
79	52.1586 0317	50.0164 9027	46.1034 3335	42.6303 3359	39.5394 0386
80	52.5673 1092	50.3866 5706	46.4073 2349	42.8799 3474	39.7445 1359
81	52.9713 8286	50.7522 5389	46.7067 2265	43.1252 4298	39.9456 0156
82	53.3709 5957	51.1133 3717	47.0016 9720	43.3663 3217	40.1427 4663
83	53.7660 9104	51.4699 6264	47.2923 1251	43.6032 7486	40.3360 2611
84	54.1568 2674	51.8221 8532	47.5786 3301	43.8361 4237	40.5255 1579
85	54.5432 1557	52.1700 5958	47.8607 2218	44.0650 0479	40.7112 8999
86	54.9253 0588	52.5136 3909	48.1386 4254	44.2899 3099	40.8934 2156
87	55.3031 4549	52.8529 7688	48.4124 5571	44.5109 8869	41.0719 8192
88	55.6767 8169	53.1881 2531	48.6822 2237	44.7282 4441	41.2470 4110
89	56.0462 6126	53.5191 3611	48.9480 0234	44.9417 6355	41.4186 6774
90	56.4116 3041	53.8460 6035	49.2098 5452	45.1516 1037	41.5869 2916
91	56.7729 3490	54.1689 4850	49.4678 3696	45.3578 4803	41.7518 9133
92	57.1302 1992	54.4878 5037	49.7220 0686	45.5605 3860	41.9136 1895
93	57.4835 3021	54.8028 1518	49.9724 2055	45.7597 4310	42.0721 7545
94	57.8329 0997	55.1138 9154	50.2191 3355	45.9555 2147	42.2276 2299
95	58.1784 0294	55.4211 2744	50.4622 0054	46.1479 3265	42.3800 2254
96	58.5200 5235	55.7245 7031	50.7016 7541	46.3370 3455	42.5294 3386
97	58.8579 0096	56.0242 6698	50.9376 1124	46.5228 8408	42.6759 1555
98	59.1919 9106	56.3202 6368	51.1700 6034	46.7055 3718	42.8195 2505
99	59.5223 6446	56.6126 0610	51.3990 7422	46.8850 4882	42.9603 1867
100	59.8490 6251	56.9013 3936	51.6247 0367	47.0614 7304	43.0983 5164

TABLE XX (Continued)

PRESENT VALUE OF ANNUITY OF 1 PER PERIOD

$$a_{\overline{n}|} = \frac{1 - (1 + i)^{-n}}{i}$$

n	$2\frac{1}{4}\%$	$2\frac{1}{2}\%$	$2\frac{3}{4}\%$	3%	$3\frac{1}{2}\%$
1	0.9779 9511	0.9756 0976	0.9732 3601	0.9708 7379	0.9661 8357
2	1.9344 6955	1.9274 2415	1.9204 2434	1.9134 6970	1.8996 9428
3	2.8698 9687	2.8560 2356	2.8422 6213	2.8286 1135	2.8016 3698
4	3.7847 4021	3.7619 7421	3.7394 2787	3.7170 9840	3.6730 7921
5	4.6794 5253	4.6458 2850	4.6125 8186	4.5797 0719	4.5150 5238
6	5.5544 7680	5.5081 2536	5.4623 6678	5.4171 9144	5.3285 5302
7	6.4102 4626	6.3493 9060	6.2894 0806	6.2302 8296	6.1145 4398
8	7.2471 8461	7.1701 3717	7.0943 1441	7.0196 9219	6.8739 5554
9	8.0657 0622	7.9708 6553	7.8776 7826	7.7861 0892	7.6076 8651
10	8.8662 1635	8.7520 6393	8.6400 7616	8.5302 0284	8.3166 0532
11	9.6491 1134	9.5142 0871	9.3820 6926	9.2526 2411	9.0015 5104
12	10.4147 7882	10.2577 6460	10.1042 0366	9.9540 0399	9.6633 3433
13	11.1635 9787	10.9831 8497	10.8070 1086	10.6349 5533	10.3027 3849
14	11.8959 3924	11.6909 1217	11.4910 0814	11.2960 7314	10.9205 2028
15	12.6121 6551	12.3813 7773	12.1566 9892	11.9379 3509	11.5174 1090
16	13.3126 3131	13.0550 0266	12.8045 7315	12.5611 0203	12.0941 1681
17	13.9976 8343	13.7121 9772	13.4351 0769	13.1661 1847	12.6513 2059
18	14.6676 6106	14.3533 6363	14.0487 6661	13.7535 1308	13.1896 8173
19	15.3228 9590	14.9788 9134	14.6460 0157	14.3237 9911	13.7098 3742
20	15.9637 1237	15.5891 6229	15.2272 5213	14.8774 7486	14.2124 0330
21	16.5904 2775	16.1845 4857	15.7929 4612	15.4150 2414	14.6979 7420
22	17.2033 5232	16.7654 1324	16.3434 9987	15.9369 1664	15.1671 2484
23	17.8027 8955	17.3321 1048	16.8793 1861	16.4436 0839	15.6204 1047
24	18.3890 3624	17.8849 8583	17.4007 9670	16.9355 4212	16.0583 6760
25	18.9623 8263	18.4243 7642	17.9083 1795	17.4131 4769	16.4815 1459
26	19.5231 1260	18.9506 1114	18.4022 5592	17.8768 4242	16.8903 5226
27	20.0715 0376	19.4640 1087	18.8829 7413	18.3270 3147	17.2853 6451
28	20.6078 2764	19.9648 8866	19.3508 2640	18.7641 0823	17.6670 1885
29	21.1323 4977	20.4535 4991	19.8061 5708	19.1884 5459	18.0357 6700
30	21.6453 2985	20.9302 9259	20.2493 0130	19.6004 4135	18.3920 4541
31	22.1470 2186	21.3954 0741	20.6805 8520	20.0004 2849	18.7362 7576
32	22.6376 7419	21.8491 7796	21.1003 2623	20.3887 6553	19.0688 6547
33	23.1175 2977	22.2918 8094	21.5088 3332	20.7657 9178	19.3902 0818
34	23.5868 2618	22.7237 8628	21.9064 0712	21.1318 3668	19.7006 8423
35	24.0457 9577	23.1451 5734	22.2933 4026	21.4872 2007	20.0006 6110
36	24.4946 6579	23.5562 5107	22.6699 1753	21.8322 5250	20.2904 9381
37	24.9336 5848	23.9573 1812	23.0364 1609	22.1672 3544	20.5705 2542
38	25.3629 9118	24.3486 0304	23.3931 0568	22.4924 6159	20.8410 8736
39	25.7828 7646	24.7303 4443	23.7402 4884	22.8082 1513	21.1024 9987
40	26.1935 2221	25.1027 7505	24.0781 0106	23.1147 7197	21.3550 7234
41	26.5951 3174	25.4661 2200	24.4069 1101	23.4123 9997	21.5991 0371
42	26.9879 0390	25.8206 0683	24.7269 2069	23.7013 5920	21.8348 8281
43	27.3720 3316	26.1664 4569	25.0383 6563	23.9819 0213	22.0626 8870
44	27.7477 0969	26.5038 4945	25.3414 7507	24.2542 7392	22.2827 9102
45	28.1151 1950	26.8330 2386	25.6364 7209	24.5187 1254	22.4954 5026
46	28.4744 4450	27.1541 6962	25.9235 7381	24.7754 4907	22.7009 1813
47	28.8258 6259	27.4674 8255	26.2029 9154	25.0247 0783	22.8994 3780
48	29.1695 4777	27.7731 5371	26.4749 3094	25.2667 0664	23.0912 4425
49	29.5056 7019	28.0713 6947	26.7395 9215	25.5016 5693	23.2765 6450
50	29.8343 9627	28.3623 1168	26.9971 6998	25.7297 6401	23.4556 1757

TABLE XX (Continued)

PRESENT VALUE OF ANNUITY OF 1 PER PERIOD

$$a_{\overline{n}|} = \frac{1 - (1 + i)^{-n}}{i}$$

n	$2\frac{1}{4}\%$	$2\frac{1}{2}\%$	$2\frac{3}{4}\%$	3%	$3\frac{1}{2}\%$
51	30.1558 8877	28.6461 5774	27.2478 5400	25.9512 2719	23.6286 1630
52	30.4703 0687	28.9230 8072	27.4918 2871	26.1662 3999	23.7957 6454
53	30.7778 0623	29.1932 4948	27.7292 7368	26.3749 9028	23.9572 6043
54	31.0785 3910	29.4568 2876	27.9603 6368	26.5776 6047	24.1132 9510
55	31.3726 5438	29.7139 7928	28.1852 6879	26.7744 2764	24.2640 5323
56	31.6602 9768	29.9048 5784	28.4041 5454	26.9654 6373	24.4097 1327
57	31.9416 1142	30.2096 1740	28.6171 8203	27.1509 3566	24.5504 4760
58	32.2167 3489	30.4484 0722	28.8245 0806	27.3310 0549	24.6864 2281
59	32.4858 0429	30.6813 7290	29.0262 8522	27.5058 3058	24.8177 9981
60	32.7489 5285	30.9086 5649	29.2226 6201	27.6755 6367	24.9447 3412
61	33.0063 1086	31.1303 9657	29.4137 8298	27.8403 5307	25.0673 7596
62	33.2580 0573	31.3467 2836	29.5997 8879	28.0003 4279	25.1858 7049
63	33.5041 6208	31.5577 8377	29.7808 1634	28.1556 7261	25.3003 5796
64	33.7449 0179	31.7636 9148	29.9569 9887	28.3064 7826	25.4109 7388
65	33.9803 4405	31.9645 7705	30.1284 6605	28.4528 9152	25.5178 4916
66	34.2106 0543	32.1605 6298	30.2953 4409 ·	28.5950 4031	25.6211 1030
67	34.4357 9993	32.3517 6876	30.4577 5581	28.7330 4884	25.7208 7951
68	34.6560 3905	32.5383 1099 ·	30.6158 2074	28.8670 3771	25.8172 7489
69	34.8714 3183	32.7203 0340	30.7696 5522	28.9971 2399	25.9104 1052
70	35.0820 8492	32.8978 5698	30.9193 7247	29.1234 2135	26.0003 9664
71	35.2881 0261	33.0710 7998	31.0650 8270	29.2460 4015	26.0873 3975
72	35.4895 8691	33.2400 7803	31.2068 9314	29.3650 8752	26.1713 4275
73	35.6866 3756	33.4049 5417	31.3449 0816	29.4806 6750	26.2525 0508
74	35.8793 5214	33.5658 0895	31.4792 2936	29.5928 8106	26.3309 2278
75	36.0678 2605	33.7227 4044	31.6099 5558	29.7018 2628	26.4066 8868
76	36.2521 5262	33.8758 4433	31.7371 8304	29.8075 9833	26.4798 9244
77	36.4324 2310	34.0252 1398	31.8610 0540	29.9102 8964	26.5506 2072
78	36.6087 2675	34.1709 4047	31.9815 1377	30.0099 8994	26.6189 5721
79	36.7811 5085	34.3131 1265	32.0987 9685	30.1067 8635	26.6849 8281
80	36.9497 8079	34.4518 1722	32.2129 4098	30.2007 6345	26.7487 7567
81	37.1147 0004	34.5871 3875	32.3240 3015	30.2920 0335	26.8104 1127
82	37.2759 9026	34.7191 5976	32.4321 4613	30.3805 8577	26.8699 6258
83	37.4337 3130	34.8479 6074	32.5373 6850	30.4665 8813	26.9275 0008
84	37.5880 0127	34.9736 2023	32.6397 7469	30.5500 8556	26.9830 9186
85	37.7388 7655	35.0962 1486	32.7394 4009	30.6311 5103	27.0368 0373
86	37.8864 3183	35.2158 1938	32.8364 3804	30.7098 5537	27.0886 9926
87	38.0307 4018	35.3325 0671	32.9308 3994	30.7862 6735	27.1388 3986
88	38.1718 7304	35.4463 4801	33.0227 1527	30.8604 5374	27.1872 8489
89	38.3099 0028	35.5574 1269	33.1121 3165	30.9324 7936	27.2340 9168
90	38.4448 9025	35.6657 6848	33.1991 5489	31.0024 0714	27.2793 1564
91	38.5769 0078	35.7714 8144	33.2838 4905	31.0702 9820	27.3230 1028
92	38.7060 2423	35.8746 1604	33.3662 7644	31.1362 1184	27.3652 2732
93	38.8322 9754	35.9752 3516	33.4464 9776	31.2002 0567	27.4060 1673
94	38.9557 9221	36.0734 0016	33.5245 7202	31.2623 3560	27.4454 2680
95	39.0765 6940	36.1691 7089	33.6005 5671	31.3226 5592	27.4835 0415
96	39.1946 8890	36.2626 0574	33.6745 0775	31.3812 1934	27.5202 9387
97	39.3102 0920	36.3537 6170	33.7464 7956	31.4380 7703	27.5558 3948
98	39.4231 8748	36.4426 9434	33.8165 2512	31.4932 7867	27.5901 8308
99	39.5336 7968	36.5294 5790	33.8846 9598	31.5468 7250	27.6233 6529
100	39.6417 4052	36.6141 0526	33.9510 4232	31.5989 0534	27.6554 2540

TABLE XX (Continued)

PRESENT VALUE OF ANNUITY OF 1 PER PERIOD

$$a_{\overline{n}|} = \frac{1 - (1 + i)^{-n}}{i}$$

n	4%	$4\frac{1}{2}$%	5%	$5\frac{1}{2}$%	6%
1	0.9615 3846	0.9569 3780	0.9523 8095	0.9478 6730	0.9433 9623
2	1.8860 9467	1.8726 6775	1.8594 1043	1.8463 1971	1.8333 9267
3	2.7750 9103	2.7489 6435	2.7232 4803	2.6979 3338	2.6730 1195
4	3.6298 9522	3.5875 2570	3.5459 5050	3.5051 5012	3.4651 0561
5	4.4518 2233	4.3899 7674	4.3294 7667	4.2702 8448	4.2123 6379
6	5.2421 3686	5.1578 7248	5.0756 9206	4.9955 3031	4.9173 2433
7	6.0020 5467	5.8927 0094	5.7863 7340	5.6829 6712	5.5823 8144
8	6.7327 4487	6.5958 8607	6.4632 1276	6.3345 6599	6.2097 9381
9	7.4353 3161	7.2687 9050	7.1078 2168	6.9521 9525	6.8016 9227
10	8.1108 9578	7.9127 1818	7.7217 3493	7.5376 2583	7.3600 8705
11	8.7604 7671	8.5289 1692	8.3064 1422	8.0925 3633	7.8868 7458
12	9.3850 7376	9.1185 8078	8.8632 5164	8.6185 1785	8.3838 4394
13	9.9856 4785	9.6828 5242	9.3935 7299	9.1170 7853	8.8526 8296
14	10.5631 2293	10.2228 2528	9.8986 4094	9.5896 4790	9.2949 8393
15	11.1183 8743	10.7395 4573	10.3796 5804	10.0375 8094	9.7122 4899
16	11.6522 9561	11.2340 1505	10.8377 6956	10.4621 6203	10.1058 9527
17	12.1656 6885	11.7071 9143	11.2740 6625	10.8646 0856	10.4772 5969
18	12.6592 9697	12.1599 9180	11.6895 8690	11.2460 7447	10.8276 0348
19	13.1339 3940	12.5932 9359	12.0853 2086	11.6076 5352	11.1581 1649
20	13.5903 2634	13.0079 3645	12.4622 1034	11.9503 8249	11.4699 2122
21	14.0291 5995	13.4047 2388	12.8211 5271	12.2752 4406	11.7640 7662
22	14.4511 1533	13.7844 2476	13.1630 0258	12.5831 6973	12.0415 8172
23	14.8568 4167	14.1477 7489	13.4885 7388	12.8750 4240	12.3033 7898
24	15.2469 6314	14.4954 7837	13.7986 4179	13.1516 9895	12.5503 5753
25	15.6220 7994	14.8282 0896	14.0939 4457	13.4139 3266	12.7833 5616
26	15.9827 6918	15.1466 1145	14.3751 8530	13.6624 9541	13.0031 6619
27	16.3295 8575	15.4513 0282	14.6430 3362	13.8980 9991	13.2105 3414
28	16.6630 6322	15.7428 7351	14.8981 2726	14.1214 2172	13.4061 6428
29	16.9837 1463	16.0218 8853	15.1410 7358	14.3331 0116	13.5907 2102
30	17.2920 3330	16.2888 8854	15.3724 5103	14.5337 4517	13.7648 3115
31	17.5884 9356	16.5443 9095	15.5928 1050	14.7239 2907	13.9290 8599
32	17.8735 5150	16.7888 9086	15.8026 7667	14.9041 9817	14.0840 4339
33	18.1476 4567	17.0228 6207	16.0025 4921	15.0750 6936	14.2302 2961
34	18.4111 9776	17.2467 5796	16.1929 0401	15.2370 3257	14.3681 4114
35	18.6646 1323	17.4610 1240	16.3741 9429	15.3905 5220	14.4982 4636
36	18.9082 8195	17.6660 4058	16.5468 5171	15.5360 6843	14.6209 8713
37	19.1425 7880	17.8622 3979	16.7112 8734	15.6739 9851	14.7367 8031
38	19.3678 6423	18.0499 9023	16.8678 9271	15.8047 3793	14.8460 1916
39	19.5844 8484	18.2296 5522	17.0170 4067	15.9286 6154	14.9490 7468
40	19.7927 7388	18.4015 8442	17.1590 8635	16.0461 2469	15.0462 9687
41	19.9930 5181	18.5661 0949	17.2943 6796	16.1574 6416	15.1380 1592
42	20.1856 2674	18.7235 4975	17.4232 0758	16.2629 9920	15.2245 4332
43	20.3707 9494	18.8742 1029	17.5459 1198	16.3630 3242	15.3061 7294
44	20.5488 4129	19.0183 8305	17.6627 7331	16.4578 5063	15.3831 8202
45	20.7200 3970	19.1563 4742	17.7740 6982	16.5477 2572	15.4558 3209
46	20.8846 5356	19.2883 7074	17.8800 6650	16.6329 1537	15.5243 6990
47	21.0429 3612	19.4147 0884	17.9810 1571	16.7136 6386	15.5890 2821
48	21.1951 3088	19.5356 0654	18.0771 5782	16.7902 0271	15.6500 2661
49	21.3414 7200	19.6512 9813	18.1687 2173	16.8627 5139	15.7075 7227
50	21.4821 8462	19.7620 0778	18.2559 2546	16.9315 1790	15.7618 6064

TABLE XX (*Continued*)

PRESENT VALUE OF ANNUITY OF 1 PER PERIOD

$$a_{\overline{n}|} = \frac{1 - (1 + i)^{-n}}{i}$$

n	4%	$4\frac{1}{2}\%$	5%	$5\frac{1}{2}\%$	6%
51	21.6174 8521	19.8679 5003	18.3389 7663	16.9966 9943	15.8130 7607
52	21.7475 8193	19.9693 3017	18.4180 7298	17.0584 8287	15.8613 9252
53	21.8726 7493	20.0663 4466	18.4934 0284	17 1170 4538	15.9069 7408
54	21.9929 5667	20.1591 8149	18.5651 4556	17 1725 5486	15.9499 7554
55	22.1086 1218	20.2480 2057	18.6334 7196	17 2251 7048	15.9905 4297
56	22.2189 1940	.20.3330 3404	18.6985 4473	17 2750 4311	16.0288 1412
57	22.3267 4943	20.4143 8664	18.7605 1879	17.3223 1575	16.0649 1898
58	22.4295 6676	20.4922 3602	18.8195 4170	17.3671 2393	16.0989 8017
59	22.5284 2957	20.5667 3303	18.8757 5400−	17 4095 9614	16.1311 1337
60	22.6234 8997	20.6380 2204	18.9292 8952	.17 4498 5416	16.1614 2771
61	22.7148 9421	20.7062 4118	18.9802 7574	17 4880 1343	16.1900 2614
62	22.8027 8289	20.7715 2266	19.0288 3404	17.5241 8334	16.2170 0579
63	22.8872 9124	20.8339 9298	19.0750 8003	17 5584 6762	16.2424 5829
64	22.9685 4927	20.8937 7319	19.1191 2384	17.5909 6457	16.2664 7009
65	23.0466 8199	20.9509 7913	19 1610 7033	17 6217 6737.	16.2891 2272
66	23.1218 0961	21.0057 2165	19.2010 1936	17.6509 6433	16.3104 9314
67	23.1940 4770	21.0581 0684	19.2390 6606	17.6786 3917	16.3306 5390
68	23.2635 0740	21 1082 3621	19.2753 0101	17 7048 7125	16.3496 7349
69	23.3302 9558	21.1562 0690	19.3098 1048	17 7297 3579	16.3676 1650
70	23.3945 1498	21.2021 1187	19.3426 7665	17 7533 0406	16.3845 4387
71	23.4562 6440	.21.2460 4007	19.3739 7776	17 7756 4366	16.4005 1308
72	23.5156 3885	21.2880 7662	19.4037 8834	17 7968 1864	16.4155 7838
73	23.5727 2966	21 3283 0298	19.4321 7937	17.8168 8970	16.4297 9093
74	23.6276 2468	21.3667 9711	19.4592 1845	17.8359 1441	16.4431 9899
75	23.6804 0834	21.4036 3360	19.4849 6995	17 8539 4731	16.4558 4810
76	23.7311 6187	21.4388 8383	19.5094 9519	17 8710 4010	16.4677 8123
77	23.7799 6333	21.4726 1611	19.5328 5257	17.8872 4180	16.4790 3889
78	23.8268 8782	21.5048 9579	19.5550 9768	17.9025 9887	16.4896 5933
79	23.8720 0752	21.5357 8545	19.5762 8351	17.9171 5532	16.4996 7862
80	23.9153 9185	21.5653 4493	19.5964 6048	17 9309 5291	16.5091 .3077
81	23.9571 0754	21.5936 3151	19.6156 7665	17.9440 3120	16.5180 4790
82	23.9972 1879	21.6207 0001	19.6339 7776	17 9564 2768	16.5264 6028
83	24.0357 8730	21.6466 0288	19.6514 0739	17 9681 7789	16.5343 9649
84	24.0728 7240	21.6713 9032	19.6680 0704	17.9793 1554	16.5418 8348
85	24.1085 3116	21.6951 1035	19.6838 1623	17 9898 7255	16.5489 4668
86	24.1428 1842	21.7178 0895	19.6988 .7260	17.9998 7919	16.5556 1008
87	24.1757 8694	21.7395 3009	19.7132 1200	18.0093 6416	16.5618 9630
88	24.2074 8745	21.7603 1588	19.7268 6857	18.0183 5466	16.5678 2670
89	24.2379 6870	21.7802 0658	19.7398 7483	18.0268 7645	16.5734 2141
90	24.2672 7759	21.7992 4075	19.7522 6174	18.0349 5398	16.5786 9944
91	24.2954 5923	21.8174 5526	19.7640 5880	18.0426 1041	16.5836 7872
92	24.3225 5695	21.8348 8542	·19.7752 9410	18.0498 6769	16.5883 7615
93	24.3486 1245	21.8515 6499	19.7859 9438	18.0567 4662	16.5928 0769
94	24.3736 6582	21.8675 2631	19.7961 8512	18.0632 6694	16.5969 8839
95	24.3977 5559	21.8828 0030	19.8058 9059	18.0694 4734	16.6009 3244
96	24.4209 1884	21.8974 1655	19.8151 3390	18.0753 0553	16.6046 5325
97	24.4431 9119	21.9114 0340	19.8239 3705	18.0808 5833	16.6081 6344
98	24.4646 0692	21.9247 8794	19.8323 2100	18.0861 2164	16.6114 7494
99	24.4851 9896	21.9375 9612	19.8403 0571	18.0911 1055	16.6145 9900
100	24.5049 9900	21.9498 5274	19.8479 1020	18.0958 3939	16.6175 4623

HIGH-SPEED MATHEMATICS

TABLE XX (Continued)

PRESENT VALUE OF ANNUITY OF 1 PER PERIOD

$$a_{\overline{n}|} = \frac{1 - (1 + i)^{-n}}{i}$$

n	$6\frac{1}{2}\%$	7%	$7\frac{1}{2}\%$	8%	$8\frac{1}{2}\%$
1	0.9389 6714	0.9345 7944	0.9302 3256	0.9259 2593	0.9216 5899
2	1.8206 2642	1.8080 1817	1.7955 6517	1.7832 6475	1.7711 1427
3	2.6484 7551	2.6243 1604	2.6005 2574	2.5770 9699	2.5540 2237
4	3.4257 9860	3.3872 1126	3.3493 2627	3.3121 2684	3.2755 9666
5	4.1556 7944	4.1001 9744	4.0458 8490	3.9927 1004	3.9406 4208
6	4.8410 1356	4.7665 3966	4.6938 4642	4.6228 7966	4.5535 8717
7	5.4845 1977	5.3892 8940	5.2966 0132	5.2063 7006	5.1185 1352
8	6.0887 5096	5.9712 9851	5.8573 0355	5.7466 3894	5.6391 8297
9	6.6561 0419	6.5152 3225	6.3788 8703	6.2468 8791	6.1190 6264
10	7 1888 3022	7.0235 8154	6.8640 8096	6.7100 8140	6.5613 4806
11	7.6890 4246	7.4986 7434	7.3154 2415	7.1389 6426	6.9689 8439
12	8.1587 2532	7.9426 8630	7.7352 7827	7.5360 7802	7.3446 8607
13	8.5997 4208	8.3576 5074	8.1258 4026	7.9037 7594	7.6909 5490
14	9.0138 4233	8.7454 6799	8.4891 5373	8.2442 3698	8.0100 9668
15	9.4026 6885	9.1079 1401	8.8271 1974	8.5594 7869	8.3042 3658
16	9.7677 6418	9.4466 4860	9.1415 0674	8.8513 6916	8.5753 3325
17	10.1105 7670	9.7632 2299	9.4339 5976	9.1216 3811	8.8251 9194
18	10.4324 6638	10.0590 8691	9.7060 0908	9.3718 8714	9.0554 7644
19	10.7347 1022	10.3355 9524	9.9590 7821	9.6035 9920	9.2677 2022
20	11.0185 0725	10.5940 1425	10.1944 9136	9.8181 4741	9.4633 3661
21	11.2849 8333	10.8355 2733	10.4134 8033	10.0168 0316	9.6436 2821
22	11.5351 9562	11.0612 4050	10.6171 9101	10.2007 4366	9.8097 9559
23	11.7701 3673	11.2721 8738	10.8066 8931	10.3710 5895	9.9629 4524
24	11.9907 3871	11.4693 3400	10.9829 6680	10.5287 5528	10.1040 9700
25	12.1978 7672	11.6535 8318	11.1469 4586	10.6747 7619	10.2341 9078
26	12.3923 7251	11.8257 7867	11.2994 8452	10.8099 7795	10.3540 9288
27	12.5749 9766	11.9867 0904	11.4413 8095	10.9351 6477	10.4646 0174
28	12.7464 7668	12.1371 1125	11.5733 7763	11.0510 7849	10.5664 5321
29	12.9074 8984	12.2776 7407	11.6961 6524	11.1584 0601	10.6603 2554
30	13.0586 7591	12.4090 4118	11.8103 8627	11.2577 8334	10.7468 4382
31	13.2006 3465	12.5318 1419	11.9166 3839	11.3497 9939	10.8265 8416
32	13.3339 2925	12.6465 5532	12.0154 7757	11.4349 9944	10.9000 7757
33	13.4590 8850	12.7537 9002	12.1074 2099	11.5138 8837	10.9678 1343
34	13.5766 0892	12.8540 0936	12.1929 4976	11.5869 3367	11.0302 4279
35	13.6869 5673	12.9476 7230	12.2725 1141	11.6545 6822	11.0877 8137
36	13.7905 6970	13.0352 0776	12.3465 2224	11.7171 9279	11.1408 1233
37	13.8878 5887	13.1170 1660	12.4153 6953	11.7751 7851	11.1896 8878
38	13.9792 1021	13.1934 7345	12.4794 1351	11.8288 6899	11.2347 3620
39	14.0649 8611	13.2649 2846	12.5389 8931	11.8785 8240	11.2762 5457
40	14.1455 2687	13.3317 0884	12.5944 0866	11.9246 1333	11.3145 2034
41	14.2211 5199	13.3941 2041	12.6459 6155	11.9672 3457	11.3497 8833
42	14.2921 6149	13.4524 4898	12.6939 1772	12.0066 9867	11.3822 9339
43	14.3588 3708	13.5069 6167	12.7385 2811	12.0432 3951	11.4122 5197
44	14.4214 4327	13.5579 0810	12.7800 2615	12.0770 7362	11.4398 6357
45	14.4802 2842	13.6055 2159	12.8186 2898	12.1084 0150	11.4653 1205
46	14.5354 2575	13.6500 2018	12.8545 3858	12.1374 0880	11.4887 6686
47	14.5872 5422	13.6916 0764	12.8879 4287	12.1642 6741	11.5103 8420
48	14.6359 1946	13.7304 7443	12.9190 1662	12.1891 3649	11.5303 0802
49	14.6816 1451	13.7667 9853	12.9479 2244	12.2121 6341	11.5486 7099
50	14.7245 2067	13.8007 4629	12.9748 1157	12.2334 8464	11.5655 9538

TABLE XXI

PERIODICAL PAYMENT OF ANNUITY WHOSE PRESENT VALUE IS 1

$$\frac{1}{a_{\overline{n}|}} = \frac{1}{s_{\overline{n}|}} + i$$

n	$\frac{5}{12}\%$	$\frac{1}{2}\%$	$\frac{7}{12}\%$	$\frac{3}{4}\%$	1%
1	1.0041 6667	1.0050 0000	1.0058 3333	1.0075 0000	1.0100 0000
2	0.5031 2717	0.5037 5312	0.5043 7924	0.5056 3200	0.5075 1244
3	0.3361 1496	0.3366 7221	0.3372 2976	0.3383 4579	0.3400 2211
4	0.2526 0958	0.2531 3279	0.2536 5644	0.2547 0501	0.2562 8109
5	0.2025 0693	0.2030 0997	0.2035 1357	0.2045 2242	0.2060 3980
6	0.1691 0564	0.1695 9546	0.1700 8594	0.1710 6891	0.1725 4837
7	0.1452 4800	0.1457 2854	0.1462 0986	0.1471 7488	0.1486 2828
8	0.1273 5512	0.1278 2886	0.1283 0351	0.1292 5552	0.1306 9029
9	0.1134 3876	0.1139 0736	0.1143 7698	0.1153 1929	0.1167 4037
10	0.1023 0596	0.1027 7057	0.1032 3632	0.1041 7123	0.1055 8208
11	0.0931 9757	0.0936 5903	0.0941 2175	0.0950 5094	0.0964 5408
12	0.0856 0748	0.0860 6643	0.0865 2675	0.0874 5148	0.0888 4879
13	0.0791 8532	0.0796 4224	0.0801 0064	0.0810 2188	0.0824 1482
14	0.0736 8082	0.0741 3609	0.0745 9295	0.0755 1146	0.0769 0117
15	0.0689 1045	0.0693 6436	0.0698 1999	0.0707 3639	0.0721 2378
16	0.0647 3655	0.0651 8937	0.0656 4401	0.0665 5879	0.0679 4460
17	0.0610 5387	0.0615 0579	0.0619 5966	0.0628 7321	0.0642 5806
18	0.0577 8053	0.0582 3173	0.0586 8499	0.0595 9766	0.0609 8205
19	0.0548 5191	0.0553 0253	0.0557 5532	0.0566 6740	0.0580 5175
20	0.0522 1630	0.0526 6645	0.0531 1889	0.0540 3063	0.0554 1532
21	0.0498 3183	0.0502 8163	0.0507 3383	0.0516 4543	0.0530 3075
22	0.0476 6427	0.0481 1380	0.0485 6585	0.0494 7748	0.0508 6371
23	0.0456 8531	0.0461 3465	0.0465 8663	0.0474 9846	0.0488 8584
24	0.0438 7139	0.0443 2061	0.0447 7258	0.0456 8474	0.0470 7347
25	0.0422 0270	0.0426 5186	0.0431 0388	0.0440 1650	0.0454 0675
26	0.0406 6247	0.0411 1163	0.0415 6376	0.0424 7693	0.0438 6888
27	0.0392 3645	0.0396 8565	0.0401 3793	0.0410 5176	0.0424 4553
28	0.0379 1239	0.0383 6167	0.0388 1415	0.0397 2871	0.0411 2444
29	0.0366 7974	0.0371 2914	0.0375 8186	0.0384 9723	0.0398 9502
30	0.0355 2936	0.0359 7892	0.0364 3191	0.0373 4816	0.0387 4811
31	0.0344 5330	0.0349 0304	0.0353 5633	0.0362 7352	0.0376 7573
32	0.0334 4458	0.0338 9453	0.0343 4815	0.0352 6634	0.0366 7089
33	0.0324 9708	0.0329 4727	0.0334 0124	0.0343 2048	0.0357 2744
34	0.0316 0540	0.0320 5586	0.0325 1020	0.0334 3053	0.0348 3997
35	0.0307 6476	0.0312 1550	0.0316 7024	0.0325 9170	0.0340 0368
36	0.0299 7090	0.0304 2194	0.0308 7710	0.0317 9973	0.0332 1431
37	0.0292 2003	0.0296 7139	0.0301 2698	0.0310 5082	0.0324 6805
38	0.0285 0875	0.0289 6045	0.0294 1649	0.0303 4157	0.0317 6150
39	0.0278 3402	0.0282 8607	0.0287 4258	0.0296 6893	0.0310 9160
40	0.0271 9310	0.0276 4552	0.0281 0251	0.0290 3016	0.0304 5560
41	0.0263 8352	0.0270 3631	0.0274 9379	0.0284 2276	0.0298 5102
42	0.0260 0303	0.0264 5622	0.0269 1420	0.0278 4452	0.0292 7563
43	0.0254 4961	0.0259 0320	0.0263 6170	0.0272 9338	0.0287 2737
44	0.0249 2141	0.0253 7541	0.0258 3443	0.0267 6751	0.0282 0441
45	0.0244 1675	0.0248 7117	0.0253 3073	0.0262 6521	0.0277 0505
46	0.0239 3409	0.0243 8894	0.0248 4905	0.0257 8495	0.0272 2775
47	0.0234 7204	0.0239 2733	0.0243 8798	0.0253 2532	0.0267 7111
48	0.0230 2929	0.0234 8503	0.0239 4624	0.0248 8504	0.0263 3384
49	0.0226 0468	0.0230 6087	0.0235 2265	0.0244 6292	0.0259 1474
50	0.0221 9711	0.0226 5376	0.0231 1611	0.0240 5787	0.0255 1273

HIGH-SPEED MATHEMATICS

TABLE XXI (Continued)

PERIODICAL PAYMENT OF ANNUITY WHOSE PRESENT VALUE IS 1

$$\frac{1}{a_{\overline{n}|}} = \frac{1}{s_{\overline{n}|}} + i$$

n	$\frac{5}{12}\%$	$\frac{1}{2}\%$	$\frac{7}{12}\%$	$\frac{3}{4}\%$	1%
51	0.0218 0557	0.0222 6269	0.0227 2563	0.0236 6888	0.0251 2680
52	0.0214 2916	0.0218 8675	0.0223 5027	0.0232 9503	0.0247 5603
53	0.0210 6700	0.0215 2507	0.0219 8919	0.0229 3546	0.0243 9956
54	0.0207 1830	0.0211 7686	0.0216 4157	0.0225 8938	0.0240 5658
55	0.0203 8234	0.0208 4139	0.0213 0671	0.0222 5605	0.0237 2637
56	0.0200 5843	0.0205 1797	0.0209 8390	0.0219 3478	0.0234 0823
57	0.0197 4593	0.0202 0598	0.0206 7251	0.0216 2496	0.0231 0156
58	0.0194 4426	0.0199 0481	0.0203 7196	0.0213 2597	0.0228 0573
59	0.0191 5287	0.0196 1392	0.0200 8170	0.0210 3727	0.0225 2020
60	0.0188 7123	0.0193 3280	0.0198 0120	0.0207 5836	0.0222 4445
61	0.0185 9888	0.0190 6096	0.0195 2999	0.0204 8873	0.0219 7800
62	0.0183 3536	0.0187 9796	0.0192 6762	0.0202 2795	0.0217 2041
63	0.0180 8025	0.0185 4337	0.0190 1366	0.0199 7560	0.0214 7125
64	0.0178 3315	0.0182 9681	0.0187 6773	0.0197 3127	0.0212 3013
65	0.0175 9371	0.0180 5789	0.0185 2946	0.0194 9460	0.0209 9667
66	0.0173 6156	0.0178 2627	0.0182 9848	0.0192 6524	0.0207 7052
67	0.0171 3639	0.0176 0163	0.0180 7449	0.0190 4286	0.0205 5136
68	0.0169 1788	0.0173 8366	0.0178 5716	0.0188 2716	0.0203 3888
69	0.0167 0574	0.0171 7206	0.0176 4622	0.0186 1785	0.0201 3280
70	0.0164 9971	0.0169 6657	0.0174 4138	0.0184 1464	0.0199 3282
71	0.0162 9952	0.0167 6693	0.0172 4239	0.0182 1728	0.0197 3870
72	0.0161 0493	0.0165 7289	0.0170 4901	0.0180 2554	0.0195 5019
73	0.0159 1572	0.0163 8422	0.0168 6100	0.0178 3917	0.0193 6706
74	0.0157 3165	0.0162 0070	0.0166 7814	0.0176 5796	0.0191 8910
75	0.0155 5253	0.0160 2214	0.0165 0024	0.0174 8170	0.0190 1609
76	0.0153 7816	0.0158 4832	0.0163 2709	0.0173 1020	0.0188 4784
77	0.0152 0836	0.0156 7908	0.0161 5851	0.0171 4328	0.0186 8416
78	0.0150 4295	0.0155 1423	0.0159 9432	0.0169 8074	0.0185 2488
79	0.0148 8177	0.0153 5360	0.0158 3436	0.0168 2244	0.0183 6984
80	0.0147 2464	0.0151 9704	0.0156 7847	0.0166 6821	0.0182 1885
81	0.0145 7144	0.0150 4439	0.0155 2650	0.0165 1790	0.0180 7180
82	0.0144 2200	0.0148 9552	0.0153 7830	0.0163 7136	0.0179 2851
83	0.0142 7620	0.0147 5028	0.0152 3373	0.0162 2847	0.0177 8886
84	0.0141 3391	0.0146 0855	0.0150 9268	0.0160 8908	0.0176 5273
85	0.0139 9500	0.0144 7021	0.0149 5501	0.0159 5308	0.0175 1998
86	0.0138 5935	0.0143 3513	0.0148 2060	0.0158 2034	0.0173 9050
87	0.0137 2685	0.0142 0320	0.0146 8935	0.0156 9076	0.0172 6417
88	0.0135 9740	0.0140 7431	0.0145 6115	0.0155 6423	0.0171 4089
89	0.0134 7088	0.0139 4837	0.0144 3588	0.0154 4064	0.0170 2056
90	0.0133 4721	0.0138 2527	0.0143 1347	0.0153 1989	0.0169 0306
91	0.0132 2629	0.0137 0493	0.0141 9380	0.0152 0190	0.0167 8832
92	0.0131 0803	0.0135 8724	0.0140 7679	0.0150 8657	0.0166 7624
93	0.0129 9234	0.0134 7213	0.0139 6236	0.0149 7382	0.0165 6673
94	0.0128 7915	0.0133 5950	0.0138 5042	0.0148 6356	0.0164 5971
95	0.0127 6837	0.0132 4930	0.0137 4090	0.0147 5571	0.0163 5511
96	0.0126 5992	0.0131 4143	0.0136 3372	0.0146 5020	0.0162 5284
97	0.0125 5374	0.0130 3583	0.0135 2880	0.0145 4696	0.0161 5284
98	0.0124 4976	0.0129 3242	0.0134.2608	0.0144 4592	0.0160 5503
99	0.0123 4790	0.0128 3115	0.0133 2549	0.0143 4701	0.0159 5936
100	0.0122 4811	0.0127 3194	0.0132 2696	0.0142 5017	0.0158 6574

TABLE XXI (Continued)

PERIODICAL PAYMENT OF ANNUITY WHOSE PRESENT VALUE IS 1

$$\frac{1}{a_{\overline{u}|}} = \frac{1}{s_{\overline{n}|}} + i$$

n	$\frac{5}{12}\%$	$\frac{1}{2}\%$	$\frac{7}{12}\%$	$\frac{3}{4}\%$	1%
101	0.0121 5033	0.0126 3473	0.0131 3045	0.0141 5533	0.0157 7413
102	0.0120 5449	0.0125 3947	0.0130 3587	0.0140 6243	0.0156 8446
103	0.0119 6054	0.0124 4611	0.0129 4319	0.0139 7143	0.0155 9668
104	0.0118 6842	0.0123 5457	0.0128 5234	0.0138 8226	0.0155 1073
105	0.0117 7809	0.0122 6481	0.0127 6238	0.0137 9487	0.0154 2656
106	0.0116 8948	0.0121 7679	0.0126 7594	0.0137 0922	0.0153 4412
107	0.0116 0256	0.0120 9045	0.0125 9029	0.0136 2524	0.0152 6336
108	0.0115 1727	0.0120 0575	0.0125 0628	0.0135 4291	0.0151 8423
109	0.0114 3358	0.0119 2264	0.0124 2385	0.0134 6217	0.0151 0669
110	0.0113 5143	0.0118 4107	0.0123 4298	0.0133 8296	0.0150 3069
111	0.0112 7079	0.0117 6102	0.0122 6361	0.0133 0527	0.0149 5620
112	0.0111 9161	0.0116 8242	0.0121 8571	0.0132 2905	0.0148 8317
113	0.0111 1386	0.0116 0526	0.0121 0923	0.0131 5425	0.0148 1156
114	0.0110 3750	0.0115 2948	0.0120 3414	0.0130 8084	0.0147 4133
115	0.0109 6249	0.0114 5506	0.0119 6041	0.0130 0878	0.0146 7245
116	0.0108 8880	0.0113 8195	0.0118 8799	0.0129 3803	0.0146 0488
117	0.0108 1639	0.0113 1013	0.0118 1686	0.0128 6857	0.0145 3860
118	0.0107 4524	0.0112 3956	0.0117 4698	0.0128 0037	0.0144 7356
119	0.0106 7530	0.0111 7021	0.0116 7832	0.0127 3338	0.0144 0973
120	0.0106 0655	0.0111 0205	0.0116 1085	0.0126 6758	0.0143 4709
121	0.0105 3896	0.0110 3505	0.0115 4454	0.0126 0294	0.0142 8561
122	0.0104 7251	0.0109 6918	0.0114 7936	0.0125 3942	0.0142 2525
123	0.0104 0715	0.0109 0441	0.0114 1528	0.0124 7702	0.0141 6599
124	0.0103 4288	0.0108 4072	0.0113 5228	0.0124 1568	0.0141 0780
125	0.0102 7965	0.0107 7808	0.0112 9033	0.0123 5540	0.0140 5065
126	0.0102 1745	0.0107 1647	0.0112 2940	0.0122 9614	0.0139 9452
127	0.0101 5625	0.0106 5586	0.0111 6948	0.0122 3788	0.0139 3939
128	0.0100 9603	0.0105 9623	0.0111 1054	0.0121 8060	0.0138 8524
129	0.0100 3677	0.0105 3755	0.0110 5255	0.0121 2428	0.0138 3203
130	0.0099 7844	0.0104 7981	0.0109 9550	0.0120 6888	0.0137 7975
131	0.0099 2102	0.0104 2298	0.0109 3935	0.0120 1440	0.0137 2837
132	0.0098 6449	0.0103 6704	0.0108 8410	0.0119 6080	0.0136 7788
133	0.0098 0883	0.0103 1197	0.0108 2972	0.0119 0808	0.0136 2825
134	0.0097 5403	0.0102 5775	0.0107 7619	0.0118 5621	0.0135 7947
135	0.0097 0005	0.0102 0436	0.0107 2349	0.0118 0516	0.0135 3151
136	0.0096 4689	0.0101 5179	0.0106 7161	0.0117 5493	0.0134 8437
137	0.0095 9453	0.0101 0002	0.0106 2052	0.0117 0550	0.0134 3801
138	0.0095 4295	0.0100 4902	0.0105 7021	0.0116 5684	0.0133 9242
139	0.0094 9213	0.0099 9879	0.0105 2067	0.0116 0894	0.0133 4759
140	0.0094 4205	0.0099 4930	0.0104 7187	0.0115 6179	0.0133 0349
141	0.0093 9271	0.0099 0055	0.0104 2380	0.0115 1536	0.0132 6012
142	0.0093 4408	0.0098 5250	0.0103 7644	0.0114 6965	0.0132 1746
143	0.0092 9615	0.0098 0516	0.0103 2978	0.0114 2464	0.0131 7549
144	0.0092 4890	0.0097 5850	0.0102 8381	0.0113 8031	0.0131 3419
145	0.0092 0233	0.0097 1252	0.0102 3851	0.0113 3664	0.0130 9356
146	0.0091 5641	0.0096 6719	0.0101 9386	0.0112 9364	0.0130 5358
147	0.0091 1114	0.0096 2250	0.0101 4986	0.0112 5127	0.0130 1423
148	0.0090 6650	0.0095 7844	0.0101 0649	0.0112 0953	0.0129 7551
149	0.0090 2247	0.0095 3500	0.0100 6373	0.0111 6841	0.0129 3739
150	0.0089 7905	0.0094 9217	0.0100 2159	0.0111 2790	0.0128 9988

TABLE XXI (*Continued*)

PERIODICAL PAYMENT OF ANNUITY WHOSE PRESENT VALUE IS 1

$$\frac{1}{a_{\overline{n}|}} = \frac{1}{s_{\overline{n}|}} + i$$

n	$1\frac{1}{8}\%$	$1\frac{1}{4}\%$	$1\frac{1}{2}\%$	$1\frac{3}{4}\%$	2%
1	1.0112 5000	1.0125 0000	1.0150 0000	1.0175 0000	1.0200 0000
2	0.5084 5323	0.5093 9441	0.5112 7792	0.5131 6295	0.5150 4950
3	0.3408 6130	0.3417 0117	0.3433 8296	0.3450 6746	0.3467 5467
4	0.2570 7058	0.2578 6102	0.2594 4478	0.2610 3237	0.2626 2375
5	0.2068 0034	0.2075 6211	0.2090 8932	0.2106 2142	0.2121 5839
6	0.1732 9034	0.1740 3381	0.1755 2521	0.1770 2256	0.1785 2581
7	0.1493 5762	0.1500 8872	0.1515 5616	0.1530 3059	0.1545 1196
8	0.1314 1071	0.1321 3314	0.1335 8402	0.1350 4292	0.1365 0980
9	0.1174 5432	0.1181 7055	0.1196 0982	0.1210 5813	0.1225 1544
10	0.1062 9131	0.1070 0307	0.1084 3418	0.1098 7534	0.1113 2653
11	0.0971 5984	0.0978 6839	0.0992 9384	0.1007 3038	0.1021 7794
12	0.0895 5203	0.0902 5831	0.0916 7999	0.0931 1377	0.0945 5960
13	0.0831 1626	0.0838 2100	0.0852 4036	0.0866 7283	0.0881 1835
14	0.0776 0138	0.0783 0515	0.0797 2332	0.0811 5562	0.0826 0197
15	0.0728 2321	0.0735 2646	0.0749 4436	0.0763 7739	0.0778 2547
16	0.0686 4363	0.0693 4672	0.0707 6508	0.0721 9958	0.0736 5013
17	0.0649 5698	0.0656 6023	0.0670 7966	0.0685 1623	0.0699 6984
18	0.0616 8113	0.0623 8479	0.0638 0578	0.0652 4492	0.0667 0210
19	0.0587 5120	0.0594 5548	0.0608 7847	0.0623 2061	0.0637 8177
20	0.0561 1531	0.0568 2039	0.0582 4574	0.0596 9122	0.0611 5672
21	0.0537 3145	0.0544 3748	0.0558 6550	0.0573 1464	0.0587 8477
22	0.0515 6525	0.0522 7238	0.0537 0331	0.0551 5638	0.0566 3140
23	0.0495 8833	0.0502 9666	0.0517 3075	0.0581 8796	0.0546 6810
24	0.0477 7701	0.0484 8665	0.0499 2410	0.0513 8565	0.0528 7110
25	0.0461 1144	0.0468 2247	0.0482 6345	0.0497 2952	0.0512 2044
26	0.0445 7479	0.0452 8729	0.0467 3196	0.0482 0269	0.0496 9923
27	0.0431 5273	0.0438 6677	0.0453 1527	0.0467 9079	0.0482 9309
28	0.0418 3299	0.0425 4863	0.0440 0108	0.0454 8151	0.0469 8967
29	0.0406 0498	0.0413 2228	0.0427 7878	0.0442 6424	0.0457 7836
30	0.0394 5953	0.0401 7854	0.0416 3919	0.0431 2975	0.0446 4992
31	0.0383 8866	0.0391 0942	0.0405 7430	0.0420 7005	0.0435 9635
32	0.0373 8535	0.0381 0791	0.0395 7710	0.0410 7812	0.0426 1061
33	0.0364 4349	0.0371 6786	0.0386 4144	0.0401 4779	0.0416 8653
34	0.0355 5763	0.0362 8387	0.0377 6189	0.0392 7363	0.0408 1867
35	0.0347 2299	0.0354 5111	0.0369 3363	0.0384 5082	0.0400 0221
36	0.0339 3529	0.0346 6533	0.0361 5240	0.0376 7507	0.0392 3285
37	0.0331 9072	0.0339 2270	0.0354 1437	0.0369 4257	0.0385 0678
38	0.0324 8589	0.0332 1983	0.0347 1613	0.0362 4990	0.0378 2057
39	0.0318 1773	0.0325 5365	0.0340 5463	0.0355 9399	0.0371 7114
40	0.0311 8349	0.0319 2141	0.0334 2710	0.0349 7209	0.0365 5575
41	0.0305 8069	0.0313 2063	0.0328 3106	0.0343 8170	0.0359 7188
42	0.0300 0709	0.0307 4906	0.0322 6426	0.0338 2057	0.0354 1729
43	0.0294 6064	0.0302 0466	0.0317 2465	0.0332 8666	0.0348 8993
44	0.0289 3949	0.0296 8557	0.0312 1038	0.0327 7810	0.0343 8794
45	0.0284 4197	0.0291 9012	0.0307 1976	0.0322 9321	0.0339 0962
46	0.0279 6652	0.0287 1675	0.0302 5125	0.0318 3043	0.0334 5342
47	0.0275 1173	0.0282 6406	0.0298 0342	0.0313 8836	0.0330 1792
48	0.0270 7632	0.0278 3075	0.0293 7500	0.0309 6569	0.0326 0184
49	0.0266 5910	0.0274 1563	0.0289 6478	0.0305 6124	0.0322 0396
50	0.0262 5898	0.0270 1763	0.0285 7168	0.0301 7391	0.0318 2321

TABLE XXI (*Continued*)

PERIODICAL PAYMENT OF ANNUITY WHOSE PRESENT VALUE IS 1

$$\frac{1}{a_{\overline{n}|}} = \frac{1}{s_{\overline{n}|}} + i$$

n	$1\frac{1}{8}\%$	$1\frac{1}{4}\%$	$1\frac{1}{2}\%$	$1\frac{3}{4}\%$	2%
51	0.0258 7494	0.0266 3571	0.0281 9469	0.0298 0269	0.0314 5856
52	0.0255 0606	0.0262 6897	0.0278 3287	0.0294 4665	0.0311 0909
53	0.0251 5149	0.0259 1653	0.0274 8537	0.0291 0492	0.0307 7392
54	0.0248 1043	0.0255 7760	0.0271 5138	0.0287 7672	0.0304 5226
55	0.0244 8213	0.0252 5145	0.0268 3018	0.0284 6129	0.0301 4337
56	0.0241 6592	0.0249 3739	0.0265 2106	0.0281 5795	0.0298 4656
67	0.0238 6116	0.0246 3478	0.0262 2341	0.0278 6606	0.0295 6120
58	0.0235 6726	0.0243 4303	0.0259 3661	0.0275 8503	0.0292 8667
59	0.0232 8366	0.0240 6158	0.0256 6012	0.0273 1430	0.0290 2243
60	0.0230 0985	0.0237 8993	0.0253 9343	0.0270 5336	0.0287 6797
61	0.0227 4534	0.0235 2758	0.0251 3604	0.0268 0172	0.0285 2278
62	0.0224 8969	0.0232 7410	0.0248 8751	0.0265 5892	0.0282 8643
63	0.0222 4247	0.0230 2904	0.0246 4741	0.0263 2455	0.0280 5848
64	0.0220 0329	0.0227 9203	0.0244 1534	0.0260 9821	0.0278 3855
65	0.0217 7178	0.0225 6268	0.0241 9094	0.0258 7952	0.0276 2624
66	0.0215 4758	0.0223 4065	0.0239 7386	0.0256 6813	0.0274 2122
67	0.0213 3037	0.0221 2560	0.0237 6376	0.0254 6372	0.0272 2316
68	0.0211 1985	0.0219 1724	0.0235 6033	0.0252 6596	0.0270 3173
69	0.0209 1571	0.0217 1527	0.0233 6329	0.0250 7459	0.0268 4665
70	0.0207 1769	0.0215 1941	0.0231 7235	0 0248 8930	0.0266 6765
71	0.0205 2552	0.0213 2941	0.0229 8727	0.0247 0985	0.0264 9446
72	0.0203 3896	0.0211 4501	0.0228 0779	0.0245 3600	0.0263 2683
73	0.0201 5779	0.0209 6600	0.0226 3368	0.0243 6750	0.0261 6454
74	0.0199 8177	0.0207 9215	0.0224 6473	0.0242 0413	0.0260 0736
75	0.0198 1072	0.0206 2325	0.0223 0072	0.0240 4570	0.0258 5508
76	0.0196 4442	0.0204 5910	0.0221 4146	0.0238 9200	0.0257 0751
77	0.0194 8269	0.0202 9953	0.0219 8676	0.0237 4284	0.0255 6447
78	0.0193 2536	0.0201 4435	0.0218 3645	0.0235 9806	0.0254 2576
79	0.0191 7226	0.0199 9341	0.0216 9036	0.0234 5748	0.0252 9123
80	0.0190 2323	0.0198 4652	0.0215 4832	0.0233 2093	0.0251 6071
81	0.0188 7812	0.0197 0356	0.0214 1019	0.0231 8828	0.0250 3405
82	0.0187 3678	0.0195 6437	0.0212 7583	0.0230 5936	0.0249 1110
83	0.0185 9908	0.0194 2881	0.0211 4509	0.0229 3406	0.0247 9173
84	0.0184 6489	0.0192 9675	0.0210 1784	0.0228 1223	0.0246 7581
85	0.0183 3409	0.0191 6808	0.0208 9396	0.0226 9375	0.0245 6321
86	0.0182 0654	0.0190 4267	0.0207 7333	0.0225 7850	0.0244 5381
87	0.0180 8215	0.0189 2041	0.0206 5584	0.0224 6636	0.0243 4750
88	0.0179 6081	0.0188 0119	0.0205 4138	0.0223 5724	0.0242 4416
89	0.0178 4240	0.0186 8490	0.0204 2984	0.0222 5102	0.0241 4370
90	0.0177 2684	0.0185 7146	0.0203 2113	0.0221 4760	0.0240 4602
91	0.0176 1403	0.0184 6076	0.0202 1516	0.0220 4690	0.0239 5101
92	0.0175 0387	0.0183 5271	0.0201 1182	0.0219 4882	0.0238 5859
93	0.0173 9629	0.0182 4724	0.0200 1104	0.0218 5327	0.0237 6868
94	0.0172 9119	0.0181 4425	0.0199 1273	0.0217 6017	0.0236 8118
95	0.0171 8851	0.0180 4366	0.0198 1681	0.0216 6944	0.0235 9602
96	0.0170 8816	0.0179 4540	0.0197 2321	0.0215 8101	0.0235 1313
97	0.0169 9007	0.0178 4941	0.0196 3186	0.0214 9480	0.0234 3242
98	0.0168 9418	0.0177 5560	0.0195 4268	0.0214 1074	0.0233 5383
99	0.0168 0041	0.0176 6391	0.0194 5560	0.0213 2876	0.0232 7729
100	0.0167 0870	0.0175 7428	0.0193 7057	0.0212 4880	0.0232 0274

TABLE XXI (*Continued*)

PERIODICAL PAYMENT OF ANNUITY WHOSE PRESENT VALUE IS 1

$$\frac{1}{a_{\overline{n}|}} = \frac{1}{s_{\overline{n}|}} + i$$

n	$2\frac{1}{4}\%$	$2\frac{1}{2}\%$	$2\frac{3}{4}\%$	3%	$3\frac{1}{2}\%$
1	1.0225 0000	1.0250 0000	1.0275 0000	1.0300 0000	1.0350 0000
2	0.5169 3758	0.5188 2716	0.5207 1825	0.5226 1084	0.5264 0049
3	0.3484 4458	0.3501 3717	0.3518 3243	0.3535 3036	0.3569 3418
4	0.2642 1893	0.2658 1788	0.2674 2059	0.2690 2705	0.2722 5114
5	0.2137 0021	0.2152 4686	0.2167 9832	0.2183 5457	0.2214 8137
6	0.1800 3496	0.1815 4997	0.1830 7083	0.1845 9750	0.1876 6821
7	0.1560 0025	0.1574 9543	0.1589 9747	0.1605 0635	0.1635 4449
8	0.1379 8462	0.1394 6735	0.1409 5795	0.1424 5639	0.1454 7665
9	0.1239 8170	0.1254 5689	0.1269 4095	0.1284 3386	0.1314 4601
10	0.1127 8768	0.1142 5876	0.1157 3972	0.1172 3051	0.1202 4137
11	0.1036 3649	0.1051 0596	0.1065 8629	0.1080 7745	0.1110 9197
12	0.0960 1740	0.0974 8713	0.0989 6871	0.1004 6209	0.1034 8395
13	0.0895 7686	0.0910 4827	0.0925 3252	0.0940 2954	0.0970 6157
14	0.0840 6230	0.0855 3653	0.0870 2457	0.0885 2634	0.0915 7073
15	0.0792 8852	0.0807 6646	0.0822 5917	0.0837 6658	0.0868 2507
16	0.0751 1663	0.0765 9899	0.0780 9710	0.0796 1085	0.0826 8483
17	0.0714 4039	0.0729 2777	0.0744 3186	0.0759 5253	0.0790 4313
18	0.0681 7720	0.0696 7008	0.0711 8063	0.0727 0870	0.0758 1684
19	0.0652 6182	0.0667 6062	0.0682 7802	0.0698 1388	0.0729 4033
20	0.0626 4207	0.0641 4713	0.0656 7173	0.0672 1571	0.0703 6108
21	0.0602 7572	0.0617 8733	0.0633 1941	0.0648 7178	0.0680 3659
22	0.0581 2821	0.0596 4661	0.0611 8640	0.0627 4739	0.0659 3207
23	0.0561 7097	0.0576 9638	0.0592 4410	0.0608 1390	0.0640 1880
24	0.0543 8023	0.0559 1282	0.0574 6863	0.0590 4742	0.0622 7283
25	0.0527 3599	0.0542 7592	0.0558 3997	0.0574 2787	0.0606 7404
26	0.0512 2134	0.0527 6875	0.0543 4116	0.0559 3829	0.0592 0540
27	0.0498 2188	0.0513 7687	0.0529 5776	0.0545 6421	0.0578 5241
28	0.0485 2525	0.0500 8793	0.0516 7738	0.0532 9323	0.0566 0265
29	0.0473 2081	0.0488 9127	0.0504 8935	0.0521 1467	0.0554 4538
30	0.0461 9934	0.0477 7764	0.0493 8442	0.0510 1926	0.0543 7133
31	0.0451 5280	0.0467 3900	0.0483 5453	0.0499 9893	0.0533 7240
32	0.0441 7415	0.0457 6831	0.0473 9263	0.0490 4662	0.0524 4150
33	0.0432 5722	0.0448 5938	0.0464 9253	0.0481 5612	0.0515 7242
34	0.0423 9655	0.0440 0675	0.0456 4875	0.0473 2196	0.0507 5966
35	0.0415 8731	0.0432 0558	0.0448 5645	0.0465 3929	0.0499 9835
36	0.0408 2522	0.0424 5158	0.0441 1132	0.0458 0379	0.0492 8416
37	0.0401 0643	0.0417 4090	0.0434 0953	0.0451 1162	0.0486 1325
38	0.0394 2753	0.0410 7012	0.0427 4764	0.0444 5934	0.0479 8214
39	0.0387 8543	0.0404 3615	0.0421 2256	0.0438 4385	0.0473 8775
40	0.0381 7738	0.0398 3623	0.0415 3151	0.0432 6238	0.0468 2728
41	0.0376 0087	0.0392 6786	0.0409 7200	0.0427 1241	0.0462 9822
42	0.0370 5364	0.0387 2876	0.0404 4175	0.0421 9167	0.0457 9828
43	0.0365 3364	0.0382 1688	0.0399 3871	0.0416 9811	0.0453 2539
44	0.0360 3901	0.0377 3037	0.0394 6100	0.0412 2985	0.0448 7768
45	0.0355 6805	0.0372 6752	0.0390 0693	0.0407 8518	0.0444 5343
46	0.0351 1921	0.0368 2676	0.0385 7493	0.0403 6254	0.0440 5108
47	0.0346 9107	0.0364 0669	0.0381 6358	0.0399 6051	0.0436 6919
48	0.0342 8233	0.0360 0599	0.0377 7158	0.0395 7777	0.0433 0646
49	0.0338 9179	0.0356 2348	0.0373 9773	0.0392 1314	0.0429 6167
50	0.0335 1836	0.0352 5806	0.0370 4092	0.0388 6550	0.0426 3371

TABLE XXI (*Continued*)

PERIODICAL PAYMENT OF ANNUITY WHOSE PRESENT VALUE IS 1

$$\frac{1}{a_{\overline{n}|}} = \frac{1}{s_{\overline{n}|}} + i$$

n	$2\frac{1}{4}\%$	$2\frac{1}{2}\%$	$2\frac{3}{4}\%$	3%	$3\frac{1}{2}\%$
51	0.0331 6102	0.0349 0870	0.0367 0014	0.0385 3382	0.0423 2156
52	0.0328 1884	0.0345 7446	0.0363 7444	0.0382 1718	0.0420 2429
53	0.0324 9094	0.0342 5449	0.0360 6297	0.0379 1471	0.0417 4100
54	0.0321 7654	0.0339 4799	0.0357 6491	0.0376 2558	0.0414 7090
55	0.0318 7489	0.0336 5419	0.0354 7953	0.0373 4907	0.0412 1323
56	0.0315 8530	0.0333 7243	0.0352 0612	0.0370 8447	0.0409 6730
57	0.0313 0712	0.0331 0204	0.0349 4404	0.0368 3114	0.0407 3245
58	0.0310 3977	0.0328 4244	0.0346 9270	0.0365 8848	0.0405 0810
59	0.0307 8268	0.0325 9307	0.0344 5153	0.0363 5593	0.0402 9366
60	0.0305 3533	0.0323 5340	0.0342 2002	0.0361 3296	0.0400 8862
61	0.0302 9724	0.0321 2294	0.0339 9767	0.0359 1908	0.0398 9249
62	0.0300 6795	0.0319 0126	0.0337 8402	0.0357 1385	0.0397 0480
63	0.0298 4704	0.0316 8790	0.0335 7866	0.0355 1682	0.0395 2513
64	0.0296 3411	0.0314 8249	0.0333 8118	0.0353 2760	0.0393 5308
65	0.0294 2878	0.0312 8463	0.0331 9120	0.0351 4581	0.0391 8826
66	0.0292 3070	0.0310 9398	0.0330 0837	0.0349 7110	0.0390 3031
67	0.0290 3955	0.0309 1021	0.0328 3236	0.0348 0313	0.0388 7892
68	0.0288 5500	0.0307 3300	0.0326 6285	0.0346 4159	0.0387 3375
69	0.0286 7677	0.0305 6206	0.0324 9955	0.0344 8618	0.0385 9453
70	0.0285 0458	0.0303 9712	0.0323 4218	0.0343 3663	0.0384 6095
71	0.0283 3816	0.0302 3790	0.0321 9048	0.0341 9266	0.0383 3277
72	0.0281 7728	0.0300 8417	0.0320 4420	0.0340 5404	0.0382 0973
73	0.0280 2169	0.0299 3568	0.0319 0311	0.0339 2053	0.0380 9160
74	0.0278 7118	0.0297 0222	0.0317 6698	0.0337 9191	0.0379 7816
75	0.0277 2554	0.0296 5358	0.0316 3560	0.0336 6796	0.0378 6019
76	0.0275 8457	0.0295 1956	0.0315 0878	0.0335 4849	0.0377 6450
77	0.0274 4808	0.0293 8997	0.0313 8633	0.0334 3331	0.0376 6390
78	0.0273 1589	0.0292 6463	0.0312 6806	0.0333 2224	0.0375 6721
79	0.0271 8784	0.0291 4438	0.0311 5382	0.0332 1510	0.0374 7426
80	0.0270 6376	0.0290 2605	0.0310 4342	0.0331 1175	0.0373 8489
81	0.0269 4350	0.0289 1248	0.0309 3674	0.0330 1201	0.0372 9894
82	0.0268 2692	0.0288 0254	0.0308 3361	0.0329 1576	0.0372 1628
83	0.0267 1387	0.0286 9608	0.0307 3389	0.0328 2284	0.0371 3676
84	0.0266 0423	0.0285 9298	0.0306 3747	0.0327 3313	0.0370 6025
85	0.0264 9787	0.0284 9310	0.0305 4420	0.0326 4650	0.0369 8662
86	0.0263 9467	0.0283 9633	0.0304 5397	0.0325 6284	0.0369 1576
87	0.0262 9452	0.0283 0255	0.0303 6667	0.0324 8202	0.0368 4756
88	0.0261 9730	0.0282 1165	0.0302 8219	0.0324 0393	0.0367 8190
89	0.0261 0291	0.0281 2353	0.0302 0041	0.0323 2848	0.0367 1868
90	0.0260 1126	0.0280 3809	0.0301 2125	0.0322 5556	0.0366 5781
91	0.0259 2224	0.0279 5523	0.0300 4460	0.0321 8508	0.0365 9919
92	0.0258 3577	0.0278 7486	0.0299 7038	0.0321 1694	0.0365 4273
93	0.0257 5176	0.0277 9690	0.0298 9850	0.0320 5107	0.0364 8834
94	0.0256 7012	0.0277 2126	0.0298 2887	0.0319 8737	0.0364 3594
95	0.0255 9078	0.0276 4786	0.0297 6141	0.0319 2577	0.0363 8546
96	0.0255 1366	0.0275 7662	0.0296 9605	0.0318 6619	0.0363 3682
97	0.0254 3868	0.0275 0747	0.0296 3272	0.0318 0856	0.0362 8995
98	0.0253 6578	0.0274 4034	0.0295 7134	0.0317 5281	0.0362 4478
99	0.0252 9489	0.0273 7517	0.0295 1185	0.0316 9886	0.0362 0124
100	0.0252 2594	0.0273 1188	0.0294 5418	0.0316 4667	0.0361 5927

TABLE XXI (*Continued*)

PERIODICAL PAYMENT OF ANNUITY WHOSE PRESENT VALUE IS 1

$$\frac{1}{a_{\overline{n}|}} = \frac{1}{s_{\overline{n}|}} + i$$

n	4%	$4\frac{1}{2}\%$	5%	$5\frac{1}{2}\%$	6%
1	1.0400 0000	1.0450 0000	1.0500 0000	1.0550 0000	1.0600 0000
2	0.5301 9608	0.5339 9756	0.5378 0488	0.5416 1800	0.5454 3689
3	0.3603 4854	0.3637 7336	0.3672 0856	0.3706 5407	0.3741 0981
4	0.2754 9005	0.2787 4365	0.2820 1183	0.2852 9449	0.2885 9149
5	0.2246 2711	0.2277 9164	0.2309 7480	0.2341 7644	0.2373 9640
6	0.1907 6190	0.1938 7839	0.1970 1747	0.2001 7895	0.2033 6263
7	0.1666 0961	0.1697 0147	0.1728 1982	0.1759 6442	0.1791 3502
8	0.1485 2783	0.1516 0965	0.1547 2181	0.1578 6401	0.1610 3594
9	0.1344 9299	0.1375 7447	0.1406 9008	0.1438 3946	0.1470 2224
10	0.1232 9094	0.1263 7882	0.1295 0458	0.1326 6777	0.1358 6796
11	0.1141 4904	0.1172 4818	0.1203 8889	0.1235 7065	0.1267 9294
12	0.1065 5217	0.1096 6619	0.1128 2541	0.1160 2923	0.1192 7703
13	0.1001 4373	0.1032 7535	0.1064 5577	0.1096 8426	0.1129 6011
14	0.0946 6897	0.0978 2032	0.1010 2397	0.1042 7912	0.1075 8491
15	0.0899 4110	0.0931 1381	0.0963 4229	0.0996 2560	0.1029 6276
16	0.0858 2000	0.0890 1537	0.0922 6991	0.0955 8254	0.0989 5214
17	0.0821 9852	0.0854 1758	0.0886 9914	0.0920 4197	0.0954 4480
18	0.0789 9333	0.0822 3690	0.0855 4622	0.0889 1992	0.0923 5654
19	0.0761 3862	0.0794 0734	0.0827 4501	0.0861 5006	0.0896 2086
20	0.0735 8175	0.0768 7614	0.0802 4259	0.0836 7933	0.0871 8456
21	0.0712 8011	0.0746 0057	0.0779 9611	0.0814 6478	0.0850 0455
22	0.0691 9881	0.0725 4565	0.0759 7051	0.0794 7123	0.0830 4557
23	0.0673 0906	0.0706 8249	0.0741 3682	0.0776 6965	0.0812 7848
24	0.0655 8653	0.0689 8703	0.0724 7090	0.0760 3580	0.0796 7900
25	0.0640 1196	0.0674 3903	0.0709 5246	0.0745 4935	0.0782 2672
26	0.0625 6738	0.0660 2137	0.0695 6432	0.0731 9307	0.0769 0435
27	0.0612 3854	0.0647 1946	0.0682 9186	0.0719 5228	0.0756 9717
28	0.0600 1298	0.0635 2081	0.0671 2253	0.0708 1440	0.0745 9255
29	0.0588 7993	0.0624 1461	0.0660 4551	0.0697 6857	0.0735 7961
30	0.0578 3010	0.0613 9154	0.0650 5144	0.0688 0539	0.0726 4891
31	0.0568 5535	0.0604 4345	0.0641 3212	0.0679 1665	0.0717 9222
32	0.0559 4859	0.0595 6320	0.0632 8042	0.0670 9519	0.0710 0234
33	0.0551 0357	0.0587 4453	0.0624 9004	0.0663 3469	0.0702 7293
34	0.0543 1477	0.0579 8191	0.0617 5545	0.0656 2958	0.0695 9843
35	0.0535 7732	0.0572 7045	0.0610 7171	0.0649 7493	0.0689 7386
36	0.0528 8688	0.0566 0578	0.0604 3446	0.0643 6635	0.0683 9483
37	0.0522 3957	0.0559 8402	0.0598 3979	0.0637 9993	0.0678 5743
38	0.0516 3192	0.0554 0169	0.0592 8423	0.0632 7217	0.0673 5812
39	0.0510 6083	0.0548 5567	0.0587 6462	0.0627 7991	0.0668 9377
40	0.0505 2349	0.0543 4315	0.0582 7816	0.0623 2034	0.0664 6154
41	0.0500 1738	0.0538 6158	0.0578 2229	0.0618 9090	0.0660 5886
42	0.0495 4020	0.0534 0868	0.0573 9471	0.0614 8927	0.0656 8342
43	0.0490 8989	0.0529 8235	0.0569 9333	0.0611 1337	0.0653 3312
44	0.0486 6454	0.0525 8071	0.0566 1625	0.0607 6128	0.0650 0606
45	0.0482 6246	0.0522 0202	0.0562 6173	0.0604 3127	0.0647 0050
46	0.0478 8205	0.0518 4471	0.0559 2820	0.0601 2175	0.0644 1485
47	0.0475 2189	0.0515 0734	0.0556 1421	0.0598 3129	0.0641 4768
48	0.0471 8065	0.0511 8858	0.0553 1843	0.0595 5854	0.0638 9766
49	0.0468 5712	0.0508 8722	0.0550 3965	0.0593 0230	0.0636 6356
50	0.0465 5020	0.0506 0215	0.0547 7674	0.0590 6145	0.0634 4429

TABLE XXI (*Continued*)

PERIODICAL PAYMENT OF ANNUITY WHOSE PRESENT VALUE IS 1

$$\frac{1}{a_{\overline{n}|}} = \frac{1}{s_{\overline{n}|}} + i$$

n	4%	$4\frac{1}{2}\%$	5%	$5\frac{1}{2}\%$	6%
51	0.0462 5885	0.0503 3232	0.0545 2867	0.0588 3495	0.0632 3880
52	0.0459 8212	0.0500 7679	0.0542 9450	0.0586 2186	0.0630 4617
53	0.0457 1915	0.0498 3469	0.0540 7334	0.0584 2130	0.0628 6551
54	0.0454 6910	0.0496 0519	0.0538 6438	0.0582 3245	0.0626 9602
55	0.0452 3124	0.0493 8754	0.0536 6686	0.0580 5458	0.0625 3696
56	0.0450 0487	0.0491 8105	0.0534 8010	0.0578 8698	0.0623 8765
57	0.0447 8932	0.0489 8506	0.0533 0343	0.0577 2900	0.0622 4744
58	0.0445 8401	0.0487 9897	0.0531 3626	0.0575 8006	0.0621 1574
59	0.0443 8836	0.0486 2221	0.0529 7802	0.0574 3959	0.0619 9200
60	0.0442 0185	0.0484 5426	0.0528 2818	0.0573 0707	0.0618 7572
61	0.0440 2398	0.0482 9462	0.0526 8627	0.0571 8202	0.0617 6642
62	0.0438 5430	0.0481 4284	0.0525 5183	0.0570 6400	0.0616 6366
63	0.0436 9237	0.0479 9848	0.0524 2442	0.0569 5258	0.0615 6704
64	0.0435 3780	0.0478 6115	0.0523 0365	0.0568 4737	0.0614 7615
65	0.0433 9019	0.0477 3047	0.0521 8915	0.0567 4800	0.0613 9066
66	0.0432 4921	0.0476 0608	0.0520 8057	0.0566 5413	0.0613 1022
67	0.0431 1451	0.0474 8765	0.0519 7757	0.0565 6544	0.0612 3454
68	0.0429 8578	0.0473 7487	0.0518 7986	0.0564 8163	0.0611 6330
69	0.0428 6272	0.0472 6745	0.0517 8715	0.0564 0242	0.0610 9625
70	0.0427 4506	0.0471 6511	0.0516 9915	0.0563 2754	0.0610 3313
71	0.0426 3253	0.0470 6759	0.0516 1563	0.0562 5675	0.0609 7370
72	0.0425 2489	0.0469 7465	0.0515 3633	0.0561 8982	0.0609 1774
73	0.0424 2190	0.0468 8606	0.0514 6103	0.0561 2652	0.0608 6505
74	0.0423 2334	0.0468 0159	0.0513 8953	0.0560 6665	0.0608 1542
75	0.0422 2900	0.0467 2104	0.0513 2161	0.0560 1002	0.0607 6807
76	0.0421 3869	0.0466 4422	0.0512 5709	0.0559 5645	0.0607 2463
77	0.0420 5221	0.0465 7094	0.0511 9580	0.0559 0577	0.0606 8315
78	0.0419 6939	0.0465 0104	0.0511 3756	0.0558 5781	0.0606 4407
79	0.0418 9007	0.0464 3434	0.0510 8222	0.0558 1243	0.0606 0724
80	0.0418 1408	0.0463 7069	0.0510 2962	0.0557 6948	0.0605 7254
81	0.0417 4127	0.0463 0995	0.0509 7963	0.0557 2884	0.0605 3984
82	0.0416 7150	0.0462 5197	0.0509 3211	0.0556 9036	0.0605 0903
83	0.0416 0463	0.0461 9663	0.0508 8694	0.0556 5395	0.0604 7998
84	0.0415 4054	0.0461 4379	0.0508 4399	0.0556 1947	0.0604 5261
85	0.0414 7909	0.0460 9334	0.0508 0316	0.0555 8683	0.0604 2681
86	0.0414 2018	0.0460 4516	0.0507 6433	0.0555 5593	0.0604 0249
87	0.0413 6370	0.0459 9915	0.0507 2740	0.0555 2667	0.0603 7956
88	0.0413 0953	0.0459 5522	0.0506 9228	0.0554 9896	0.0603 5795
89	0.0412 5758	0.0459 1325	0.0506 5888	0.0554 7273	0.0603 3757
90	0.0412 0775	0.0458 7316	0.0506 2711	0.0554 4788	0.0603 1836
91	0.0411 5995	0.0458 3486	0.0505 9689	0.0554 2435	0.0603 0025
92	0.0411 1410	0.0457 9827	0.0505 6815	0.0554 0207	0.0602 8318
93	0.0410 7010	0.0457 6331	0.0505 4080	0.0553 8096	0.0602 6708
94	0.0410 2789	0.0457 2991	0.0505 1478	0.0553 6097	0.0602 5190
95	0.0409 8738	0.0456 9799	0.0504 9003	0.0553 4204	0.0602 3758
96	0.0409 4850	0.0456 6749	0.0504 6648	0.0553 2410	0.0602 2408
97	0.0409 1119	0.0456 3834	0.0504 4407	0.0553 0711	0.0602 1135
98	0.0408 7538	0.0456 1048	0.0504 2274	0.0552 9101	0.0601 9935
99	0.0408 4100	0.0455 8385	0.0504 0245	0.0552 7577	0.0601 8803
100	0.0408 0800	0.0455 5839	0.0503 8314	0.0552 6132	0.0601 7736

TABLE XXI (*Continued*)

PERIODICAL PAYMENT OF ANNUITY WHOSE PRESENT VALUE IS 1

$$\frac{1}{a_{\overline{n}|}} = \frac{1}{s_{\overline{n}|}} + i$$

n	$6\frac{1}{2}\%$	7%	$7\frac{1}{2}\%$	8%	$8\frac{1}{2}\%$
1	1.0650 0000	1.0700 0000	1.0750 0000	1.0800 0000	1.0850 0000
2	0.5492 6150	0.5530 9179	0.5569 2771	0.5607 6923	0.5646 1631
3	0.3775 7570	0.3810 5166	0.3845 3763	0.3880 3351	0.3915 3925
4	0.2919 0274	0.2952 2812	0.2985 6751	0.3019 2080	0.3052 8789
5	0.2406 3454	0.2438 9069	0.2471 6472	0.2504 5645	0.2537 6575
6	0.2065 6831	0.2097 9580	0.2130 4489	0.2163 1539	0.2196 0708
7	0.1823 3137	0.1855 5322	0.1888 0032	0.1920 7240	0.1953 6922
8	0.1642 3730	0.1674 6776	0.1707 2702	0.1740 1476	0.1773 3065
9	0.1502 3803	0.1534 8647	0.1567 6716	0.1600 7971	0.1634 2372
10	0.1391 0469	0.1423 7750	0.1456 8593	0.1490 2949	0.1524 0771
11	0.1300 5521	0.1333 5690	0.1366 9747	0.1400 7634	0.1434 9293
12	0.1225 6817	0.1259 0199	0.1292 7783	0.1326 9502	0.1361 5286
13	0.1162 8256	0.1196 5085	0.1230 6420	0.1265 2181	0.1300 2287
14	0.1109 4048	0.1143 4494	0.1177 9737	0.1212 9685	0.1248 4244
15	0.1063 5278	0.1097 9462	0.1132 8724	0.1168 2954	0.1204 2046
16	0.1023 7757	0.1058 5765	0.1093 9116	0.1129 7687	0.1166 1354
17	0.0989 0633	0.1024 2519	0.1060 0003	0.1096 2943	0.1133 1198
18	0.0958 5461	0.0994 1260	0.1030 2896	0.1067 0210	0.1104 3041
19	0.0931 5575	0.0967 5301	0.1004 1090	0.1041 2763	0.1079 0140
20	0.0907 5640	0.0943 9293	0.0980 9219	0.1018 5221	0.1056 7097
21	0.0886 1333	0.0922 8900	0.0960 2937	0.0998 3225	0.1036 9541
22	0.0866 9120	0.0904 0577	0.0941 8687	0.0980 3207	0.1019 3892
23	0.0849 6078	0.0887 1393	0.0925 3528	0.0964 2217	0.1003 7193
24	0.0833 9770	0.0871 8902	0.0910 5008	0.0949 7796	0.0989 6975
25	0.0819 8148	0.0858 1052	0.0897 1067	0.0936 7878	0.0977 1168
26	0.0806 9480	0.0845 6103	0.0884 9961	0.0925 0713	0.0965 8016
27	0.0795 2288	0.0834 2573	0.0874 0204	0.0914 4809	0.0955 6025
28	0.0784 5305	0.0823 9193	0.0864 0520	0.0904 8891	0.0946 3914
29	0.0774 7440	0.0814 4865	0.0854 9811	0.0896 1854	0.0938 0577
30	0.0765 7744	0.0805 8640	0.0846 7124	0.0888 2743	0.0930 5058
31	0.0757 5393	0.0797 9691	0.0839 1628	0.0881 0728	0.0923 6524
32	0.0749 9665	0.0790 7292	0.0832 2599	0.0874 5081	0.0917 4247
33	0.0742 9924	0.0784 0807	0.0825 9397	0.0868 5163	0.0911 7588
34	0.0736 5610	0.0777 9674	0.0820 1461	0.0863 0411	0.0906 5984
35	0.0730 6226	0.0772 3396	0.0814 8291	0.0858 0326	0.0901 8937
36	0.0725 1332	0.0767 1531	0.0809 9447	0.0853 4467	0.0897 6006
37	0.0720 0534	0.0762 3685	0.0805 4533	0.0849 2440	0.0893 6799
38	0.0715 3480	0.0757 9505	0.0801 3197	0.0845 3894	0.0890 0966
39	0.0710 9854	0.0753 8676	0.0797 5124	0.0841 8513	0.0886 8193
40	0.0706 9373	0.0750 0914	0.0794 0031	0.0838 6016	0.0883 8201
41	0.0703 1779	0.0746 5962	0.0790 7663	0.0835 6149	0.0881 0737
42	0.0699 6842	0.0743 3591	0.0787 7789	0.0832 8684	0.0878 5576
43	0.0696 4352	0.0740 3590	0.0785 0201	0.0830 3414	0.0876 2512
44	0.0693 4119	0.0737 5769	0.0782 4710	0.0828 0152	0.0874 1363
45	0.0690 5968	0.0734 9957	0.0780 1146	0.0825 8728	0.0872 1961
46	0.0687 9743	0.0732 5996	0.0777 9353	0.0823 8991	0.0870 4154
47	0.0685 5300	0.0730 3744	0.0775 9190	0.0822 0799	0.0868 7807
48	0.0683 2506	0.0728 3070	0.0774 0527	0.0820 4027	0.0867 2795
49	0.0681 1240	0.0726 3853	0.0772 3247	0.0818 8557	0.0865 9005
50	0.0679 1393	0.0724 5985	0.0770 7241	0.0817 4286	0.0864 6334

GLOSSARY

Denominator. The part of a fraction below the dividing line; thus in the fraction $\frac{7}{12}$, 12 is the denominator.

Digit. In this book the word is used to designate any of the figures 1, 2, 3, 4, 5, 6, 7, 8 and 9. It should be noted, however, that some authorities consider 0 as a digit too.

Dividend. The number that is divided by another number; thus, in the problem 18 divided by 9, 18 is the dividend.

Divisor. The number by which any number is divided; thus, in the problem 18 divided by 9, 9 is the divisor.

Factor. Any of the quantities which, multiplied together, form a product; thus, in the problem 8 multiplied by 4, both 8 and 4 are factors. On the other hand, to factor a number means to break it up into numbers (factors) which, multiplied together, produce the original number; thus the number 6 is composed of the factors 2 and 3, because 2 multiplied by 3 equals 6.

Minuend. The number from which another number is subtracted; thus, in the problem 16 minus 12, 16 is the minuend.

Multiple. A number that is exactly divisible by a given number; thus 100 is a multiple of 10, because it is exactly divisible by 10.

Numerator. The number above the dividing line in a fraction; thus in the fraction $\frac{7}{12}$, 7 is the numerator.

Per cent. "Per hundred," or "hundredths"; thus 2 per cent means 2 hundredths.

Percentage. The result obtained by computing a certain per cent of a number; thus in computing 5 per cent of $100.00, $5.00—the result obtained—is known as the percentage.

Power. The product resulting from the continued multiplication of a number by itself; thus 4, 8, 16, 32 are powers of 2; and 100, 1000, 10000 are powers of 10.

Quotient. The number resulting from the division of one number by another; thus, in dividing 18 by 3, 6—the result obtained—is known as the quotient.

Subtrahend. The number that is subtracted from another number; thus, in the problem 16 minus 12, 12 is the subtrahend.

ALPHABETICAL LIST OF THE HUNDREDS OF PRODUCTS, MATERIALS, OPERATIONS, SERVICES, AND BUSINESS PRACTICES REPRESENTED BY THE MORE THAN 1500 ILLUSTRATIONS AND PROBLEMS IN THIS BOOK